Differential Geometry and Topology

Notes on Mathematics and its Applications

General Editors: Jacob T. Schwartz, Courant Institute of Mathematical Sciences and Maurice Lévy, Université de Paris

E. Artin, ALGEBRAIC NUMBERS AND ALGEBRAIC FUNCTIONS
R. P. Boas, COLLECTED WORKS OF HIDEHIKO YAMABE
M. Davis, A FIRST COURSE IN FUNCTIONAL ANALYSIS
M. Davis, LECTURES ON MODERN MATHEMATICS
J. Eells Jr., SINGULARITIES OF SMOOTH MAPS
K. O. Friedrichs, ADVANCED ORDINARY DIFFERENTIAL EQUATIONS
K. O. Friedrichs, SPECIAL TOPICS IN FLUID DYNAMICS
K. O. Friedrichs and H. N. Shapiro, INTEGRATION IN HILBERT SPACE
A. Guichardet, SPECIAL TOPICS IN TOPOLOGICAL ALGEBRAS
M. Hausner and J. T. Schwartz, LIE GROUPS; LIE ALGEBRAS
P. Hilton, HOMOTOPY THEORY AND DUALITY
F. John, LECTURES ON ADVANCED NUMERICAL ANALYSIS
A. M. Krall, STABILITY TECHNIQUES FOR CONTINUOUS LINEAR SYSTEMS
H. Mullish, AN INTRODUCTION TO COMPUTER PROGRAMMING
F. Rellich, PERTURBATION THEORY OF EIGENVALUE PROBLEMS
J. T. Schwartz, W-* ALGEBRAS
J. T. Schwartz, DIFFERENTIAL GEOMETRY AND TOPOLOGY
J. T. Schwartz, NONLINEAR FUNCTIONAL ANALYSIS
J. L. Soulé, LINEAR OPERATORS IN HILBERT SPACE
J. J. Stoker, NONLINEAR ELASTICITY

Additional volumes in preparation

Differential Geometry and Topology

J. T. SCHWARTZ

Courant Institute of
Mathematical Sciences
New York University

Notes by

Adil Naoum and
Joseph Roitberg

GORDON AND BREACH
SCIENCE PUBLISHERS
NEW YORK · LONDON · PARIS

Printed in Germany (East)

Editors' Preface

A large number of mathematical books begin as lecture notes; but, since mathematicians are busy, and since the labor required to bring lecture notes up to the level of perfection which authors and the public demand of formally published books is very considerable, it follows that an even larger number of lecture notes make the transition to book form only after great delay or not at all. The present lecture note series aims to fill the resulting gap. It will consist of reprinted lecture notes, edited at least to a satisfactory level of completeness and intelligibility, though not necessarily to the perfection which is expected of a book. In addition to lecture notes, the series will include volumes of collected reprints of journal articles as current developments indicate, and mixed volumes including both notes and reprints.

JACOB T. SCHWARTZ
MAURICE LÉVY

Differential Geometry and Topology
Author's Preface

The present set of notes was developed during a course given in the 1965–66 academic year. It is hoped that, in spite of the rather fragmentary character of the notes, they will be of use to graduate students and others wishing to survey the material with which they are concerned.

Our emphasis lies on the development and application of intersection theoretic methods for the calculation of various interesting topological invariants. Chapter 1 gives a summary of the usual basic generalities of differential topology. The fundamental lemma of Sard is proved and yields an elementary proof for the Brouwer fixed point theorem. Chapter 2 uses Sard's lemma, and the transversality arguments originally developed by Rene Thom, to derive the classical connections between geometric intersection theory and algebraic homology on a rigorous basis. In the following chapter we use these intersection theoretic results to calculate the cohomology ring of the Grassmann spaces; the facts derived in this way form the basis for our subsequent discussion of Whitney and Chern classes. In the second part of Chapter 3 we use intersection theoretic arguments, combined with arguments taken from Morse theory, to prove the Poincare duality theorem for differentiable manifolds. Chapter 4 summarizes various basic facts concerning fiber bundles, especially linear bundles. Chapter 5 gives an outline of the algebraic theory of spectral sequences. In Chapter 6 we combine the general principles discussed in the two preceding chapters with the intersection theoretic methods developed in Chapter 3 and discuss the characteristic classes of linear bundles. In the following chapter we develop various fundamental formulae of Riemannian geometry; then, combining these with the topological material developed in the preceding chapters, we derive the very interesting generalization of the Riemann–Roch theorem due to Chern.

The remaining chapters are intended to serve as a quick introduction to the generalized cohomology theory, and particularly to K-theory, which has played an important role in various recent topological advances. Chapter 8 begins with the simple proof of the fact that certain families of homotopy classes define generalized cohomology theories and then applies this general result to define K-theory as a particular generalized cohomology theory. Chapter 9 continues the discussion of K-theory, deriving various product relations belonging to this theory as well as the special properties of K-theory which follow from the Bott periodicity theorem. In the third section of Chapter 9, we show that the Chern classes define a homomorphism of the K-theory into ordinary cohomology theory. This fact is then used to derive a number of interesting properties of K-theory. The Atiyah–Hirzebruch spectral sequence for K-theory is derived in Section 4 of Chapter 9. Mapping this spectral sequence by the Chern character discussed in the preceding section of Chapter 9, we are able to develop the various interesting relations between the K-function and the ordinary cohomology theory. In Section 5 of Chapter 9 the K-theory operations originally introduced by Adams are discussed. Our concluding Chapter 10 gives an incomplete, but hopefully helpful, sketch of the proof of Adams' result on the number of linearly independent vector fields on n-spheres.

Contents

CHAPTER I

General Theory of Manifolds

We begin with the concept of a *differentiable manifold*, or more briefly *manifold*.

Definition (1): A manifold M is a separable metric space with a system of open subsets $\{U_\alpha\}$ satisfying the following properties: (i) $M \subseteq \bigcup_\alpha U_\alpha$, (ii) for each α, there is a map $h_\alpha : U_\alpha \to E^m$ (E^m is the m-dimensional Euclidean space) such that h_α is a homeomorphism of U_α with an open ball in E^m, (iii) for arbitrary α and β, the map $h_\alpha h_\beta^{-1}$ of $h_\beta (U_\alpha \cap U_\beta) \to E^m$ is smooth, i.e. C^∞. The sets U_α are called "coordinate patches on M" and the maps $h_\alpha h_\beta^{-1}$ are called "change of coordinate maps"; m is called the dimension of M.

One can apply the notions of ordinary local analysis to manifolds. For example, if $\phi : M \to M_1$ is a map from the manifold M into the manifold M_1, we say ϕ is C^∞ or *smooth* at the point $p \in M$ if there exist coordinate patches $U_p \subseteq M$, $V_{\phi(p)} \subseteq M_1$ such that $p \in U_p$, $\phi(p) \in V_{\phi(p)}$ and such that the composite map $g_{\phi(p)}\phi h_p^{-1} : h_p(U_p) \to E^{m_1}$ is C^∞ at $h_p(p) \in E^m$. Here, h_p is the map associated with U_p and $g_{\phi(p)}$ is the map associated with $V_{\phi(p)}$. We say that $\phi' : M \to M_1$ is a *diffeomorphism* between M and M' if ϕ is a homeomorphism which is C^∞ at each point $p \in M$ and which is such that ϕ^{-1} is C^∞ at each point $q \in M_1$. Let us note, incidentally, that if $\phi : M \to M_1$ is C^∞ at $p \in M$, then $g_\gamma \phi h_\alpha^{-1} : h_\alpha(U_\alpha) \to E^{m_1}$ is a C^∞ map at $h_\alpha(p)$ for all coordinate patches U_α, V_γ such that $p \in U_\alpha \subseteq M$, $\phi(p) \in V_\gamma \subseteq M_1$. In fact, $g_\gamma \phi h_\alpha^{-1}$, when restricted to an appropriate subdomain, is equal to

$$g_\gamma g_{\phi(p)}^{-1} g_{\phi(p)} \phi h_p^{-1} h_p h_\alpha^{-1} = (g_\gamma \circ g_{\phi(p)}^{-1}) \circ (g_{\phi(p)} \circ \phi \circ h_p^{-1}) \circ (h_p \circ h_\alpha^{-1}).$$

Condition (iii) of Definition (1) tells us that $g_\gamma g_{\phi(p)}^{-1}$ and $h_p h_\alpha^{-1}$ are C^∞, while $g_{\phi(p)} \phi h_p^{-1}$ is C^∞ by assumption. Hence the composite map is C^∞, as asserted. This shows that the notion of differentiability at a point is invariant, i.e. coordinate free.

1

Let $f: M \to E^1$ be a smooth function at each point $p \in M$. We say that f is *horizontal* at p if, in coordinates, all first partial derivatives of f vanish at p. It follows easily from the chain rule that the notion of being horizontal at a point is invariant under coordinate changes.

Definition (2): Let τ be a linear functional, acting on the set of real-valued smooth functions on M. If, whenever f is horizontal at p, we have $\tau f = 0$, we say τ is a *tangent vector* to M at p.

The following definition is easily seen to be equivalent to Definition (2).

Definition (2′): Let τ be a linear functional, acting on the set of real-valued smooth functions on M. If $\tau(fg) = f(p)\,\tau(g) + g(p)\,\tau(f)$, we say τ is a *tangent vector* to M at p.

If f is a C^∞ real function of a real variable, then integration by parts yields

$$f(1) - f(0) = \int_0^1 f'(s)\,ds = f'(0) + \cdots$$

$$+ \frac{1}{n!} f^{(n)}(0) + \frac{1}{n!} \int_0^1 (1 - s)^n f^{(n+1)}(s)\,ds.$$

If now g is a C^∞ real function of m real variables and if $x \in E^m$, set $f(s) = g(sx)$, and then substitute in the above formula. We obtain

$$g(x) = g(0) + \sum (\partial_i g)(0)\, x^i + \frac{1}{2!} \sum (\partial_{i_1 i_2} g)(0)\, x^{i_1} x^{i_2} + \cdots$$

$$+ \frac{1}{n!} \sum (\partial_{i_1 \cdots i_n} g)(0)\, x^{i_1} \cdots x^{i_n}$$

$$+ \frac{1}{n!} \int_0^1 (1 - s)^n \sum (\partial_{i_1 \cdots i_{n+1}} g)(sx)\, x^{i_1} \cdots x^{i_{n+1}}\,ds,$$

where

$$(\partial_{i_1 \cdots i_j} g)(0) = \left. \frac{\partial^j g}{(\partial x^{i_1}) \cdots (\partial x^{i_j})} \right|_{x=0}, \qquad x = (x^1, \ldots, x^m).$$

Let $g: M \to E^1$ be smooth. We say that g is *n-horizontal* at $p \in M$ if, in coordinates, all partials of g up to and including order n vanish at p. In the above formula, it is clear that the integral term is n-horizontal at $x = (0, \ldots, 0)$. The term $g(0)$ is a constant and we call the sum of the remaining terms the principal part of $g(x)$. Hence, near $x = 0$, $g(x)$ can be written as the sum of a constant, a principal part, and an n-horizontal part.

Definition (3): Let τ be a linear functional, acting on the set of real-valued smooth functions on M. If, whenever f is n-horizontal at p, we have $\tau f = 0$, we say τ is a *jet of order n* (or more briefly, n-jet) to M at p.

Clearly, the notion of tangent vector and 1-jet coincide.

We shall now see how to express an n-jet at p in terms of coordinates at p. Se let $g : M^m \to E^1$ be smooth at $p \in M$ and suppose that in coordinates p corresponds to $(x^1, \ldots, x^m) = (0, \ldots, 0) = 0$. Suppose τ is an arbitrary n-jet at p. From above, we have $g(x) = C + p(x) + H_n(x)$ near $x = 0$. Here, C is a constant, $p(x)$ is the principal part of $g(x)$, and $H_n(x)$ is the n-horizontal part of $g(x)$.

By definition $\tau\,(H_n(x)) = 0$. Moreover, if C is a constant, C is k-horizontal at p for all $k \geq 1$, in particular for $k = n$. So $\tau(C) = 0$. By the linearity of τ, we have

$$\tau(g) = \tau\,(p(x)) = \tau\left(\sum (\partial_i g)\,(0)\,x^i + \cdots + \frac{1}{n!}\sum (\partial_{i_1} \cdots \partial_{i_n} g)\,(0)\,x^{i_1} \cdots x^{i_n}\right)$$

$$= \sum (\partial_i g)\,(0)\,\tau(x^i) + \cdots + \frac{1}{n!}\sum (\partial_{i_1} \cdots \partial_{i_n} g)\,(0)\,\tau\,(x^{i_1} \cdots x^{i_n}).$$

Setting

$$\tau(x^i) = a_i(\tau), \ldots, \tau\,(x^{i_1} \cdots x^{i_n}) = a_{i_1 \ldots i_n}(\tau),$$

we obtain

$$\tau(g) = \sum (\partial_i g)\,(0)\,a_i(\tau) + \cdots + \frac{1}{n!}\sum (\partial_{i_1 \ldots i_n} g)\,(0)\,a_{i_1 \ldots i_n}(\tau).$$

The real numbers $a_i(\tau), \ldots, a_{i_1 \ldots i_n}(\tau)$ are called the coordinates of τ at p. If we put $n = 1$, we have

$$\tau(g) = \sum_{i=1}^{m} a_i(\tau)\,\frac{\partial g}{\partial x^i}$$

or

$$\tau = \sum a_i(\tau)\,\frac{\partial}{\partial x^i}.$$

We can define the sum of two n-jets τ, τ_1 and the product of an n-jet by a scalar in the obvious manner. So the set of n-jets at a point p forms a linear space, *the n-jet space at p*. We call the 1-jet space at p the *tangent space at p*.

If $f : N^n \to E^1$ is a smooth function on the manifold N, we write $f \in C^\infty(N)$. If now $\phi : M^n \to N^m$ is smooth, then $f \in C^\infty(N)$ implies $f \circ \phi \in C^\infty(M)$.

Lemma (1): If $\phi(p) = q$ and $f \in C^\infty(N)$ is k-horizontal at q, then $f \circ \phi$ is k-horizontal at p.

Proof: Locally, ϕ is represented in coordinates by $y_j = \phi_j(x_1, \ldots, x_m)$ $(j = 1, 2, \ldots, n)$. Here $(x_1, \ldots, x_m)$ are coordinates at p and $(y_1, \ldots, y_n)$ are coordinates at q. So

$$\frac{\partial f(\phi(x))}{\partial x_i} = \frac{\partial f(\phi_1(x), \ldots, \phi_n(x))}{\partial x_i}$$

$$= \sum_{j=1}^{n} \frac{\partial f(\phi_1(x), \ldots, \phi_n(x))}{\partial y_j} \cdot \frac{\partial \phi_j(x_1, \ldots, x_m)}{\partial x_i}.$$

Therefore, since $\left.\dfrac{\partial f(\phi(x))}{\partial y_j}\right|_{x=0} = 0$ for $j = 1, 2, \ldots, n$, $\left.\dfrac{\partial f(\phi(x))}{\partial x_i}\right|_{x=0} = 0$

for $i = 1, 2, \ldots, m$. Similarly we can prove that all partials of $f \circ \phi$ up to order k vanish at $x = 0$.

Q.E.D.

If now τ is a k-jet on M at p, we define $\hat{\tau}(f) = \tau(f \circ \phi)$ for $f \in C^{\infty}(N)$. From Lemma (1), it follows that $\hat{\tau}$ is a k-jet on N at $q = \phi(p)$. We write $\hat{\tau} = \phi_*(\tau)$ and call $\hat{\tau}$ an "image k-jet". The following properties follow immediately from the definition.

(a) $\phi_*(\tau + \tau_1) = \phi_*(\tau) + \phi_*(\tau_1)$
(b) 1-jets $\subseteq$ 2-jets $\subseteq$ 3-jets $\subseteq$ $\cdots$

Definition (4): If $\tau(p)$ is, for all $p \in M$, a tangent vector at p, we say $\tau(p)$ is a *tangent vector field*. Define the real-valued function g by $g(p) = \tau(p)(f)$, $f \in C^{\infty}(M)$. This gives rise to a mapping $T : f \to g$. If g is a smooth function for all $f \in C^{\infty}(M)$, we say T is a *smooth vector field*. Clearly $T(fg) = fTg + gTf$.

Similarly, we can define the notion of a k-jet field.

Lemma (2): If T_1 is a k_1-jet field and T_2 is a k_2-jet field, then $(T_1T_2)f = T_1(T_2f)$ is a $k_1 + k_2$-jet field.

Proof: If T_1 and T_2 are both smooth, the composite map T_1T_2 is also smooth. It remains to show that at each point $p \in M$, T_1T_2 gives rise to a $k_1 + k_2$-jet. But, as we have shown above, in coordinates at p, T_2 is a partial differential operator of order k_2 and T_1 is a partial differential operator of order k_1. Hence, T_1T_2 is a partial differential operator of order $k_1 + k_2$.

Q.E.D.

Let $\phi : M \to N$ be smooth, $p \in M$. Denote by $\tau_p(M)$ the tangent space at p. We have shown that there is a linear map $\phi_* : \tau_p(M) \to \tau_{\phi(p)}(N)$. We define the *rank* of ϕ at p to be the dimension of the image of $\tau_p(M)$ under ϕ_*. We denote the rank of ϕ at p by $\mathrm{rank}_p \phi$. If x is a coordinate vector on M at p and y is coordinate vector on N at $\phi(p)$, then ϕ can be written locally as $\Phi(x) = y$. It is easily seen that the linear map ϕ_* is represented in matrix form by the Jacobian matrix $\left\| \dfrac{\partial \Phi_i}{\partial x_j} \right\|_{x=x(p)}$. Hence $\mathrm{rank}_p \phi$ is equal to the rank of this Jacobian matrix.

Remark: If $p_n \to p$, then $\lim\limits_{n \to \infty} \mathrm{rank}_{p_n} \phi \geqq \mathrm{rank}_p \phi$. Indeed, choose a coordinate patch U around p. For n sufficiently large, $p_n \in U$. If now $\mathrm{rank}_p \phi = r$, the Jacobian determinant evaluated at p has a nonvanishing minor of order r. But since the determinant is a continuous function of its entries, it follows that the chosen minor of order r will not vanish for p_n sufficiently near p.

Note however that the Jacobian determinant evaluated at p_n may contain nonvanishing minors of order exceeding r. When this does not occur, we say ϕ is locally of constant rank.

If $\phi : M^m \to N^n$, the maximum possible value of $\mathrm{rank}_p \phi$ is min (m, n).

If $\mathrm{rank}_p \phi$ is maximal, we say p is a *regular* point of ϕ; otherwise, we say p is a *singular* point of ϕ.

Lemma (3): If at p, ϕ is locally of constant rank, then there are coordinates in M at p and N at $\phi(p)$ such that ϕ appears as $\Phi[\tilde{x}, \tilde{y}] = [\tilde{x}, 0]$.

Proof: Let $x = (x_1, x_2, \ldots, x_m)$ be a coordinate vector on M at p and suppose p corresponds to $x = 0$. By assumption, $\mathrm{rank}_p \phi = r$ in a neighborhood of p. Hence, in a neighborhood of $x = 0$, the Jacobian matrix $\left\| \dfrac{\partial \Phi_i}{\partial x_j} \right\|$ has a nonvanishing $r \times r$ minor. Without loss of generality, assume

$$\det \left\| \frac{\partial \Phi_i}{\partial x_j}; \quad 1 \leqq i, j \leqq r \right\| \neq 0$$

near $x = 0$. Let

$$u_k = \Phi_k(x_1, \ldots, x_m), \qquad k = 1, 2, \ldots, r,$$
$$u_k = x_k, \qquad\qquad\quad k = r + 1, \ldots, m.$$

Then $u = (u_1, \ldots, u_m)$ can be taken as a new coordinate vector on M at p. In fact, the determinant of the Jacobian of the transformation $(x_1, \ldots, x_m) \to (u_1, \ldots, u_m)$ at $x = 0$ is easily seen to be non-zero and we can apply the implicit function theorem. In this new coordinate system, ϕ is represented by a new function $\Phi'(u)$ and moreover,

$$\Phi'_k(u_1, \ldots, u_m) = u_k, \qquad k = 1, 2, \ldots, r.$$

1 Schwartz, Differential

The new Jacobian matrix is

$$
\left\| \frac{\partial \Phi_i'}{\partial u_j} ; \quad 1 \leq i \leq n, \quad 1 \leq j \leq m \right\| =
\begin{pmatrix}
\begin{smallmatrix} 1 & & \\ & \ddots & \\ & & 1 \end{smallmatrix} & 0 \\
\hline
* & \begin{smallmatrix} \dfrac{\partial \Phi_{r+1}'}{\partial u_{r+1}} & \cdots & \\ & \ddots & \\ & & \dfrac{\partial \Phi_m'}{\partial u_n} \end{smallmatrix}
\end{pmatrix}
$$

Since the rank of this matrix is exactly r in a whole neighborhood of $u = 0$, we must have $\partial \Phi_\alpha'/\partial u_\beta \equiv 0$ in this neighborhood for $\alpha, \beta > r$. Hence, for $\alpha > r$, $\Phi_\alpha'(u_1, \ldots, u_m)$ is actually a function of only the first r coordinates $u_1, \ldots, u_r$, i.e. $\Phi_\alpha'(u_1, \ldots, u_n) = \Phi_\alpha''(u_1, \ldots, u_r)$. If now y is the coordinate vector on N at $\phi(p)$, we set

$$
\begin{aligned}
z_k &= y_k, & k &= 1, \ldots, r, \\
z_k &= y_k - \Phi_k''(y_1, \ldots, y_r), & k &= r + 1, \ldots, n.
\end{aligned}
$$

Since the Jacobian of this transformation is nonzero at p we see that the transformation $(y_1, \ldots, y_n) \to (z_1, \ldots, z_n)$ is a valid coordinate change at $\phi(p)$. Using the coordinate systems u on M at p and z on N at $\phi(p)$, we see that ϕ is represented by a new function $\tilde{\Phi}(u)$ and

$$
\begin{aligned}
\tilde{\Phi}_k(u_1, \ldots, u_m) &= u_k, & k &= 1, \ldots, r, \\
\tilde{\Phi}_k(u_1, \ldots, u_m) &= 0, & k &= r + 1, \ldots, n.
\end{aligned}
$$

This is the desired result if we write $\tilde{x} = (u_1, \ldots, u_r)$, $\tilde{y} = (u_{r+1}, \ldots, u_m)$. Q.E.D.

Corollary (1): If $\operatorname{rank}_p \phi$ is maximal and $m \geq n$, then for given coordinates x on N at $\phi(p)$, we can choose coordinates $[x, y]$ on M at p such that ϕ is represented by $\Phi[x, y] = x$.

Corollary (2): If $\operatorname{rank}_p \phi$ is maximal and $m \leq n$, then for given coordinates $[x, y]$ on N at $\phi(p)$, we can choose coordinates x on M at p such that ϕ is given by $\Phi(x) = [x, 0]$.

Definition (5): Let M^m and V^v be manifolds such that $V \subseteq M, v \leq m$. We say that V is a *submanifold* of M if in appropriate coordinates V appears locally as a plane. This means that there is a system of coordinate patches $\{U_\alpha\}$ on M such that $\{U_\alpha \cap V\}$ is a system of coordinate patches covering V

and if $x = (x_1, \ldots, x_m)$ is the coordinate vector on U_α, then $U_\alpha \cap V$ appears as $(x_{v+1}, \ldots, x_m) = (0, \ldots, 0)$.

Corollary (3): Let $m \geqq n$ and suppose $\phi : M^m \to N^n$. If W is a submanifold of N and if $\phi^{-1}(W)$ contains only regular points of ϕ, then $\phi^{-1}(W)$ is a submanifold of M and codim $(\phi^{-1}(W)) =$ codim (W).

Proof: Let $p \in \phi^{-1}(W)$ be arbitrary. Then $q = \phi(p) \in W$. Now, there is a coordinate neighborhood V on N at $\phi(p)$ with corresponding coordinate vector $x = (x_1, \ldots, x_n)$ such that $V \cap W$ is a coordinate neighborhood on W at $\phi(p)$ and where x restricted to W is of the form $(x_1, \ldots, x_w, 0, \ldots, 0)$. By Corollary (1), we can choose coordinates $[x, y]$ in M such that ϕ is given by $\Phi [x_1, \ldots, x_w, x_{w+1}, \ldots, x_n, y_{n+1}, \ldots, y_m] = (x_1, \ldots, x_n)$. Hence, if U is the coordinate patch on M at p corresponding to the coordinate vector $[x, y]$, $\phi^{-1}(W) \cap U$ appears as $[x_1, \ldots, x_w, 0, \ldots, 0, y_{n+1}, \ldots, y_m]$. This proves that $\phi^{-1}(W)$ is a submanifold of M. Finally, codim $(\phi^{-1}(W)) = m - (w + (m - n)) = n - w =$ codim (W).

Definition (6): A subset e of a manifold M is said to have *measure zero* if $h_\alpha (e \cap U_\alpha)$ has Lebesgue measure zero for every coordinate patch U_α on M.

Notice that a set of measure zero has empty interior. The following important lemmas will be very useful in the future discussion.

Lemma (4) (Sard): Let $\phi : M \to N$ be smooth and let $S \subseteq M$ be the set of all singular points of ϕ. Then $\phi(S)$ has measure zero.

Lemma (5): Every connected one-dimensional manifold is diffeomorphic to either an open interval or a circle.

Before proceding with the proofs of these lemmas, we shall show how the Brouwer Fixed-Point Theorem can be derived from them. The following proof of Brouwer's theorem is completely non-combinatorial and serves to illustrate the power of the differentiable approach to topological questions. Later, we shall apply these lemmas in a more serious way.

Recall that Brouwer's theorem states that every continuous self-map of the closed n-dimensional ball has a fixed point. Let $B_r^n = \{x = (x_1, \ldots, x_n)| \ \|x\| \leqq r\}$ be the closed n-ball of radius r. We claim that it suffices to prove Brouwer's theorem for differentiable maps. For suppose $f : B_1^n \to B_1^n$ is continuous. Let $\pi_\varepsilon : B_1^n \to B_{1-\varepsilon}^n$ be the retraction of B_1^n onto its subset $B_{1-\varepsilon}^n$. In formulas, we can write

$$\pi_\varepsilon(x) = \begin{cases} x & \text{if } \|x\| < 1 - \varepsilon \\ \dfrac{x}{\|x\|} (1 - \varepsilon) & \text{if } \|x\| \geqq 1 - \varepsilon. \end{cases}$$

It is clear that $d(f, \pi_\varepsilon f) \leq \varepsilon$ where d is the supremum metric. Consider now the maps
$$\pi_{1/m}f : B_1^n \to B_{1-1/m}^n, \qquad m = 2, 3, \ldots$$

By the Weierstrass Approximation Theorem, we can find C^∞ maps ϕ_m such that $d(\pi_{1/m}f, \phi_m) \leq 1/m$. In particular, this means $\phi_m(B_1^n) \subseteq B_1^n$. Assuming Brouwer's Theorem for smooth maps, there is an $x^m \in B_1^n$ such that $\phi_m(x^m) = x^m$, $m = 2, 3, \ldots$ Using the compactness of B_1^n and passing to a subsequence if necessary, we may assume $x^m \to x_\infty \in B_1^n$. It follows from the continuity of f and the triangle inequality that $f(x_\infty) = x_\infty$.

To prove Brouwer's theorem for smooth maps, it suffices to prove that there exists no smooth map $\phi : B_1^n \to \partial B_1^n$ such that $\phi|\partial B_1^n$ is the identity $(\partial B_1^n = \{x | \|x\| = 1\})$. It is a standard result that this last statement is equivalent to Brouwer's theorem and we do not stop to prove it [see Hurewicz and Wallman—*Dimension Theory*]. We should note, however, that the proof is geometric and completely elementary. What remains then is to prove the no-retraction theorem for smooth maps. Suppose that there were a C^∞ map $\phi : B^n \to \partial B^n$ whose restriction to ∂B^n is the identity map. To say that ϕ is smooth on B^n means that there is an extension of ϕ to an open neighborhood $N(B^n)$ of B^n which is C^∞. (Later, we shall use this definition of differentiability when we speak about manifolds with boundary.) Now $\phi : N(B^n) \to \partial B^n$ is a smooth map from an n-dimensional manifold onto an n-1-dimensional submanifold. If S is the set of singular points of ϕ, then by Sard's Lemma, $\phi(S)$ has measure zero. In particular, there is a $p \in \partial B^n$ such that $p \notin \phi(S)$. By Corollary (3), $\phi^{-1}(p)$ is a one dimensional submanifold of $N(B^n)$. Let K be the connected component of $\phi^{-1}(p)$ containing p. There are two possibilities (Lemma (5)):

(i) K is diffeomorphic to an open interval. Now K is a closed subset of $N(B^n)$ and hence $K \cap B^n$ is closed in B^n. Let K be parametrized by $\{\eta(s) : -\infty < s < +\infty\}$ and suppose $\eta(0) = p$. Now first of all, K must pierce ∂B^n at p i.e. it cannot be that $K \subseteq B^n$ or $K \subseteq N(B^n) - B^n$. For otherwise K would be tangent to ∂B^n at p which would contradict the regularity of ϕ at p. (Later, we shall meet this situation in a more general setting when we talk about transversality.) As $\eta(0) = p$, $\eta(-\varepsilon)$ must lie either inside or outside B^n for small ε. We suppose $\eta(-\varepsilon)$ is in the interior of B^n. Then $\eta(s) \in \text{Int } B^n$ for all $s < 0$. Otherwise, $q = \eta(s_0) \in \partial B^n$ for some $s_0 < 0$. Now $q \neq p$ for otherwise K would not be diffeomorphic to an open interval. But, since $\phi|\partial B^n$ is the identity, $q = \phi(q) = \phi(\eta(s_0)) = p$. Hence s_0 cannot exist. Similarly, $\eta(s) \in N(B^n) - B^n$ for all $s > 0$. So consider the set of points in B^n of the form $\eta(s)$, $s < 0$. Let $\{s_n\}$ be a sequence of real numbers tending monotonely to $-\infty$ and consider the sequence of points $\{\eta(s_n)\}$. Passing to a subsequence if necessary, we may assume $\lim_{n\to\infty} \eta(s_n) = p_\infty \in B^n$ exists. Now $\phi(\eta(s_n)) = p$ for all n and by continuity of ϕ, $\phi(p_\infty) = p$. Thus $p_\infty \in \phi^{-1}(p) \cap \bar{K} \cap B^n = K \cap B^n$ since $K \cap B^n$ is closed in B^n. But this clearly contradicts the fact that K is diffeomorphic to an open interval. Hence case (i) is completed.

(ii) K is diffeomorphic to a circle—As in (i), it cannot be that K lies completely inside B^n or completely inside $N(B^n) - B^n$. But since K is essentially a circle, K must intersect ∂B^n in two points, i.e. $K \cap \partial B^n = \{p, q\}$, $q \neq p$. But, as in (i), $q = \phi(q) = \phi(p) = p$, a contradiction. This proves case (ii) and completely proves the no-retraction theorem.

Proof of Lemma (4): Let $p \in M$ and set $q = \phi(p)$. Pick a coordinate patch V_q around q and then, by continuity of ϕ, find a coordinate patch U_p around p such that $\phi(U_p) \subseteq V_q$. We can then find a coordinate neighborhood U'_p around p such that $\bar{U}'_p \subseteq U_p$, $\bar{U}'_p$ is compact, $\bar{U}'_p$ is homeomorphic to an m-ball B^m and U'_p is homeomorphic to Int B^m. Now $\phi(U'_p) \subseteq V_q$ and V_q is homeomorphic to the interior of some open ball B^n. So ϕ can be regarded locally as a map $\phi :$ Int $B^m \to$ Int B^n. Now M is a separable metric space and we can therefore cover M with a countable collection of coordinate patches of the form U'_p. If we can therefore prove Sard's lemma in the case $\phi :$ Int $B^m \to$ Int B^n, we may then use the complete additivity of Lebesgue measure to prove Sard's lemma in the general case. Denote Int B^k by W^k. We prove that if S is the set of singular points of the map $\phi : W^m \to W^n$, then $\phi(S)$ has measure zero. We may regard $\phi : W^m \to W^n$ as a restriction of the corresponding map $\phi : B^m \to B^n$, and we observe that all functions and their derivatives are uniformly continuous.

Case 1, $m < n$: In this case, we show $\phi(W^m)$ has measure zero. We write W^m as a union of small cubes, each of side ε (and therefore each of volume ε^m). We can choose the ε-cubes in such a way that their total number does not exceed c/ε^m where c is a constant independent of ε (c is essentially the volume of W^m). Denote the ε-cubes by $R_i^{(\varepsilon)}$. Now $\phi(W^m) \equiv \phi\left(\bigcup_i R_i^{(\varepsilon)}\right) = \bigcup_i \phi(R_i^{(\varepsilon)})$. Since ϕ is differentiable, diam $(\phi(R_i^{(\varepsilon)}) \leq K\varepsilon$ where K is independent of ε. Hence, Vol $(\phi(R_i^{(\varepsilon)})) \leq K'\varepsilon^n$ where K' is independent of ε.

Finally, Vol $(\phi(W^m)) \leq K'\varepsilon^n \dfrac{c}{\varepsilon^m} = K'c \, \varepsilon^{n-m}$. This converges to zero as $\varepsilon \to 0$ because $n > m$.

Case 2, $m \geqq n$: Let S_k be the set of points in W^m where the rank of ϕ exactly equals k. It is enough to prove that $\phi(S_k)$ has measure zero for each $k < n$. Let P be the mapping of E^n into itself which projects every n-vector $(\alpha_1, \alpha_2, ..., \alpha_n)$ into $(\alpha_1, \alpha_2, ..., \alpha_{k+1}, 0, ..., 0)$. Clearly $P\phi$ is still singular on S_k. If we suppose Sard's lemma holds for the case $n = k + 1$, then $P\phi(S_k)$ has measure zero (in this subspace). By a result in measure theory (essentially Fubini's theorem), we know that if a set $e \subseteq E^n$ is such that $P(e)$ has measure zero, then $P^{-1}(P(e))$ has measure zero. As $e \subseteq P^{-1}(P(e))$, this means that e itself has measure zero. In our case, we have $\phi(S_k) = e$ and hence $\phi(S_k)$ has measure zero. It remains therefore to prove the following statement: If $\phi: W^m \to W^{k+1}$, then $\phi(S_k')$ has measure zero. We proceed by induction on m. For $m = 1$, we must have $k = 0$ and $\phi: W^1 \to W^1$ i.e. ϕ is a smooth self-mapping of an open interval. S_0 is just the set of points where $d\phi(x)/dx = 0$. Cover S_0 with a set of intervals $R_i^{(\varepsilon)}$ of length ε in such a way that the total number of intervals does not exceed c/ε where c is independent of ε. For each i, we claim that $\phi(R_i^{(\varepsilon)})$ is a set of diameter not exceeding $K\varepsilon^2$ where K is independent of ε. In fact let $x_0 \in R_i^{(\varepsilon)} \cap S_0$. Then $d\phi/dx|_{x=x_0} = 0$. If x is any other point in $R_i^{(\varepsilon)}$, we apply Taylor's formula to obtain

$$|\phi(x) - \phi(x_0)| \leqq K |x - x_0|^2 \leqq K\varepsilon^2.$$

Hence, $\phi(S_0) \subseteq \phi \left(\bigcup_i R_i^{(\varepsilon)} \right) = \bigcup_i \phi(R_i^{(\varepsilon)})$ and hence

$$\text{Vol} (\phi(S_0)) \leqq \frac{c}{\varepsilon} K\varepsilon^2 = cK \cdot \varepsilon.$$

Letting $\varepsilon \to 0$, we have

$$\text{Vol} (\phi(S_0)) = 0.$$

We now assume the theorem true for all integers less than m and try to deduce the theorem for the integer m. First of all, assume $k = 0$. Then $\phi: W^m \to W^1$ is a smooth real valued function. Let S_0^m be the set of all points in W^m where all the partials of ϕ up to and including order m vanish. By exactly the same argument as in the case $m = 1$, we can prove that $\phi(S_0^m)$ has measure zero. Now let $\hat{S}_0^j$ be the set of all points in W^m where all the partials of ϕ up to order j vanish, but where some $j + 1$-st partial does not vanish, i.e. if $p \in \hat{S}_0^j$, there is a $\psi = \partial^j \phi$ such that $\psi(p) = 0$ but $\partial \psi (p) \neq 0$. Now ψ is a map from $W^m \to W^1$ and is regular at p. Let U be a neighborhood of p in which $\partial \psi (x) \neq 0$. By Corollary (3), the set $\psi^{-1}(0) \cap U$ is a submanifold of W^m of dimension $m - 1$. Since W^m is separable, this means that $\hat{S}_0^j$ is contained in a countable union of submanifolds of W^m of dimension $m - 1$.

By the induction assumption and the complete additivity of the measure, it follows that $\phi(\hat{S}_0^j)$ has measure zero. Now $S_0 = \hat{S}_0^1 \cup \hat{S}_0^2 \cup \cdots \cup \hat{S}_0^{m-1} \cup S_0^m$; hence $\phi(S_0)$ has measure zero.

Suppose now $\phi: W^m \to W^{k+1}$, $k + 1 \leq m$, $k > 0$. We want to show $\phi(S_k)$ has measure zero. Let $p \in S_k$; in a neighborhood of p, there is a $k \times k$ minor of the Jacobian matrix $\|\partial\Phi_j/\partial x_i\|$ which is nonvanishing. By the implicit function theorem, we can find local coordinates at p and $\phi(p)$ such that the map ϕ is given by $\tilde{\Phi}(x, y) = [x, f(x, y)]$. Here $x = (x_1, x_2, \ldots, x_k)$, $y = (y_{k+1}, \ldots, y_m)$ and $f(x, y)$ is a real-valued function. If U is the coordinate neighborhood corresponding to the coordinate vector $[x, y]$, then clearly

$$S_k \cap U = \left\{ [x, y] \,\Big|\, \frac{\partial f(x, y)}{\partial y_j} = 0 \right\}.$$ Again using the separability of W^m, we

see that S_k is contained in a countable union of sets of the type

$$\left\{ [x, y] \,\Big|\, \frac{\partial f(x, y)}{\partial y_j} = 0 \right\}.$$

Hence it suffices to prove that the measure of the image (under ϕ) of such a set has measure zero.

Now, $\phi(S_k) = \left\{ [x, t] \mid t = f(x, y), \dfrac{\partial f(x, y)}{\partial y_j} = 0; \ j = k + 1, \ldots, m \right\}.$

Fix $x = \bar{x} = (\bar{x}_1, \ldots, \bar{x}_k)$ and consider $\left\{ [\bar{x}, t] \mid t = f(\bar{x}, y), \dfrac{\partial f(\bar{x}, y)}{\partial y_j} = 0; \right.$

$\left. j = k + 1, \ldots, m \right\}.$ For fixed $\bar{x}, f$ can be regarded as mapping the coordinates

$y_{k+1}, \ldots, y_m$ into the real numbers $t = f(\bar{x}, y)$, i.e. $\tilde{f}: W^{m-k} \to W^1$. If we denote by $\tilde{S}_0$ the set of singular points of $\tilde{f}$, it is clear that $\tilde{S}_0$ coincides with

the set of all y such that $\dfrac{\partial f(\bar{x}, y)}{\partial y_j} = 0, j = k + 1, \ldots, m$. But here we have

just the situation discussed above (namely, when $k + 1 \leq m$, $k = 0$) and it follows that $\phi(\tilde{S}_0)$ has measure zero. But $\phi(\tilde{S}_0)$ is essentially

$$\left\{ [\bar{x}, t] \mid t = f(\bar{x}, y), \frac{\partial f(\bar{x}, y)}{\partial y_j} = 0, \ j = k + 1, \ldots, m \right\}$$

and hence this latter set has measure zero. Thus $\phi(S_k)$ is such that its intersection with each vertical line $\{[\bar{x}, t] \mid -t_1 < t < t_2\}$ has measure zero. Again appealing to Fubini's theorem, we deduce that $\phi(S_k)$ itself has measure zero. This completes the proof of Sard's lemma.

Q.E.D.

Let $\mathscr{D}$ be a smooth vector field on the smooth manifold M. If $\gamma(t)$ is a differentiable curve in M, then we can define $\frac{d}{dt}\gamma(t) \circ f = \frac{d}{dt}f(\gamma(t))$. This gives a tangent vector at each point $\gamma(t) \in M$. Given $p_0 \in M$, we want to find a differentiable curve $\gamma(t, p_0)$ in M passing through p_0 such that $\frac{d}{dt}\gamma(t) \circ f$ $= \mathscr{D} \circ f$. This leads to the initial-value problem $\frac{d}{dt}\gamma(t, p_0) = \mathscr{D}(\gamma(t, p_0))$, $\gamma(0, p_0) = p_0$. Expressing the problem in local coordinates, we are able to apply the classical theory of ordinary differential equations. See S. Long's book for the relevant theory of differential equations.

We now proceed to the proof of Lemma (5) on one-dimensional connected manifolds. Suppose M is a connected one-dimensional manifold. Let U be a maximal coordinate patch on M. The existence of U will be established later. Now U is diffeomorphic to the open interval $(-1, 1)$; let $p(t)$, $-1 < t < 1$, be a $1-1$ parametrization of U. If U is closed in M, we are finished. In fact, U is open and closed in M and since M is connected, $U = M$. Thus, in this case, M is diffeomorphic to an open interval. We assume then that U is not closed. Then, there exists a sequence $t_n \to 1$ (for definiteness) such that $p(t_n) \to p_\infty$ $\notin U$. We take a coordinate patch $\hat{V}$ around p_∞. Now $\hat{V}$ contains some point in U, say $p(A)$ (where $-1 < A < 1$). We choose a coordinate patch V around p_∞ such that V has compact closure $\bar{V}$ in $\hat{V}$. As $\bar{V}$ is diffeomorphic to a closed interval, we can moreover require that one of the endpoints of $\bar{V}$ be $p(A)$. It follows readily that all points $p(t)$ for $t > A$ lie in V and then plainly $p(t) \to p_\infty$ as $t \to 1$. We claim that $U \cap V$ is one of the two following sets:

(a) $\{p(t) \mid t > A\}$,
(b) $\{p(t) \mid t > A\} \cup \{p(t) \mid t < B$ for some B between -1 and $+1\}$.

To see this, we observe that one of the following statements is true:

(1) As $t \to -1$, $p(t)$ has no limit point,
(2) As $t \to -1$, $p(t) \to p_{-\infty}$ and $p_{-\infty} \neq p_\infty$,
(3) As $t \to -1$, $p(t) \to p_\infty$ i.e. $p_{-\infty} = p_\infty$.

If either (1) or (2) holds, we can choose V and $\varepsilon > 0$ so small that $V \cap \{p(t)\mid t < -1 + \varepsilon\} = \phi$. For otherwise, there would exist a sequence $p(t_n)$, $t_n \to -1$ such that $p(t_n) \to p_\infty$. But this would imply that $p_{-\infty}$ exists and that $p_{-\infty} = p$. Thus, if either (1) or (2) holds, then (a) is true. On the other hand, if (3) holds, then clearly (b) is true.

We consider first case (a): We shall prove that there exists on $U \cup V$ a vector field $\mathscr{D}$ such that (i) on U, and in the coordinates of U, $\mathscr{D}$ is positive and bounded, (ii) on V, and in the coordinates of V, $\mathscr{D}$ is positive and bounded. To see this, we note first of all that we may assume that the change of coordinates map from U to V has positive derivative. For otherwise, we reverse the coordinate on V (i.e. if s is the coordinate on V, replace s by $-s$). We now construct a vector field $\mathscr{D}_1$ on U which is nonnegative and bounded on U. To do this, construct a C^∞ real function f_1 on the interval $-1 < t < 1$ such that $f_1 = 1$ on $(-1, A)$ and such that f_1 tapers off smoothly to 0 before reaching $t = +1$. Let $\mathscr{D}_1$ be the vector field on U which, when expressed in coordinates, is of the form $f_1(t)\dfrac{d}{dt}$. Assume now $\hat{V}$ is diffeomorphic to the interval $-1 < s < 1$ while V is given by $-\frac{1}{2} < s < \frac{1}{2}$. Construct a C^∞ real function f_2 on the interval $-1 < s < 1$ such that $f_2 = 1$ on $[-\frac{1}{2}, \frac{1}{2}]$ and such that f_2 tapers off smoothly to 0 before reaching $s = -1$ and $s = 1$. Let $\mathscr{D}_2$ be the vector field on V which, when expressed in coordinates, is of the form $f_2(s)\dfrac{d}{ds}$. If we put $\mathscr{D} = \mathscr{D}_1 + \mathscr{D}_2$, then $\mathscr{D}$ clearly satisfies (i) and (ii) above.

Take $p_0 \in U \cap V$ and consider the initial value problem

$$\frac{d\gamma\,(x, p_0)}{dx} = \mathscr{D}\,(\gamma\,(x, p_0)),\ \gamma\,(0, p_0) = p_0.$$

Let $\gamma\,(x, p_0)$ be the solution to this problem. It follows from the fact that $\mathscr{D}$ is positive and bounded that $x \to \gamma\,(x, p_0)$ covers all of V monotonely and all of U monotonely. But then γ gives a $1 - 1$ parametrization of $U \cup V$ which contradicts the maximality of U. Hence, we conclude that p_∞ does not exist in this case, i.e. $U = M$.

Case (b) may be treated in exactly the same way.

We consider case (c): We have $p(t) \to p_\infty$ as $t \to \pm 1$. If $K = \{p(t)\,|\,-1 < t < 1\} \cup \{p_\infty\}$, then K is both open and closed and therefore $K = M$. Now K is topologically a circle and it remains only to prove that M is also diffeomorphic to a circle. Note that, there is a continuous parametrization of M by $\theta\,(0 \leq 0 \leq 2\pi)$ and any coordinate system can be oriented using θ. More precisely, we can cover M by coordinate patches such that each change of coordinates map has positive derivative. Hence, the notion of a positive vector field on M is well-defined. Since M is compact, we can construct (by using a partition of unity) a vector field $\mathscr{D}$ on M which is everywhere positive and bounded. Again, let $p_0 \in U \cap V$ and consider the initial value problem $d\gamma\,(x, p_0)/dx = \mathscr{D}\,(\gamma\,(x, p_0), \gamma\,(0, p_0) = p_0$.

The range of the solution $\gamma\,(x, p_0)$ includes $U \cup V$. Now γ cannot be $1 - 1$ and so there is an $x_0 \neq 0$ such that $\gamma\,(x_0, p_0) = \gamma\,(0, p_0)$.

Then the set $\{\gamma\,(x, p_0)|0 \leq x \leq x_0\}$ is a circle embedded in M and thus must be all of M.

It remains to prove the existence of a maximal coordinate patch U in M. We use Zorn's lemma: Take an ascending chain $\{U_n\}$ of coordinate patches (i.e. $U_j \subseteq U_k$ if $j \leq k$). Note that since M has a countable base, it is unnecessary to consider uncountable chains. We can assume that all the change of coordinate maps have positive derivative. Let $L = \bigcup\limits_{n=1}^{\infty} U_n$. If we can show that L is covered by a single coordinate patch, we will have proved that every chain has a least upper bound and we can then appeal to Zorn's lemma. We shall construct on L a positive and bounded vector field. On each U_j, we can construct a vector field $\mathscr{D}_j$ which is positive and bounded. We may even assume each $\mathscr{D}_j$ is bounded above by 1. Let $\mathscr{D} = \sum\limits_{n=1}^{\infty} \dfrac{1}{n!} \mathscr{D}_n$. Then $\mathscr{D}$ is the desired vector field. Using the previous arguments, we find that L is indeed covered by a single coordinate patch. This completes the proof of the lemma. Q.E.D.

Definition (7): Let M^m be a manifold. If U and V are two overlapping coordinate neighborhoods on M, we say U and V are *positively related* if the change of coordinates map from U to V has positive Jacobian determinant. M is said to be *orientable* if it can be covered by coordinate neighborhoods, any two of which are positively related. Otherwise, M is said to be *nonorientable*.

The following construction is useful: If N is a connected, nonorientable manifold, there exists a connected, orientable manifold $\hat{N}$ which is a twofold covering of N. To define $\hat{N}$, we take the collection S of all pairs (p, U) where U is a coordinate neighborhood around p. We take two copies of S, say S_+ and S_-. Then $S_+ = \{(p, U)_+|p \in U\}$, $S_- = \{(p, U)_-|p \in U\}$. We make the following identification: Identify $(p, U)_+$ with $(q, V)_+$ iff $p = q$ and the change of coordinates map from U to V has positive Jacobian determinant at the point p, identify $(p, U)_+$ with $(q, V)_-$ iff $p = q$ and the change of coordinates map from U to V has negative Jacobian determinant at the point p, and identify $(p, U)_-$ with $(q, V)_-$ iff $p = q$ and the change of coordinates map from U to V has positive Jacobian determinant at p. Let $\hat{N}$ be the set obtained from $S_+ \cup S_-$ by virtue of this identification. To define a topology on $\hat{N}$, we define neighborhoods as follows: Denote by $[(p, U)_+]$ the equivalence class (i.e. the element in $\hat{N}$) containing $(p, U)_+$. For a neighborhood of $[(p, U)_+]$, take all points in $\hat{N}$ of the form $[(q, U)_+]$ where q ranges over U. Similarly, we define the neighborhood of $[(p, U)_-]$. It is easy to check that with this definition of neighborhoods $\hat{N}$ becomes a topological space. To make $\hat{N}$ a manifold, we define coordinates on the neighborhoods as follows: For coordinates around $[(p, U)_+]$, take the coordinates of U. For coordinates around $[(p, U)_-]$, take the reversed coordinates of U. That is, if $(x_1, \ldots, x_n)$ are the coordinates of U, take $(x_1, \ldots, x_{n-1}, -x_n)$ to be the coordinates around $[(p, U)_-]$. With this structure, $\hat{N}$ becomes a C^∞ manifold. It is easy to see that $\hat{N}$ is orientable and that the map $[(p, U)_\pm] \to p$ is a two to one differentiable covering map. It follows from the fact that $\hat{N}$ is nonorientable that N is connected.

Definition (8): Let A be closed subset of a separable metric space M. M is a *relative manifold modulo A* if $M - A$ is a manifold. We say (M, A) or (M/A) is a relative manifold.

Definition (9): Let $M \subseteq N$ (N is a manifold), $p \in M$. Then p is a *j-corner* point if there is a coordinate patch U in N such that in these coordinates, $M \cap U$ appears as a j-corner in E^n ($n = \dim (N)$). A j-corner in E^n is $\{x = [x_1, x_2, \ldots, x_n] \mid \|x\| < 1, \ x_1 \geq 0, \ldots, x_j \geq 0\}$. Here, p corresponds to the origin $x = [0, 0, \ldots, 0]$.

Definition (10): A *manifold with corners* is a space such that every point is a j-corner point for some $j \geq 0$. A *manifold with boundary* is a space such that every point is either a 0-corner point or a 1-corner point.

The notion of j-corner point is independent of the coordinate patch; in fact if p is a j-corner point, then the set of all vectors tangent "in both directions" to the manifold at p is an $m - j$-dimensional vector space and this number is invariant under any nonsingular linear transformation. If M^m is a manifold with boundary ∂M, then ∂M is a manifold of dim $m - 1$. ∂M inherits its differentiable structure from M.

Let M^m, A^a be manifolds, N^n a submanifold of M. Locally, if $[x, y]$ are coordinates on M, N appears as $x = 0$, i.e. the coordinates on N are $[0, y]$.

Definition (11): Let $\phi \mathbf{I} A \to M$ be C^∞; then ϕ is *transverse* to N at $q \in \phi^{-1}(N)$ if
$$T_p(N) + \phi_* (T_q(A)) = T_p(M).$$

Here $p = \phi(q)$, $T_p(N)$ and $T_p(M)$ are the respective tangent spaces, and ϕ_* is the map of tangent spaces induced by ϕ.

Note: (a) if $\dim(A) + \dim(N) < \dim(M)$, then $N \cap \phi(A) = \phi$;

(b) if $\dim(A) + \dim(N) = \dim(M)$, then the solutions of $\phi(q) \in N$ are isolated points;

(c) let P_x be the projection $[x, y] \to x$.

The definition of transversality is equivalent to: $P_x\phi$ is regular at q. (In this case, $P_x\phi$ is regular at q means $(P_x\phi)_*$ is an onto map).

(d) if ϕ is transverse to N at each point of $\phi^{-1}(N)$, then $\phi^{-1}(N)$ is a submanifold of A and codim $(\phi^{-1}(N))$ in $A = $ codim (N) in M. This follows from the lemmas given previously.

Definition (12): Let N, $\bar{N}$ be submanifolds of the manifold M, $N \cap \bar{N} \neq \phi$. N and $\bar{N}$ are said to be *transverse* at their intersection if the injection $i:$ $N \to M$ is transverse to $\bar{N}$ at each intersection point; i.e. $T_p(N) + T_p(\bar{N})$ $= T_p(M) \, (p \in N \cap \bar{N})$.

As an example, let M be E^3, N the plane $x_3 = 0$, and $\bar{N}$ the line $x_1 = 0$, $x_2 = 0$. Then N, $\bar{N}$ are transverse at $(0, 0, 0)$.

Lemma (6): If N, $\bar{N}$ are transverse at their intersection, $p \in N \cap \bar{N}$, then it is possible to choose suitable coordinates near p such that both N, $\bar{N}$ appear as planes (in fact, as linear subspaces whose sum is the whole space).

Proof: Let $[x, y]$ be coordinates on M at p, such that N appears as $[0, y]$. Let $P_x: [x, y] \to x$. Introduce coordinates z on $\bar{N}$, $i(z): \bar{N} \to M$. As $P_x i$ is regular at p, change coordinates $z \to [u, v]$ such that $P_x i \, [(u, v)] = u$ (see remark (c) above). Then $i \, ([u, v]) = [u, \psi \, (u, v)]$. As $\bar{N}$ is regularly embedded, i has maximal rank. Hence

$$[u, \psi \, (u, v)] = [u, \eta \, (u, v), x \, (u, v)], \quad \det \left(\frac{\partial \eta}{\partial v}\right) \neq 0.$$

Change coordinates in $\bar{N}$: $[u, v] \to [u, \eta]$. Then $i \, ([u, \eta]) = [u, \eta, x \, (u, \eta)]$. Change coordinates in M: $[u, \eta, x] \to [u, \eta, x - x \, (u, \eta)]$. Then $i \, ([u, \eta])$ $= [u, \eta, 0]$ and the assertion is proved.

Q.E.D.

Corollary: $N \cap \bar{N}$ is a submanifold.

Proof: Clearly, $N \cap \bar{N}$ is locally a plane at $p \in N \cap \bar{N}$.

Lemma (7): Let $\phi: M \to A$ and let $N \subseteq M$, $B \subseteq A$ be submanifolds. Suppose ϕ is transverse to B everywhere and $\phi|N$ is transverse to B everywhere. Then N and $\phi^{-1}(B)$ are transverse in M.

Proof: Since transversality pertains to tangent spaces, we can restate the lemma in the following linearized form: if $\bar{N} \subseteq \bar{M}$, $\bar{B} \subseteq \bar{A}$ (considered as

subspaces of linear spaces), $\bar{\phi} : \bar{M} \to \bar{A}$ is a linear map, $\bar{\phi}(\bar{M}) + \bar{B} = \bar{A}$ and $\bar{\phi}(\bar{N}) + \bar{B} = \bar{A}$, then $\bar{N} + \bar{\phi}^{-1}(\bar{B}) = \bar{M}$. To prove the last statement, take any $\bar{m} \in \bar{M}$. Then $\bar{\phi}(\bar{m}) = \bar{a} = \bar{\phi}(\bar{n}) + \bar{b} \Rightarrow \bar{m} - \bar{n} \in \bar{\phi}^{-1}(\bar{B})$.
Q.E.D.

If M is a manifold with boundary ∂M, we always assume M is contained in some larger manifold M_0. A map $\phi : M \to A$ (A is a manifold) is understood to be the restriction of the map $\phi : M_0 \to A$. Suppose now B is a submanifold of A. Suppose ϕ is transverse to B everywhere, $\phi|\partial M$ is transverse to B everywhere (in ∂M). By the first condition, we know $\phi^{-1}(B)$ is a submanifold of M_0. By the previous lemma, $\phi^{-1}(B)$ is transverse to ∂M wherever it intersects ∂M. It is easy to see that $M \cap \phi^{-1}(B)$ is a manifold with boundary $\partial (M \cap \phi^{-1}(B)) = \phi^{-1}(B) \cap \partial M$.

Example: Suppose the above hypotheses are satisfied. Moreover, assume M is *compact*, $B = \{b\}$ (i.e. only one point), $\dim (M) = 1 + \dim (A)$. Then $\phi^{-1}(b)$ is a submanifold of M of dimension 1. Therefore $\phi^{-1}(b)$ is a union of open arcs and circles. $C = \phi^{-1}(b) \cap M$ is then a collection of *closed* arcs and circles; ∂C is a set of points in $\partial M \cap \phi^{-1}(b)$. This set of points is finite because M is compact and the parity of this set of points is even (because the intersection of an open arc or a circle with ∂M consists of an even number of points).

This Lemma will play an important role in the next chapter, when we discuss the theory of degree.

We state this result for future reference as a lemma.

Lemma (8): Let M be a compact manifold with boundary ∂M, and A a manifold of the same dimension as ∂M. Let $\phi : M \to A$ be a smooth map. Suppose that $a \in A$ is chosen in such a way that $\mathfrak{z}$ is transverse to a everywhere and $\phi|\partial M$ is transverse to a everywhere. Then $\phi^{-1}(a) \cap M$ decomposes into a number of smooth closed curves lying in $M - \partial M$ and a number of smooth closed arcs in M intersecting ∂M only at their end-points. These arcs intersect ∂M transversally at their end-points. All the points of $\phi^{-1}(a) \cap \partial M$ are end-points of such arcs.

CHAPTER II

Degree of a Map and Intersection Theory. Applications

Definition (1): Let M, A be manifolds, both of dimension m. Suppose M is *compact* and let $\phi : M \to A$ be C^∞. If ϕ is transverse to $\{p\}$, $p \in A$, then the parity of the number of points in $\phi^{-1}(p)$ is called *the degree of ϕ at p (mod 2)* and is denoted by $\deg_2(\phi)|_p$.

Let M and A be as before and let $\psi : M \to A$, $\bar{\psi} : M \to A$ be (smoothly) homotopic; i.e. there exists a $\Psi : M \times [0, 1] \to A$ such that $\Psi | M \times \{0\} = \psi$, $\Psi | M \times \{1\} = \bar{\psi}$. (We assume ψ, $\bar{\psi}$, Ψ are C^∞ and say that Ψ is a smooth homotopy.) Take $p \in A$ and suppose all maps involved are transverse to the submanifold $\{p\}$ of A. Let $M' = M \times [0, 1]$. Then M' is a manifold with boundary $\partial M' = (M \times \{0\}) \cup (M \times \{1\})$ and $\dim (M') = m + 1$. By Lemma 8 of the last chapter, $\partial (\Psi^{-1}(p) \cap M')$ contains an even number of points. This means that if the number of solutions of $\Psi(x) = p$, $x \in M \times \{0\}$, is n_0 and the number of solutions of $\Psi(x) = p$, $x \in M \times \{1\}$, is n_1, then $n_0 \equiv n_1 \pmod{2}$. But $\Psi(x) = \psi(x)$ for $x \in M \times \{0\}$ and $\Psi(x) = \bar{\psi}(x)$ for $x \in M \times \{1\}$, and hence the parity number of points in $\psi^{-1}(p) =$ the parity number of points in $\bar{\psi}^{-1}(p)$. We shall show later that it is not necessary to assume that the homotopy Ψ is transverse to A at $\{p\}$. We will then have proved:

Theorem (1): $\deg_2(\phi)|_p$ is a (smooth) homotopy invariant.

Remark: It follows from an approximation theorem that we will discuss later that if two smooth maps are homotopic then they are actually smoothly homotopic.

Remark: Assume the manifolds M and A are compact and also that A is connected. Then the set $B \subseteq A$ of all points p such that a smooth map $\phi : M \to A$ is transverse to $\{p\}$ is open and everywhere dense (Sard's Lemma).

It will be shown below that $\deg_2 \phi|_p$ is the same for all points $p \in B$. It will then be called the *degree of ϕ (mod 2)*.

In fact, let x be a coordinate system with origin at the point $a \in A$, let V be a spherical neighborhood of $\mathscr{A}$ in this coordinate system, and further let b_0 and b_1 be two points of $V \cap B$. It is easy to construct a diffeomorphism ψ of A onto itself, under which all points of the set $A - V$ remain fixed and which maps b_0 to b_1. The map ψ is homotopic to the identity (see the "Homotopy Lemma" below). It is easy to see that the degree of $\psi\phi$ at b_1 is equal to the degree of ϕ at b_0; but since $\psi\phi$ and ϕ are homotopic, their degrees at b_1 coincide. Thus the degrees of ϕ at all points $b \in V \cap B$ are equal. Since A is connected and B is everywhere dense in A it follows that the degrees of ϕ at all points of B are the same.

Corollary: Let M be a compact manifold. Then, since the identity map of M onto itself has degree 1, and the constant map has degree zero, these two maps are not homotopic.

Remark: Assume the manifolds M and A in Definition (1) above are oriented, while A is also connected. $\phi^{-1}(p)$ consists of a finite number of points $m_1, m_2, \ldots, m_k$, at each of which the Jacobian determinant of ϕ is not zero and has a definite sign. Denote by $\varepsilon_i \, (= \pm 1)$ the sign of the Jacobian determinant of ϕ at m_i, $i = 1, 2, \ldots, k$. We may now state the following proposition.

Proposition: Let M^{m+1} be a compact oriented manifold with boundary ∂M, A^m a compact connected manifold which is oriented, ϕ a smooth map of $M \to A$ such that $\phi/\partial M$ is transverse to A at p. Then the map $\phi/\partial M$ has degree zero at p.

Proof: Using Lemma 8 of the preceding chapter, we have only to show that if $\sigma = \sigma(t)$, $0 \le t \le 1$, is a smooth closed arc in M intersecting ∂M only in its end-points, if $\phi(\sigma(t)) \equiv p$, and if σ intersects ∂M transversally at its end points, then the following statement holds:

A: Let N_q denote the tangent space to any manifold N at one of its points q. Suppose that the jacobian transformation ϕ_* maps a positively oriented basis for $(\partial M)_{\sigma(0)}$ to a positively oriented basis for A_p. Then ϕ_* maps a positively oriented basis for $(\partial M)_{\sigma(1)}$ to a negatively oriented basis for A_p.

To see this, note that ∂M is oriented by the following rule: call a basis β of $(\partial M)_q$ positively oriented if, when supplemented by a vector of M_q pointing into M, it gives a positively oriented basis of the (oriented) space M_q. Now let $\sigma'(t)$ denote the tangent vector to σ at $\sigma(t)$. Then, by hypothesis, ϕ_* in duces an isomorphism of the factor space $M_{\sigma(t)}/(\sigma'(t))$ onto A_p. Call a set $\alpha = \{v_1, \ldots, v_n\}$ of n vectors in $M_{\sigma(t)}$ σ-*positive* if $\{v_1, \ldots, v_n, \sigma'(t)\}$ is a positively oriented basis for $M_{\sigma(t)}$. Since $\sigma'(0)$ points into M, it follows from the above that if α is σ-positive set of vectors in $M_{\sigma(t)}$, $t = 0$, then $\phi_*\alpha$ is a positively oriented set of vectors in A_p. By continuity, the same holds for all $0 \leq t \leq 1$. Since $\sigma'(1)$ points out of M, a σ-positive set of vectors in $(\partial M)_{\sigma(1)}$ is negatively oriented in the space $(\delta M)_{\sigma(1)}$. Hence the above statement A follows. Q.E.D.

Definition (1A): Let M, A be oriented manifolds, both of dimension m. Suppose M is compact, and let $\phi: M \to A$ be C^∞. If ϕ is transverse to $\{p\}, p \in A$, then the number of points in $\phi^{-1}(p)$, counted with the sign convention of the above Remark, is the *degree of ϕ at p*, and is denoted by $\deg(\phi)|_p$.

Using the above proposition, and arguing exactly as in the proof of Theorem 1, we may obtain the following result.

Theorem (1A): $\deg(\phi)|_p$ is a (smooth) homotopy invariant of mappings between compact oriented manifolds.

In the next few pages, we shall show that the restrictions arising from the proof of Theorems 1 and 1A, namely that ϕ be smooth, that ϕ be transverse to p, as well as the condition of smoothness of homotopies, may be relaxed.

In the course of doing this, we will develop lemmas in terms of which a more general and powerful "intersection theory" can be built up.

Let X be a metric space, $Y \subseteq X$. Then Y is said to be of *first category* if Y is the countable union of nowhere dense subsets of X. Y is said to be a *prevalent* subset if $X - Y$ is of first category. If P is a property of points, P is said to be true at *most points* if the set of points on which P is true is prevalent.

Any manifold has a metric which makes it complete: For M compact, this is obvious. Otherwise take the one-point compactification $M \cup \{p_\infty\}$. If $\varrho\,(x, y)$ is a complete metric on $M \cup \{p_\infty\}$, introduce $\varrho_1\,(x, y) = \varrho\,(x, y) + |\varrho\,(x, p_\infty)^{-1} - \varrho\,(y, p_\infty)^{-1}|$ for $x, y \in M$. Then ϱ_1 is a complete metric on M.

As M is separable and locally compact, $M = \overset{\infty}{\underset{m=1}{U}} K_m$, with $K_1, K_2, \ldots,$ compact, $K_1 \subset \operatorname{int} K_2 \subset K_2 \subset \operatorname{int} K_3 \subset \ldots$ We consider the set of continuous maps of M into itself. Define

$$d\,(\phi, \psi) = \sum_{i=1}^{\infty} \frac{1}{2^i} \frac{\underset{p \in K_i}{\sup} \varrho\,(\phi(p), \psi(p))}{1 + \underset{p \in K_i}{\sup} \varrho\,(\phi(p), \psi(p))}.$$

Then the set of maps of M into M forms a complete metric space. Clearly, convergence in d is the same as uniform convergence on compact subsets.

If M is a manifold, let $J_K(M)$ be the collection of all K-jets at all points of M. $J_K(M)$ is called the K-jet space of M. We can make $J_K(M)$ a manifold. For $K = 1$ this manifold is called the tangent space of M and its dimension is $2m$. We introduce coordinates in $J_1(M)$ as follows: if (m^0, α^0) is a pair from $J_1(M)$ ($m^0 \in M$, α^0 is a tangent vector at m^0), there is a coordinate neighborhood U of m^0 with coordinates $(x_1, \ldots, x_m)$. Let $\pi : J_1(M) \to M$ be defined by $\pi(\tilde{m}, \alpha) = \tilde{m}$. Then $\pi^{-1}(U)$ is the set of all pairs $(\tilde{m}, \alpha)$ such that $\tilde{m} \in U$. If $(\tilde{m}, \alpha) \in \pi^{-1}(U)$, then $\tilde{m} = (x_1, \ldots, x_m)$ and

$$\alpha = a_1 \frac{\partial}{\partial x_1} + \cdots + a_m \frac{\partial}{\partial x_m}.$$

The map

$$(\tilde{m}, \alpha) \to (x_1, x_2, \ldots, x_m, a_1, a_2, \ldots, a_m)$$

is a $1 - 1$ map between $\pi^{-1}(U)$ and an open subset of E^{2m}. There is a unique topology on $J_1(M)$ which makes this map a homeomorphism. We take $\{\pi^{-1}(U)\}$ as coordinate neighborhoods of $J_1(M)$ with homeomorphisms

$$(\tilde{m}, \alpha) \to (x_1, x_2, \ldots, x_m, a_1, a_2, \ldots, a_m)$$

as coordinate mappings.

It is left to the reader to verify that these coordinate neighborhoods are compatible with one another.

A similar construction, based on the fact that in local coordinates a K-jet has a unique expression as a partial differential operator of order K, can be used to define a manifold structure for $J_K(M)$. We leave details to the reader.

Let ϱ_K be a complete metric on $J_K(M)$. A map $\phi : M \to M$ induces a map $\phi_* : J_K(M) \to J_K(M)$ (Chapter I). Introduce $d_K(\phi_*, \psi_*)$ as above. Define $\hat{d}_K(\phi, \psi) = d_K(\phi_*, \psi_*)$. Then convergence in $\hat{d}_K$ is the same as uniform convergence of all derivatives up to order K on compact subsets. Finally, define

$$\hat{d}_\infty(\phi, \psi) = \sum_{K=1}^\infty \frac{1}{2^K} \frac{\hat{d}_K(\phi, \psi)}{1 + \hat{d}_K(\phi, \psi)}.$$

Then convergence in $\hat{d}_\infty$ is the same as uniform convergence of all derivatives on compact subsets. All the metrics defined above are complete.

Auxiliary Lemma (1): Let (M, A) be a relative manifold. Suppose $\phi : (M^m, A) \to N^m$, $p \in N^m - \phi(A)$. Assume M is compact and ϕ is transverse to $\{p\}$. If ψ is sufficiently close to ϕ in the C^1-topology then the number of points in $\psi^{-1}(p) = $ the number of points in $\phi^{-1}(p)$.

Proof: Since M is compact, $\phi^{-1}(p)$ has only a finite number of points, call them $\{q_1, ..., q_K\}$. Surround each q_j with a coordinate neighborhood U_j such that $U_j \cap U_i = \phi$ $(i \neq j)$. We can do this because each $q_j \in M - A$ (which is a manifold). Then $\phi\left(M - \overset{K}{\underset{j=1}{\cup}} U_j\right) \not\ni p$. For ψ sufficiently close (even in the C^0-sense) $\psi\left(M - \overset{K}{\underset{j=1}{\cup}} U_j\right) \not\ni p$. We want to show that for ψ sufficiently close to ϕ in the C^1-sense, each U_j contains exactly one point of $\psi^{-1}(p)$. Now, as ϕ is transverse to $\{p\}$ at q_j,

$$T_p(\{p\}) + \phi_*(T_{a_j}(M)) = T_p(N).$$

As $T_p(\{p\})$ is 0-dimensional, $\phi_*(T_{a_j}(M))$ must be m-dimensional. Hence the Jacobian of ϕ must be nonzero. If ψ is close to ϕ in the C^1-sense, then the Jacobian of ψ at q_j must also be different from zero. By the implicit function theorem, ψ maps U_j diffeomorphically onto a neighborhood of p. In particular, there exists exactly one point $x_j \in U_j$ such that $\psi(x_j) = p$.
Q.E.D.

Corollary: Suppose the manifolds in the auxiliary lemma are oriented. We count a point in $\phi^{-1}(p)$ with a plus sign if the Jacobian of ϕ is positive at the point, and with a negative sign if the Jacobian is negative. Then with obvious modifications in the statement of the above lemma, the result is still true. The proof is along similar lines.

Lemma (2): Let N be a compact, connected manifold, $\phi : N \to N$ a self-diffeomorphism. If ψ is sufficiently close to ϕ in the C^1-sense, then ψ is also a self-diffeomorphism.

Proof: ϕ_* is nonsingular everywhere; therefore, for ψ sufficiently close to ϕ in the C^1 sense, ψ_* has the same property. So ψ is locally $1-1$ and takes open sets onto open sets by the implicit function theorem. As N is compact, ψ takes closed sets to closed sets. By the connectedness of N, $\psi(N) = N$. It remains to show ψ is globally $1-1$: Suppose it is not. Then there exists a sequence of maps $\{\psi_n\}$, $\psi_n \to \phi$ in the C^1-topology and sequences of points $\{q_n\}$, $\{q_n'\}$, such that $\psi_n(q_n) = \psi_n(q_n')$. Using the compactness of N and passing to subsequences if necessary, assume $q_n \to q_\infty$, $q_n' \to q_\infty'$. Clearly $\phi(q_\infty) = \phi(q_\infty')$. Hence $q_\infty = q_\infty'$. But then for n sufficiently large, q_n, q_n' lie in a single arbitrarily neighborhood. This contradicts the fact that ψ_n is locally $1-1$.
Q.E.D.

Let $\mathcal{M}$ be the space of all maps $\phi : N \to N$ with the C^∞-topology. The above lemma shows that the subset $D \subseteq \mathcal{M}$ of self-diffeomorphisms is open. Let $d_\infty (\phi, \psi)$ be the complete metric on the space of C^∞-maps of $N \to N$. Introduce

$$\hat{d}_\infty (\phi, \psi) = d_\infty (\phi, \psi) + \left| \left(\inf_{K \in \mathcal{M} - D} d_\infty (\phi, K) \right)^{-1} - \left(\inf_{K \in \mathcal{M} - D} d_\infty (\psi, K) \right)^{-1} \right|$$

for $\phi, \psi \in D$. $\hat{d}_\infty$ is a complete metric on D.

Jiggling Lemma (3): Let $\Psi : M^m \to N^n$ be C^∞ and let V be a submanifold of N. Assume M, N are compact. Then the set of self-diffeomorphisms η of N such that $\eta \Psi$ is transverse to V is a prevalent open set of D.

Corollary: Let $\phi, \psi : M^m \to N^m$ be smoothly homotopic and let $p \in N$. If ϕ and ψ are both transverse to $\{p\}$, then the parity of the number of points in $\phi^{-1}(p)$ is equal to the parity of the number of points in $\psi^{-1}(p)$.

Proof of Corollary: Let Φ be a homotopy between ϕ and ψ. By the Jiggling Lemma, there is a self-diffeomorphism η of N which is close to the identity such that $\eta \Phi, \eta \phi, \eta \psi$ are all transverse to N at $\{p\}$. Now, $\eta \phi$ and $\eta \psi$ are smoothly homotopic (via the homotopy $\eta \Phi$) and we are able to apply the remarks preceding Theorem 1. Thus, the parity of the number of points in $(\eta \phi)^{-1}(p)$ is equal to the parity of the number of points in $(\eta \psi)^{-1}(p)$. Since η is close to the identity, we can apply the auxiliary Lemma (1) to the maps ϕ, $\eta \phi$ as well as to the maps $\psi, \eta \psi$.
Q.E.D.

Proof of Jiggling Lemma: We shall show that the set of diffeomorphisms η of N such that $\eta \psi$ is transverse to V is a prevalent set. It clearly suffices to prove that the set of diffeomorphisms η such that $\eta \psi$ restricted to a small coordinate neighborhood U on M is transverse to V is a prevalent set. We call this set of diffeomorphisms $TR(U)$. For η close to a fixed $\eta_1, \eta \psi (U) \subseteq W$, a fixed coordinate neighborhood on N. We choose coordinates $[x, y]$ in W (x and y are themselves vectors) such that V appears locally as $y = 0$. Let P be the projection $[x, y] \to y$. Transversality of $\eta \psi$ restricted to U means that at each point in $(P \eta \psi)^{-1} (0)$, the Jacobian of $P \eta \psi$ is of maximal rank, i.e. there is an $r \times r$ nonvanishing minor, where r is as large as possible. It is clear that $TR(U)$ is open. We must show that $TR(U)$ is dense; for this it suffices to prove that arbitrarily near each fixed η_2, there is an η_3 such that $P \eta_3 \psi$ has a Jacobian of maximum rank at each point of $(P \eta_3 \psi)^{-1} (0)$. Let Σ be the set of points in U where $P \eta_2 \psi$ does not have maximum rank. By

Sard's lemma, $P\eta_2\psi(\Sigma)$ has measure zero. If $\varepsilon > 0$ is an arbitrary number, there then exists a vector δ whose norm $\|\delta\| < \varepsilon$ and $\delta \notin P\eta_2\psi(\Sigma)$, i.e. the Jacobian of $P\eta_2\psi$ has maximal rank at every point of $(P\eta_2\psi)^{-1}(\delta)$. It is possible to define a diffeomorphism $\eta_0 : N \to N$ which is such that $\eta_0([x, y]) = [x, y - \delta]$ holds for all $x, y \in W$ (we may assume that W is such that it is itself contained in a coordinate neighborhood W', thereby insuring that $[x, y - \delta] \in W'$) and such that η_0 tapers off smoothly to the identity away from W. If δ is small, η_0 is very near the identity, and $\eta_3 = \eta_0\eta_2$ is very near η_2. Now, $(P\eta_0\eta_2\psi)^{-1}(0) = P\eta_2(\psi)^{-1}(\delta)$ and the proof is complete.
Q.E.D.

Remark: If, in the above lemma, N is not a genuine manifold but rather a relative manifold modulo some closed subset A, and if $V \subseteq N - A$, then the set of diffeomorphisms $\eta : (N, A) \to (N, A)$ such that (i) $\eta\psi$ is transverse to V, (ii) η coincides with the identity in a neighborhood of A, is a prevalent open set.

The proof of this assertion closely resembles the proof of the Jiggling Lemma. Details are left to the reader.

Lemma (4): Any compact manifold N^n can be embedded in a sufficiently high dimensional Euclidean space E^K.

Proof: We can cover N with coordinate neighborhoods U_α such that for each α there exist coordinate neighborhoods V_α and W_α satisfying $U_\alpha \subseteq \bar{U}_\alpha \subseteq V_\alpha \subseteq \bar{V}_\alpha \subseteq W_\alpha$. By compactness, we may assume the number of U_α is finite, say $N \subseteq \overset{l}{\underset{i=1}{\cup}} U_{\alpha_i}$. We may also assume that none of the n-dimensional balls which are homeomorphic to the coordinate neighborhoods $U_{\alpha_j}, j = 1, \dots, l$, and which give the coordinates on these coordinate neighborhoods contain the origin. Let $f_\alpha : N^n \to E^n$ be a C^∞ function such that

$$f_\alpha(p) = \begin{cases} \text{coordinate vector of } p \text{ in } U_\alpha, \text{ if } p \in U_\alpha \\ 0, \text{ if } p \in N - V_\alpha \end{cases}$$

Let g_α be a C^∞ function such that

$$g_\alpha(p) = \begin{cases} \text{coordinate vector of } p \text{ in } V_\alpha, \text{ if } p \in V_\alpha \\ 0, \text{ if } p \in N - W_\alpha \end{cases}$$

Define $F : N^n \to E^{2nl}$ by $F(p) = [f_{\alpha_1}(p), \dots, f_{\alpha_l}(p), g_{\alpha_1}(p), \dots, g_{\alpha_l}(p)]$. The map F is $1-1$: For suppose $F(p) = F(q)$. If $p \in U_{\alpha_j}$, then $f_{\alpha_j}(p) \neq 0$ and therefore also $f_{\alpha_j}(q) \neq 0$. By the definition of the f_α, this means $p, q \in V_\alpha$. Now $g_{\alpha_i}(p) = g_{\alpha_i}(q)$, $i = 1, \dots, l$, and by the definition of g_α, it follows that $g_{\alpha_j}(p)$ is the coordinate vector of p in V_{α_j} while $g_{\alpha_j}(q)$ is also the coordinate vector of q in V_{α_j}. But then we must have $p = q$ and F is $1-1$. On the other hand, F is C^∞ and since F is clearly of maximal rank also F^{-1} is C^∞. So F is a diffeomorphic embedding of N^n into E^K, where $K = 2nl$.

Corollary: Any compact manifold can be given a Riemannian metric. (This observation will be useful in our subsequent discussion of Riemannian geometry.)

Note: The previous lemma is a special case of a more general result called the Whitney Embedding Theorem: this asserts that if N^n is an arbitrary (not necessarily compact) manifold, then there is an embedding $\tau : N^n \to E^{2n+1}$ such that $\tau(N)$ is a closed subset of E^{2n+1}. The proof can be found (for example) in *Introduction to Differentiable Manifolds* by Auslander and Mac-Kenzie.

Lemma (5): If N^n is a smooth manifold embedded in E^K, then there is a tubular neighborhood U of N^n in E^K and a map $\varrho : U \to N^n$ such that ϱ is a smooth retraction of U onto N^n.

Proof: Consider the K-manifold Σ^K consisting of pairs $\sigma = [a, b]$ such that $a \in N^n$, and b is a vector in E^K orthogonal to N at its foot a. It is clear the map $f : \Sigma^K \to E^K$ given by $f[a, b] = a + b$ is a smooth map whose Jacobian determinant is nonzero at every point σ in the set of points Σ_0 in which b has zero length. By the implicit function theorem, there is a neighborhood U of Σ_0 such that the map $f : U \to E^K$ is smooth, $1-1$, and maps onto an open set V in E^K; f^{-1} on V is also smooth by the implicit function theorem. We put $g[a, b] = a$ and $\varrho = g \circ f^{-1}$.
Q.E.D.

Homotopy Lemma (6): Let M^m and N^n be compact manifolds and let $\eta_1, \eta_2 : M \to N$ be smooth maps. Let d be the metric on N where N is considered as a topological subspace of some E^K (see Lemma 4). Then there exists an $\varepsilon > 0$ such that if $d(\eta_1(p), \eta_2(p)) < \varepsilon$ for all $p \in M$, then η_1 and η_2 are homotopic.

Proof: Considering N as an embedded submanifold of E^K, we take the neighborhood U guaranteed by Lemma 5. If $\varepsilon > 0$ is chosen small enough, $t\eta_1(p) + (1 - t)\eta_2(p) \in U$ for all $p \in M$, $t \in [0, 1]$. Set $\varrho_t(p) = \varrho(t\eta_1(p) + (1 - t)\eta_2)(p)$ where ϱ is the restraction of U on N. Clearly, ϱ_t is a homotopy between η_1 and η_2.
Q.E.D.

Approximation Lemma (7): Let M^m and N^n be compact manifolds and let $f: M^m \to N^n$ be a *continuous* map. Then (using the notation of Lemma 6) there exists, for any preassigned $\varepsilon > 0$, a smooth map $\phi_\varepsilon: M \to N$ such that $d(f(m), \phi_\varepsilon(m)) < \varepsilon$ for all $m \in H$.

Proof: Follows at once from Lemma 5 and the Weierstrass approximation theorem. Q. E. D.

Definition (2): Let M^m and N^n be compact manifolds and let $\phi : M \to N$ be a continuous map. Let $p \in N$ be arbitrary. By Lemma 7, we can find a sequence $\{\phi_j\}$ of smooth maps such that $d(\phi(m), \phi_j(m)) < 1/j$. By the Jiggling Lemma, we can assume ϕ_j is transverse to $\{p\}$ for all j. By the Homotopy Lemma, ϕ_k and ϕ_l are homotopic if $k, l \geq A$, for some integer A. By the corollary to the Jiggling Lemma, the parity of the number of points in $\phi_k^{-1}(p)$ is equal to the parity of the number of points in $\phi_l^{-1}(p)$ (for $k, l \geq A$). We define $\deg_2 \phi|_p$ to be this parity number.

Theorem (1'): $\deg_2 \phi|_p$ is a homotopy invariant.
The proof is obvious.

Theorem (1'A): $\deg \phi|_p$ is a homotopy invariant of maps between orientable manifolds.

Intersection Theory (mod 2)

We recall first a few definitions from singular homology theory. By a singular m-cube in a space X, we mean a map $\sigma: I^n \to X$ ($I^n = \{x = (x_1, x_2, \ldots, x_n) \in E^n \,|\, 0 \leq x_i \leq 1\}$.) If $n = 0$, then σ is interpreted as a single point in X. If $n > 0$, we define the i-th lower and upper faces $\lambda_i^0 \sigma$ and $\lambda_i^1 \sigma$ of σ to be the singular $(n-1)$-cubes given by

$$(\lambda_i^\varepsilon \sigma)(x_1, \ldots, x_{n-1}) = \sigma(x_1, \ldots, x_{i-1}, \varepsilon, x_i, \ldots, x_{n-1})$$

for every $i = 1, 2, \ldots, n$, where $\varepsilon = 0, 1$, and $(x_1, \ldots, x_{n-1}) \in I^{n-1}$. Then for $i < j$ we have $\lambda_i^\varepsilon \lambda_j^\eta = \lambda_{j-1}^\eta \lambda_i^\varepsilon$; ε, η are 0 or 1. Define $Q_n(X)$ to be the free abelian group generated by all singular n-cubes in X if $n \geq 0$ and $Q_n(X) = 0$ if $n < 0$. Then the operation

$$\partial \sigma = \sum_{i=1}^{n} (-1)^i (\lambda_i^1 \sigma - \lambda_i^0 \sigma)$$

determines a homomorphism $\partial : Q_n(X) \to Q_{n-1}(X)$ for every n. It is straightforward to verify that $\partial\partial = 0$.

For each singular $(n-1)$-cube σ in X, $n > 0$, we define a singular n-cube $D\sigma$ in X by setting

$$(D\sigma)\,(x_1, \ldots, x_{n-1}, x_n) = \sigma\,(x_1, \ldots, x_{n-1}).$$

A singular n-cube V in X is said to be *degenerate* if $V = D\sigma$ for some σ. In other words, V is degenerate iff it does not depend on the last coordinate x_n of the point $(x_1, \ldots, x_n)$ in I^n. The degenerate singular n-cubes in X, $n > 0$, generate a subgroup $D_n(X)$ of $Q_n(X)$. Since $\lambda_i^\varepsilon D = D\lambda_i^\varepsilon$, $i < n$, $\lambda_n^\varepsilon D = 1$, it follows that

$$\partial D\sigma = \sum_{i=1}^{n}(-1)^i\,(\lambda_i^1 D\sigma - \lambda_i^0 D\sigma) = \sum_{i=1}^{n-1}(-1)^i\,(D\lambda_i^1\sigma - D\lambda_i^0\sigma),$$

and hence ∂ carries $D_n(X)$ into $D_{n-1}(X)$.

For each integer n, the quotient group $C_n(X) = Q_n(X)/D_n(X)$ is obviously a free abelian group and will be called the group of normalized cubical singular n-chains in X. Since ∂ carries $D_n(X)$ into $D_{n-1}(X)$, it induces a homomorphism

$$\partial\colon C_n(x) \to C_{n-1}(X),$$

for every n. Since $\partial\partial = 0$, we can define singular cycles and singular boundaries with coefficients in an arbitrary abelian group G as in simplicial homology theory and then we can define the singular homology group $H_n(X, G)$ = (cycles)/(boundaries).

Let (M^m, A) be a relative manifold, $V^v \subseteq M$ a submanifold. Assume $V \cap A = \phi$. We say the chain $\Sigma\,k_\sigma\sigma$ is carried by A and write $\Sigma\,k_\sigma\sigma \subseteq A$ if $\sigma(I^n) \subseteq A$, all σ. A singular n-chain α called a *cycle modulo A* if its boundary $\partial\alpha \subseteq A$.

Suppose $\alpha = \Sigma k_\sigma\sigma$. Then arbitrarily near the identity, there exists a diffeomorphism η of M such that $\eta \equiv$ identity near A and such that $\eta\sigma$ is transverse to V for each σ, and such that $\eta\sigma$ restricted to any face of I^n is transverse to V. This follows immediately from the remark following the Jiggling Lemma.

Definition (3): Let $m - v = k$. (m, v as in the last paragraph.) Suppose α is a k-cycle of M mod A, $\alpha = \Sigma k_\sigma\sigma$. We wish to define $\alpha \cdot V$, *the intersection number of α and V (mod 2)*.

Take any diffeomorphism η sufficiently close to the identity and with the properties described above. First of all there are no solutions of $\eta\sigma(x) \in V$ on the boundary of I^k. For suppose there is such an x on a face of I^k. Since, dim (face) $< k =$ codim (V), the existence of such an x contradicts remark (a) following the definition of transversality in Chapter I. From remark (b) it follows that the set of solutions of $\eta\sigma(x) \in V$ is an isolated set. As I^k is compact, there can be only finitely many such points. Call this finite number $\#(\sigma)$ and *define* $\sigma \cdot V = parity\,(\#(\sigma)), \alpha \cdot V = \Sigma k_\sigma \cdot parity\,(\# \sigma)$. This defines the intersection number of α with V (mod 2). It is easy to see that $\alpha \cdot V$ as defined is independent of η. We argue as follows. If $\alpha = \Sigma k_\sigma \sigma$, then by definition $\eta\alpha = \Sigma k_\sigma \cdot \eta\sigma$. Let η' be another diffeomorphism having the same properties as η. By the Homotopy Lemma, η and η' are homotopic. We claim then that $\eta\alpha$ and $\eta'\alpha$ are homologous mod A, i.e. $\eta\alpha - \eta'\alpha = \partial\beta + \gamma$, where $\gamma \subseteq A$, and β a is a $k+1$-dim singular chain. To see this, note that there exists a homotopy η_t between η, η' i.e. $\eta_0 = \eta, \eta_1 = \eta'$. Define $\beta = \Sigma k_\sigma \cdot \hat{\sigma}$ where $\hat{\sigma}(t, x) = \eta_t \cdot \sigma(x)$. It follows from the preceding definition of the operator ∂ that $\eta\alpha - \eta'\alpha - \partial\beta \subseteq A$.

Lemma (8): If α is homologous to 0 mod A, then $\alpha \cdot V = 0$ i.e. if $\alpha = \Sigma k_\sigma \sigma = \partial\beta + \gamma, \gamma \subseteq A$, then $\Sigma k_\sigma \cdot parity\, \#(\sigma) = 0$.

Proof: By the preceding definition and the jiggling lemma, we may M slightly to make all the singular cubes of α, β, γ transverse to V. The singular cubes of γ lie on A and are therefore disjoint from V. $\beta = \Sigma l_\tau \tau$ implies that $\partial\beta = \Sigma l_\tau \cdot \partial\tau$. We shall show that for each cube τ, the number of points x in ∂I^{k+1} such that $\tau(x) \in V$ is even. Indeed, $\tau^{-1}(V)$ is a 1-dim manifold with boundary, and all the boundary points are in ∂I^{k+1} by the Lemma 8 of the preceding chapter. So $\tau^{-1}(V)$ is a set of arcs and circles and the set of end points $= \{x \in \partial I^{k+1} | \tau(x) \in V\}$ is even.

Q.E.D.

If the manifold M and its submanifold V are oriented, then we may state a more precise version of Lemma 8, i.e., one which refers to signed integers rather than merely to a parity. We proceed as follows. As above, we call the number of solutions of $\eta\sigma(x_0) \in V$ (in the transverse case) $\#(\sigma)$. Now, however, we count solutions with sign ± 1, in the following manner. Let $\{u_i\}$ be a positively oriented basis for the tangent space to I^k at x_0, and let $\{v_j\}$ be a positively oriented basis for the tangent space to V at $\eta\sigma(x_0)$. If $\{(\eta\sigma)_* u_i, v_j\}$ is a positively oriented basis for the tangent space to M, we count x_0 with the sign $+1$, otherwise -1. Adopting this sign convention, we put $\sigma \cdot V = \#(\sigma)$, $\alpha \cdot V = (\Sigma n_\sigma \sigma) \cdot V = \Sigma n_\sigma \cdot (\#(\sigma))$. Then we may state the following lemma.

Lemma 8A: If α is homologous to zero mod A, then $\alpha \cdot V = 0$, i.e., if $\alpha = \Sigma n_\sigma \sigma = \partial\beta + \gamma, \gamma \subseteq A$, then $\Sigma n_\sigma(\#\sigma) = 0$.

The proof is very much like the proof of Lemma 8; however, it uses the Proposition following Theorem 1 of the present chapter in the place of Lemma 8 of the preceding chapter. We leave the details of the proof of Lemma $8A$ to the reader.

Corollary: $\alpha \cdot V$ depends only on the homology class $\{\alpha\}$ of α, *so we may define* $\{\alpha\} \cdot V = \alpha \cdot V$.

Corollary: $(\alpha_1 + \alpha_2) \cdot V = \alpha_1 \cdot V + \alpha_2 \cdot V$. i.e. $\{\alpha\} \cdot V$ is linear in $\{\alpha\}$.
Let $\sigma\colon I^k \to M$, $\sigma'\colon I^l \to M'$. We define

$$\sigma \times \sigma'\colon I^k \times I^l = I^{k+l} \to M \times M'$$

by

$$\sigma \times \sigma' (x_1, \ldots, x_k, x_{k+1}, \ldots, x_{k+l})$$
$$= [\sigma (x_l, \ldots, x_k), \sigma' (x_{k+1}, \ldots, x_{k+l})].$$

If $\alpha = \Sigma k_\sigma \cdot \sigma$, $\alpha' = \Sigma l_{\sigma'} \cdot \sigma'$, we define $\alpha \times \alpha' = \Sigma k_\sigma l_{\sigma'} \cdot \sigma \times \sigma'$. It is left to the reader to verify that

$$\partial (\alpha \times \alpha') = (\partial\alpha) \times \alpha' + (-1)^k \alpha \times (\partial\alpha')$$

where ∂ is the boundary operator defined previously.

Now suppose (M, A) and (M', A') are relative manifolds. Let α be a cycle of M mod A, and α' a cycle of M' mod A'. Using the above formula, we can easily verify the following statements:

(1) $\alpha \times \alpha'$ is a cycle of $M \times M'$ mod $(M \times A') \cup (A \times M')$.

(2) If α is a boundary of M mod A or if α' is a boundary of M' mod A', then $\alpha \times \alpha'$ is a boundary of $M \times M'$ mod $(M \times A') \cup (M' \times A)$. (Note that $(\alpha + \beta) \times \alpha' = \alpha \times \alpha' + \beta \times \alpha'$.)

Combining (1) and (2) we see that the map $[\alpha, \alpha'] \to \alpha \times \alpha'$ induces a map of $H_k(M, A) \times H_l(M', A') \to H_{k+l}(M \times M', (M \times A') \cup (M' \times A))$. Assume now that both M, M' are contained in a genuine manifold M_0; moreover assume that M, M' and M_0 all have the same dimension m and that $A \cap M' = A' \cap M = \phi$.

Finally, define $N = \text{diag } M_0 = \{[x, x] | x \in M_0\}$; N is an m-dimensional manifold. Assume that α is a cycle of M mod A, α' a cycle of M' mod A'. From the previous paragraph, $\alpha \times \alpha'$ is a cycle of $M \times M'$ mod $(M \times A')$ $\cup (M' \times A)$. As $N \cap \{M \times A' \cup M' \times A\} = \phi$, we can define the intersection number $\{\alpha \times \alpha'\} \cdot N$ if we assume that $\dim \alpha + \dim \alpha' = k + l = m$. This follows from the theory developed above since codim (N) in M_0 is $2m - m = m$.

Definition (4): Define the intersection number $\{\alpha\} \cdot \{\alpha'\}$ of the two homology classes $\{\alpha\}$, $\{\alpha'\}$ (mod 2) by $\{\alpha\} \cdot \{\alpha'\} = \{\alpha \times \alpha'\} \cdot N$.

Lemma (9): The intersection number as thus defined is
(a) well defined for $\{\alpha\} \in H_k(M_1, A)$, $\{\alpha'\} \in H_l(M_2, A')$ if $k + l = m$.
(b) Bilinear in $\{\alpha\}$, $\{\alpha'\}$.
(c) Satisfies $\gamma \cdot \gamma' = \gamma' \cdot \gamma$ where $\gamma = \{\alpha\}$, $\gamma' = \{\alpha'\}$.

Proof: To check (a) we have to show that $\gamma \cdot \gamma'$ does not depend on the choice of representatives α, α'. But this is true because the homology class of $\alpha \times \alpha'$ depends only on the homology classes of α and α'.

(b) is obvious.

(c) Define a diffeomorphism ϱ of $M \times M$ by $\varrho: [m_1, m_2] \to [m_2, m_1]$, and a homeomorphism of $(I^{k+l}, \partial I^{k+l})$ onto itself by

$$\varrho_{k,l}: (x_1, \ldots, x_k, x_{k+1}, \ldots, x_{k+l}) \to [x_{k+1}, \ldots, x_{k+l}, x_1, \ldots, x_k].$$

Note that $\varrho_{k,l}$ is homotopic as a map of $(I^{k+l}, \partial I^{k+l})$ to the identity if kl is even, but to the map $[x_1, \ldots, x_{k+l}] \to [1 - x_1, x_2, \ldots, x_{k+l}]$ if kl is odd. If $\beta = \Sigma n_\sigma \sigma$ is a singular $k + l$ dimensional cycle, it follows that $\Sigma n_\sigma (\sigma \cdot \alpha_{k,l})$ belongs to the same homology class as $(-1)^{kl}\beta$. Plainly, if $\sigma: I^k \to M$ and $\tau: I^l \to M$, we have $\varrho(\sigma \times \tau) = (\tau + \sigma)\alpha_{k,l}$. Thus, for k- and l-dimensional homology classes, we have $\delta_*(\gamma \times \gamma') = (-1)^{kl}\gamma' \times \gamma$. Since $N = \text{diag}$ $(M \times M)$ is invariant under ϱ, we have $(\gamma \times \gamma') \cdot N = (-1)^k (\gamma' \times \gamma) \cdot N$, which by reduction mod 2 gives (c).
Q.E.D.

Remark: If the manifolds above are oriented, we can, as in degree theory, develop a more specific integer-coefficient intersection theory. In this case, these two important formulas hold. We shall leave the proofs as an exercise, cf., however, Lemma 8A.

(1) $\alpha \cdot \beta = (-1)^{kl}\beta \cdot \alpha$, where $k = \dim \alpha$, $l = \dim \beta$,
(2) if ε and η are such that $\dim \varepsilon + \dim \eta = \dim M_0 + 1$ and if $\partial \varepsilon \cap \partial \eta = \phi$, then $\partial \varepsilon \cdot \eta = (-1)^l \varepsilon \cdot \partial \eta$ where $l = \dim \varepsilon$.

Lemma (10): Let α and α' be of dimensions k and l where $k + l = m$. If at each intersection point p of a cell σ of α with a cell σ' of α', the intersecting cells are "transverse" i.e. $\sigma_*(T_{p_1}(I^k)) + \sigma'_*(T_{p_2}(I^l)) = T_p(M)$ (where $p_1 \in \sigma^{-1}(p)$, $p_2 \in \sigma'^{-1}(p)$ and where σ_*, σ'_* are the maps of tangent spaces induced by σ, σ'), then $\alpha \cdot \alpha' = \text{parity } \#$ of intersections of all cells of α with all cells of α'.

The proof is left as an exercise to the reader.

Example (1): Let S^n be the n-sphere. We know $H_k(S^n, Z_2) = 0$ if $k \neq 0, n$, $H_k(S^n, Z_2) = Z_2$ if $k = 0, n$. Let γ^0, γ^n be the homology classes of dimensions 0 and n which generate their respective homology groups. Take representatives α^0, α^n of γ^0, γ^n (i.e. $\{\alpha^0\} = \gamma^0$, $\{\alpha^n\} = \gamma^n$) as follows: let α^n: $I^n \rightarrow S^n$ be the map that takes the interior of I^n onto the interior of I^n by the identity map, and let α^n take the entire boundary of I^n into a single boundary point p_∞. So $\alpha^n(I^n)$ is the n-cube with the boundary identified to one point p_∞, which is topologically S^n. Let $\alpha^0\colon I^0 \rightarrow p_0$, $p_0 \in S^n$, $p_0 \neq p_\infty$. Then by the above lemma $\gamma^0 \cdot \gamma^n = 1$.

Theorem (2): Let M, M' be two manifolds and suppose γ_1, γ_2 are homology classes on M and γ_1', γ_2' are homology classes on M' such that dim (γ_1) + dim (γ_2) = dim M, dim (γ_1') + dim (γ_2') = dim M'. Then $(\gamma_1 \times \gamma_1') \cdot (\gamma_2 \times \gamma_2')$ = $(\gamma_1 \cdot \gamma_2)(\gamma_1' \cdot \gamma_2')$. If the above conditions on dimensions are not satisfied, but the former intersection is defined, then $(\gamma_1 \times \gamma_1') \cdot (\gamma_2 \times \gamma_2') = 0$.

Proof: The proof follows immediately from the definition of intersection number and is left as an exercise to the reader.

We now quote a theorem of Künneth on homology groups of a topological product. For notations and proof, see *Homology Theory*—Hilton and Wylie, Chapter 5.

Theorem (Künneth): Let $|K|$, $|L|$ be polyhedra. Then

(i) $H_p(|K| \times |L|) \cong \sum_{m+n=p} H_m(|K|) \otimes H_n(|L|) \oplus \sum_{m+n=p-1} H_m(|K|) * H_n(|L|)$

where the group of coefficients is taken to be the group of integers. ("*" is the torsion product.)

(ii) If $\mathscr{J}$ is a field,

$$H_p(|K| \times |L|; \mathscr{J}) \cong \sum_{m+n=p} H_m(|K|) \otimes H_n(|L|) \otimes \mathscr{J}.$$

(iii) If q is prime, and Z_q is the group of integers mod q,

$$H_p(|K| \times |L|); Z_q) \cong \sum_{m+n=p} H_m(|K|; Z_q) \otimes H_n(|L|; Z_q).$$

Example (2): Consider $S^n \times S^n$. Künneth's theorem, the only non trivial homology classes of $S^n \times S^n$ are $\gamma^0 \times \gamma^0$, $\gamma^n \times \gamma^0$, $\gamma^0 \times \gamma^n$, $\gamma^n \times \gamma^n$. Using the previous theorem,

$$(\gamma^n \times \gamma^0) \cdot (\gamma^0 \times \gamma^n) = 1$$
$$(\gamma^0 \times \gamma^0) \cdot (\gamma^n \times \gamma^n) = 1$$

and all other intersections (which are defined) are 0.

Remark: If the intersection number of a homology class on $S^n \times S^n$ with all other classes (of appropriate complementary dimension) is 0, then the class is the zero class.

Proof: It suffices to consider n-cycles (because of the above formulas). The most general n-cycle on $S^n \times S^n$ is $C_1(\gamma^0 \times \gamma^n) + C_2(\gamma^n \times \gamma^0)$. By hypothesis, $C_2 = \{C_1(\gamma^0 \times \gamma^n) + C_2(\gamma^n \times \gamma^0)\} \cdot (\gamma^0 \times \gamma^n) = 0$. Similarly, $C_1 = 0$.

Suppose $\phi : S^n \to S^n$ is smooth. Let $\Gamma^\phi : S^n \to S^n \times S^n$ be defined by $\Gamma^\phi(x) = [x, \phi(x)]$ and let Λ_ϕ be the image of Γ^ϕ. Γ^ϕ induces a map $\Gamma^\phi_* : H_p(S^n) \to H_p(S^n \times S^n)$ for all p. Now $\Gamma^\phi_*(\gamma^n) = C_1(\gamma^n \to \gamma^0) + C_2(\gamma^0 \to \gamma^n)$ (because $\gamma^n \times \gamma^0$, $\gamma^0 \times \gamma^n$ form a basis for $H_n(S^n \times S^n)$). Take for representative of γ^n the singular n-cube σ described in example (1). A representative of $\Gamma^\phi_*(\gamma^n)$ is thus given by $x \to [\sigma(x), \phi(\sigma(x))]$. A representative of $\gamma^n \to \gamma^0$ is given by $\gamma \to [\sigma(x), x_0]$ where $x_0 = \gamma^0(I^0)$. A representative of $\gamma^0 \to \gamma^n$ is given by $x \to [x_0, \sigma(x)]$. By the last lemma, we find easily that $(\gamma^0 \times \gamma^n) \cdot \Gamma^\phi_*(\gamma^n) = 1$, $(\gamma^n \to \gamma^0) \cdot \Gamma_*(\gamma^n) = $ parity # of solution of $\phi(\sigma(x)) = x_0 = $ parity # of solutions of $\phi(p) = x_0$ which is just $\deg_2(\phi)|_{x_0}$. Therefore,

$$1 = (\gamma^0 \times \gamma^n) \cdot \Gamma^\phi_*(\gamma^n) = (\gamma^0 \times \gamma^n) \cdot \{C_1(\gamma^n \times \gamma^0) + C_2(\gamma^0 \times \gamma^n)\} = C_1$$

and

$$\deg_2(\phi)|_{x_0} = (\gamma^n \times \gamma^0) \cdot \Gamma^\phi_*(\gamma^n)$$

$$= (\gamma^n \times \gamma^0) \cdot \{C_1(\gamma^n \times \gamma^0) + C_2(\gamma^0 \times \gamma^n)\} = C_2$$

Thus,

$$\Gamma^\phi_*(\gamma^n) = (\gamma^n \times \gamma^0) + (\deg_2(\phi)|_{x_0})(\gamma^0 \times \gamma^n).$$

If ψ is another map $S^n \to S^n$, then $\Gamma^\psi_*(\gamma^n) = (\gamma^n \to \gamma^0) + (\deg_2(\psi)|_{x_0})(\gamma^0 \times \gamma^n)$. Therefore

$$\Gamma^\phi_*(\gamma^n) \cdot \Gamma^\psi_*(\gamma^n) = \deg_2(\phi)|_{x_0} + \deg_2(\psi)|_{x_0}.$$

Now $\Gamma^\phi_*(\gamma^n)$ is a chain carried by Λ_ϕ and $\Gamma^\psi_*(\gamma^n)$ is a chain carried by Λ_ψ. Therefore if $\deg_2(\phi)|_{x_0} \neq \deg_2(\psi)|_{x_0}$, then $\Gamma^\phi_*(\gamma^n) \cdot \Gamma^\psi_*(\gamma^n) = 1$ and consequently $\Lambda_\phi \cap \Lambda_\psi \neq \phi$. That is, there exists an $x_1 \in S^n$ such that $\phi(x_1) = \psi(x_1)$. This gives us a so-called coincidence theorem.

Corollary: If $\deg_2\phi|_{x_0} = 0$, then ϕ has a fixed point.

Proof: Take $\psi = $ identity and apply the above result.

We now quote a fixed point theorem without proof. For the terminology and notation, see for example *Algebraic Topology* by Lefschetz.

Theorem (Lefschetz): Let X be a finitely triangulated space, $\phi : X \to X$. Consider the induced map

$$\phi_* : H_k(X) \to H_k(X)$$

Let $l(\phi) = \sum_{k=0}^{\dim X} (-1)^k \, tr \, (\phi_* | H_k(X))$. If $l(\phi) \neq 0$, then ϕ has a fixed point of homology with coefficients in some field.

Application: If $X = S^n$, $l(\phi) = 1 + (-1)^n \deg \phi$.

Let $\phi_1, \phi_2 : S^n \to S^n$, $\psi_1, \psi_2 : S^n \to S^n$. Define $\Phi : S^n \to S^n \times S^n$ by $\Phi(p) = [\phi_1(p), \phi_2(p)]$ and define Ψ analogously. Then

$$\Phi_*(\gamma^n) = \deg_2(\phi_1) \, (\gamma^n \times \gamma^0) + \deg_2(\phi_2) \, (\gamma^0 \times \gamma^n).$$

$$\Psi_*(\gamma^n) = \deg_2(\psi_1) \, (\gamma^n \times \gamma^0) + \deg_2(\psi_2) \, (\gamma^0 \times \gamma^n).$$

$$\Phi_*(\gamma^n) \cdot \Psi_*(\gamma^n) = \deg_2(\phi_1) \deg_2(\psi_2) + \deg_2(\psi_1) \deg_2(\phi_2).$$

If this number is $\neq 0$, there exists x_1, x_2 such that

$$[\phi_1(x_1), \phi_2(x_1)] = [\psi_1(x_2), \psi_2(x_2)].$$

We now define the cohomology ring of a space.

If X is a topological space, let $H(X)$ be the direct sum of the singular homology groups of X of all dimensions. If the coefficient group is a field, $H(X)$ can be considered as a vector space over this field. Define the (total) cohomology group $H^*(X)$ of X to be the dual space of $H(X)$.

Let $\phi : X \to Y$. Then ϕ induces a map $\phi_* : H(X) \to H(Y)$ and a dual map $\phi^* : H^*(Y) \to H^*(X)$.

Let diag: $X \to X \times X$ be the diagonal map defined by diag $(x) = (x, x)$.

Therefore diag: $H(X) \to H(X \times X) = H(X) \otimes H(X)$ and diag$^* : H^*(X) \otimes H^*(X) \to H^*(X)$.

Let $\gamma_1^*, \gamma_2^* \in H^*(X)$; define the *cup product* of γ_1^* and γ_2^* (denoted by $\gamma_1^* \cup \gamma_2^*$) by

$$\gamma_1^* \cup \gamma_2^* = \text{diag}^* (\gamma_1^* \otimes \gamma_2^*).$$

This operation of product turns $H^*(X)$ into a ring, called the cohomology ring of X.

Let X be a topological space containing a closed subset A. A finite sequence $X = X_n \supseteq X_{n-1} \supseteq \cdots \supseteq X_0 = A$ of closed subsets is called a *filtration* of X or a *normal series* of closed subsets of X. A filtration of X is said to give a *cell complex* if for each pair (X_j, X_{j-1}), $j = 1, \ldots, n$, there exists a set $C_1^{(j)}$, $C_2^{(j)}, \ldots, C_{m_j}^{(j)}$ of j-cubes and a corresponding set of maps $\sigma_1^{(j)}, \ldots, \sigma_{m_j}^{(j)}$ satisfying the following:

(i) For each $p = 1, 2, \ldots, m_j$, $\sigma_p^{(j)} : C_p^{(j)} \to X_j$
(ii) $\sigma_p^{(j)} : \partial C_p^{(j)} \to X_{j-1}$

(iii) $\sigma_p^{(j)}$ maps the interior of $C_p^{(j)}$, call it $C_p^{0(j)}$, homeomorphically onto its image.

(iv) $\bigcup\limits_{p=1}^{m_j} \sigma_p^{(j)}(C_p^{0(j)}) = X_j - X_{j-1}$.

The $\sigma_p^{(j)}$ are called the *singular j-cells* of the cell complex and the subsets $\sigma_p^{(j)}(C_p^{0(j)})$ are called the *open j-cells* of the cell complex.

The reason for introducing the above notions is to aid us in computing the homology groups of various spaces. In order to carry this out, we need two basic lemmas (which we do not prove). For a proof, cf. Cooke and Finrey, *Homology of Cell Complexes*, Princeton University Press 1967.

Lemma (11): (a) Any singular j-cycle of (X, A) ($X \bmod A$) is homologous to a linear combination of the $\sigma_p^{(j)}$.

(b) The homology of (X, A) may be calculated from the cell complex as follows: We know $\partial C_p^{(j)}$ is a $(j-1)$-sphere. We take a basic $j-1$ dimensional integer homology class α on $\partial C_p^{(j)}$. As a map from $\partial C_p^{(j)}$ into X_{j-1}, $\sigma_p^{(j)}$ induces a homomorphism $\sigma_{p_*}^{(j)}$ from $H(\partial C_p^{(j)})$ into $H(X_{j-1}, A)$. Therefore, $\sigma_{p_*}^{(j)}(\alpha) \in H_{j-1}(X_{j-1}, A)$. From (a) any singular $j-1$ cycle of (X_{j-1}, A) can be expressed as a linear combination of certain of the $j-1$ cells of the cell complex. In particular,

$$\sigma_{p_*}^{(j)}(\alpha) = \{\textstyle\sum n_q \sigma_q^{(j-1)}\}$$

where, in general, $\{\beta\}$ is the homology class of β. We now introduce formal boundary operators $\tilde{\partial}$ by defining $\tilde{\partial}\sigma_p^{(j)} = \sum n_q \sigma_q^{(j-1)}$. It is easily proved that $\tilde{\partial}\tilde{\partial} = 0$. Hence, in the usual way, we can define formal cycles, formal boundaries, and show that the group of formal j-boundaries is contained in the group of formal j-cycles. We can then pass to the quotient group and obtain the formal j-th homology group. We assert that these formal homology groups are isomorphic with the actual singular homology groups. In addition, we assert that the integer n_q in the formula displayed above is the degree of the map

$$(\sigma_q^{(j-1)})^{-1}\,\sigma_p^{(j)}: \quad \partial C_p^{(j)} \cap U \to C_q^{0(j-1)}\,,$$

where U is the inverse image of $C_q^{0(j-1)}$ under this map.

These facts with be used as a basis for calculation in what follow.

Let (X, A), (Y, B) be two cell complexes,

$$X = X_n \supseteq X_{n-1} \supseteq \cdots \supseteq X_0 = A$$

$$Y = Y_n \supseteq Y_{n-1} \supseteq \cdots \supseteq Y_0 = B.$$

Let $f: (X, A) \to (Y, B)$, i.e. $f(X) \subseteq Y$, $f(A) \subseteq B$. f is called a *cellular map* if:

(i) $f(X_j) \subseteq Y_j$,

(ii) f maps each open cell of $X_j - X_{j-1}$ homeomorphically onto an open cell of $Y_j - Y_{j-1}$ (recall that $X_j - X_{j-1}$ is the finite union of open j-cells).

An orientation of the open cells e of a cell complex is a choice for each e of a homeomorphism h from e to the open unit ball B_j. We say two homeomorphisms have the same orientation or opposite orientation depending on the following: let $h_1 : e \to B_j$, $h_2 : e \to B_j$, so that $h_1 h_2^{-1} : B_j \to B_j$. If $h_1 h_2^{-1}$ is orientation preserving, we say h_1, h_2 give the same orientation. If $h_1 h_2^{-1}$ is orientation reversing, we say h_1, h_2 give the opposite orientation to e.

Lemma (12): Let $f: (X, A) \to (Y, B)$ be a cellular map. Introduce the formal map $\tilde{f}$ on the open oriented cells e of (X, A) as follows: e has an orientation given by a homeomorphism $h : e \to B_j$. $f(e)$ has an orientation given by a homeomorphism $g : f(e) \to B_j$ (recall $f(e)$ is an open j-cell).

Therefore $gf : e \to B_j$. If now h and gf give the same orientation to e, we put $\tilde{f}(e) = +f(e)$. If h and gf give opposite orientations, we put $\tilde{f}(e) = -f(e)$. By linearity, we may introduce the formal map on formal linear combinations of open oriented cells. Then it is easily proved that $\tilde{f}$ commutes with $\tilde{\partial}$. Hence, as usual, $\tilde{f}$ induces a map $\tilde{f}_*$ of formal homology groups. We assert that this $\tilde{f}_*$ represents the map f_* of the singular homology groups.

We proceed now to the calculation of some homology groups.

(1) $X = S^n$, the n sphere: Note that we are cheating here because we have already used (in Lemma 11) the fact that $H_n(S^n)$ is isomorphic to the group of coefficients. However, we shall deduce that $H_k(S^n)$ is trivial for $0 < k < n$. For the cell decomposition $X_n \supseteq X_{n-1} \supseteq \cdots \supseteq X_0$, we choose $X_{n-1} = \cdots = X_0 =$ one point p. For the n-cell, we choose $\sigma^n : C^{(n)} \to S^n$ by mapping $C^{0(n)}$ identically and mapping $\partial C^{(n)}$ to the single point p. We define no k-cells for $0 < k < n$. We define one 0-*cell*, namely $\sigma^{(0)} : C^{(0)} \to p$. It is easy to verify that we have a cell complex. Moreover, all the operators $\tilde{\partial}$ are obviously 0. The calculation of the homology groups of S^n now results at once from the previous lemmas.

(2) $X = P_n^{\mathcal{C}}$, the complex projective n-space: For our filtration, we take $P_n^{\mathcal{C}} \supseteq P_{n-1}^{\mathcal{C}} \supseteq \cdots \supseteq P_0^{\mathcal{C}}$. Let $E_n^{\mathcal{C}}$ be the complex Euclidean space. We compactify $E_n^{\mathcal{C}}$ by introducing points ω^* at ∞ corresponding to all unit vectors ω as follows: We say $z(n) \to \omega^*$ if $z(n)/|z(n)| \to \omega$. It is easy to see that $E_n^{\mathcal{C}}$ so compactified is homeomorphic to the real $2n$-dimensional ball. For our $2n$-cell, we choose $\sigma^{(2n)} : B^{2n} \to P_n^{\mathcal{C}}$ to be the identification map. The map is

easily seen to be continuous. In the interior of B^{2n} (i.e. $E_n^{\mathcal{C}}$), $\sigma^{(2n)}$ is the identity and hence $\sigma^{(2n)}|E_n^{\mathcal{C}}$ is a homeomorphism onto $P_n^{\mathcal{C}} - P_{n-1}^{\mathcal{C}}$. Defining cells $\sigma^{(2n-2)}, \ldots, \sigma^{(0)}$ similarly and defining no odd dimensional cells, we obtain a cell decomposition of $P_n^{\mathcal{C}}$. Again, all boundaries $\tilde{\partial}$ are zero because there are no odd dimensional cells (check the definition of $\tilde{\partial}$). It follows readily that $H_j(P_n^{\mathcal{C}}) = Z, j = 0, 2, \ldots, 2n, H_j(P_n^{\mathcal{C}}) = 0, j = 1, 3, \ldots, 2n-1$.

(3) $X = P_n$, the real projective n-space: For a filtration, take $P_n \supseteq P_{n-1} \supseteq \cdots \supseteq P_0$. For each j, $0 \leq j \leq n$, we have one j-cell, namely $\sigma^{(j)} : C^{(j)} \to P_j$ where $C^{(j)}$ is the j-cube and $\sigma^{(j)}$ is the identification map. Thus the filtration gives a cell complex. We shall define a cellular map from (S^n, S^0) to (P_n, P_0) as follows: We begin by choosing a cell decomposition of S^n (different from the one defined in (1)). We write $S^n \supseteq S^{n-1} \supseteq \cdots \supseteq S^0$ where we regard S^{j-1} as the equator of S^j, $j = 1, 2, \ldots, n$. We define two j-cells $\sigma_1^{(j)}$, $\sigma_2^{(j)}$ for each dimension j. For $C_1^{(j)}$ we take the closed upper hemisphere U_j of S^j defined by $x_{j+1} \geq 0$. For $C_2^{(j)}$ we take the closed lower hemisphere L_j of S^j defined by $x_{j+1} \leq 0$. More precisely, since the standard j-cubes $C_1^{(j)}$, $C_2^{(j)}$ are homeomorphic to U_j, L_j, we let $\sigma_1^{(j)}$, $\sigma_2^{(j)}$ be the homeomorphisms taking $C_1^{(j)}$, $C_2^{(j)}$, onto U_j, L_j. Clearly $\sigma_1^{(j)}(\partial C_1^{(j)}) \subseteq S^{j-1}$ (because we regard S^{j-1} as the equator of S^j) and similarly $\sigma_2^{(j)}(\partial C_2^{(j)}) \subseteq S^{j-1}$. Moreover, it is clear that $S^j - S^{j-1} = \sigma_1^{(j)}(C_1^{0(j)}) \cup \sigma_2^{(j)}(C_2^{0(j)})$. So all the a cell complex conditions are satisfied. Now we define the cellular map f. Let $f : S^j \to P_j$ be the identification map, i.e. we regard P_j as S^j with x and $-x$ identified. From our construction, it is clear that f is indeed a cellular map. We now calculate the homology map $\tilde{f}$. The open j-cells of S^n are U_j^0 and L_j^0 (the open hemispheres). Moreover, the open j-cell of P_n can be regarded as U_j^0. Therefore $\tilde{f}(U_j^0) = U_j^0$. But f restricted to L_j^0 is the map taking x into $-x$. This map preserves (respectively, reserves) orientation if $j+1$ is even (respectively, odd), i.e. $\tilde{f}(L_j^0) = (-1)^{j+1}U_j^0$. Now, by Lemma (11), $\tilde{\partial}\sigma^{(j)} = k_j\sigma^{(j-1)}$ for some integer k_j. It follows easily by Lemma (12) that

$$k_j = \begin{cases} 2 & \text{if } j \text{ is even} \\ 0 & \text{if } j \text{ is odd} \end{cases}$$

since the fundamental cycle on S^j is $U_j + L_j$ and its image is either $2U_j$ or 0. Using this relation, the homology of P_n is readily calculated. We obtain the following result.

If n is even,

$$H_0(P_n, Z) \cong Z, H_1(P_n, Z) \cong H_3(P_n, Z)$$
$$\cong \cdots \cong H_{n-1}(P_n, Z) \cong Z_2;$$
$$H_2(P_n, Z) \cong H_4(P_n, Z) \cong \cdots \cong H_n(P_n, Z) \cong \{0\}.$$

If n is odd,

$$H_0(P_n, Z) \cong H_n(P_n, Z) \cong Z;$$

$$H_1(P_n, Z) \cong H_3(P_n, Z) \cong \cdots \cong H_{n-2}(P_n, Z) \cong Z_2;$$

$$H_2(P_n, Z) \cong H_4(P_n, Z) \cong \cdots \cong H_{n-1}(P_n, Z) \cong \{0\}.$$

Cohomology Ring of P_n (mod 2)

We now calculate the cohomology ring (mod Z_2) of P_n, the real projective space. We saw above that $H_j(P_n, Z_2)$ is generated by one element, say α_j. We claim $\alpha_j \cdot \alpha_{n-j} = 1$. In fact α_j is represented by the map $\sigma^{(j)}$ which takes $C^{(j)}$ onto P_j. Similarly α_{n-j} is represented by the map $\sigma^{(n-j)}$ which takes $C^{(n-j)}$ onto P_{n-j}. As the maps $\sigma^{(j)}$ and $\sigma^{(n-j)}$ are nonsingular on the interiors of $C^{(j)}$ and $C^{(n-j)}$, it follows that $\alpha_j \cdot \alpha_{n-j}$ is equal to the number of intersections of P_j with P_{n-j} if we take P_j and P_{n-j} to be in general position in P_n. But $P_j \cap P_{n-j}$ is just one point and hence the assertion follows.

By Künneth's theorem, $H_j(P_n \times P_n, Z_2)$ has as generators $\alpha_0 \times \alpha_j, \ldots,$ $\alpha_j \times \alpha_0$. By appealing to the product rule, we see that $(\alpha_0 \times \alpha_j) \cdot (\alpha_n \times \alpha_{n-j})$ $= 1$, $(\alpha_1 \times \alpha_{j-1}) \cdot (\alpha_{n-1} \times \alpha_{n-j+1}) = 1, \ldots, (\alpha_j \times \alpha_0) \cdot (\alpha_{n-j} \times \alpha_n) = 1$. All other intersections are 0. Consider the diagonal map of $P_n \to P_n \times P_n$. We calculate the image of α_j. We claim that $\mathrm{diag}_*(\alpha_j) = (\alpha_0 \times \alpha_j) + (\alpha_1 \times \alpha_{j-1}) + \cdots$ $+ (\alpha_j \times \alpha_0)$. First of all, we know $\mathrm{diag}_*(\alpha_j) = C_0(\alpha_0 \times \alpha_j) + \cdots + C_j(\alpha_j \times \alpha_0)$. If we can show that $\mathrm{diag}_*(\alpha_j) \cdot (\alpha_l \times \alpha_m) = 1$ for all l such that $j + l + m$ $= 2n$, we will have proved the assertion. Now, as before, $\mathrm{diag}_*(\alpha_j) \cdot (\alpha_l \times \alpha_m)$ is just the number of points in $P_j \cap P_l \cap P_m$ when P_j, P_l, P_m are regarded as being in general position in $P_n \times P_n$. But $P_j \cap P_l \cap P_m = P_{j+l-n} = P_{j+l+m-2n}$ $= P_0$ which is one point. Now introduce a dual basis $\beta_0, \beta_1, \ldots, \beta_n$ for the cohomology groups of P_n mod Z_2. Then β_j is the linear functional defined by $\beta_j(\alpha_i) = \delta_{ji}, i = 1, 2, \ldots, n$. We claim $\beta_j \cup \beta_k = \beta_{j+k}$. In fact,

$$\beta_j \cup \beta_k(\alpha_{j+k}) = \mathrm{diag}^*(\beta_j \otimes \beta_k)(\alpha_{j+k})$$

$$= \beta_j \otimes \beta_k (\mathrm{diag}_*(\alpha_{j+k}))$$

$$= \beta_j \otimes \beta_k (\alpha_0 \times \alpha_{j+k} + \cdots + \alpha_j \times \alpha_k + \cdots + \alpha_{j+k} \times \alpha_0)$$

$$= 1.$$

Similarly $\beta_j \cup \beta_k(\alpha_l) = 0$ if $l \neq j + k$. This proves the assertion. It follows that the cohomology ring of P_n (mod Z_2) is isomorphic to $Z_2[x]/(x^{n+1})$.

Exercise

Calculate the cohomology ring (mod Z) for $P_n^{\mathscr{C}}$. Using this and the Lefschetz fixed point theorem, prove that the spaces $P_{2k}^{\mathscr{C}}$ have the fixed point property. (A space X is said to have the fixed point property if every continuous self-mapping of X has a fixed point.)

CHAPTER III

Further Applications of Intersection Theory

This chapter is divided into two parts. The first part will be devoted to computing the homology groups and the cohomology ring of the Grassman manifold (see the definition below). The importance of the homology and cohomology structure of this manifold will become apparant later on when its central connection with the theory of fibre bundles is shown (see Chapters IV, VI). The method of computation itself is quite similar to the method used at the end of Chapter II in calculating the homology and co-homology structure of the projective spaces. The results of Chapter II are needed in the present chapter. On the other hand, in certain special cases (see below), the Grassman manifold turns out to be merely projective space. Hence, the results of this chapter can be regarded as a generalization of the results of Chapter II.

In the second part of this chapter, we shall prove the classical Poincare Duality Theorem by a differential method. Rather than using the cumbersome methods of combinational topology (see e.g. Alexandrov— *Combinatorial Topology*), we shall use as our main tool Morse Theory. This is in accord with the general philosophy developed in Chapters I and II, namely, to treat topological questions (as far as possible) by "differentiable" methods.

Part A: Homology of Grassman Manifolds

Let $G_{\varkappa,n}$ denote the set of $\varkappa$-dimensional linear subspaces ($\varkappa$-planes through the origin) of E^n. When we talk about real (resp. complex) $\varkappa$-planes in real (resp. complex) Euclidean n-space, we shall sometimes write $G_{\varkappa,n}^R$ (resp. $G_{\varkappa,n}^C$) for emphasis. It is easy to see that the orthogonal group $O(n)$ acts transitively on $G_{\varkappa,n}^R$. Moreover, if π is a fixed $\varkappa$-plane and $\pi^\perp$ is its orthogonal complement, the subgroup of $O(n)$ mapping π onto itself splits up into the direct product $O(\varkappa) \times O(n - \varkappa)$, the first of which leaves $\pi^{\perp}$ pointwise fixed and the second of which leaves π pointwise fixed. Hence, we may identify $G_{\varkappa,n}^{R}$ with the (analytic) manifold $O(n)/O(\varkappa) \times O(n - \varkappa)$. In this way, we see that $G_{\varkappa,n}^{R}$ is a compact manifold of dimension $\varkappa (n - \varkappa)$. Similarly, we can identify $G_{\varkappa,n}^{C}$ with $U(n)/U(\varkappa) \times U(n - \varkappa)$ where $U(n)$ is the unitary group. Thus, $G_{\varkappa,n}^{C}$ is a compact manifold of complex dimension $\varkappa (n - \varkappa)$ and hence of real dimension $2\varkappa(n - \varkappa)$.

Observe that the correspondence between any $\varkappa$-plane and its orthogonal complement gives rise to a $1 - 1$ correspondence between $G_{\varkappa,n}$ and $G_{n-\varkappa,n}$. Note also that $G_{1,n} = P_{n-1}$, ordinary projective space.

In E^n, we pick an ascending sequence $E^0 \subseteq E^1 \subseteq \cdots \subseteq E^{n-1} \subseteq E^n$, where E^j is a subspace of E^n of dimension j. For a given plane $\pi \in G_{\varkappa,n}$ we set

$$m_j(\pi) = \inf_{m} \{m \mid \dim (\pi \cap E^m) \geqq j\}, \qquad j = 1, 2, ..., \varkappa.$$

From now on, we shall write πE^m instead of $\pi \cap E^m$. Observe that

$$m_1(\pi) < m_2(\pi) < \cdots < m_\varkappa(\pi).$$

We now set

$$C_{m_1, ..., m_\varkappa} (E^0, E^1, ..., E^n) = \{\pi \in G_{\varkappa,n} \mid m_j(\pi) = m_j, j = 1, 2, ..., \varkappa\}.$$

For brevity, we write $C_{m_1, ..., m_\varkappa}$ instead of $C_{m_1, ..., m_\varkappa} (E^0, E^1, ..., E^n)$. $C_{m_1, ..., m_\varkappa}$ is called the *Schubert Cell* corresponding to the multiindex $(m_1, m_2, ..., m_\varkappa)$.

Lemma (1): The Schubert cells are topological cells. Moreover, the collection of all Schubert cells gives a cell decomposition of $G_{\varkappa,n}$.

Proof: Let $\pi \in C_{m_1, ..., m_\varkappa}$. Then πE^{m_1} is one-dimensional and $\pi E^{m_1 - 1} = \{0\}$. As a basis for E^n, we can take the vectors

$$e_i = (0, ..., 0, 1, 0, ..., 0), \qquad i = 1, ..., n,$$

where the "1" in e_i appears in the i-th place. We can assume moreover that $E^\varkappa$ is generated by the vectors $e_1, e_2, ..., e_\varkappa$. Then πE^{m_1} is generated by a vector of the form $x = (x_1, ..., x_{m_1}, 0, ..., 0)$ where $x_{m_1} \neq 0$. In fact, if x_{m_1} were equal to zero, then we would have $\dim (\pi E^{m_1 - 1}) = 1$, which is impossible. Hence, we may assume $x_{m_1} = 1$. Now, πE^{m_2} is 2-dimensional and $\pi E^{m_2 - 1}$ has dimension less than two. Then πE^{m_2} is generated by x and a vector of the form

$$\eta = (\eta_1, ..., \eta_{m_1}, \eta_{m_1+1}, ..., \eta_{m_2}, 0, ..., 0).$$

As the linear transformation $x \to x$, $\eta \to \eta - \eta_{m_1} x$ is invertible, it follows that the vectors x and $y = \eta - \eta_{m_1} x$ also generate πE^{m_2}. Now y is of the form

$$y = (y_1, \ldots, y_{m-1}, 0, y_{m_1+1}, \ldots, y_{m_2}, 0, \ldots, 0).$$

As above, $y_{m_2} \neq 0$ and hence we may suppose $y_{m_2} = 1$. We now continue the procedure, finding a basis for $\pi E^{m_2}, \ldots, \pi E^{m_\varkappa}$. We arrive at a $\varkappa \times n$ matrix

$$x_1 \cdots x_{m_1-1} \quad 1 \quad 0 \qquad \cdots \qquad\qquad\qquad\qquad\qquad 0$$

$$y_1 \cdots y_{m_1-1} \quad 0 \quad y_{m_1+1} \cdots y_{m_2-1} \quad 1 \quad 0 \qquad \cdots \qquad\qquad 0$$

$$z_1 \cdots z_{m_1-1} \quad 0 \quad z_{m_1+1} \cdots z_{m_2-1} \quad 0 \quad z_{m_2+1} \cdots z_{m_3-1} \quad 1 \quad 0 \cdots 0$$

$$\vdots \qquad\qquad \vdots \qquad\qquad \vdots \qquad\qquad \vdots \qquad\qquad \vdots$$

The first j rows represent j vectors generating πE^j ($j = 1, 2, \ldots, \varkappa$). The components of this matrix are real or complex parameters (depending on whether we are considering $G_{\varkappa,n}^{R}$ or $G_{\varkappa,n}^{\mathcal{C}}$) and can be chosen arbitrarily otherwise. Thus, we have defined coordinates on $C_{m_1, \ldots, m_\varkappa}$ and hence $C_{m_1, \ldots, m_\varkappa}$ becomes an open cell (although not necessarily an open subset of $G_{\varkappa,n}$) of dimension

$$(m_1 - 1) + (m_2 - 2) + \cdots + (m_\varkappa - \varkappa) = (m_1 + \cdots + m_\varkappa) - \frac{\varkappa(\varkappa+1)}{2}.$$

There is a unique Schubert cell of dimension 0, namely $C_{1,2,\ldots,\varkappa}$ and a unique Schubert cell of dimension $\varkappa(n - \varkappa)$, namely $C_{n-\varkappa+1,\ldots,n}$.

We shall show that the Schubert cells give a cell decomposition of the space $G_{\varkappa,n}$. Denote by D^α the closed α-dimensional unit disc and by B^α the interior of D^α. For brevity, write $D_i = D^{m_i-1}$ and finally, write $D = D_1 \times D_2 \times \cdots \times D_\varkappa$, $B = $ interior of D. Clearly, D is homeomorphic to a closed disc of dimension $(m_1 + \cdots + m_\varkappa) - \varkappa(\varkappa+1)/2$. We want to define a continuous map $\phi : D \to G_{\varkappa,n}$ such that

(1) $\phi(D) = C_{m_1, \ldots, m_\varkappa} \cup \{$Schubert cells of lower dimension$\}$

(2) ϕ maps B homeomorphically onto $C_{m_1, \ldots, m_\varkappa}$

(3) ϕ maps $\partial D = D - B$ into the union of Schubert cells of lower dimension.

Consider the set of all unit vectors $u \in E^{m_1}$ such that the m_1-th component $(u)_{m_1} \geq 0$; this set is homeomorphic with $D_1 = D^{m_1-1}$. Let $R_u^{(1)}$ be a rotation of E^n, depending continuously on u, such that

$$\text{(a)} \quad R_u^{(1)} e_{m_1} = u, \qquad \text{(b)} \quad R_u^{(1)} \mid E^n \ominus E^{m_1} = \text{identity}.$$

Consider the set of all unit vectors $v \in E^{m_2} \ominus \{e_{m_1}\}$ such that $(v)_{m_2} \geqq 0$; this set is homeomorphic with $D_2 = D^{m_2-2}$. Let $R_v^{(2)}$ be a rotation of E^n, depending continuously on v, such that

(a) $R_v^{(2)} e_{m_2} = v$,   (b) $R_v^{(2)} \mid E^n \ominus [E^{m_2} \ominus \{e_{m_1}\}] = $ identity.

Consider the set of all unit vectors $w \in E^{m_3} \ominus \{e_{m_1}, e_{m_2}\}$ with $(w)_{m_3} \geqq 0$; this set is homeomorphic with $D_3 = D^{m_3-3}$. Let $R_w^{(3)}$ be a rotation of E^n, depending continuously on w, such that

(a) $R_w^{(3)} e_{m_3} = w$,   (b) $R_w^{(3)} \mid E^n \ominus [E^{m_3} \ominus \{e_{m_1}, e_{m_2}\}] = $ identity.

We continue this process $\varkappa$ times. We define ϕ as follows:

$$\phi((u, v, w, \ldots)) = \{u, R_u^{(1)} v, R_u^{(1)} R_v^{(2)} w, \ldots\} = \pi,$$

i.e. π is the plane spanned by the vectors $u, R_u^{(1)} v, R_u^{(1)} R_v^{(2)} w, \ldots$ The fact that π is actually a $\varkappa$-plane follows from the fact that the generating vectors of π defined above are mutually orthogonal. Let us show, for example, that $(u, R_u^{(1)} v) = 0 : (u, R_u^{(1)} v) = (R_u^{(1)} e_{m_1}, R_u^{(1)} v) = (e_{m_1}, v) = 0$. Note that we use here the fact that $R_u^{(1)}$ is unitary.

Clearly, ϕ is continuous. We shall prove (1) above. By the construction, we have $\dim(\pi E^{m_i}) \geqq i$ for $i = 1, 2, \ldots, \varkappa$. By definition, we have then $m_i(\phi(d)) \leqq m_i$ for $d \in D$, $i = 1, 2, \ldots, \varkappa$. But this means

$$\phi(d) \in \bigcup_{(l_1, \ldots, l_\varkappa)} C_{l_1, \ldots, l_\varkappa}$$

where the summation extends over all multi-indices $(l_1, \ldots, l_\varkappa)$ satisfying $l_1 \leqq m_1, l_2 \leqq m_2, \ldots, l_\varkappa \leqq m_\varkappa$. This proves (1). To prove (2), we shall construct a continuous map

$$\psi : C_{m_1, \ldots, m_\varkappa} \to B$$

which will clearly be a 2-sided inverse of the map $\phi \mid B$. So let $\pi \in C_{m_1, \ldots, m_\varkappa}$. We know $\dim(\pi E^{m_1}) = 1$ and hence there is a *unique* unit vector $u \in \pi E^{m_1}$ with $(u)_{m_1} > 0$ such that u generates πE^{m_1}. As $\dim(\pi E^{m_2}) = 2$, πE^{m_2} is generated by u and a unit vector $v \in \{(R_u^{(1)})^{-1} \pi\} \cap \{E^{m_2} - \{e_{m_1}\}\}$. If we require $(v)_{m_2} > 0$, then v is uniquely determined by π. We continue the procedure in the obvious way and define

$$\psi(\pi) = (u, v, \ldots).$$

It is clear that ψ has the required properties.

Statement (3) above is easily verified also and the proof of Lemma 1 is completed.

To calculate the homology of $G_{\varkappa,n}$, we shall apply the previously developed theory. We must therefore look at the boundary relations.

In the complex case (i.e. $G_{\varkappa,n}^{\mathcal{C}}$), there are only even dimensional cells. Hence, all boundary relations are trivial.

In the real case, we let $(\partial D)_1$ be the part of the boundary ∂D which is mapped by ϕ into the union of Schubert cells, each of whose dimensions is exactly one less than the dimension of $C_{m_1,\ldots,m_\varkappa}$. It is easy to see that such a cell has the form $C_{m_1,\ldots,m_{s-1},m_s-1,m_{s+1},\ldots,m_\varkappa}$ where $m_s-1 > m_{s-1}$. Then, if $d \in (\partial D)_1$ and $d = (u, v, w, \ldots)$, we assert that not more than one of the unit vectors $u, v, w, \ldots$ can lie on the boundary of its corresponding hemisphere $D_1, D_2, D_3, \ldots$ Suppose, for example, that u lies on the boundary of D_1 and v lies on the boundary of D_2. Then $\dim(\pi E^{m_1-1}) \geq 1$, $\dim(\pi E^{m_2-1}) \geq 2$ and hence $m_1(\pi) \leq m_1 - 1$, $m_2(\pi) \leq m_2 - 1$ contradicting our dimensional assumption. It follows readily that on $(\partial D)_1$, the map ϕ is exactly 2 to 1.

Let now $C = C_{m_1,\ldots,m_\varkappa}$. Then $\tilde{\partial}C = \sum n_i C^i$ where the C^i are the cells of dimension one smaller than the dimension of C and the n_i are integers (or integers mod 2 if we are interested in homology mod 2) determined as follows (see the general discussion in Chapter 2): if C^i is not contained in $\phi(\partial D)$, then $n_i = 0$. If $C^i \subseteq \phi(\partial D)$, consider the map $\phi : \phi^{-1}(C^i) \to C^i$; then n_i is the degree of this map. Thus, n_i is the algebraic number of points in ∂D mapping into a single point of C^i. Since ϕ has been shown to be two to one on $(\partial D)_1$, it follows that, modulo 2, $\tilde{\partial}C = 0$.

We thus have the following

Theorem (1): $H_l(G_{\varkappa,n}^{\mathcal{C}}, \mathbf{Z})$ is isomorphic to the direct sum of N_l copies of $\mathbf{Z}$ where N_l is the number of Schubert cells of dimension l. $H_l(G_{\varkappa,n}^{R}, \mathbf{Z}_2)$ is isomorphic to the direct sum of N_l copies of $\mathbf{Z}_2$ where N_l is as above.

Corollary: By duality, we see that $H^l(G_{\varkappa,n}^{\mathcal{C}}, \mathbf{Z}) \cong H_l(G_{\varkappa,n}^{\mathcal{C}}, \mathbf{Z})$ and $H^l(G_{\varkappa,n}^{R}, \mathbf{Z}_2) \cong H_l(G_{\varkappa,n}^{R}, \mathbf{Z}_2)$. Hence, Theorem 1 gives us the cohomology groups of $G_{\varkappa,n}$.

We shall now carry out some intersection theoretic calculations on the manifold $G_{\varkappa,n}$. Denote by $E_\perp^\beta$ the orthogonal complement of E^β in E^n ($\beta \leq n$). Let $\pi \in G_{\varkappa,n}$ satisfy the following conditions:

$$
\begin{array}{ll}
\dim(\pi E^{m_1}) \geq 1 & \dim(\pi E_\perp^{m_1-1}) \geq \varkappa \\
\dim(\pi E^{m_2}) \geq 2 & \dim(\pi E_\perp^{m_2-1}) \geq \varkappa - 1 \\
\quad\vdots & \quad\vdots \\
\dim(\pi E^{m_\varkappa}) \geq \varkappa & \dim(\pi E_\perp^{m_\varkappa-1}) \geq 1
\end{array} \tag{*}
$$

The first condition tells us that π contains e_{m_1}, the unique vector (up to scalar multiples) in $E^{m_1} \cap E^{m_1-1}$. The second condition tells us that π contains e_{m_2}, the unique vector (up to scalar multiples) in $E^{m_2} \cap E^{m_2-1}$. In general, the j-th condition tells us that π contains e_{m_j}, the unique vector (up to scalar multiples) in $E^{m_j} \cap E^{m_j-1}$. Hence $\pi = \{e_{m_1}, e_{m_2}, \ldots, e_{m_\varkappa}\}$ and thus there is a unique plane π satisfying (*). It is therefore plain that (*) implies that fact $\pi \in C_{m_1, \ldots, m_\varkappa}$. Now, since

$$E^0 \subseteq E^1 \subseteq \cdots \subseteq E^n$$

we have also

$$E_\perp^0 \supseteq E_\perp^1 \supseteq \cdots \supseteq E_\perp^n.$$

Let $F^j = E_\perp^{n-j}$ $(j = 0, 1, \ldots, n)$. Then

$$F^0 \subseteq F^1 \subseteq \cdots \subseteq F^n.$$

We define

$$\hat{m}_j(\pi) = \inf_m \{m \mid \dim(\pi F^m) \geq j\}$$

and we put

$$C_{m_1, \ldots, m_\varkappa}^\perp = \{\pi \in G_{\varkappa, n} \mid \hat{m}_j(\pi) = m_j\}.$$

Observe that $C_{m_1, \ldots, m_\varkappa}^\perp = C_{m_1, \ldots, m_\varkappa}(F^0, F^1, \ldots, F^n)$. Now, conditions (*) clearly imply $\pi \in C_{n-m_\varkappa+1, \ldots, n-m_1+1}^\perp$. We also have, by direct calculation,

$$\dim(C_{m_1, \ldots, m_\varkappa}) + \dim(C_{n-m_\varkappa+1, \ldots, n-m_1+1}^\perp) = \dim G_{\varkappa, n}.$$

It can moreover be shown that the cells $C_{m_1, \ldots, m_\varkappa}$ and $C_{n-m_\varkappa+1, \ldots, n-m_1+1}^\perp$ are in general position in $G_{\varkappa, n}$. We call each of these cells the *dual Shubert cell* of the other. It follows then that

$$C_{m_1, \ldots, m_\varkappa} \cdot C_{n-m_\varkappa+1, \ldots, n-m_1+1}^\perp = 1.$$

We shall now show that the set of $\pi \in G_{\varkappa, n}$ satisfying conditions

$$
\begin{array}{ll}
\dim(\pi E^{m_1}) \geq 1 & \dim(\pi E_\perp^{l_1-1}) \geq \varkappa \\
\dim(\pi E^{m_2}) \geq 2 & \dim(\pi E_\perp^{l_2-1}) \geq \varkappa - 1 \\
\quad\vdots & \quad\vdots \\
\dim(\pi E^{m_\varkappa}) \geq \varkappa & \dim(\pi E_\perp^{l_\varkappa-1}) \geq 1
\end{array}
\qquad (**)
$$

in addition to the condition $\sum_{i=1}^{\varkappa} l_i = \sum_{i=1}^{\varkappa} m_i$, is nonempty only if $l_j = m_j$ $(j = 1, \ldots, \varkappa)$.

Suppose, for example, $l_1 > m_1$. Then $E^{m_1} \cap E_\perp^{l_1-1} = \{0\}$ and the first line of (**) would be violated. Therefore, $l_1 \leq m_1^\perp$. Similarly, $l_2 \leq m_2, \ldots,$ $l_\varkappa \leq m_\varkappa$. As $\sum_{i=1}^{\varkappa} l_i = \sum_{i=1}^{\varkappa} m_i$, we must have $l_j = m_j$ $(j = 1, \ldots, \varkappa)$.

Thus, if $(l_1, l_2, \ldots, l_\varkappa)$ is a $\varkappa$-tuple of strictly increasing integers such that $l_{j_0} \neq m_{j_0}$ for some $j_0 \in \{1, 2, \ldots, \varkappa\}$, while $\sum\limits_{i=1}^{\varkappa} l_i = \sum\limits_{i=1}^{\varkappa} m_i$, then

$$C_{m_1, \ldots, m_\varkappa} \cdot C^{\perp}_{n-l_\varkappa+1, \ldots, n-l_1+1} = 0.$$

We have already observed that the Schubert cells depend upon the sequence $E^0 \subseteq E^1 \subseteq \cdots \subseteq E^n$. Suppose then we have two such sequences,

$$E^0 \subseteq E^1 \subseteq \cdots \subseteq E^n \quad \text{and} \quad \tilde{E}^0 \subseteq \tilde{E}^1 \subseteq \cdots \subseteq \tilde{E}^n$$

where $E^0 = \tilde{E}^0$, $E^n = \tilde{E}^n$ and where E^i and $\tilde{E}^i$ are Euclidean i-dimensional spaces embedded in Euclidean n-space. Let

$$C_{m_1, \ldots, m_\varkappa} = C_{m_1, \ldots, m_\varkappa} (E^0, \ldots, E^n),$$

$$\tilde{C}_{m_1, \ldots, m_\varkappa} = C_{m_1, \ldots, m_\varkappa} (\tilde{E}^0, \ldots, \tilde{E}^n).$$

We have the following

Lemma (2): $C_{m_1, \ldots, m_\varkappa}$ and $\tilde{C}_{m_1, \ldots, m_\varkappa}$ define the same homology class in $H(G_{\varkappa,n})$.

Proof: The sequence $E^0 \subseteq \cdots \subseteq E^n$ gives rise to a basis $e_1, e_2, \ldots, e_n$ where $E^i = \{e_1, \ldots, e_i\}$. The sequence $\tilde{E}^0 \subseteq \tilde{E}^1 \subseteq \cdots \subseteq \tilde{E}^n$ gives rise to a similar basis $\tilde{e}_1, \tilde{e}_2, \ldots, \tilde{e}_n$. Let $T: E^n \to \tilde{E}^n = E^n$ be the linear transformation defined by

$$Te_i = \tilde{e}_i, \qquad i = 1, \ldots, n.$$

The map T induces naturally a map

$$T': G_{\varkappa,n} \to G_{\varkappa,n}$$

which in turn induces a map

$$T_*: H(G_{\varkappa,n}) \to H(G_{\varkappa,n}).$$

Clearly, $T'(C_{m_1, \ldots, m_\varkappa}) = \tilde{C}_{m_1, \ldots, m_\varkappa}$. If we are dealing with $G^{\mathscr{C}}_{\varkappa,n}$, then $T \in GL(n, \mathscr{C})$; since $GL(n, \mathscr{C})$ is arcwise connected, T can be joined to I (the identity matrix) by a path in $GL(n, \mathscr{C})$. This induces a homotopy between T' and I' (the identity map of $G_{\varkappa,n}$). Hence, T_* is the identity map of $H(G^{\mathscr{C}}_{\varkappa,n})$ and the assertion is proved. If we are dealing with $G^{\mathscr{R}}_{\varkappa,n}$, then $T \in GL(n, \mathscr{R})$ and then either $\det T > 0$ or $\det T < 0$. If $\det T > 0$, then T can be joined to I by a path in $GL(n, \mathscr{R})$ since T lies in the connected component of $GL(n, R)$ which contains I. In this case, T_* is the identity map, as above. If $\det T < 0$, then T can be joined to the matrix

$$\hat{I} = \begin{pmatrix} -1 & & & & \\ & 1 & & 0 & \\ & & 1 & & \\ & & & \ddots & \\ 0 & & & & 1 \end{pmatrix}$$

by a path in $GL(n, R)$ since T lies in the connected component of $GL(n, R)$ which contains $\hat{I}$. But the map

$$\hat{I}' : G_{\varkappa,n} \to G_{\varkappa,n}$$

induced by $\hat{I}$ is the identity map on $G_{\varkappa,n}$ because we have assumed that $G_{\varkappa,n}$ consists of unoriented $\varkappa$-planes. Hence, as above, T_* is the identity map. This proves the lemma.

Observing that $C^\perp_{m_1,\dots,m_\varkappa} = C_{m_1,\dots,m_\varkappa}(F^0, F^1, \dots, F^n)$, we have

Theorem (2): Let $m_1 + m_2 + \cdots + m_\varkappa = l_1 + l_2 + \cdots + l_\varkappa$. Then

$$C_{m_1,\dots,m_\varkappa} \cdot C_{n-l_\varkappa+1,\dots,n-l_1+1} = \delta^{l_1 l_2 \dots l_\varkappa}_{m_1 m_2 \dots m_\varkappa}$$

where

$$\delta^{l_1 \dots l_\varkappa}_{m_1 \dots m_\varkappa} = 1 \quad \text{if} \quad l_i = m_i, \qquad (i = 1, \dots, \varkappa),$$
$$= 0 \quad \text{otherwise.}$$

That is, the intersection of each Schubert cell with its dual cell is 1, while all other intersections are 0.

We now consider the cohomology ring of $G_{\varkappa,n}$. Let $P^{(1)}_{n-1} \times \cdots \times P^{(\varkappa)}_{n-1}$ be the product of $\varkappa$ copies of projective space P_{n-1}. From a result of Chapter 2,

$$H^*(P^C_{n-1}, Z) \cong Z(z)/(z^n), \qquad H^*(P^R_{n-1}, Z_2) \cong Z_2(z)/(z^n).$$

From Künneth's Theorem,

$$H^*(P^C_{n-1} \times \cdots \times P^C_{n-1}) \cong Z(z_1, \dots, z_\varkappa)/(z_1^n, \dots, z_\varkappa^n)$$
$$H^*(P^R_{n-1} \times \cdots \times P^R_{n-1}) \cong Z_2(z_1, \dots, z_\varkappa)/(z_1^n, \dots, z_\varkappa^n).$$

Again from Künneth's theorem, the homology classes of $P^{(1)}_{n-1} \times \cdots \times P^{(\varkappa)}_{n-1}$ can be represented by products

$$P^{(1)}_{l_1} \times P^{(2)}_{l_2} \times \cdots \times P^{(\varkappa)}_{l_\varkappa}, \quad l_i \leq n-1; \quad (i = 1, 2, \dots, \varkappa).$$

We define a "natural" map

$$N : P^{(1)}_{n-1} \times \cdots \times P^{(\varkappa)}_{n-1} \to G_{\varkappa,\varkappa n}$$

as follows. An element of $P_{n-1}^{(i)}$ is the equivalence class of an n-vector $(x_0, x_1, \ldots, x_{n-1})$. This equivalence class gives a one-dimensional subspace of a Euclidean space E_i^n ($i = 1, 2, \ldots, \varkappa$).

Let $E^{\varkappa n} = E_1^n \oplus \cdots \oplus E_\varkappa^n$. If $v_i \in P_{n-1}^{(i)}$, define

$$N((v_1, v_2, \ldots, v_\varkappa)) = \{v_1, v_2, \ldots, v_\varkappa\} = \pi$$

i.e. π is the plane in $E^{\varkappa n}$ generated by the vectors $v_1, v_2, \ldots, v_\varkappa$.

Let $\{P_{\alpha_1}^{(1)} \times \cdots \times P_{\alpha_\varkappa}^{(\varkappa)}\}$ denote the homology class of $P_{\alpha_1}^{(1)} \times \cdots \times P_{\alpha_\varkappa}^{(\varkappa)}$ in $H(P_{n-1}^{(1)} \times \cdots \times P_{n-1}^{(n)})$; similarly, let $\{C_{\beta_1, \ldots, \beta_\varkappa}\}$ denote the homology class of $C_{\beta_1, \ldots, \beta_\varkappa}$ in $H(G_{\varkappa, n})$.

Suppose that we introduce a lexicographic ordering of the homology classes of a Grassmann manifold by writing $\{C_{m_1, \ldots, m_k}\} > \{C_{n_1, \ldots, n_k}\}$ if $m_1 > n_1$, or if $m_1 = n_1$ while $m_2 > n_2$, or if $m_1 = n_1$ and $m_2 = n_2$ while $m_3 > n_3$, etc. Then, if $l_1 \leq l_2 \leq \cdots \leq l_x \leq n - 1$, we will show that

(†) $N_*(\{P_{l_1}^{(1)} \times \cdots \times P_{l_x}^{(x)}\}) = \{C_{l_1+1, l_2+2, \ldots, l_x+x}\}$ + lower classes of like dimension, where N_* denotes the mapping of homology induced by the continuous mapping N. We prove this as follows. Let p, m, k be positive integers such that $p \geq m + k$; let $C_{m_1, \ldots, m_k}$ be a Schubert cell of the Grassmann manifold $G_{k, p}$; and suppose that $m_k < m + k$. Consider the mapping M: $G_{k, p} \times P^m \to G_{k, p+m+1}$ which maps $\pi \times (x) \in G_{k, p} \times P^m$ into the hyperplane π_x in E^{p+m+1} generated by the vectors $[y, x]$, where $y \in \pi$. We shall show, using intersection theory, that

(††) $M_*(\{C_{m_1, \ldots, m_k}\} \times \{P^m\}) = a\{C_{m_1, \ldots, m_k, m+k}\}$ + lower classes of like dimension, and that the coefficient a is equal to 1. Indeed, regard $E^1 \subseteq E^2 \subseteq E^3 \subseteq \ldots$ as in the preceding paragraphs, let $n_1 < n_2 < \cdots n_{k+1}$, and suppose that π_x lies in the dual cell of $C_{n_1, \ldots, n_{k+1}}$, so that dim $(\pi_x E_{n_j-1}^\perp) \geq k + 2 - j$. Since $\pi \subseteq \pi_x$ is a hyperplane of codimension 1, it follows that dim $(\pi E_{n_j-1}^\perp) \geq k + 1 - j$, so that dim $(\pi E_{n_j-1}^\perp E_{m_j}) \geq 1$ and $n_j \leq m_j$, $j = 1, \ldots, k$. Thus, if the image $M(C_{m1, \ldots, m_k} \times P^m)$ has a non-zero intersection with the dual cell of $C_{n_1, \ldots, n_{k+1}}$, we have $\{C_{n_1, \ldots, n_{k+1}}\} < \{C_{m_1, \ldots, m_k, m+k}\}$ in the lexicographic ordering. Using Theorem 2, we may at once conclude that (††) is true; however, it remains for us to evaluate the coefficient a. To this end, we proceed as follows. Let $Tx: E^{m+1} \to E^p$ be the linear transformation defined by

$$Tx = (x_1, \ldots, x_{n_1-1}, 0, x_{n_1}, \ldots, x_{n_2-2}, 0, \ldots, x_{m-1}, x_m, 0, \ldots, 0).$$

Let $M^t: G_{k, p} \times P^m \to G_{k, p+m+1}$ map $\pi \times (x)$ into the plane $\pi_x^{(t)}$ generated by the vectors $[y + tTx, x]$, where $y \in \pi$. Then $M^0 = M$, while M^t clearly depends continuously upn t. To prove that $a = 1$ in (††) we have therefore only to show that the intersection number of $M_*^{(1)}(\{C_{m_1,\ldots,m_k}\} \times \{P^m\})$ with the dual class of $C_{m_1,\ldots,m_k,m+k}$ is 1. But if $\pi_x^{(1)}$ belongs to the corresponding dual cell, we have $\dim(\pi_x^{(1)}E_{m_j-1}^\perp) \geq k + 2 - j$ as above, and it follows as above that $\dim(\pi_x^{(1)}E_{m_j}E_{m_j-1}^\perp) \geq 1$. Thus the basis vector e_{m_j} belongs to $\pi_x^{(1)}$ for $1 \leq j \leq k$. We may therefore write $[e_{m_j},0] = [y + zTx, zx]$ for some $y \in \pi$ and scalar z, from which it follows that $z = 0$, $e_{m_j} \in \pi$, $1 \leq j \leq k$, so that π is uniquely determined. Moreover, since $\dim(\pi_x^{(1)}E_{m+k}^\perp) = 1$, $Tx = 0$; thus the $m + 1$-dimensional vector x is a multiple of the basis vector e_{m+1}, i.e., x is determined up to a scalar factor. The intersection with which we are concerned thus consists of precisely one point; since it is readily seen to be transverse, the intersection number a of (††) is equal to 1, and (††) is fully proved.

It is clear that (†) follows from (††), by induction on x; thus (†) is also established.

We assert further that

$$N_*(\{P_{l_1}^{(1)} \times \cdots \times P_{l_x}^{(x)}\}) = \{C_{l_1'+1, l_2'+2, \ldots, l_x'+x}\}$$

$$+ \text{ lower classes of like dimension,}$$

where $l_1, l_2, \ldots, l_x$ is an arbitrary sequence of integers such that $l_i \leq n - 1$ ($i = 1, \ldots, x$) and where the sequence $l_1', l_2', \ldots, l_n'$ is the sequence $l_1, l_2, \ldots, l_n$ rearranged in ascending order. To see this, let

$$\psi : P_{n-1}^{(1)} \times \cdots \times P_{n-1}^{(x)} \to P_{n-1}^{(1)} \times \cdots \times P_{n-1}^{(x)}$$

be defined by $\psi((v_1, \ldots, v_x)) = (v_{i_1}, \ldots, v_{i_x})$. Then, ψ permutes the vectors $v_1, \ldots, v_x$ among themselves, and

$$\psi(P_{l_1}^{(1)} \times \cdots \times P_{l_x}^{(x)}) = P_{l_{i_1}}^{(1)} \times \cdots \times P_{l_{i_x}}^{(x)}.$$

By choosing ψ appropriately, we can insure $l_{i_1} \leq l_{i_2} \leq \cdots \leq l_{i_x}$.

Observe that $N \circ \psi = T' \circ N$ where $T' : G_{x,n} \to G_{x,n}$ is induced by an appropriate (nonsingular) linear transformation of E^{xn}. From the proof of Lemma 2, it follows that

$$N_* \circ \psi_* = N_*, \quad \psi^* \circ N^* = N^*$$

where N^*, ψ^* are the induced mappings in chomology. The desired result follows directly.

Let now $\gamma_{m_1,\ldots,m_x}$ be the cohomology class dual to $\{C_{m_1,\ldots,m_x}\}$. By the above assertion, it follows that $N^*\gamma_{m_1,\ldots,m_x}(\{P_{l_1}^{(1)} \times \cdots \times P_{l_x}^{(x)}\}) = 1$ if $(l_1, l_2, \ldots, l_x)$ is a permutation of $(m_1 - 1, m_2 - 2, \ldots, m_x - x)$ and equals zero if $(l_1, \ldots, l_x) < (m_1 - 1, m_2 - 2, \ldots, m_x - x)$ in the lexicographic ordering of x-tuples introduced above.

Let $\delta_l^{(i)}$ be the cohomology class in $H^l(P_{n-1}^{(i)})$ dual to $\{P_l^{(i)}\}$ ($i = 1, \ldots, x$).

Any cohomology class of $H^*(P_{n-1}^{(1)} \times \cdots \times P_{n-1}^{(x)})$ can be written uniquely as a combination of the basis vectors $\delta_{l_1}^{(1)} \otimes \cdots \otimes \delta_{l_x}^{(x)}$. Suppose that we order these basis vectors by the same lexicographic ordering of $(l_1, \ldots, l_x)$. We know from Chapter 2 that $\delta_l^{(i)} = (\delta_1^{(i)})^l = \delta_1^{(i)} \cup \delta_1^{(i)} \cup \cdots \cup \delta_1^{(i)}$ (l times). It follows from the above that

$$N^* \gamma_{m_1, \ldots, m_x} = \text{Symm} \, (\delta_{m_1-1}^{(1)} \otimes \delta_{m_2-2}^{(2)} \otimes \cdots \otimes \delta_{m_x-x}^{(x)})$$

$$+ \text{ a combination of higher basis vectors}$$

where "Symm" is the symmetrization operator. Writing $\delta_{m_j-j}^{(j)} = (\delta_1^{(j)})^{m_j-j}$, we get

$$N^* \gamma_{m_1, \ldots, m_x} = \text{Symm} \, ((\delta_1^{(1)})^{m_1-1} \otimes \cdots \otimes (\delta_1^{(x)})^{m_x-x})$$

$$+ \text{ a combination of higher basis vectors.}$$

From this, the following theorem is evident.

Theorem (3): N^* maps $H^*(G_{x,xn}^{C})$ onto the subring of $Z(z_1, \ldots, z_x)/(z_1^n, \ldots, z_x^n)$ consisting of symmetric polynomials. Also, N^* maps $H^*(G_{x,xn}^{R})$ onto the subring of $Z_2(z_1, \ldots, z_x)/(z_1^n, \ldots, z_x^n)$ consisting of symmetric polynomials.

Consider now an increasing sequence of Euclidean spaces $E^x \subseteq E^{x+1} \subseteq \cdots \subseteq E^N \subseteq \cdots$. Then,

$$E^n = \{(x_1, \ldots, x_n) \, (x_n \in R)\}, \qquad n \geq x.$$

The inclusion $E^n \subseteq E^{n+1}$ gives rise to an inclusion map

$$i_n : G_{x,n} \to G_{x,n+1}$$

which is clearly a cellular map. Since there are no nontrivial boundary relations among the Schubert cells, it follows that

$$(i_n)_* : H(G_{x,n}) \to H(G_{x,n+1})$$

is an injective homomorphism.

Now let E^∞ denote the set of all sequences of real numbers, all but a finite number of which are 0. Then E^∞ can be viewed as the direct limit space of the sequence $E^x \subseteq E^{x+1} \subseteq \cdots$. Then define $G_{x,\infty}$ to be the direct limit space of the sequence $G_{x,x} \subseteq G_{x,x+1} \subseteq \cdots$. Clearly, $G_{x,\infty}$ can be regarded as the set of $\varkappa$-planes in E^{∞}. Using the fact that the maps $(i_n)_*$ are injective, it can be shown that

$$H(G_{\varkappa,\infty}) = \operatorname*{dir\,lim}_{n\to\infty} H(G_{\varkappa,n}).$$

Using this, the following theorem can be demonstrated.

Theorem (4): $H^*(G_{\varkappa,\infty})$ is isomorphic to the ring of all symmetric polynomials in $\varkappa$ variables $z_1, \ldots, z_\varkappa$.

From a classical theorem in algebra, any symmetric polynomial in $\varkappa$ variables can be written as a polynomial in the elementary symmetric polynomials $\sigma_1, \ldots, \sigma_\varkappa$. Denote by $c_1, \ldots, c_\varkappa$ the elements of $H^*(G_{\varkappa,\infty})$ which correspond to $\sigma_1, \ldots, \sigma_\varkappa$ under the isomorphism given by Theorem 4. The elements $c_1, \ldots, c_\varkappa$ are called the *Whitney Classes* (in the real case) and the *Chern Classes* (in the complex case). Thus, Theorem 4 asserts that any cohomology class in $H^*(G_{\varkappa,\infty})$ can be written as a sum of cup products of Whitney (Chern) Classes.

Note that in the real case, $c_j \in H^j(G^R_{\varkappa,\infty}, Z_2)$, while in the complex case, $c_j \in H^{2j}(G^C_{\varkappa,\infty}, Z)$.

Part B: The Poincaré Duality Theorem

We recall some of the facts from the theory of character groups. (For a full exposition of results, see Loomis—*An Introduction to Abstract Harmonic Analysis* or Pontryagin—*Topological Groups*.) Let G be a locally compact abelian group with a countable basis. Then we can define the character group $\hat{G}$ of G to be the group of continuous homomorphisms of G into R mod 1, the additive group of reals modulo 1. It is known that (i) if $G \cong R^n$, then $\hat{G} \cong R^n$, (ii) if G is finite and has the discrete topology, then $G \cong \hat{G}$, (ii) if $G \cong Z$, then $\hat{G} \cong R$ mod 1. There is a pairing of the groups G, $\hat{G}$ to the group R mod 1, i.e. for $g \in G$, $\hat{g} \in \hat{G}$, there is a natural "multiplication" $g\hat{g} = r$, $r \in R$ mod 1. In particular, if $g, \hat{g} \in R$, then $g\hat{g}$ is just the ordinary multiplication reduced modulo 1. It is known that G is compact $\Leftrightarrow$ $\hat{G}$ is discrete and that $\hat{\hat{G}} \cong G$ for any locally compact G. We say that two groups G and G' are dually paired to R mod 1 if there is a multiplication $gg' \in R$ mod 1 such that if ϕ_g is the element of $\hat{G}'$ defined by $\phi_g(g') = gg'$ and if $\psi_{g'}$ is the element of $\hat{G}$ defined by $\psi_{g'}(g) = gg'$, then the maps $g \to \phi_g$ and $g' \to \psi_{g'}$ are isomorphisms of G onto $\hat{G}'$ and G' onto $\hat{G}'$.

We are now in a position to state the *Poincaré Duality Theorem: Let M^m be a compact orientable manifold without boundary and let G be a locally compact abelian group with a countable basis. Then $H_k(M; G)$ and $H_{m-k}(M; \hat{G})$*

are dually paired to R mod 1 *if the multiplication between* $H_k(M; G)$ *and* $H_{m-k}(M; \hat{G})$ *is defined as the intersection number of homology classes.*

Corollary (1): Let M^m be a compact orientable manifold without boundary. If α is a singular (k)-cycle on M with real (respectively integer) coefficients, and if $\alpha \cdot \beta = 0$ for all singular $(m-k)$-cycles β on M with real (respectively R mod 1) coefficients, then α is a boundary.

If G is a field, the singular homology groups of H are vector spaces. We define the p-h Betti number b_p of M to be the dimension of $H_p(M; G)$. As a consequence of the Poincaré Duality Theorem, we have the following

Corollary (2): $b_k = b_{m-k}$.

If M is not orientable, the intersection theory mod Z cannot be applied. However, we still have *Poincaré Duality Theorem Mod* 2: *If* M^m *is a compact manifold without boundary, then* $H_k(M; Z_2)$ *and* $H_{m-k}(M; Z_2)$ *are dually paired to* R mod 1 *if the multiplication between* $H_k(M; Z_2)$ *and* $H_{m-k}(M; Z_2)$ *is defined as the intersection number mod* 2 *of homology classes.*

Our proof of the Poincaré Duality Theorem will make use of Morse Theory. We shall state the results we need without proof. The proofs can be found in Milnor—*Morse Theory*.

Suppose then that f is a smooth real-valued function on a manifold M^m. A point $p \in M$ is called a *critical* point of f if, in local coordinates at p, $\frac{\partial f}{\partial x_1}(p) = \cdots = \frac{\partial f}{\partial x_m}(p) = 0$. A critical point p is called *nondegenerate* if the matrix $\left\| \frac{\partial^2 f}{\partial x_i \partial x_j}(p) \right\|$ is nonsingular. A lemma of Morse states that if p is a nondegenerate critical point of f, then there exist local coordinates at p such that $f = f(p) - x_1^2 - \cdots - x_k^2 + x_{k+1}^2 + \cdots + x_m^2$ in the entire coordinate patch. The integer k is called the *index* of the critical point p. It is an immediate consequence of Morse's lemma that nondegenerate critical points are isolated. Hence, if M is a compact manifold, the number of nondegenerate critical points is finite. The following lemma, which is closely related to the jiggling lemma, and the details of whose proof we leave to the reader, plays a crucial role in what follows.

Lemma (1): Let f be a smooth real-valued function on the compact manifold M. Arbitrarily near f (in the sense of the d_k-metric, for any k), there exists a smooth real-valued function g on M such that g has only nondegenerate critical points. If, moreover, $p_1, p_2, \ldots, p_k$ are the critical points of g, then g can be chosen so that $g(p_1), g(p_2), \ldots, g(p_k)$ are distinct real numbers.

The following theorem is one of the central results of Morse Theory. First, we give some definitions. Let f be a smooth real-valued function on a compact manifold M. The real number c is called a critical *level* of f if there exists a critical point p of f such that $f(p) = c$. Denote by $(r_1 \leq f \leq r_2)$ the set of all points $q \in M$ such that $r_1 \leq f(q) \leq r_2$, where r_1 and r_2 are any real numbers. Similarly, we denote by $(f \leq r)$ (respectively $(f \geq r)$) the set of all points $q \in M$ such that $f(q) \leq r$ (respectively $f(q) \geq r$). We then have

Morse's Theorem: *Let a and b be real numbers, $a < b$. If there are no critical levels of f between a and b, then $(f \leq a)$ is a deformation retract of $(f \leq b)$. In particular, the relative singular homology group $H((f \leq b)/(f \leq a))$ $= 0$. On the other hand, suppose there is exactly one critical level of f between a and b corresponding to exactly one nondegenerate critical point of f of index k. Then $H_l((f \leq b)/(f \leq a)) = 0$ for $k \neq l$ and $H_k((f \leq b)/(f \leq a); G)$ $\cong G$.*

For a proof of this result, cf. Milnor, *op. cit.*

We now proceed to the proof of the Poincaré Duality Theorem. By Lemma (1), we can find a smooth real-valued function f on M, all of whose critical points are nondegenerate. Moreover, if $p_1, p_2, \ldots, p_{n-1}$ are these critical points, we may suppose that $f(p_1), f(p_2), \ldots, f(p_{n-1})$ are all distinct. Without loss of generality, we may assume $f(p_1) < f(p_2) < \cdots < f(p_{n-1})$. It is clear that $f(p_1)$ is the minimum value, and $f(p_{n-1})$ the maximum value, of the function f. We now choose any real numbers $c_1, c_2, \ldots, c_n$ such that $c_1 < f(p_1) < c_2 < f(p_2) < \cdots < c_{n-1} < f(p_{n-1}) < c_n$. It suffices to prove (by induction on i) that $H_k((f \leq c_i); G)$ and $H_{m-k}((f \leq c_i)/(f = c_i); \hat{G})$ are dually paired to R mod 1 by the intersection number. Indeed, setting $i = n$, we have $(f \leq c_n) = M$, $(f = c_n) = \phi$ and the assertion follows directly. For $i = 1$, the proposition is obvious because $(f \leq c_1) = \phi$. Let $c = f(p_1)$ denote the minimum value of f. There is a coordinate patch at p_1 such that f is given by $f = c + x_1^2 + \cdots + x_m^2$. Since p_1 is the only point in M at which f takes on its minimum, it follows easily from the compactness of M that there exists a number $\varepsilon > 0$ such that $(f \leq c + \varepsilon)$ is homeomorphic to $B_\varepsilon^m = \{(x_1, \ldots, x_m) \mid x_1^2 + \cdots + x_m^2 \leq \varepsilon\}$. Now $H_k(B_\varepsilon^m, G)$ and $H_{m-k}(B_\varepsilon^m/\partial B_\varepsilon^m, \hat{G})$ are dually paired to R mod 1 by the intersection number. In fact, if $k \neq 0$, $H_k(B_\varepsilon^m, G) = 0 = H_{m-k}(B_\varepsilon^m/\partial B_\varepsilon^m, \hat{G})$. Moreover, $H_0(B_\varepsilon^m, G) \cong G$ and $H_m(B_\varepsilon^m/\partial B_\varepsilon^m, \hat{G}) \cong \hat{G}$. It follows from the first part of Morse's theorem that $H_k((f \leq c_2), G) \cong H_k(B_\varepsilon^m, G)$ and $H_{m-k}((f \leq c_2)/(f = c_2), \hat{G}) \cong H_{m-k}(B_\varepsilon^m/\partial B_\varepsilon^m, \hat{G})$. The proposition is thus verified for $i = 2$. We now proceed inductively, assuming the result for $i \leq j$ and proving it for $i = j + 1$. Let the index of the critical point p_j be λ. Set $T = (f \leq c_{j+1})$, $U = (f = c_{j+1})$, $T_- = (f \leq c_{j+1} - \varepsilon)$, $T_0 = (c_j + \varepsilon \leq f \leq c_{j+1})$, $L = (f \leq c_j)$. Here, ε is chosen so small that $c_{j+1} - \varepsilon > f(p_j) > c_j + \varepsilon$. We consider two exact homology sequences; the sequence of the pair (T_-, L) and the sequence of the triple (T, T_0, U). We have

$$\cdots \to H_{k+1}(T_-/L, G) \to H_k(L, G) \to H_k(T_-, G) \to \tag{1}$$
$$\to H_k(T_-/L, G) \to H_{k-1}(L, G) \to \cdots$$

$$\cdots \leftarrow H_{m-k-1}(T_0/U, \hat{G}) \leftarrow H_{m-k}(T/T_0, \hat{G}) \leftarrow H_{m-k}(T/U, \hat{G}) \leftarrow \tag{2}$$
$$\leftarrow H_{m-k}(T_0/U, \hat{G}) \leftarrow H_{m+k-1}(T/T_0, \hat{G}) \leftarrow \cdots$$

We want to show that $H_k(T, G)$ and $H_{m-k}(T/U, \hat{G})$ are dually paired to $R \bmod 1$ by the intersection number. By virtue of Morse's theorem, it is just as well to consider $H_k(T_-, G)$ as $H_k(T, G)$. In general, $\alpha \cdot \beta$ is defined whenever $\partial\alpha \cap \beta = \phi, \alpha \cap \partial\beta = \phi$. Hence, intersection numbers are defined between elements of $H_r(L, G)$ and $H_{m-r}(T/T_0, \hat{G})$, $H_r(T_-, G)$ and $H_{m-r}(T/U, \hat{G})$, and $H_r(T_-/L, G)$ and $H_{m-r}(T_0/U, \hat{G})$. Indeed, $L \cap T_0 = T_- \cap U = \phi$. We shall show that $H_k(L, G)$ and $H_{m-k}(T/T_0, G)$ are dually paired to $R \bmod 1$ by the intersection number. By excision, $H_{m-k}(T/T_0, \hat{G}) \cong H_{m-k}((f \leq c_j + \varepsilon)/(f = c_j + \varepsilon), \hat{G})$ and by the first part of Morse's theorem, $H_k(L, G) \cong H_k((f \leq c_j + \varepsilon), G)$. The assertion now follows by induction and another application of Morse's theorem. The same result is true, of course, for the groups $H_{k-1}(L, G)$ and $H_{m-k+1}(T/T_0, \hat{G})$. We claim moreover that $H_k(T_-/L), G)$ and $H_{m-k}(T_0/U, \hat{G})$ are dually paired to $R \bmod 1$ by the intersection number. Indeed, it follows directly the second part of Morse's theorem that $H_k(T_-/L, G) \cong \begin{cases} 0 & \text{if } k \neq \lambda \\ G & \text{if } k = \lambda. \end{cases}$ By excision,

$$H_{m-k}(T_0/U, \hat{G}) \cong H_{m-k}((f \geq c_j + \varepsilon)/(f \geq c_{j+1}), \hat{G})$$
$$\cong H_{m-k}((-f \leq -c_j - \varepsilon)/(-f \leq -c_{j+1})\, \hat{G}).$$

As p_j is a critical point of f of index λ, it is clearly a critical point of $-f$ of of index $m - \lambda$. It follows again from the second part of Morse's theorem that $H_{m-k}(T_0/U, \hat{G}) \cong \begin{cases} 0 & \text{if } k \neq \lambda \\ \hat{G} & \text{if } k = \lambda \end{cases}$: This proves the claim. The same result is true, of course, for the groups $H_{k+1}(T_-/L, G)$ and $H_{m-k-1}(T_0/U, \hat{G})$. We claim, now, that the sequences (1) and (2) are dual exact sequences in the following sense. Consider abstractly two exact sequences of groups

$$\cdots \longrightarrow A_{j+1} \xrightarrow{\phi_{j+1}} A_j \xrightarrow{\phi_j} A_{j-1} \longrightarrow \cdots \tag{1'}$$
$$\cdots \longleftarrow B_{j+1} \xleftarrow{\psi_j} B_j \xleftarrow{\psi_{j-1}} B_{j-1} \longleftarrow \cdots \tag{2'}$$

Suppose we have defined a product $a \cdot b$ for $a \in A_j$, $b \in B_j$. We say that the sequences (1′) and (2′) are dual exact sequences if $\phi_{j+1} a' \cdot b = a' \cdot \psi_j b$ holds for $a' \in A_{j+1}$, $b \in B_j$. Let us assume for the moment that (1) and (2) above are dual exact sequences. Our theorem will then be deduced from the

Algebraic Lemma: Suppose (1′) and (2′) are dual exact sequences. Suppose further that A_{3j} and B_{3j} are dually paired to R mod 1 and also that A_{3j+1} and B_{3j+1} are dually paired to R mod 1. Then, A_{3j+2} and B_{3j+2} are dually paired to R mod 1.

To prove this, let $C_i = \hat{B}_i$, the character group of B_i. The exact sequence (2′) gives rise to a corresponding exact sequence $\longrightarrow C_{j+1} \xrightarrow{\hat{\psi}_j} C_j \xrightarrow{\hat{\psi}_{j-1}} C_{j-1}$. We consider the diagram

$$
\begin{array}{ccccccc}
\cdots \longrightarrow & A_{j+1} & \xrightarrow{\phi_{j+1}} & A_j & \xrightarrow{\phi_j} & A_{j-1} & \longrightarrow \cdots \\
& \downarrow{\scriptstyle f_{j+1}} & & \downarrow{\scriptstyle f_j} & & \downarrow{\scriptstyle f_{j-1}} & \\
\longrightarrow & C_{j+1} & \xrightarrow{v_j} & C_j & \xrightarrow{v_{j-1}} & C_{j-1} & \longrightarrow \cdots
\end{array}
$$

The maps $f_i : A_i \to C_i$ are given by $a_i \to g_{a_i}$, where $g_{a_i}(b_i) = a_i \cdot b_i$. The relation $\phi_{j+1} a' \cdot b = a' \cdot \psi_j b$ insures that the diagram is commutative. Moreover it follows from the hypothesis that f_{3j}, g_{3j+1} are isomorphisms. By the "Five Lemma" (see Eilenberg-Steenrod), f_{3j+2} is also an isomorphism. The assertion of the lemma now follows easily.

Thus, if we can show that (1) and (2) are dual exact sequences, it will follow that $H_k(T_-; G)$ and $H_{m-k}(T/U; \hat{G})$ are dually paired to R mod 1 by the intersection number. The fact that (1) and (2) are dual exact sequences follows easily from properties of the intersection number which we have developed. We leave the details as an easy exercise.

CHAPTER IV

Introduction to the Theory of Fiber Bundles

In this chapter, we begin our study of fiber bundles and their applications to differential topology. Throughout these notes, emphasis is placed on the theory of linear bundles and their associated principal bundles (see definitions below and in Chapter VI). A most important particular case which we shall consider is the tangent bundle of a manifold (see below).

Geometrically, a fiber bundle may be considered as a generalization of a product space. In fact, as we shall see below, a fiber bundle "appears locally as a product space". However, is allowed a "twisting in the large".

The formal definition of a fiber bundle is actually rather involved. Moreover, many of the theorems in the subject are of a technical nature. Since there is a quite detailed book on the subject available, namely, Steenrod—*Topology of Fiber Bundles,* we shall be rather lax in supplying full arguments. Frequently, we state without proof theorems which can be found in Stenrod's book. As another reference for the subject (especially for the theory of linear bundles), we suggest the newer book Hirzebruch—*Neue Topologische Methoden in der Algebraischen Geometrie.*

To begin with, recall that if G is a topological group and Y is a space, then G is a *group of homeomorphisms* of Y if there is a continuous map $\eta : G \times Y \to Y$ (we write $\eta (g, y) = g \cdot y$) such that

(i) $ey = y$ for all $y \in Y$ (where e is the unit of G),
(ii) $g_1 (g_2 y) = (g_1 g_2) y$ for all $g_1, g_2 \in G$ and $y \in Y$.
    G is called *effective* if $gy = y$ for all $y \in Y$ implies $g = e$.

Definition (1): A fiber bundle is a collection (X, B, F, G, π) as follows:

(1) A space X called the *bundle space* (or *total space*).
(2) A space B called the *base space.*
(3) A space F called the *fiber.*

57

(4) An effective group G of homeomorphisms of F called the group of the bundle.

(5) A map $\pi : X \xrightarrow{\text{onto}} B$ called the projection such that $\pi^{-1}(b)$ is homeomorphic to the space F for all $b \in B$.

(6) A family $\{\mathcal{U}_\alpha\}$ of open sets covering B; the $\mathcal{U}_\alpha$'s are called coordinate neighborhoods. For each $\mathcal{U}_\alpha$, there exists a homeomorphism im_x such that $im_\alpha : \pi^{-1}(\mathcal{U}_\alpha) \xrightarrow{\text{onto}} \mathcal{U}_\alpha \times F$ is given by

$$\text{Im}_\alpha (x) = [b,f] = [\pi(x), f_\alpha(x)], \quad (b \in \mathcal{U}_\alpha, f \in F).$$

(7) If $b \in \mathcal{U}_\alpha \cap \mathcal{U}_\beta$ then $im_\beta \circ im_\alpha^{-1}[b,f] = [b, U_b(\beta,\alpha)f]$. We require that the maps $U_b(\beta,\alpha) : F \to F$ depend continuously on b and belong to the group of homeomorphisms G. The $U_b(\beta,\alpha)$ are called the *coordinate transformations* of the bundle.

Examples: (For more details concerning these examples, see Steenrod, loc. cit.)

(i)   If X is a Lie group and F a closed subgroup, then X is a bundle over the base $B = X/F$ with fiber F and group F acting on itself by left translations.

(ii) The Möbius strip is a bundle over the circle as base and the line segment as fiber. The group G is the cyclic group of order 2.

(iii) As a very simple example, we have the product space $B \times F$, which is a bundle over B with fiber F. In this case, the group G is the trivial group.

(iv) Let M^m be a manifold, $\tau(M)$ the collection of all tangent spaces at all points of M, i.e. the collection of all pairs $[p, v]$ where $p \in M$ and v is a tangent vector to M at p. Let $\pi : \tau(M) \to M$ be defined by $\pi[p, v] = p$. Then $\tau(M)$ becomes a fiber bundle over M called the *tangent bundle*. In fact, for coordinate neighborhoods $\mathcal{U}_\alpha$ we take the coordinate neighborhoods of M. Write $\mathcal{W}(m)$ for the Lie group of all non-singular $m \times m$ matrices. The maps $U_b(\beta,\alpha)$ of the last definition are just the Jacobian matrices of transformations of coordinate maps and therefore belong to $\mathcal{W}(m)$; therefore $\tau(M)$ is a $\mathcal{W}(m)$-*bundle* over M.

Remark: The coordinate change functions $U_b(\beta,\alpha)$ of a bundle satisfy the following properties

(i) $U_b(\alpha,\alpha) = $ identity homeomorphism $e \in G$

(ii) $U_b(\gamma, \beta) \circ U_b(\beta,\alpha) = U_b(\gamma,\alpha)$

Clearly, (i) and (ii) imply that $U_b(\alpha, \beta) \circ U_b(\beta,\alpha) = e$. A set of functions $U_b(\beta,\alpha)$ defined on the set $\mathcal{U}_\alpha \cap \mathcal{U}_\beta$, which satisfy conditions (i) and (ii) and which are continuous functions of b (i.e. the map from $\mathcal{U}_\alpha \cap \mathcal{U}_\beta \to G$ given by $b \to U_b(\beta, \alpha)$ is continuous) is said to define a *G-bundle structure* on B.

Now let B be a space and let $\{\mathcal{U}_\alpha\}$ be an open covering of B. Suppose that a topological G acts on a space F as a group of homeomorphisms. Finally, suppose functions $U_b(\beta, \alpha)$ are given on $\mathcal{U}_\alpha \cap \mathcal{U}_\beta$ which define a G-bundle structure on B. Then we have the

Existence Theorem (See Steenrod, loc. cit., p. 14)

There exists a G-bundle X over B with fiber F and coordinate transformations $U_b(\beta, \alpha)$. X can be constructed as follows. Let $\tilde{X}$ be the collection of all triples $\{[b, f, \alpha] \mid b \in \mathcal{U}_\alpha, f \in F\}$. X is given the relative topology of the product space (where the index set is assumed to have the discrete topology). X is obtained from $\tilde{X}$ via the equivalence relation $[b, f, \alpha] \sim [b, U_b(\beta, \alpha) f, \beta]$, i.e. X is defined as the resulting set of equivalence classes. The theorem also asserts that X is unique up to equivalence (see directly below).

Equivalence of G-bundles

Let X, X' be two G-bundles with the same base B and fiber F, and with projections π, π' respectively. Then the two bundle structures are *equivalent* if there exists a homeomorphism $\phi : X \xrightarrow{\text{onto}} X'$ satisfying the following:

(i) $\pi'\phi = \pi$. Thus, $\phi : \pi^{-1}(b) \to \pi'^{-1}(b)$ is a homeomorphism,

(ii) if $\mathcal{U}_\alpha, \mathcal{V}_{\beta'}$ are coordinate neighborhoods of the G-bundles X, X' respectively and if $\text{im}_{\beta'} \circ \phi \circ \text{im}_\alpha^{-1}[b, f] = [b, \Phi_b(\beta', \alpha) f]$, then we require that Φ_b depend continuously on b and belong to G.

Notation: We use the symbol "$\cong$" for equivalence.

Remark: The following relation follows immediately from the definitions:

$$U_b(\gamma', \beta') \, \Phi_b(\beta', \alpha) \, U_b(\alpha, \delta) = \Phi_b(\gamma', \delta).$$

Another way of putting this is as follows:

$$U_b(\gamma', \beta') = \Phi_b(\gamma', \delta) \, U_b(\delta, \alpha) \, \Phi_b^{-1}(\beta', \alpha).$$

The last relation could be taken as the definition of equivalence of G-bundle structures over B.

Definition (2): Let ξ be a bundle structure over B with fiber F and group G, and let $\psi : B' \to B$ be a continuous map. The *induced* bundle structure $\psi^\dagger \xi$

having base space B', fiber F, and group G is defined as follows. The co-ordinate neighborhoods are the inverse images of those of ξ: $\mathcal{U}'_\alpha = \psi^{-1}(\mathcal{U}_\alpha)$. The coordinate transformations are given by $U_{\psi(b')}(\beta, \alpha)$ where $\psi(b') \in \mathcal{U}_\alpha \cap \mathcal{U}_\beta$.

Notice that if ξ_1, ξ_2 are equivalent bundle structures over B, then $\psi^\dagger \xi_1$ and $\psi^\dagger \xi_2$ are equivalent over B'. Moreover, $(\psi_1 \psi_2)^\dagger = (\psi_2)^\dagger (\psi_1)^\dagger$, $(\text{ident})^\dagger = \text{ident}$.

Definition (3): Let ξ be a G-bundle structure on B, G' a subgroup of G. We say ξ is *reducible* to G' if there exists an equivalent bundle structure ξ' such that all coordinate changes $U_b(\beta, \alpha)$ are in G'. If $G' = \{e\}$, we call ξ a *trivial bundle*. Then ξ is equivalent to the product space bundle.

If $G = \mathcal{W}(n)$, the general linear group, and if ξ is reducible to $\mathcal{W}^+(n)$, i.e. the subgroup of $\mathcal{W}(n)$ of all $n \times n$ matrices with positive determinant, then we say that ξ is an *orientable bundle*.

Lemma (1): A manifold M^m is orientable iff the tangent bundle $\tau(M)$ is an orientable bundle (see last definition).

Proof: Recall that a manifold M is orientable if it can be covered by co-ordinate neighborhoods such that the Jacobian matrices of coordinate maps have positive determinants. From this and from the definition of tangent bundle the sufficiency follows.

Necessity: Let $\tau_1, \ldots, \tau_m$ be a frame of vectors at some point $p \in M$, i.e. a set of linearly independent vectors at p. Let x be a coordinate system in some neighborhood of p. Let the components of τ_1 in this coordinate system be given by $\tau_i^{(j)}(x)$ $(j = 1, 2, \ldots, m)$. We say that the frame of vectors τ_i is positively oriented if $\|\tau_i^j\|$ has positive determinant. This notion is well defined since $\tau(M)$ is oriented. Now, given a coordinate system x_α on M, let $\tau_1, \ldots, \tau_m$ be the directional derivatives in the coordinate directions. Call this system positive if $\tau_1, \ldots, \tau_m$ forms a positive frame, negative otherwise. Cover M with coordinates as follows: take x_α if x_α is positive, take x'_α = the reverse of x_α otherwise. (Recall that the reverse of $[x_1, \ldots, x_n]$ is $[x_1, \ldots, x_{n-1}, -x_n]$.) This orients M.
Q.E.D.

Cross-Section of a Bundle

Definition (4): Let X be a bundle over the base B, with projection $\pi: X \to B$. Then a cross-section of X is a continuous map $k: B \to X$ such that $\pi k = \text{identity}$.

Example: A continuous vector field on a manifold is a cross-section of the tangent bundle of the manifold.

Note: Not all bundles have cross-sections; for example let $\hat{\tau}(M)$ be the set of all non-zero vectors in $\tau(M)$. Then $\hat{\tau}(M)$ is a bundle over M and $\hat{\tau}(M)$ may not have a cross-section. Indeed, the following result holds.

Theorem: There is a continuous nonvanishing vector field on M iff the Euler characteristic of $M = 0$.
See Steenrod, op. cit., for a proof.

Linear Bundles

Definition (4): A fiber bundle is said to be a *linear bundle* or a *vector space bundle* if the fiber is a vector space V^k of some dimension k and the group is $\mathscr{W}(k)$.

Definition (5): Let $(X, B, V^k, \mathscr{W}(k), \pi)$ be a linear bundle. Let $X' \subseteq X$ be such that $\pi(X') = B$. Then $(X', B, V^j, \mathscr{W}(j), \pi|X')$ is said to be a *linear sub-bundle* of $(X, B, V^k, \mathscr{W}(k), \pi)$ if

(1) $\pi^{-1}(b) \cap X' = V'(b)$ is a linear subspace of V^k, always of the same dimension j, i.e. $j = \dim(V'(b))$ does not depend on b.
(2) $V'(b)$ depends continuously on b, i.e. $V'(b)$ has a basis which depends continuously on b.

Let $b_0 \in B$. We pick a basis $\{v_1(b_0), \ldots, v_j(b_0)\}$ for $V'(b_0)$ and then we find vectors $v_{j+1}, \ldots, v_k$ in $V(b_0) = \pi^{-1}(b_0)$ such that the system $\{v_1(b_0), \ldots, v_j(b_0), v_{j+1}, \ldots, v^k\}$ forms a basis for all of $V(b_0)$. By property (2) of Definition 5, we find a basis $\{v_1(b), \ldots, v_j(b)\}$ for $V'(b)$ such that $v_i(b)$ is close to $v_i(b_0)$ whenever b is close to b_0 $(1 \leq i \leq j)$. Then, if b is sufficiently near b_0, the system $\{v_1(b), \ldots, v_j(b), v_{j+1}, \ldots, v_k\}$ forms a basis for $V'(b)$ (as one clearly sees). Thus, there is a unique nonsingular linear transformation $L(b)$, which is continuous in b, and which maps

$$\{v_1(b_0), \ldots, v_j(b_0), v_{j+1}, \ldots, v_k\} \to \{v_1(b), \ldots, v_j(b), \ldots, v_j(b), v_{j+1}, \ldots, v_k\}.$$

Now, X "appears locally" as $\mathscr{U} \times V(b_0)$ for some coordinate neighborhood $\mathscr{U}$ and some $b_0 \in B$ (see Definition 1). The above argument shows that X' "appears locally" as $\mathscr{U} \times V'(b_0)$. The reader should now be able to satisfy himself that a linear sub-bundle is actually a bundle.

Definition (6): Let X be a linear bundle and X' a linear sub-bundle. (By abuse of language, we call X and X' bundles, although they are actually only the bundle spaces.) We define an equivalence relation in X as follows: $x_1 \sim x_2$ if

(i) $\pi(x_1) = \pi(x_2)$,   and
(ii) $x_2 - x_1 \in X'$.

Denote by X/X' the resulting set of equivalence classes. X/X' then forms the bundle space of a linear bundle called the *factor bundle*.

To verify that X/X' can be turned into the bundle space of a linear bundle, we observe that locally, we can write $X = \mathcal{U} \times V(b_0)$, $X' = \mathcal{U} \times V'(b_0)$; whence $X/X' = \mathcal{U} \times V(b_0)/V'(b_0)$. To define a natural linear bundle structure on X/X', use this "coordinatization".

Lemma (2): Suppose

(1) $X \xrightarrow{\pi} B$ is a linear bundle,
(2) X' is a linear sub-bundle,
(3) X is orientable.

Then X' is orientable iff X/X' is orientable. Moreover, any orientation of either of these bundles induces naturally an orientation of the other.

Proof: If X is a linear bundle with fiber V^k, then a k-frame in X is a set $x_1, x_2, \ldots, x_k$ of k linearly independent elements of X such that $\pi(x_i) = b$. (This makes sense since $\pi^{-1}(b) = V^k$.) Notice that a bundle is orientable if the set of frames can be divided "continuously" into right handed frames and left handed frames, i.e. if $x_1, \ldots, x_k$ is a right handed frame, then any frame sufficiently close to it is a right handed frame. Now, suppose X' is orientable. Call a frame $x_{j+1}, \ldots, x_k$ of X/X' right handed if, when supplemented with a right handed frame of X', we get a right handed frame for X. This orients X/X'. Conversely, suppose X/X' is orientable. Call a frame $x_1, \ldots, x_j$ in X' right handed if, when supplemented with a right handed frame for X/X', we get a right handed frame for X. This orients X', and proves our lemma. Q.E.D.

Let M be a manifold, $M' \subseteq H$ a submanifold. Let $\tau(M)$ be the tangent bundle of M, $\tau_0(M)$ the restriction of $\tau(M)$ to M', i.e. the set of all vectors tangent to M at points of M'. Then

$$\tau_0(M) \supseteq \tau(M').$$

Suppose M has a Riemannian metric, and let $\nu(M')$ be the set of vectors in $\tau_0(M)$ which are normal to M'. We call $\nu(M')$ the *normal bundle* of M'. It is easy to see that $\tau_0(M') \cong \tau(M) \oplus \nu(M')$. (A precise definition of $\oplus$

is given in a later section.) If M is orientable, then $\tau(M)$ is orientable and hence $\tau_0(M)$ is orientable (because it is a restriction of the orientable bundle $\tau(M)$). Therefore by the last lemma, $\tau(M')$ is orientable iff $\nu(M')$ is orientable, which implies that M' is orientable if $\nu(M')$ is orientable by Lemma 1.

Special Case: Assume M is an orientable manifold with boundary, $M' = \partial M$. Then $\nu(M')$ is trivial. To see this, let $n(b)$ be the unit normal vector at a point b in the boundary M' of M pointing inward; $n(b)$ depends continuously on b. Given any normal vector v at b, assign coordinates $[b, v \cdot n(b)]$ to v. (The dot means inner product.) Then

$$\nu(M') \cong M' \times R$$

where R is the real line. But this means that $\nu(M')$ is the trivial bundle, hence orientable. Therefore, if M is an orientable manifold, then ∂M is also orientable.

Remark: As we have observed above, we have the relation $\nu(M') \oplus \tau(M') \cong \tau_0(M)$. This means that we have a natural equivalence of the bundles $\nu(M')$ and $\tau_0(M)/\tau(M')$. Now, $\tau_0(M)/\tau(M')$ is clearly independent of the choice of a Riemannian metric for the manifold. Hence, $\nu(M')$, which seems to depend on the choice of the metric, is actually determined (up to equivalence) by the internal structure of M.

Now suppose M and M' are manifolds, both contained in another manifold M_0. Assume that M and M' intersect transversely, i.e. at each point $p \in M \cap M' = MM'$, we have

$$\tau(M)|_p + \tau(M')|_p = \tau(M_0)|_p.$$

We claim that if M_0, M and M' are all orientable and oriented in some way, then MM' is also orientable (and inherits a natural orientation). To see this, note that

$$\{\tau(M)|_{MM'} + \tau(M')|_{MM'}\}/\tau(MM') \cong \tau(M_0)|_{MM'}.$$

(By $\tau(M)|_{MM'}$, we mean the set of all tangent vectors to M at points of MM'. Similarly for $\tau(M')|_{MM'}$ and $\tau(M_0)|_{MM'}$.) Now, by assumption, $\tau(M)|_{MM'}$, $\tau(M')|_{MM'}$ and $\tau(M_0)|_{MM'}$ are all oriented. Therefore, $\tau(MM')$ is oriented; whence MM' is oriented, as asserted.

To complete the circle of ideas centering about orientation of submanifolds, etc., we state the following lemma and corollary. The proof of the lemma is left as an exercise (see Steenrod, loc. cit., pp. 47–49).

Lemma (3): Suppose that $\phi : M \to M'$ is a smooth map between two manifolds M and M'. Let N' be a submanifold of M' and suppose ϕ is everywhere transverse to N'. Then, as we know, $N = \phi^{-1}(N')$ is a submanifold of M. We assert that

$$\nu(N) \cong \phi^\dagger(\nu(N'))$$

where $\phi^\dagger$ is the induced map on bundles.

Corollary: If M, M' and N' are orientable, then N is also orientable.

Proof: Since M' and N' are orientable, $\nu(N')$ is orientable (see discussion after Lemma 2 above). This means that $\nu(N')$ is reducible to $\mathscr{W}^+(n')$ where n' is the dimension of N'. Now, $\phi^\dagger$ does not "enlarge" the group $\mathscr{W}^+(n)$, i.e. $\phi^\dagger(\nu(N'))$ is an orientable bundle. By Lemma 3, $\nu(N)$ is also orientable. But then, since M is orientable, it follows that N is orientable.

Q.E.D.

CHAPTER V

Spectral Sequences

If X is a topological space and A a closed subset of X, we call (X, A) a pair. A *normal series* for (X, A) is a sequence

$$X = X_n \supseteq X_{n-1} \supseteq \cdots \supseteq X_0 = A$$

where all the X_j are closed subsets of X.

Let $H(X, A) = \sum_{d=1}^{\infty} \oplus H_d(X, A)$ where $H_d(X, A)$ is the dth relative homology group of (X, A). The inclusion map $(X_j, A) \to (X_n, A)$ induces a homomorphism of $H(X_j, A) \to H(X_n, A)$ and we denote by Im $H(X_j, A)$ the image of the group $H(X_j, A)$ in the group $H(X_n, A)$. (In general, if (R, U) and (S, V) are pairs such that $R \subseteq S$, $U \subseteq V$, we denote by "Im $H(R, U)$ in $H(S, V)$" the image of the group $H(R, U)$ in the group $H(S, V)$ under the homomorphism which is induced by the inclusion map $(R, U) \to (S, V)$.) We consider the sequence

$$H(X, A) = H(X_n, A) \supseteq \text{Im } H(X_{n-1}, A)$$
$$\supseteq \text{Im } H(X_{n-2}, A) \supseteq \cdots \supseteq \text{Im } H(A, A) = 0.$$

Since all the groups involved are abelian, the above sequence of groups is actually a normal series for $H(X, A)$ (in the group-theoretic sense). Denote by F_j the j-th factor of this normal series, i.e.

$$F_j = \frac{\text{Im } H(X_j, A)}{\text{Im } H(X_{j-1}, A)}.$$

By convention, set $X_{-k} = A$ ($k = 0, 1, 2, \ldots$) and $X_l = X$ ($l = n, n+1, \ldots$). We wish to find relations between the groups $H(X_j, X_{j-1})$ and the groups of the normal series for (X, A). For this purpose, we define the *Leray intermediate groups* E_r^j: we set

$$E_r^j = \frac{\text{Im } H(X_j, X_{j-r}) \text{ in } H(X_{j+r-1}, X_{j-r})}{\text{Im } H(X_{j-1}, X_{j-r}) \text{ in } H(X_{j+r-1}, X_{j-r})}.$$

5 Schwartz, Differential

It is easy to verify that $E_1^j = H(X_j, X_{j-1})$ and $E_\infty^j = F_j$. The main result to be proved in this section is the following.

Theorem (1): *We can define boundary operators $\partial_r^j \colon E_r \to E_r^{j-r}$ such that $\partial^r \partial^r = 0$. If $Z(E_r^j) = \{z \in E_r^j | \partial^r z = 0\}$ and $B(E_r^j) = \{\partial^r \omega | \omega \in E_r^{j+r}\}$, then, as usual, $B(E_r^j) \subseteq Z(E_r^j)$. Set $H(E_r^j) = Z(E_r^j)/B(E_r^j)$. Then $H(E_r^j) \cong E_{r+1}^j$.*

Proof: We define ∂^r as follows: Consider the sequence

$$H(X_j, X_{j-r}) \xrightarrow{\ \partial\ } H(X_{j-r}) \longrightarrow H(X_{j-r}, X_{j-2r}) \longrightarrow H(X_{j-1}, X_{j-2r}).$$

Here ∂ is a boundary operator and the other maps are induced by the respective inclusions. The composite map from $H(X_j, X_{j-r})$ to $H(X_{j-1}, X_{j-2r})$ will be denoted by ∂_0^r. Note that ∂_0^r can be regarded as a map from $H(X_j, X_{j-r})$ to "Im $H(X_{j-r}, X_{j-2r})$ in $H(X_{j-1}, X_{j-2r})$" and a fortiori as a map from $H(X_j, X_{j-r})$ to E_r^{j-r} where

$$E_r^{j-r} = \frac{\text{Im } H(X_{j-r}, X_{j-2r}) \text{ in } H(X_{j-1}, X_{j-2r})}{\text{Im } H(X_{j-r-1}, X_{j-2r}) \text{ in } H(X_{j-1}, X_{j-2r})}.$$

If now $\{\gamma\} \in E_r^j$ and if $\gamma \in$ "Im $H(X_j, X_{j-r})$ in $H(X_{j+r-1}, X_{j-r})$" is a representative of $\{\gamma\}$, we set $\partial^r\{\gamma\} = \{\partial_0^r \alpha\}$ where $\alpha \in H(X_j, X_{j-r})$ is an element whose image in $H(X_{j+r-1}, X_{j-r})$ is γ and where $\{\partial_0^r \alpha\}$ is the equivalence class (i.e. the element of E_r^{j-r}) containing $\partial_0^r \alpha$. To see that ∂^r is a well-defined homomorphism from E_r^j to E_r^{j-r}, the following assertions must be verified:

(a) Let $\alpha \in H(X_j, X_{j-r})$. If the image of α in $H(X_{j+r-1}, X_{j-r})$ is 0, then $\partial_0^r \alpha = 0$.
(b) If $\alpha \in$ "Im $H(X_{j-1}, X_{j-r})$ in $H(X_j, X_{j-r})$", then $\partial_0^r \alpha = 0$.

We prove (a): Consider the sequence

$$H(X_{j+r-1}, X_j) \xrightarrow{\ \partial\ } H(X_j, X_{j-r}) \longrightarrow H(X_{j+r-1}, X_{j-r}).$$

This is the exact sequence of the triple $(X_{j+r-1}, X_j, X_{j-r})$. Since α is mapped to 0, we must have $\alpha = \partial\beta$ (by exactness) where $\beta \in H(X_{j+r-1}, X_j)$. We now consider the sequence

$$H(X_{j+r-1}, X_j) \xrightarrow{\ \partial\ } H(X_j) \longrightarrow H(X_j, X_{j-r}) \xrightarrow{\ \partial\ } H(X_{j-r})$$

$$\longrightarrow H(X_{j-r}, X_{j-2r}) \longrightarrow H(X_{j-1}, X_{j-2r}).$$

Now ∂ in the second display above is just the composite map of ∂ and the "inclusion" $H(X_j) \to H(X_j, X_{j-r})$. To show that the image of $\partial\alpha$ in

$H(X_{j-1}, X_{j-2r})$ is 0, it suffices to show that the image of $\partial\beta$ in $H(X_{j-1}, X_{j-2r})$ is 0. Indeed, the image of $\partial\beta$ in $H(X_{j-r})$ is already 0 because the section $H(X_j) \to H(X_j, X_{j-r}) \to H(X_{j-r})$ of the above sequence is just part of the exact sequence of the pair (X_j, X_{j-r}). This proves (a).

We next prove (b). Consider the following diagram.

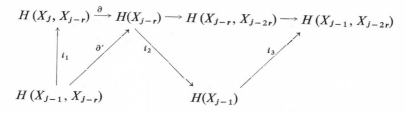

Let $\alpha \in H(X_j, X_{j-r})$ be such that $i_1(\beta) = \alpha$ where $\beta \in H(X_{j-1}, X_{j-r})$. Now $\partial_0^r\alpha = \partial_0^r i_1(\beta) = i_3 i_2 \partial'(\beta)$. But $i_2 \partial'(\beta) = 0$ because the section

$$H(X_{j-1}, X_{j-r}) \xrightarrow{\partial'} H(X_{j-r}) \xrightarrow{i_2} H(X_{j-1}),$$

is a portion of the exact sequence of the pair (X_{j-1}, X_{j-r}). Hence $\partial_0^r\alpha = 0$, as asserted.

We now prove that $\partial^r\partial^r = 0$. We show more, namely that $\partial_0^r\partial_0^r = 0$. In fact, consider the following diagram.

$$H(X_j, X_{j-r}) \xrightarrow{\partial_1} H(X_{j-r}) \xrightarrow{i_1} H(X_{j-r}, X_{j-2r}) \longrightarrow H(X_{j-1}, X_{j-2r})$$

$$H(X_{j-2}, X_{j-3r}) \xleftarrow{i_3} H(X_{j-2r}, X_{j-3r}) \xleftarrow{i_2} H(X_{j-2r})$$

with ∂^1 and ∂_2 maps.

Now $\partial_0^r\partial_0^r\alpha = i_3 i_2 \partial^1 i_1 \partial_1(\alpha)$. Put $\beta = \partial_1(\alpha)$. Then as in our previous arguments, $\partial^1 i_1(\beta) = 0$. Hence, $\partial_0^r\partial_0^r\alpha = 0$.

We now prove $H(E_r^j) \cong E_{r+1}^j$. For each $x_0 \in H(X_j, X_{j-r})$ such that $\{x_0\} \in Z(E_r^j)$ (i.e. $\{\partial_0^r x_0\} = 0$), we will define an element $\{\omega_0\} \in E_{r+1}^j$ such that the map $\{x_0\} \to \{\omega_0\}$ determines a homomorphism of $Z(E_r^j)$ into E_{r+1}^j. We then prove that this map is onto and that the kernel of the map is precisely $B(E_r^j)$. The proof will be split into three lemmas.

Lemma (1): Let $\partial^r\{x_0\} = 0$. Then there exist $z_0 \in H(X_{j-1}, X_{j-r})$ and $\omega_0 \in H(X_j, X_{j-r-1})$ such that $x_0 = \text{im } z_0 + \text{im } \omega_0$. (Recall that by im z_0 we mean the image of z_0 in $H(X_j, X_{j-r})$. Similarly for im ω_0.)

Proof: Consider first the diagram

$$H(X_j, X_{j-r}) \xrightarrow{\partial} H(X_{j-r}, X_{j-2r}) \longrightarrow H(X_{j-1}, X_{j-2r})$$

$$\uparrow i$$

$$H(X_{j-r-1}, X_{j-2r})$$

Since $\partial^r\{x_0\} = 0$, we see by looking at the definition of E_r^{j-r} that there exists $y_0 \in H(X_{j-r-1}, X_{j-2r})$ such that $\partial x_0 - i y_0$ has zero image in $H(X_{j-1}, X_{j-2r})$. Consider next the diagram

$$H(X_j, X_{j-r}) \xrightarrow{\partial} H(X_{j-r}, X_{j-r-1}) \longrightarrow H(X_{j-1}, X_{j-r-1})$$

$$\uparrow$$

$$H(X_{j-r-1}, X_{j-r-1})$$

Since $H(X_{j-r-1}, X_{j-r-1}) = 0$, it follows easily from the above that ∂x_0 in $H(X_{j-r}, X_{j-r-1})$ has zero image in $H(X_{j-1}, X_{j-r-1})$. Using the exact sequence of the triple $(X_{j-1}, X_{j-r}, X_{j-r-1})$, we see that there exists $z_0 \in H(X_{j-1}, X_{j-r})$ such that $\partial x_0 = \partial z_0$ in $H(X_{j-r}, X_{j-r-1})$. Consider the image of z_0 under the map $H(X_{j-1}, X_{j-r}) \to H(X_j, X_{j-r})$; call this element im z_0. Then $\partial (x_0 - \text{im } z_0) = 0$ in $H(X_{j-r}, X_{j-r-1})$. Using the exact sequence of the triple $(X_j, X_{j-r}, X_{j-r-1})$, we see that there exists $\omega_0 \in H(X_j, X_{j-r-1})$ such that $x_0 - \text{im } z_0 = \text{im } \omega_0$, i.e. $x_0 = \text{im } z_0 + \text{im } \omega_0$.

Q.E.D.

We define the map from $Z(E_r^j)$ to E_{r+1}^j as follows: Let $\{x_0\} \in Z(E_r^j)$ and let x_0 be an element in $H(X_j, X_{j-r})$ representing $\{x_0\}$. By Lemma 1, $x_0 = \text{im } z_0 + \text{im } \omega_0$. Now $\omega_0 \in H(X_j, X_{j-r-1})$ and

$$E_{r+1}^j = \frac{\text{Im } H(X_j, X_{j-r-1}) \text{ in } H(X_{j+r}, X_{j-r-1})}{\text{Im } H(X_{j-1}, X_{j-r-1}) \text{ in } H(X_{j+r}, X_{j-r-1})}.$$

Let $\{\omega_0\}$ be the element in E_{r+1}^j determined by ω_0. We define the map by sending $\{x_0\} \to \{\omega_0\}$. We show this map is well-defined.

Lemma (2): If $\{x_0\} = 0$, then $\{\omega_0\} = 0$.

Proof: We have to prove two statements:

(a) If the image of x_0 in $H(X_{j+r-1}, X_{j-r})$ is 0, then $\{\omega_0\} = 0$.

(b) If $x_0 \in$ "Im $H(X_{j-1}, X_{j-r})$ in $H(X_j, X_{j-r})$" then $\{\omega_0\} = 0$.

We prove (a): From Lemma 1, write $x_0 = \text{im } z_0 + \text{im } \omega_0$. It follows directly from the hypothesis that the image of x_0 in $H(X_{j+r}, X_{j-1})$ is 0.

Moreover, the image of z_0 in $H(X_{j+r}, X_{j-1})$ is 0. This follows immediately from the commutativity of the diagram

$$H(X_{j-1}, X_{j-r}) \longrightarrow H(X_{j+r}, X_{j-1})$$
$$\searrow \quad \nearrow$$
$$H(X_{j-1}, X_{j-1})$$

Hence, the image of ω_0 in $H(X_{j+r}, X_{j-1})$ is 0. Let $\bar{\omega}_0$ be the image of ω_0 under the map $H(X_j, X_{j-r-1}) \to H(X_{j+r}, X_{j-r-1})$. Then the image of $\bar{\omega}_0$ in $H(X_{j+r}, X_{j-1})$ is 0. Using the exact sequence of the triple $(X_{j+r}, X_{j-1}, X_{j-r-1})$, we find that $\bar{\omega}_0 \in$ "Im $H(X_{j-1}, X_{j-r-1})$ in $H(X_{j+r}, X_{j-r-1})$". It follows immediately from the definition of E_{r+1}^j that $\{\omega_0\} = 0$. This proves (a).

To prove (b), we note that, by hypothesis, there exists z_0 in $H(X_{j-1}, X_{j-r})$ such that $x_0 = \text{im } z_0'$. Thus im $\omega_0 = \text{im } (z_0' - z_0)$; and therefore the image of ω_0 in the group $H(X_j, X_{j-1})$ is zero. By the exactness of the homology sequence for the triple $(X_j, X_{j-1}, X_{j-r-1})$ it follows that there exists $u_0 \in H(X_{j-1}, X_{j-r-1})$ such that $\omega_0 = \text{im } u_0$, proving that $\{\omega_0\} = 0$.

Q.E.D.

Lemmas 1 and 2 show that the map $\{x_0\} \to \{\omega_0\}$ is a homomorphism of $Z(E_r^j)$ into E_{r+1}^j. This map is onto because given $\{\omega_0\} \in E_{r+1}^j$, we may just choose $x_0 \in H(X_j, X_{j-r})$ such that $x_0 = \text{im } \omega_0$. To complete the proof of the theorem, we show that the kernel of the map $\{x_0\} \to \{\omega_0\}$ is $B(E_r^j)$.

Lemma (3): If $\{\omega_0^j\} = 0$, then $\{x_0\} \in B(E_r^j)$.

Proof: We have $x_0 = \text{im } z_0 + \text{im } \omega_0$. Now, $\{\omega_0\} = 0$ iff there exists $u_0 \in H(X_{j-1}, X_{j-r-1})$ such that the image of ω_0 in $H(X_{j+r}, X_{j-r-1})$ coincides with the image of u_0 in $H(X_{j+r}, X_{j-r-1})$. Let us denote by $\tilde{u}_0, \tilde{z}_0$ the images of u_0, z_0 in $H(X_j, X_{j-r})$. Also, denote by $\bar{x}_0, \bar{u}_0, \bar{z}_0$ the images of x_0, u_0, z_0 in $H(X_{j+r}, X_{j-r})$. It follows that $\bar{x}_0 = \bar{z}_0 + \bar{u}_0$. If we put $r_0 = x_0 - \tilde{u}_0 - \tilde{z}_0$, then r_0 has image zero in $H(X_{j+r}, X_{j-r})$. Using the exact sequence of the triple (X_{j+r}, X_j, X_{j-r}), we see that $r_0 = \partial s_0$, $s_0 \in H(X_{j+r}, X_j)$. Therefore $x_0 = \partial s_0 + \tilde{z}_0 + \tilde{u}_0$. If $\{\tilde{z}_0\}$ and $\{\tilde{u}_0\}$ are the elements in E_r^j determined by $\tilde{z}_0$ and $\tilde{u}_0$, it is easy to see that $\{\tilde{z}_0\} = \{\tilde{u}_0\} = 0$. Noting that

$$E_r^{j+r} = \frac{\text{Im } H(X_{j+r}, X_j) \text{ in } H(X_{j+2r-1}, X_j)}{\text{Im } H(X_{j+r-1}, X_j) \text{ in } H(X_{j+2r-1}, X_j)}$$

and hence that s_0 determines an element $\{s_0\} \in E_r^{j+r}$, it follows from the definition of ∂^r that $\{x_0\} = \partial^r\{s_0\}$. Thus $\{\omega_0\} = 0$ iff $\{x_0\} \in \partial^r E_r^{j+r}$.

Q.E.D.

This completes the proof of the theorem. Notice that in the course of the proof, we have not made use of all of the axioms for a homology theory (see Eilenberg-Steenrod). In particular, we have not used the dimension axiom. The fact that the Leray relation $H(E_r^j) \cong E_{r+1}^j$ holds independent of this axiom lends importance to the so-called generalized homology theories where the dimension axiom is not postulated. Notice also that the proof of the Leray relation is completely algebraic; there are no really vital references to topological spaces or continuous maps. Indeed the theory of spectral sequences has a wide range of applicability and is not restricted solely to topological questions. Before discussing an application of the theory of spectral sequences to fiber bundles, we make a few further remarks. If we set

$$E_{r,d}^j = \frac{\operatorname{Im} H_d\,(X_j,\,X_{j-r}) \text{ in } H_d\,(X_{j+r-1},\,X_{j-r})}{\operatorname{Im} H_d\,(X_{j-1},\,X_{j-r}) \text{ in } H_d\,(X_{j+r-1},\,X_{j-r})},$$

then ∂^r is a homomorphism taking $E_{r,d}^j$ into $E_{r,d-1}^{j-r}$. As before

$$Z(E_{r,d}^j)/B(E_{r,d}^j) \cong E_{r+1,d}^j.$$

A sequence E_r^j of groups, with boundary operators ∂_r^j as in Theorem 1, and such that $H(E_r^j) \cong E_{r+1}^j$, is called a *spectral sequence*. If there exists r_0 such that $r \geq r_0$ implies $\partial_r^j = 0$, so that $E_r^j \cong E_{r+1}^j$ for $r \geq r_0$, we say that the spectral sequence is *convergent*. The groups E_r^j for $r \geq r_0$ are then written as E_∞^j, and called the *limit groups* of the spectral sequence. If G is a group with a normal sequence whose factor groups are isomorphic to the groups E_∞^j, we say that the spectral sequence converges to normal factors for G, and we write $E_1^j \Rightarrow G, E_2^j \Rightarrow G, E_3^j \Rightarrow G$, etc.
We mention finally the spectral sequence in cohomology. Here we take a different normal series from the one we took in homology. The series is given as

$$H^*\,(X,\,A) = \ker\,(H^*\,(X,\,A) \to H^*\,(A,\,A)) \supseteq \ker\,(H^*\,(X,\,A) \to H^*\,(X_1,\,A))$$

$$\supseteq \ker\,(H^*\,(X,\,A) \to H^*\,(X_2,\,A)) \supseteq \cdots$$

$$\supseteq \ker\,(H^*\,(X,\,A) \to H^*\,(X,\,A)) = 0.$$

We set

$$E_r^{*j} = \frac{\ker\,(H^*\,(X_{j+r-1},\,X_{j-r}) \to H^*\,(X_{j-1},\,X_{j-r}))}{\ker\,(H^*\,(X_{j+r-1},\,X_{j-r}) \to H^*\,(X_j,\,X_{j-r}))}.$$

As before, we can prove that $E_1^{*j} = H^*(X_j,\,X_{j-1})$ and that E_∞^{*j} is the j-th factor of the above normal series. The theory then proceeds in much the same was as for homology.

One of the main applications of spectral sequences is to help find relationships between the homology and cohomology groups of the bundle space, base space and fiber of a fiber bundle. We shall give a brief glimpse of the method.

Let then X be a bundle over a (finitely) triangulable base B, with fiber F and projection π. We shall need the following proposition about bundles, the proof of which can be found in Steenrod—*The Topology of Fiber Bundles*, p. 53.

Proposition: Any bundle over a cell is a trivial bundle.

Let σ be a single simplex in B, $\partial\sigma$ its boundary. Let $(\partial\sigma)_\tau$ be the "thickened" boundary and let $\hat{\sigma} = \sigma - \overline{(\partial\sigma)_\tau}$. Thus, in the figure to the right, the whole (closed) triangle represents σ, the shaded part (including the boundaries) represents $(\partial\sigma)_\tau$ and the inner (closed) triangle represents $\hat{\sigma}$.

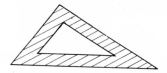

By the above proposition, $\pi^{-1}(\sigma) = \sigma \times F$, $\pi^{-1}(\partial\sigma) = \partial\sigma \times F$, $\pi^{-1}((\partial\sigma)_\tau)$ $= (\partial\sigma)_\tau \times F$. Since $\partial\sigma$ is clearly a deformation retract of $(\partial\sigma)_\tau$, $\partial\sigma \times F$ $= \pi^{-1}(\partial\sigma)$ is also a deformation retract of $(\partial\sigma)_\tau \times F = \pi^{-1}((\partial\sigma)_\tau)$. Let X_j denote the part of X lying over the j-skeleton of B and let $(X_k)_\tau$ denote the part of X lying over the union of the $k-1$ skeleton of B and the thickened boundaries of dimension k. Then, X_{j-1} is a deformation retract of $(X_{j-1})_\tau$ and therefore $H(X_j, X_{j-1}) \cong H(X_j, (X_{j-1})_\tau)$. By excision, $H(X_j, X_{j-1})$ $\cong H\left(\pi^{-1}\left(\bigcup_\alpha \hat{\sigma}_\alpha^j\right), \pi^{-1}\left(\bigcup_\alpha \partial\hat{\sigma}_\alpha^j\right)\right)$ where we sum over all j-simplices in B. But observe that the simplices $\hat{\sigma}_\alpha^j$ are mutually disjoint. Hence, we may write

$$H\left(\pi^{-1}\left(\bigcup_\alpha \hat{\sigma}_\alpha^j\right), \pi^{-1}\left(\bigcup_\alpha \partial\hat{\sigma}_\alpha^j\right)\right) = \sum_\alpha \oplus H\left(\pi^{-1}(\hat{\sigma}_\alpha^j), \pi^{-1}(\partial\hat{\sigma}_\alpha^j)\right)$$

$$= \sum_\alpha \oplus H(\hat{\sigma}_\alpha^j \times F, \partial\hat{\sigma}_\alpha^j \times F).$$

An elementary calculation, using Kunneth's theorem, shows that $\sum_\alpha \oplus H(\hat{\sigma}_\alpha^j \times F, \partial\hat{\sigma}_\alpha^j \times F) \cong \sum_\alpha \oplus H(F)$. Recalling the summation range of α, it follows that

$$H(X_j, X_{j-1}) \cong C_j(B, H(F))$$

where $C_j(B, H(F))$ is the group of j-chains of B with coefficients in $H(F)$.

Now, $X = X_n \supseteq X_{n-1} \supseteq \cdots$ is a filtration of X, corresponding to the filtration $B = B_n \supseteq B_{n-1} \supseteq \cdots$ of the complex B. By definition, $E_1^j = H(X_j, X_{j-1})$. Hence, the above result can be restated as

$$E_1^j \cong C_J(B, H(F)).$$

Finally, we assert without proof that

$$E_2^j \cong H_J(B, H(F)).$$

This formula can be considered to be the fundamental relationship which we have been seeking. The proof of the formula follows without difficulty from the Leray relation $H(E_r^j) \cong E_{r+1}^j$. We leave the details to the reader.

The preceding theory now implies that there exists, a convergent spectral sequence through which $H(B, H(F)) \Rightarrow H(X)$. This fundamental result in the homology theory of fiber bundles, due to Levay, has played a very significant role in the advance of topology during the last three decades.

CHAPTER VI

Introduction to the Theory
of Characteristic Classes

In this chapter, we study of the some the homotopy and cohomology theory of bundles. Proofs of many standard theorems are omitted; they can all be found in Steenrod—*Topology of Fiber Bundles*.

Our main aim in this chapter is to show that, at least in certain respects, the study of an arbitrary principal G-bundle (see definition below) can be reduced to the study of a particular principal G-bundle, the so-called universal G-bundle. In particular, if G is one of the classical Lie groups U_n or O_n, the base space of the corresponding universal bundle turns out to be the space $G_{n,\infty}$. We can then use our knowledge of the cohomology structure of $G_{n,\infty}$ to define and study the Chern and Whitney classes of an arbitrary principal U_n or O_n bundle. Our study of these "characteristic classes" will be continued in subsequent chapters. Finally, we mention briefly (and do not use again) the Pontryagin classes.

We begin by recalling some facts about homotopy groups. For details, see Hu—*Homotopy Theory*, Chapter IV.

Let X be a topological space, A a subspace and $x_0 \in A$ a fixed point. Denote by I^{n-1} the face of the cube I^n defined by $t_n = 0$, and by J^{n-1} the set $\overline{\partial I^n - I^{n-1}}$. Consider the set $F^n(X, A, x_0)$ of all maps f of the cube I^n into X which carry I^{n-1} into A and J^{n-1} into the point x_0. An "addition" is defined in $F^n(X, A, x_0)$ for $n > 1$ by setting

$$(f + g)(t) = \begin{cases} f(2t_1, t_2, \ldots, t_n) & 0 \leq t_1 \leq \frac{1}{2} \\ g(2t_1 - 1, t_2, \ldots, t_n) & \frac{1}{2} \leq t_1 \leq 1 \end{cases}$$

for $f, g \in F^n(X, A, x_0)$. We say two maps $f_0, f_1 \in F^n(X, A, x_0)$ are equivalent if there is a deformation f_t connecting f_0 and f_1 such that

$$f_t(I^{n-1}) \subseteq A, \quad f_t(J^{n-1}) = x_0, \quad 0 \leq t \leq 1.$$

We denote the set of equivalence classes thus obtained by $\pi_n(X, A, x_0)$. The addition in $F^n(X, A, x_0)$ induces an addition in $\pi_n(X, A, x_0)$ which turns $\pi_n(X, A, x_0)$ into a group. We call $\pi_n(X, A, x_0)$ the n-th relative homotopy group of the pair (X, A) with respect to the basepoint x_0; it is known to be abelian for $n \geq 3$. If, in particular, $A = x_0$, we put $\pi_n(X, x_0, x_0) = \pi_n(X, x_0)$ and call this group the n-th absolute homotopy group of X with respect to x_0; $\pi_n(X, x_0)$ is abelian for $n \geq 2$. For $n = 1$, we get the fundamental group of X at x_0. If the spaces X and A are arcwise connected, then the n-th homotopy groups are isomorphic for any two basepoints x_0, x_1. In this case, we will write $\pi_n(X, A)$ instead of $\pi_n(X, A, x_0)$.

If $f: (X, A, x_0) \to (Y, B, y_0)$ is such that $f(A) \subseteq B$ and $f(x_0) = y_0$, then it can be shown that f induces a homomorphism

$$f_*: \pi_n(X, A, x_0) \to \pi_n(Y, B, y_0).$$

Also, if $f \in F^n(X, A, x_0)$, then the restriction of f to the face I^{n-1} will define an element in $\pi_{n-1}(A, x_0)$ and in this way we get a homomorphism

$$\partial: \pi_n(X, A, x_0) \to \pi_{n-1}(A, x_0)$$

called the boundary homomorphism. We now have the

Lemma (1): The following sequence of homotopy groups of the pair (X, A) is exact:

$$\cdots \longrightarrow \pi_n(X, A) \xrightarrow{\partial} \pi_{n-1}(A) \xrightarrow{i_*} \pi_{n-1}(X) \xrightarrow{j_*} \pi_{n-1}(X, A) \longrightarrow \cdots$$

Here, i_* and j_* are the maps induced by the inclusion map i, j.

Remark: There is a useful extension of the notion of homotopy sequence to that of a triple (X, A, B) where $X \supseteq A \supseteq B$ and where the basepoint $x_0 \in B$. It is the sequence

$$\cdots \longrightarrow \pi_n(A, B) \xrightarrow{i_*} \pi_n(X, B) \xrightarrow{j_*} \pi_n(X, A) \xrightarrow{\tilde{\partial}} \pi_{n-1}(A, B) \longrightarrow$$

$$\cdots \longrightarrow \pi_2(X, A),$$

where i, j are inclusion maps and $\tilde{\partial}$ is the composition

$$\pi_n(X, A) \xrightarrow{\partial} \pi_{n-1}(A) \xrightarrow{k_*} \pi_{n-1}(A, B)$$

where k is the inclusion map. It follows without much difficulty from Lemma (1) that this sequence is exact.

We now turn to the homotopy properties of fiber bundles. Here, our constant reference is Steenrod, loc. cit. The key property which fiber bundles possess and from which many theorems about them follow is

Theorem (1) (Covering Homotopy Theorem): (cf. Steenrod, p. 50, and Hu, p. 65).

If X is a bundle over B with projection p and if $f: K \to K$ is a map of a "nice" space (e.g. a finite complex) into X such that there exists a homotopy $g_t: K \to B$ with $g_0 = p \circ f$, then there exists a homotopy $f_t: K \to X$ with $f_0 = f$, $p \circ f_t = g_t$.

From this theorem and Lemma (1), we can construct the

Exact Homotopy Sequence of a Bundle: (Steenrod, p. 90).

In the notation of the theorem above, let $x_0 \in X$, $b_0 = p(x_0)$, $F_0 = p^{-1}(b_0)$, so that F_0 is homeomorphic to the fiber F. It follows from Theorem 1 that $p_*: \pi_n(X, F_0, x_0) \to \pi_n(B, b_0, b_0)$ is an isomorphism for $n \geqq 2$. Using this fact, we define a homomorphism

$$\Delta: \pi_n(B, b_0) \to \pi_{n-1}(F_0, x_0)$$

by $\Delta = \partial \circ p_*^{-1}$ where $\partial: \pi_n(X, F_0) \to \pi_{n-1}(F_0)$ is the boundary homomorphism. Then the exact sequence of the pair (X, F_0) (see Lemma 1) is transformed into an exact sequence

$$\cdots \xrightarrow{\Delta} \pi_n(F_0) \xrightarrow{i_*} \pi_n(X) \xrightarrow{p_*} \pi_n(B) \xrightarrow{\Delta} \pi_{n-1}(F_0) \xrightarrow{i_*} \cdots$$

$$\cdots \xrightarrow{p_*} \pi_2(B) \xrightarrow{\Delta} \pi_1(F_0) \xrightarrow{i_*} \pi_1(X) \xrightarrow{p_*} \pi_1(B).$$

Definition (1): A bundle ξ is called a *principal G-bundle* if (a) the fiber F = the group G and (b) G operates on itself by left translation.

Given a bundle ξ, with base B, group G and fiber F, then we can construct the *associated principal bundle* $\tilde{\xi}$ in the following way. Let $\tilde{\xi}$ have the same base B, the same coordinate neighborhoods U_α, the same $U_b(\alpha, \beta)$ and the same group G as ξ, but replace the fiber F of ξ by the group G and allow G to operate on itself by left translation.

Remark: Let us observe that, up to equivalence, there is a $1 - 1$ correspondence between G-bundle structures over a space B and principal G-bundles over B. This follows from the fact that given a G-bundle structure over B, there is a unique way of constructing a principal G-bundle over B (see the Existence Theorem in Chapter IV).

Theorem (2) (Bundle Structure Theorem): (Steenrod, p. 30).

Let G be a topological group, H and K closed subgroups such that $K \subsetneqq H$, and let H admit a local cross-section. If p is the map induced by inclusion of cosets, then G/K is a bundle over G/H with projection p, fiber H/K and group H/K_0 acting on H/K by left translation (where K_0 is the largest subgroup of K invariant in H). Furthermore, any two local cross-sections lead to equivalent bundles. Finally, the left translations of G/K by elements of G are bundle maps of this bundle onto itself.

As a special case note that if we take $K = \{e\}$ then G is a principal bundle over G/H with fiber and group H.

Let us use the above ideas to prove the following lemma, which will be useful in what follows.

Lemma (2): If O_m is the group of orthogonal transformations of E^m, then O_N/O_n is "aspherical" for all $k < n$, i.e. $\pi_k(O_N/O_n) = 0$ for $k < n$.

(Notice that O_N/O_n is arc-wise connected because O_N has two components and O_n contains matrices with both positive and negative determinant.)

Proof: O_m is a Lie group, and therefore O_n has a local cross-section in O_{n+1}. We have $O_n \subset O_{n+1} \subset O_{n+2} \subset \cdots \subset O_N$. By the Bundle Structure Theorem, O_N/O_n is a bundle over O_N/O_{n+1} with fiber $O_{n+1}/O_n = S^n$. Now, $\pi_k(S^n) = 0$ if $k < n$.

By writing down the homotopy exact sequence of this bundle, we see that every third term in the sequence is zero. Therefore,

$$\pi_k (O_N/O_n) \cong \pi_k (O_N/O_{n+1}) \quad \text{if} \quad k < n.$$

By repeating this argument, we get

$$\pi_k (O_N/O_n) \cong \pi_k (O_N/O_{n+1}) \cong \cdots \cong \pi_k (O_N/O_N) = 0.$$

Q.E.D.

Lemma (2′): If U_n is the group of all unitary transformations of $\mathscr{C}^n$, then

$$\pi_k (U_N/U_n) = 0 \quad \text{if} \quad k < 2n + 1.$$

The proof is analogous to that of Lemma 2.

Definition (2): A k-frame in E^N is an ordered set of k independent vectors in E^N. Call the set of all orthonormal $(N-n)$-frames in E^N the *Stiefel Manifold* $V_{N-n,N}$. Clearly, O_N acts transitively on $V_{N-n,N}$. The subgroup leaving fixed a certain frame f_0^{N-n} is just the orthogonal group $O_{N-(N-n)} = O_n$ operating in the space orthogonal to all the vectors of f_0^{N-n}. Thus, $V_{N-n,N} = O_N/O_n$.

If we work in $\mathscr{C}^N$, we can define $V_{N-n,N}^{\mathscr{C}}$ simularly and show that $V_{N-n,N}^{\mathscr{C}} = U_N/U_n$.

We have $O_n \subseteq O_n \times O_m$. By Theorem 2, $V_{m,n+m} = O_{n+m}/O_n$ is a bundle over $O_{n+m}/O_n \times O_m = G_{m,m+n}$, with fiber $O_m \times O_n/O_n \cong O_m$ and group $O_m \times O_n/O_n \cong O_m$. I.e. the Stiefel manifold $V_{m,m+n}$ is a principal bundle over the *Grassmann manifold* $G_{m,m+n}$ with group O_m and fiber O_m.

Definition (3): Let ξ be a principal bundle over a space B with group G. Then ξ is called n-universal for the group G if for any n-complex K, subcomplex L of K, principal bundle ξ' over K with group G, and bundle map f of $\xi'|L \to \xi$, there exists an extension of f to a bundle map of $\xi' \to \xi$. (Notice that if η is a bundle with bundle space X, base space A, and projection map $p: X \to A$, and if $\hat{A} \subset A$, then we can construct, in the obvious way, a bundle $\hat{\eta}$ with bundle space $p^{-1}(\hat{A})$, base space $\hat{A}$ and projection $p|p^{-1}(\hat{A})$.)

Characterization of an n-Universal Bundle

Theorem (3): (Steenrod, p. 102).

A principal bundle ξ, with bundle space X, is n-universal iff $\pi_i(X) = 0$ for $0 \leq i < n$. (Note: $\pi_0(X) = 0$ means X is arcwise connected.)

Corollary: The real (resp. complex) Grassmannian $G_{m,n}$, with the bundle structure defined over it as described above, is an $(n-m)$-universal O_m-bundle (resp. $[2(n-m)+1]$-universal U_m-bundle).

Proof: We showed above that $V_{m,n}$ is a principal O_m bundle over $G_{m,n}$, and $\pi_k(V_{m,n}) = 0$ if $0 \leq k < n-m$. Similarly for the complex case.

Definition (4): We have a sequence of natural inclusions $E^m \subseteq E^{m+1} \subseteq \cdots$ which induces a sequence of inclusions $V_{m,n} \subseteq V_{m,n+1} \subseteq \cdots$. Let $V_{m,\infty}$ be the direct limit space; $V_{m,\infty}$ is then the set of orthogonal m-frames in E^∞.

Definition (5): Consider $V_{m,\infty}$ is a principal O_m-bundle over $G_{m,\infty}$ (U_m-bundle in the complex case). The bundle constructed in this way is r-universal for O_m-bundles (resp. U_m-bundles) for all integers $r > 0$. We are going to call the space $G_{m,\infty}$ a *universal classifying space* for O_m-bundles (resp. U_m-bundles). We will denote this principal bundle and its bundle structure by α_m.

Theorem (4) (Classification Theorem): (Steenrod, p. 101).

Let ξ be a principal G-bundle with the base space B and bundle space X. Assume $\pi_k(X) = 0$ $(0 \leq k \leq n)$. Let K be a complex of dimension n. Then the operation of assigning to each map $f: K \to B$ its induced bundle over K gives a $1-1$ correspondence between G-bundle structures on K and homotopy classes of maps of $K \to B$.

Corollary: Let K be a complex of finite dimension. Then O_m-bundle structures (resp. U_m-bundle structures) on K are in $1 - 1$ correspondence with the homotopy classes of maps of $K \to G_{m,\infty}^R$ (resp. $G_{m,\infty}^C$).

Definition (6): Recall that if $\phi : X \to Y$, then ϕ induces a map ϕ^* of the cohomology ring $H^*(Y) \to H^*(X)$, and induces a map $\phi^\dagger$ of G-bundle structures on Y into G-bundle structures on X. Let now Γ be a map assigning to each G-bundle structure ξ on an arbitrary space Y an element of $H^*(Y; C)$ such that $\Gamma(\phi^\dagger \xi) = \phi^* \Gamma(\xi)$ for all spaces X, Y and all maps $\phi : X \to Y$. Then Γ is called a *C-cohomology invariant of G-bundle structures*. Here C is a commutative ring taken as a coefficient ring for the cohomology rings of spaces.

Example of a Cohomology Invariant

Let β be an O_m-bundle over a triangulable space B with fiber F, bundle space X. Assume $\pi_i(F) = 0$ for $i \leq n - 1$ and let $n > 1$. Let B^k be the k-skeleton of B, σ^{k+1} a $(k + 1)$-dimensional simplex of B, and $\partial\sigma^{k+1}$ its boundary (which is homeomorphic to S^k, the k-dimensional sphere). Let ϕ be a cross-section defined on B^k; we want to investigate the possibility of extending ϕ to B^{k+1}. The restriction of β to the call σ^{k+1} is a trivial bundle since every bundle over a cell is trivial. Therefore $\phi | \partial\sigma^{k+1}$ is a map of $\partial\sigma^{k+1} \to \partial\sigma^{k+1} \times F$ defined by $\phi(c) = (c, f)$, and hence defines a map (call it ϕ again) of $\partial\sigma^{k+1} \to F$. Since $\partial\sigma^{k+1}$ is homeomorphic to S^k and F is simply connected, ϕ defines an element α_0 in $\pi_k(F)$. It is easy to see that ϕ can be extended to σ^{k+1} iff $\alpha_\sigma = 0$. Therefore, if $k \leq n - 1$, ϕ can always be extended to all of B^{k+1}. Assume now $k = n$; then the operation of assigning to each σ^{k+1} the element α_σ in $\pi_k(F)$ as above defines a $(k + 1)$-cochain α on B. It can be shown that α is a cocycle and does not depend on the successive extensions of ϕ on lower dimensions. Therefore we could start by ϕ defined arbitrarily on B^0. It is evident therefore that to each β, we can associate a uniquely defined element in $H^{n+1}(B, \pi_n(F))$; denote this element by $\mathrm{obst}_{n+1}(\beta, F)$. The map "obst" of O_m-bundle structures on B into $H^{n+1}(B, \pi_n(F))$ may be shown to be a $\pi_n(F)$-cohomology invariant of O_m-bundle structures.

Theorem (5): The set S of Z-cohomology invariants of U_m-bundle structures is in $1 - 1$ correspondence with the set of cohomology classes of $G_{m,\infty}^C$ with integer coefficients.

Proof: Recall that $V_{m,\infty}^C$ is a principal U_m-bundle over $G_{m,\infty}^C$. Let α_m be the corresponding bundle structure. Let Γ be an element of S. Then $\Gamma(\alpha_m)$ is an element γ of cohomology ring $H^*(G_{m,\infty}, Z)$. Let β_1 be a U_m-bundle structure over a base B. Then, by the classification theorem, there exists a map ϕ (unique up to homotopy) of $B \to G^{\mathcal{C}}_{m,\infty}$ such that $\beta_1 = \phi^\dagger(\alpha_m)$. But then

$$\Gamma(\beta_1) = \Gamma(\phi^\dagger \alpha_m) = \phi^* \Gamma(\alpha_m) = \phi^*(\gamma).$$

If Γ' is another cohomology invariant such that $\Gamma'(\alpha_m) = \gamma$, then $\Gamma'(\beta_1) = \phi^*(\gamma)$, and therefore $\Gamma(\beta_1) = \Gamma'(\beta_1)$ for all spaces B and U_m-bundle structures β_1, i.e. $\Gamma = \Gamma'$. Conversely, let γ be any element in $H^*(G^{\mathcal{C}}_{m,\infty}, Z)$; we want to define an element Γ_γ in S which corresponds to γ. Let B be any space, ξ a U_m-bundle structure on B. There is a map ϕ (unique up to homotopy) from B into $G^{\mathcal{C}}_{m,\infty}$ such that $\xi = \phi^\dagger(\alpha_m)$. Define $\Gamma_\gamma(\xi) = \phi^*(\gamma) \in H^*(B, Z)$. It is easy to check that Γ_γ is a well defined Z-cohomology invariant of U_m-bundle structures. We have only to show that if $\Gamma_\gamma = \Gamma_{\gamma'}$, then $\gamma = \gamma'$. It is clearly enough to check that $\Gamma_\gamma(\alpha_m) = \gamma$. But this is clear since if i is the identity map of $G^{\mathcal{C}}_{m,\infty} \to G^{\mathcal{C}}_{m,\infty}$, then $i^\dagger = \text{identity}$, $i^* = \text{identity}$.

This completes the proof of the theorem.

Recalling that the Chern classes $c_j \in H^{2j}(G_{m,\infty}, Z)$ form a set of ring generators of $H^*(G_{m,\infty}, Z)$, we have the following

Corollary: Every Z-cohomology invariant of U_m-bundle structures can be identified in a unique way with a linear combination of cup products of Chern classes.

Similarly, we can prove the following theorem and corollary.

Theorem (6): The set S' of Z_2-cohomology invariants of O_m-bundle structures is in $1 - 1$ correspondence with the set of cohomology classes of $G^R_{m,\infty}$ with Z_2 coefficients.

Corollary: Every Z_2-cohomology invariant of O_m-bundle structures can be identified in a unique way with a linear combination of cup products of Whitney classes.

Definition (7): Let $\xi = (X, B, U_m, p)$ be a principal U_m-bundle with base B, bundle space X and projection p. Since $G^{\mathcal{C}}_{m,\infty}$ is a universal classifying space, there exists a map $\psi : B \to G^{\mathcal{C}}_{m,\infty}$, which is unique up to homotopy, such that $\xi = \psi^\dagger(\alpha_m)$ where $\alpha_m = (V_{m,\infty}, G_{m,\infty}, U_m, p_m)$. The map ψ induces a map ψ^*, on the cohomology level, from $H^*(G^{\mathcal{C}}_{m,\infty})$ into $H^*(X)$. Notice that if ψ is homotopic to $\tilde{\psi}$, then $\psi^* = \tilde{\psi}^*$. Thus, ψ^* is determined by ξ itself and does not depend on the mapping ψ. We can then define the *Chern class* $c_j(\xi)$ of the principal bundle ξ by $c_j(\xi) = \psi^*(c_j)$, where c_j is the j-th Chern class of α_m. Notice that $c_j(\xi)$ belongs to $H^{2j}(X)$. Define the Chern classes of an arbitrary U_m-bundle to be the Chern classes of the associated principal bundle.

Definition (8): $c(\xi) = 1 + c_1(\xi) + \cdots + c_m(\xi)$ is called the *total Chern class* of ξ.

One can define the *Whitney classes* of O_m-bundles and total Whitney class of O_m-bundles analogously by using the real Grassmann manifold $G_{m,\infty}^R$ and the cohomology ring of $G_{m,\infty}^R$ with coefficients in Z_2.

Conjugate Bundle

Let ξ be a U_m-bundle structure on B with coordinate neighborhoods N_i, and coordinate transformations $U_b(i,j)$. Now $U_b(i,j)$, which is an element in U_m, can be considered as an $m \times m$ unitary matrix. Let $\bar{U}_b(i,j)$ be the complex conjugate of $U_b(i,j)$, again an element in U_m. Denote by $\bar{\xi}$ the bundle structure over B with coordinate neighborhoods N_i and coordinate transformations $\bar{U}_b(i,j)$. $\bar{\xi}$ is called the *conjugate* of ξ.

We want to find the relation between the Chern classes of ξ and those of $\bar{\xi}$. The bundle structure ξ is induced by a map $\phi : B \to G_{m,\infty}$. There is a map

$$C : G_{m,\infty} \to G_{m,\infty}$$

defined by mapping an element $\pi \in G_{m,\infty}$ (π is an m-plane through the origin in E^∞) into its complex conjugate $\bar{\pi} \in G_{m,\infty}$. It is easy to see then that the map

$$C \circ \phi : B \to G_{m,\infty}$$

induces the bundle structure $\bar{\xi}$. Let

$$C' : P_n^{(1)} \times P_n^{(2)} \times \cdots \times P_n^{(m)} \to P_n^{(1)} \times P_n^{(2)} \times \cdots \times P_n^{(m)}$$

be defined by $C'((z^{(1)}, z^{(2)}, \ldots, z^{(m)})) = (\bar{z}^{(1)}, \bar{z}^{(2)}, \ldots, \bar{z}^{(m)})$. Recall that in Chapter III A, we introduced a map $N : P_n^{(1)} \times \cdots \times P_n^{(m)} \to G_{m,m(n+1)}$. Letting $\tilde{N}$ be the composition of N and the inclusion map $G_{m,m(n+1)} \to G_{m,\infty}$, we see that

$$
\begin{array}{ccc}
P_n^{(1)} \times \cdots \times P_n^{(m)} & \xrightarrow{\tilde{N}} & G_{m,\infty} \\
\downarrow{\scriptstyle C'} & & \downarrow{\scriptstyle C} \\
P_n^{(1)} \times \cdots \times P_n^{(m)} & \xrightarrow{\tilde{N}} & G_{m,\infty}
\end{array}
$$

is a commutative diagram.

Recall that a cell decomposition of P_n is given by

$$P_n \supseteq P_{n-1} \supseteq \cdots \supseteq P_1 \supseteq P_0.$$

Clearly, the map C' takes each cell of P_n homeomorphically onto itself, but with a possible change of orientation. By looking at the coordinates on

P_j, it is not hard to see that in fact C' maps P_j onto itself homeomorphically with degree $(-1)^j$. Therefore, the induced map of cohomology classes takes the cohomology class t^j into $(-1)^j t^j$, where t is a ring generator of $H^*(P_n, Z)$. By using the commutativity of the above diagram, one can see that C^* has the same effect on $H^*(G_{m,\infty})$ as $(C')^*$ has on $H^*(P_n^{(1)} \times \cdots \times P_n^{(m)})$. If ψ is the map of Definition 7, we have $c_j(\xi) = \psi^*(c_j)$. Moreover,

$$c_j(\bar{\xi}) = (C \circ \psi)^*(c_j) = \psi^* C^*(c_j) = \psi^*((-1)^j c_j)$$

We thus arrive at the formula

$$c_j(\bar{\xi}) = (-1)^j c_j(\xi). \tag{*}$$

Pontryagin Classes

Let γ be an O_m-bundle structure on B, with coordinate neighborhoods N_i and coordinate transformations $U_b(i,j)$. As before, $U_b(i,j)$ can be considered as an $m \times m$ real orthogonal matrix. If we "enlarge" the group of γ by considering O_m as a subgroup of U_m, one can consider $U_b(i,j)$ as an element of U_m and get a U_m-bundle structure γ^c on B. Now, it is clear that $\gamma^c = \bar{\gamma}^c$. Therefore, by (*) above,

$$c_j(\gamma^c) = c_j(\bar{\lambda}^c) = (-1)^j c_j(\gamma^c).$$

Thus, we have $2c_j(\gamma^c) = 0$ if j is odd. Define the *Pontryagin classes* $p_j(\gamma)$ of the O_m-bundle structure γ by

$$p_j(\gamma) = c_{2j}(\gamma^c).$$

It is clear that $p_j(\gamma)$ is an element of $H^{4j}(B)$.

CHAPTER VII

Riemannian Geometry.
An Application of Characteristic Classes

First, we shall discuss some of the aspects of Riemannian Geometry; later we shall consider some applications of the previous theory to certain geometric problems. As a reference, we suggest Milnor—*Morse Theory*.

To begin with, we recall that a vector field V on a manifold M is a linear map from $C^\infty(M)$ into itself (here $C^\infty(M)$ denotes the algebra of C^∞ real-valued functions defined on M) which satisfies $V(\phi\psi) = (V\phi)\psi + \phi(V\psi)$ for $\phi, \psi \in C^\infty(M)$. If U and V are vector fields, it is easy to verify that the Poisson Bracket $[U, V] = UV - VU$ is also a vector field. Let $D^1(M)$ (or more briefly, D^1) denote the set of all vector fields on M.

Definition (1): A *Riemannian metric* on M is a bilinear map $g : D^1 \times D^1 \to C^\infty(M)$ such that

(i) g is local, i.e. $g(\phi U, \psi V) = \phi\psi g(U, V)$ for $U, V \in D^1$ and $\phi, \psi \in C^\infty(M)$;
(ii) g is symmetric, i.e. $g(U, V) = g(V, U)$ for $U, V \in D^1$;
(iii) g is positive definite, i.e. $g(U, U) \geqq 0$ and $g(U, U) = 0 \Leftrightarrow U = 0$.

Definition (2): An *affine connection* on M is a bilinear map $\vdash : D^1 \times D^1 \to D^1$ (we write $\vdash (U, V) = V \vdash U$) such that

(i) $\phi V \vdash U = \phi(V \vdash U)$,
(ii) $V \vdash \phi U = (V\phi)U + \phi(V \vdash U)$.

Definition (3): An affine connection is said to be *symmetric* if $(V \vdash U) - (U \vdash V) = [V, U]$ for $U, V \in D^1$.

Definition (4): An affine connection is said to be *appropriate to a given metric* if

$$W(U \circ V) = (W \vdash U) \circ V + U \circ (W \vdash V) \quad \text{for} \quad U, V, W \in D^1$$

(Here, we write $U \circ V$ for $g(U, V)$.)

Let us examine the above definitions in local coordinates. We set $g_{ij} = g(\partial_i, \partial_j)$ $= \partial_i \circ \partial_j.$ $\left(\text{Here, we have written } \partial_i = \dfrac{\partial}{\partial x_i}\right).$ Thus, if $U = u^i \partial_i, V = v^j \partial_j$ (we employ the summation convention), we have $g(U, V) = g_{ij} u^i v^j$. If $\partial_j \vdash \partial_i = \Gamma_{ji}^k \partial_k,$ $V \vdash U = v^i \partial_i \vdash u^i \partial_i = v^j (\partial_j \vdash u^i \partial_i) = v^j (u^i \partial_j \vdash \partial_i + (\partial_j u^i) \partial_i)$ $= v^i (u^i \Gamma_{ji}^k \partial_k + (\partial_j u^i) \partial_i) = (v^j u^i \Gamma_{ji}^k + v^j \partial_j u^k) \partial_k.$ It is an easy matter to check that the connection is symmetric iff $\Gamma_{ij}^k = \Gamma_{ji}^k$. Concerning Definition 4, we have the following

Theorem (1): Let M be a Riemannian manifold, i.e. a manifold with a given Riemannian metric g. Then there exists exactly one symmetric connection on M which is appropriate to g.

Proof: We shall first prove the uniqueness. Let $\vdash$ be a connection on M with the required properties. Locally, $\vdash$ is completely determined by the Γ_{ij}^k. We shall obtain an explicit formula for the Γ_{ij}^k in terms of the metric. It is clear that this establishes uniqueness. We begin by writing out the equation in Definition 4 in local coordinates. We have

$$W(U \circ V) = w^k (\partial_k (g_{ij} u^i v^j)) \quad \text{where} \quad W = w^k \partial_k.$$

Now,

$$(W \vdash U) \circ V + U \circ (W \vdash V) = (w^k u^i \Gamma_{ki}^l + (\partial_k u^l) w^k) \partial_l \circ v^j \partial_j$$
$$+ u^i \partial_i \circ (w^k v^j \Gamma_{kj}^l + (\partial_k v^l) w^k) \partial_l$$
$$= g_{lj} \{u^i v^j w^k \Gamma_{ik}^l + v^j w^k \partial_k u^l\}$$
$$+ g_{il} \{u^i v^j w^k \Gamma_{kj}^l + u^i w^k \partial_k v^l\}.$$

We put $\Gamma_{\varrho\sigma\tau} = g_{\varrho l} \Gamma_{\sigma\tau}^l$. Then $\Gamma_{l\sigma}^\varrho = g^{\varrho l} \Gamma_{l\sigma\tau}$ where the matrix $\|g^{ij}\|$ is the inverse of the (positive definite, and hence invertible) matrix $\|g_{ij}\|$. As

$$w^k (\partial_k (g_{ij} u^i v^j)) = w^k \{(\partial_k g_{ij}) u^i v^j + g_{ij} u^i (\partial_k v^j) + g_{ij} v^j (\partial_k u^i)\},$$

we get

$$\{(\partial_k g_{ij}) u^i v^j w^k\} + \{g_{ij} u^i w^k (\partial_k v^j) + g_{ij} v^j w^k (\partial_k u^i)\}$$
$$= \{g_{lj} \Gamma_{ki}^l u^i v^j w^k + g_{il} \Gamma_{kj}^l u^i v^j w^k\} + \{g_{ij} u^i w^k (\partial_k v^j) + g_{ij} v^j w^k (\partial_k u^i)\}.$$

Hence, $\partial_k g_{ij} = \Gamma_{jki} + \Gamma_{ikj}$. We write $\partial_\alpha g_{\beta\gamma} = \{\alpha\beta\gamma\}$, $\Gamma_{\alpha\beta\gamma} = [\alpha\beta\gamma]$. The previous equation gives us $\{kij\} = [jki] + [ikj]$. Taking cyclic permutations of the indices yields $\{ijk\} = [kij] + [jik]$, $\{jki\} = [ijk] + [kji]$. Since the connection is symmetric, $[\alpha\beta\gamma] = [\alpha\gamma\beta]$. Thus, the three equations give us $[ijk] = \frac{1}{2}(\{kij\} + \{jki\} - \{ijk\})$, i.e. $\Gamma_{ijk} = \frac{1}{2}(\partial_k g_{ij} + \partial_j g_{ki} - \partial_i g_{jk})$.

Therefore $\Gamma^i_{jk} = \frac{1}{2}(\partial_k g_{\alpha j} + \partial_j g_{k\alpha} - \partial_\alpha g_{jk}) g^{\alpha i}$ and we are finished. To prove existence, we just define the Γ^i_{jk} by the above formula. It is easy to verify that the resulting connection satisfies all of the required properties.

Definition (5): A covariant n-tensor field on a manifold M is an n-linear map $T: \overbrace{D^1 \times \cdots \times D^1}^{n} \to C^\infty(M)$ which is local, i.e. $T(\phi_1 U_1, \ldots, \phi_n U_n) = \phi_1 \cdots \phi_n T(U_1, \ldots, U_n)$.

A Riemannian metric is a covariant 2-tensor field. We shall now construct two other important tensor fields.

1) The covariant derivative of a covariant n-tensor field

T: Define $DT(U_1, \ldots, U_n, W) = W(T(U_1, \ldots, U_n))$

$$- T(W \vdash U_1, U_2, \ldots, U_n) - T(U_1, W \vdash U_2, U_3, \ldots, U_n)$$

$$- \cdots - T(U_1, \ldots, U_{n-1}, W \vdash U_n).$$

It is obvious that DT is $(n+1)$-linear and a short calculation shows that DT is local. In local coordinates, if $t_{i_1} \cdots {}_{i_n}$ are the coordinates of T, it turns out that the coordinates of DT are $t_{i_1 \ldots i_n; j} = \partial_j (t_{i_1 \ldots i_n}) - t_{\alpha i_2 \ldots i_n} \Gamma^\alpha_{i_1 j}$ $- t_{i_1 \alpha i_3 \ldots i_n} \Gamma^\alpha_{i_2 j} - \cdots - t_{i_1 \ldots i_{n-1} \alpha} \Gamma^\alpha_{i_n j}.$

2) The Riemann Curvature Tensor:
Define

$$[R(U, V)W] \circ Z = \{U \vdash (V \vdash W) - V \vdash (U \vdash W) - [U, V] \vdash W\} \circ Z.$$

Again, it is obvious that R is 4-linear and it is not difficult to verify that R is local. If we put $R(\partial_j, \partial_k) \cdot \partial_i = R^m_{ijk} \partial_m$, then it can easily be checked that

$$R^l_{ijk} = \partial_j \Gamma^l_{ik} - \partial_k \Gamma^l_{ij} + \Gamma^m_{ik} \Gamma^l_{mj} - \Gamma^m_{ij} \Gamma^l_{mk}.$$

Now, $R_{hijk} = g_{hm} R^m_{ijk} = [R(\partial_j, \partial_k) \cdot \partial_i] \circ \partial_h$ and we get by direct calculation $R_{hijk} = \frac{1}{2}(g_{hk,ij} + g_{ij,hk} - g_{hj,ik} - g_{ik,hj})$ + terms in the first derivatives of the metric tensor. (Note $g_{\alpha\beta,\gamma\delta}$ means $\partial^2 g_{\alpha\beta}(x)/\partial x^\gamma \partial x^\delta$.)

Let now γ be a (smooth) curve in the manifold M^n and let $V(t)$ be a vector field along γ, i.e. if $\gamma(t) = (p^1(t), \ldots, p^n(t))$ $(0 \leq t \leq 1)$, then $V(t)$ is a tangent vector at $\gamma(t)$. We say that $V(t)$ is parallel along $\gamma(t)$ if $\frac{d\gamma}{dt} \vdash V(t) = 0$. If now γ is parametrized by arc length s, we say that γ is a geodesic if $\frac{d\gamma}{ds} \vdash \frac{d\gamma}{ds} = 0$. If $\gamma(s)$ is geodesic, then we have in local coordinates

$$\frac{d^2 p^i(s)}{ds^2} + \Gamma^i_{jk}(p(s)) \frac{dp^j(s)}{ds} \cdot \frac{dp^k(s)}{ds} = 0.$$

Definition (6): A local coordinate system $(x^1, \ldots, x^n)$ on a Riemannian manifold M^n is said to be a geodesic coordinate system if we have

$$\Gamma_{jk}^i(x)\, x^j x^k = 0, \qquad i = 1, 2, \ldots, n.$$

The statement that a coordinate system is geodesic is equivalent to the assertion that geodesics through the origin appear in these coordinates as straight radii parametrized linearly. It is therefore clear that, if $\exp_p(v)$ denotes the point $\sigma(t)$ along the geodesic $\sigma(t)$ originating at p and with initial tangent vector v, then the mapping $v \to \exp_p(v)$ establishes geodesic coordinates at p. Thus geodesic coordinates exist in the neighborhood of any given point. Observe that in geodesic coordinates, $\Gamma_{ijk}(x)\, x^j x^k = 0$. Hence, since $\Gamma_{ijk} = \frac{1}{2}(\partial_k g_{ij} + \partial_j g_{ik} - \partial_i g_{jk})$, we must have

$$2\,(\partial_k g_{ji})\, x^j x^k - (\partial_i g_{jk})\, x^j x^k = 0.$$

Let us assume the $g_{\alpha\beta}(x)$ are real analytic. By direct calculation,

$$(x^k \partial_k)\,(g_{ji} x^j) = x^j x^k\,(\partial_k g_{ji}) + g_{ji} x^j,$$

$$\partial_i\,(g_{jk} x^j x^k) = (\partial_i g_{jk})\, x^j x^k + 2 g_{ij} x^j.$$

Combining results, we find that in geodesic coordinates

$$2\,(x^k \partial_k)\,(g_{ij} x^j) - \partial_i\,(g_{jk} x^j x^k) = 0. \tag{*}$$

We now set $v_i(x) = g_{ij}(x)\, x^j$ and $v_i^{(\delta)}(x) = \partial_{j_1 \ldots j_\delta}(v_i(0))\, x^{j_1} \cdots x^{j_\delta}$ where δ is any non-negative integer. Formula (*) now reads

$$2\,(x^k \partial_k)\, v_i = \partial_i\,(v_j x^j). \tag{**}$$

Taking the homogeneous terms of order δ from each side of this equation gives

$$2\,(x^k \partial_k)\, v_i^{(\delta)} = \partial_i\,(v_j^{(\delta)} x^j).$$

Now, $v_i^{(\delta)}(tx) = t^\delta v_i^{(\delta)}(x)$ and differentiation with respect to t yields

$$(x^k \partial_k)\, v_i^{(\delta)}(x) = \delta v_i^{(\delta)}(x) \qquad \text{(placing } t = 1\text{)}.$$

Formula (**) is now transformed to

$$2\delta v_i^{(\delta)} = \partial_i(v_j^{(\delta)} x^j). \tag{***}$$

We now put $f^{(\delta)} = v_j^{(\delta)} x^j$, so that (***) yields

$$v_i^{(\delta)} = \frac{1}{2\delta}\, \partial_i f^{(\delta)}, \qquad \delta > 0.$$

We thus obtain, using all the previous formulas,

$$f^{(\delta)} = \frac{1}{2\delta}\,(x^j \partial_j f^{(\delta)}) = \frac{\delta + 1}{2\delta}\, f^{(\delta)}.$$

Hence, $f^{(\delta)} = 0$ unless $\delta = 1$. Since, without loss of generality, we may assume that $g_{ij}(0) = \delta_{ij}$, it follows from $f^{(\delta)} = 0$ ($\delta > 1$) that in geodesic coordinates,

$$g_{ij}(x)\, x^j = x^i.$$

Expanding the left hand side in a Taylor series, and comparing coefficients with the right hand side, we find easily

$$g_{ij,k_1 \ldots k_m}(0)\, x^j x^{k_1} \cdots x^{k_m} = 0$$

and, in particular, since $g_{ij,k}(0) + g_{ik\,,j}(0) = g_{jk,i}(0)$, we have

$$g_{ij,k}(0) = 0.$$

Using the previous formula for R_{hijk}, we see that in geodesic coordinates

$$R_{hijk}(0) = \tfrac{1}{2}\,(g_{hk,ij}(0) + g_{ij,hk}(0) - g_{hj,ik}(0) - g_{ik,hj}(0)).$$

Additional calculation also gives us the following result.

Theorem (2): At the center of geodesic coordinates, the m-h order partial derivatives of the metric tensor are expressible algebraically in terms of the covariant derivatives of order $\leq m - 2$ of the Riemann tensor.

Proof: From the expression

$$R_{ijkl} = \tfrac{1}{2}\,(g_{ij,kl} - g_{ik,jl} + g_{kl,ij} - g_{jl,ik}) + T^{(1)},$$

where here and below we write $T^{(n)}$ for any algebraic expression in the metric tensor g and its m-th derivatives, $m \leq n$, we find on interchanging i, k and adding that

(1) $\qquad 2\,(R_{ijkl} + R_{kjil}) + T^{(1)} = g_{kl,ij} + g_{il,kj} - 2g_{jl,ik}.$

Differentiating the equation $g_{ri}(x)\, x^r = x^i$ twice we find that $-g_{ri,jk}x^r = g_{ij,k} + g_{ik,j}$. Repeated differentiation now gives $(E_n) - g_{ri,i_1 \ldots i_n}x^r = g_{ii_1,i_2 \ldots i_n} + \cdots + g_{ii_n,i_1 \ldots i_{n-1}}$. Using equation (E_2) to replace the first two terms on the right of (1), we find that

(2) $\qquad g_{rl,ijk}x^r - 2\,(R_{ijkl} + R_{kjil}) + T^{(1)} = 3g_{jl,ik}.$

Setting $x = 0$ in (2), we obtain an expression for the second derivative of the metric tensor at the origin in terms of the Riemann tensor. We now prove Theorem 2 by induction on the integer m. We have just given the proof for $m = 2$; let $m > 2$, and suppose Theorem 2 valid for $m_1 < m$. Then, taking the m-2'nd derivative of equation (2), and noting that the m-2'nd derivative of the Riemann tensor can be expressed in terms of its m-2'nd covariant derivatives and derivatives of the metric tensor of order at most $m - 1$, we see that to prove Theorem 2 it is sufficient to prove that, at the center of geodesic coordinates, the derivative $h = g_{ij, i_1 \ldots i_n}$ can be written in terms of the set of expressions

$$3g_{ij_0, j_1 \ldots j_n} + g_{ij_1, j_2 \ldots j_n j_0} + \cdots + g_{ij_{n-2}, j_{n-1} j_n j_0 \ldots j_{n-3}}.$$

Let σ denote the cyclic permutation $j_0 \cdots j_n \to j_1 \cdots j_n j_0$ of indices, so that $\sigma^{n+1} = 1$. Then we must prove that h can be expressed in terms of $3h + \sigma h + \cdots + \sigma^{n-2} h$, given the fact that $(1 + \sigma + \cdots + \sigma^n) h = 0$ which follows from (E_n) on setting $x = 0$. To prove this note that the polynomials $P(y) = 3 + y + \cdots + y^{n-2}$ and $Q(y) = 1 + y + \cdots + y^n$ have no roots in common and hence are relatively prime. Indeed, a root y_0 of $P(y) = 0$ satisfies $P(y_0) - y_0 P(y_0) = 0$, i.e. $3 - 2y_0 - y_0^{n-1} = 0$, and hence lies on the unit circle if and only if $2y_0 = 2$ and $y_0^{n-1} = 1$, so that $y_0 = 1$ and $Q(y_0) \neq 0$. We may therefore find rational polynomials $A(y)$ and $B(y)$ such that $A(y) P(y) + B(y) Q(y) = 1$, so that $h = A(\sigma) P(\sigma) h$ and the proof of Theorem 2 is complete. Q.E.D.

Corollary: The covariant derivatives of the Riemann tensor give a complete set of invariants for the Riemann metric in geodesic coordinates.

Proof: By Theorem 2, the covariant derivatives of the Riemann tensor completely determine the values of g_{ij} and all its derivatives at the center of geodesic coordinates. But g_{ij} is analytic and hence g_{ij} is completely determined in the whole coordinate neighborhood by the values of all its derivatives at the center.

We shall now consider another important instance of covariant n-tensor fields, the alternating n-tensor fields (or n-forms). By definition, ω is an alternating n-tensor field if

$$\omega (V_{\sigma(1)}, \ldots, V_{\sigma(n)}) = \text{sgn } \sigma \cdot \omega (V_1, \ldots, V_n)$$

where $V_i \in D^1$, σ is a permutation of $1, 2, \ldots, n$ and sgn σ is the sign of σ. If ω_i is an alternating k_i-tensor field $(i = 1, 2)$, then the outer product of ω_1 and ω_2 is defined by

$$\omega_1 \cdot \omega_2 (V_1, \ldots, V_{k_1}, \ldots, V_{k_i + k_2}) = \omega_1 (V_1, \ldots, V_{k_1}) \cdot \omega_2 (V_{k_1 + 1}, \ldots, V_{k_1 + k_2})$$

and the exterior product of ω_1 and ω_2 is defined by

$$\omega_1 \wedge \omega_2 = A (\omega_1 \cdot \omega_2)$$

where A is the alternating function, defined as follows:

$$A\omega\,(V_1, \ldots, V_n) = (n!)^{-1}\Sigma_\sigma\, \text{sgn}\,\sigma \cdot \omega\,(V_{\sigma(1)}, \ldots, V_{\sigma(n)}).$$

One shows easily that exterior multiplication is associative and that

$$\omega_1 \wedge \omega_2 = (-1)^{k_1 k_2}\omega_2 \wedge \omega_1.$$

If $D\omega$ is the covariant derivative of ω, we put

$$d\omega = A\,(D\omega)$$

and call d exterior differentiation. We then have the relations

$$d^2 = 0, \quad d\,(\omega_1 \wedge \omega_2) = d\omega_1 \wedge \omega_2 + (-1)^{k_1}\,\omega_1 \wedge d\omega_2.$$

Let us fix our attention on E^N, a Euclidean space of arbitrary dimension. Consider the collection of all pairs (S, T) where S is a compact subset of E^N and T is a closed subset of S. We define a collection of spaces as follows (see J. Schwartz, Amer. J. of Math., vol. 77, No. 1, Jan. 1965, pp. 29–44 for the following definitions and proofs of the next few theorems):

(i) F^k is the space of all (smooth) k-forms defined on E^N.

(ii) $V^k(S)$ is the subspace of F^k consisting of the forms which vanish near S.

(iii) $Z^k(S, T) = \{\omega \in V^k(T)|d\omega \in V^{k+1}(S)\}$.

(iv) $B^k(S, T) = \{d\omega + \theta|\omega \in V^{k-1}(T),\ \theta \in V^k(S)\}$.

(v) $D^k(S, T) = Z^k(S, T)/B^k(S, T)$.

We then have the following theorem, which we state without proof.

Theorem (3): *De Rham's Theorem* for every triangulable pair (S, T), $D^k(S, T)$ is naturally isomorphic to the k-h real relative (singular) cohomology group of (S, T).

If we let $S = M^m$, a manifold and $T = \phi$, we then obtain the classical theorem of De Rham. We call $Z^k(M)$ the space of closed k-forms and $B^k(M)$ the space of exact k-forms.

If $\phi : M^m \to N^n$ is a smooth map and if ω is a k-form on N, then we can define a k-form $\phi'\omega$ on M by setting

$$\phi'\omega\,(V_1, \ldots, V_k) = \omega\,(\phi_1 V_1, \ldots, \phi_1 V_k)$$

where $V_i \in D^1(M)$ ($i = 1, \ldots, k$) and ϕ_1 is the map on vector fields induced by ϕ. It is easy to see that $d\phi'\omega = \phi'd\omega$. Hence ϕ' induces a map, call it ϕ' again, from $D^k(N) \to D^k(M)$. It turns out that the following diagram is commutative.

$$
\begin{array}{ccc}
H^k\,(N, R) & \xrightarrow{\ \phi^*\ } & H^k\,(M, R)\\[4pt]
\big\uparrow{\scriptstyle \nu_N} & & \big\uparrow{\scriptstyle \nu_M}\\[4pt]
D^k(N) & \xrightarrow{\ \phi'\ } & D^k(M)
\end{array}
$$

Here, ν_N and ν_M are the natural isomorphisms given by De Rham's theorem and ϕ^* is the map on cohomology induced by the (continuous) map ϕ.

Let M^n be a Riemannian manifold and let $V_1, \ldots, V_n$ be smooth vector fields defined on some coordinate neighborhood $\mathcal{N}$ such that on $\mathcal{N}$, $V_i \circ V_j = g(V_i, V_j) = \delta_{ij}$. Let ω_i be the 1-form given by

$$\omega_i(V_j) = \delta_{ij}.$$

We define the 1-form ω_{ij} by

$$\omega_{ij}(V) = \omega_i(V \vdash V_j)$$

where V is a vector field on $\mathcal{N}$. If we differentiate $V_i \circ V_j = \delta_{ij}$ covariantly with respect to V, we obtain

$$(V \vdash V_j) \circ V_i + V_j \circ (V \vdash V_i) = 0$$

and, since $\omega_i(V) = V \circ V_i$, we get

$$\omega_{ij} = -\omega_{ji}.$$

If U is any vector field on $\mathcal{N}$, then $U = \omega_j(U) V_j$ (sum over repeated indices). By the definition of an affine connection,

$$\omega_i(V \vdash \omega_j(U) V_j) = \omega_j(U)\,\omega_{ij}(V) + \omega_i(V_j) \cdot V(\omega_j(U))$$

$$= \omega_j(U)\,\omega_{ij}(V) + V(\omega_i(U)).$$

Thus,

$$D\omega_i(U, V) = V(\omega_i(U)) - \omega_i(V \vdash U) = -\omega_j(U)\,\omega_{ij}(V)$$

from above. Applying the alternation operator A to both sides of this equation gives

$$d\omega_i = -\omega_j \wedge \omega_{ij}. \tag{C-1}$$

Let now $\Omega_{ij}(U, V) = \omega_i(R(U, V) V_j)$. We now prove

$$\omega_i(R(U, V) Z) = \omega_k(Z)\{\omega_{il} \wedge \omega_{lk}(U, V) - d\omega_{ik}(U, V)\}.$$

By the product rule for covariant differentiation we have $U\omega(V) = (D\omega)$ $(V, U) + \omega(U \vdash V)$ for any 1-form ω, and thus, antisymmetrizing, we have $U\omega(V) - V\omega(U) - \omega[(U, V)] = -(d\omega)(U, V)$. By definition of the Riemann form R, we have

$$\omega_i(R(U, V) Z) = \omega_i(U \vdash (V \vdash Z) - V \vdash_i (U \vdash Z) - [U, V] \vdash Z).$$

Hence, using the fundamental equation $\omega_i (V \vdash U) = \omega_{ij}(V) \, \omega_j(U) + V\omega_i(U)$, we have

$$\omega_i (R(U, V) Z) = \omega_{ij}(U) \, \omega_j (V \vdash Z) + U\omega_i (V \vdash Z)$$

$$- \text{ same terms with } U, V \text{ interchanged}$$

$$- \omega_{ij} ([U, V]) \, \omega_j(Z) - [U, V] \, \omega_j(Z)$$

$$= \omega_{ij}(U) \, \omega_{jk}(V) \, \omega_k(Z) + \omega_{ij}(U) \, V\omega_j (Z)$$

$$+ U (\omega_{ij} (V) \, \omega_j(Z)) + UV\omega_i (Z)$$

$$- \text{ same terms with } U, V \text{ interchanged}$$

$$- \omega_{ij} ([U, V]) \, \omega_j(Z) - [U, V] \, \omega_j(Z)$$

$$= \{(\omega_{ik} \wedge \omega_{kj}) (U, V) + U\omega_{ij} (V) - V\omega_{ij} (U)$$

$$- \omega_{ij} ([U, V])\} \, \omega_j(Z)$$

$$= \{\omega_{ik} \wedge \omega_{kj} (U, V) - d\omega_{ij} (U, V)\} \, \omega_j(Z),$$

proving the desired fromula.

(Summing over repeated indices here and below.) In particular, if we put $Z = V_j$, we get

$$d\omega_{ij} = \omega_{il} \wedge \omega_{lj} - \Omega_{ij}. \tag{C-2}$$

Now, taking the exterior derivative of each side of (C-2) and using the fact that $\omega_{\alpha\beta} = -\omega_{\beta\alpha}$, we get

$$d\Omega_{ij} = d\omega_{il} \wedge \omega_{lj} - d\omega_{jl} \wedge \omega_{li}. \tag{C-3}$$

The formulas (C-1), (C-2), (C-3) are called the *Cartan structure equations*.

We shall now construct an important class of forms on a Riemannian manifold M^n, the so-called curvature forms. We define

$$\Omega_{(k)} = \Omega_{i_1 i_2} \wedge \Omega_{i_2 i_3} \wedge \cdots \wedge \Omega_{i_{k-1} i_k} \wedge \Omega_{i_k i_1}.$$

If n is even and M is orientable, we also define

$$\Omega = \varepsilon^{i_1 \cdots i_n} \Omega_{i_1 i_2} \wedge \Omega_{i_3 i_4} \wedge \cdots \wedge \Omega_{i_{n-1} i_n}$$

where $\varepsilon^{i_1 \cdots i_n} = \text{sgn} \begin{pmatrix} 1 & 2 & \dots & n \\ i_1 & i_2 & \dots & i_n \end{pmatrix}$ if $i_1, \dots, i_n$ are distinct and $\varepsilon^{i_1 \cdots i_n} = 0$ if $i_1, \dots, i_n$ are not all distinct.

Theorem (4): The curvature forms $\Omega_{(k)}$ are invariantly defined on M, i.e. if $\hat{V}_1, \ldots, \hat{V}_n$ is another orthonormal system of vector fields on $\mathcal{N}$, and if $\hat{\omega}_i$, $\hat{\Omega}_{ij}$ and $\hat{\Omega}_{(k)}$ are obtained using the new system, then $\hat{\Omega}_{(k)} = \Omega_{(k)}$. Moreover, the forms $\Omega_{(k)}$ are closed i.e., $d\Omega_{(k)} = 0$. For k odd, $\Omega_{(k)} = 0$.

Proof: There exist orthogonal matrices $\|a_{ij}\|$ such that $\hat{V}_i = a_{ki}V_k$ (sum over k as usual). If then $\hat{\omega}_i$ is defined by $\hat{\omega}_i(\hat{V}_j) = \delta_{ij}$, we easily get $\hat{\omega}_i = a_{ki}\omega_k$. Using the definitions of $\hat{\Omega}_{ij}$ and Ω_{ij}, we get easily

$$\hat{\Omega}_{ij}(U, V) = a_{ki}a_{lj}\Omega_{kl}(U, V).$$

If we use this formula on each factor of $\hat{\Omega}_{j_1 j_2} \wedge \hat{\Omega}_{j_2 j_3} \wedge \cdots \wedge \hat{\Omega}_{j_k j_1}$ and use the fact that $\|a_{ij}\|$ is orthogonal, the first assertion follows directly.

To prove that $d\Omega_{(k)} = 0$ we make use of the formula

$$d\Omega_{ij} = -\Omega_{il} \wedge \omega_{lj} + \omega_{il} \wedge \Omega_{lj} \tag{*}$$

which is readily deduced from the Cartan structure equations. Now,

$$d\Omega_{(k)} = d\Omega_{i_1 i_2} \wedge (\Omega_{i_2 i_3} \wedge \Omega_{i_3 i_4} \wedge \cdots \wedge \Omega_{i_k i_1})$$
$$+ \Omega_{i_1 i_2} \wedge d(\Omega_{i_2 i_3} \wedge \cdots \wedge \Omega_{i_k i_1}).$$

But,

$$\Omega_{i_1 i_2} \wedge d(\Omega_{i_2 i_3} \wedge \cdots \wedge \Omega_{i_k i_1})$$
$$= \Omega_{i_1 i_2} \wedge \{d\Omega_{i_2 i_3} \wedge \Omega_{i_3 i_4} \wedge \cdots \wedge \Omega_{i_k i_1} + \Omega_{i_3 i_2} \wedge d(\Omega_{i_3 i_4} \wedge \cdots \wedge \Omega_{i_k i_1})\}$$
$$= \Omega_{i_1 i_2} \wedge d\Omega_{i_2 i_3} \wedge \Omega_{i_3 i_4} \wedge \cdots \wedge \Omega_{i_k i_1}$$
$$+ \Omega_{i_1 i_2} \wedge \Omega_{i_2 i_3} \wedge d(\Omega_{i_3 i_4} \wedge \cdots \wedge \Omega_{i_k i_1})$$
$$= d\Omega_{i_2 i_3} \wedge \Omega_{i_3 i_4} \wedge \cdots \wedge \Omega_{i_k i_1} \wedge \Omega_{i_1 i_2}$$
$$+ \Omega_{i_1 i_2} \wedge \Omega_{i_2 i_3} \wedge d(\Omega_{i_3 i_4} \wedge \cdots \wedge \Omega_{i_k i_1})$$

since $\Omega_{i_1 i_2}$, being a 2-form, commutes with any form. Hence, we have

$$d\Omega_{(k)} = 2d\Omega_{i_1 i_2} \wedge \Omega_{i_2 i_3} \wedge \cdots \wedge \Omega_{i_k i_1}$$
$$+ \Omega_{i_1 i_2} \wedge \Omega_{i_2 i_3} \wedge d(\Omega_{i_3 i_4} \wedge \cdots \wedge \Omega_{i_k i_1}).$$

By induction, we finally get

$$d\Omega_{(k)} = k \cdot d\Omega_{i_1 i_2} \wedge \Omega_{i_2 i_3} \wedge \cdots \wedge \Omega_{i_k i_1}.$$

To see that $d\Omega_{i_1 i_2} \wedge \Omega_{i_2 i_3} \wedge \cdots \wedge \Omega_{i_k i_1} = 0$, just apply formula (*) to $d\Omega_{i_1 i_2}$. The result follows by direct calculation.

To see that $\Omega_{(k)}$ is already 0 for k odd, observe first that $\Omega_{ij} = -\Omega_{ji}$. This follows from (C-2). Now,

$$\begin{aligned}
\Omega_{(k)} &= \Omega_{i_1 i_2} \wedge \Omega_{i_2 i_3} \wedge \cdots \wedge \Omega_{i_k i_1} \\
&= (-1)^k \Omega_{i_2 i_1} \wedge \Omega_{i_3 i_2} \wedge \cdots \wedge \Omega_{i_k i_{k-1}} \wedge \Omega_{i_1 i_k} \\
&= (-1)^k \Omega_{i_1 i_k} \wedge \Omega_{i_k i_{k-1}} \wedge \cdots \wedge \Omega_{i_3 i_2} \wedge \Omega_{i_2 i_1} \\
&= -\Omega_{(k)}
\end{aligned}$$

since k is odd. This completes the proof.

Theorem (5): The curvature form Ω is invariantly defined on an even dimensional oriented M^n, i.e. if $\hat{V}_1, \ldots, \hat{V}_n$ is another orthonormal system of vector fields on $\mathcal{N}$, giving the same orientation as $V_1, \ldots, V_n$, then $\hat{\Omega} = \Omega$. Moreover, Ω is a closed form.

Proof: As in Theorem 3, $\hat{\Omega}_{ij} = a_{ki} a_{lj} \Omega_{kl}$. But now we also have $|a_{ij}| = \det(\|a_{ij}\|) = 1$. By direct calculation, we get

$$\begin{aligned}
\hat{\Omega} &= \varepsilon^{j_1 \cdots j_n} \hat{\Omega}_{j_1 j_2} \wedge \hat{\Omega}_{j_3 j_4} \wedge \cdots \wedge \hat{\Omega}_{j_{n-1} n} \\
&= \varepsilon^{j_1 \cdots j_n} a_{i_1 j_1} a_{i_2 j_2} \cdots a_{i_n j_n} \Omega_{i_1 i_2} \wedge \Omega_{i_3 i_4} \wedge \cdots \wedge \Omega_{i_{n-1} i_n} \\
&= \varepsilon^{i_1 \cdots i_n} \Omega_{i_1 i_2} \wedge \Omega_{i_3 i_4} \wedge \cdots \wedge \Omega_{i_{n-1} i_n},
\end{aligned}$$

because of the definition of determinant. Since $d\Omega$ is of order $n + 1$ and since M is n-dimensional, it follows that $d\Omega = 0$.

Definition (7): By Theorems 4 and 5, the curvature forms $\Omega_{(k)}$, Ω define elements in the De Rham cohomology ring; we call these elements the *curvature cohomology classes*. By virtue of De Rham's theorem, these elements may be identified with elements of the ordinary cohomology ring (with real coefficients).

Suppose now that M_0^ν is a submanifold of the Riemannian manifold M^n. In a natural way, M_0 inherits a Riemannian metric g_0 from the metric g on M. By Theorem 1, g_0 determines a symmetric connection, call it $\vdash_0$, which is appropriate to g_0.

Lemma (1): $V \vdash U_0 = P_0(V \vdash U)$, where $U, V \in D^1(M_0)$, P_0 is the orthogonal projection of a tangent space to M onto the corresponding tangent space to M_0.

Proof: Put $V \vdash_1 U = P_0(V \vdash U)$. It is easy to check that $\vdash_1$ is an affine connection which is symmetric and appropriate to g_0. Appealing to the uniqueness assertion of Theorem 1, the lemma is proved.

Let now $V_1, \ldots, V_n$ be a system of orthonormal vector fields on a coordinate neighborhood $\mathcal{N}$ of M^n such that $V_1, \ldots, V_\nu$ form a system of tangent vector fields to M_0^ν while $V_{\nu+1}, \ldots, V_n$ form a system of normal vector fields to M_0^ν. Let $\omega_i^{(0)}$, $\omega_{ij}^{(0)}$, $\Omega_{ij}^{(0)}$ denote the forms on M_0 defined using the vector fields $V_1, \ldots, V_\nu$. Thus, the forms are defined only for the values $1 \leq i, j \leq \nu$.

If $1 \leq i \leq \nu$ and $V \in D^1(M_0)$, then $\omega_i(V) = \omega_i^{(0)}(V)$, i.e. $\omega_i^{(0)}$ is the restriction of ω_i $(1 \leq i \leq \nu)$.

If $1 \leq i, j \leq \nu$ and $V \in D^1(M_0)$, then

$$\omega_{ij}(V) = \omega_i \left(V \vdash V_j \right) = \omega_i \left(P_0(V \vdash V_j) \right) = \omega_i(V \vdash_0 V_j)$$
$$= \omega_i^{(0)} \left(V \vdash_0 V_j \right) = \omega_{ij}^{(0)}(V),$$

i.e. $\omega_{ij}^{(0)}$ is the restriction of ω_{ij} $(1 \leq i, j \leq \nu)$.

On M^n, we have (C-2): $\Omega_{ij} = \sum_{l=1}^{n} \omega_{il} \wedge \omega_{lj} - d\omega_{ij}$ $(1 \leq i, j \leq n)$.

Similarly, on M_0^ν, we have $\Omega_{ij}^{(0)} = \sum_{l=1}^{\nu} \omega_{il}^{(0)} \wedge \omega_{lj}^{(0)} - d\omega_{ij}^{(0)}$ $(1 \leq i, j \leq \nu)$. By the above remarks, it follows that actually

$$\Omega_{ij}^{(0)} = \sum_{l=1}^{\nu} \omega_{il} \wedge \omega_{lj} - d\omega_{ij}, \qquad 1 \leq i, j \leq \nu.$$

Subtracting, we get

$$\Omega_{ij}^{(0)} = \Omega_{ij} - \sum_{l=\nu+1}^{n} \omega_{il} \wedge \omega_{lj}, \qquad 1 \leq i, j \leq \nu. \tag{**}$$

In the sequel we make use of the following deep theorem of Nash, which we state without proof. (For a proof, cf. J. Schwartz, NYU Lecture Notes on Nonlinear Functional Analysis, 1963/64.)

Theorem (6) (Nash): Any Riemannian manifold can be isometrically embedded in E^N for some sufficiently large integer N.

Using this theorem, we take an arbitrary Riemannian manifold M_0^ν and embed it isometrically in E^N. In the above discussion, we replace M^n by E^N. Since in E^N, $\Omega_{ij} = 0$, we get from (**) above

Theorem (7) (Generalized Theorema Egregium):

$$\Omega_{ij}^{(0)} = - \sum_{l=\nu+1}^{N} \omega_{il} \wedge \omega_{lj}, \qquad 1 \leq i, j \leq \nu.$$

We change our notation and let M^n be an arbitrary Riemannian manifold, sometrically embedded in E^N. We now make a fundamental definition which will enable us to relate the curvature cohomology classes defined above with the characteristic classes of Chapter VI. (Cf. Pontryagin—"Some Topological Invariants of Closed Riemannian Manifolds", AMS Translations, Series 1, Volume 7.)

Definition (8): Let 0 be the origin in E^N. We define a map

$$T : M^n \to G_{n,N}$$

where, as in Chapter III, $G_{n,N}$ is the set of n-dimensional planes in N-space, as follows. For each $x \in M^n$, let T_x be the tangent space to M^n at x. Then, since $M^n \subseteq E^N$, T_x may be viewed as an n-plane in E^N. Let $T(x)$ be the n-dimensional subspace passing through 0 which is parallel to T_x. The map $x \to T(x)$ so defined is called a *tangential representation* of M^n.

Let $W_{n,N}$ be the subspace of $G_{n,N} \times G_{1,N}$ consisting of all pairs (π, e) such that e is a vector lying in π; $W_{n,N}$ is given the relative topology of the product space. A projection $p_2 : W_{n,N} \to G_{n,N}$ is given by $p_2(\pi, e) = \pi$. Then $W_{n,N}$ is the bundle space of a vector bundle ξ over $G_{n,N}$ (see Chapter IV, Definition 4). We can suppose the structural group of this bundle to be O_n, acting as usual on an n-dimensional vector space. If now $\tau(M)$ is the tangent bundle of M (recall that $\tau(M)$ consists of pairs (x, e_x) with $x \in M$ and e_x a vector lying in T_x) and if $p_1 : \tau(M) \to M$ is the projection $(x, e_x) \to x$, then there is a bundle map

$$\tilde{T} : \tau(M) \to W_{n,N}$$

that is,

$$\tau(M) \xrightarrow{\tilde{T}} W_{n,N}$$
$$\downarrow{p_1} \qquad \downarrow{p_2}$$
$$M \xrightarrow{T} G_{n,N}$$

is a commutative diagram. In fact, $\tilde{T}$ is given by

$$\tilde{T}((x, e_x)) = (T_x, e(x))$$

where $e(x)$ is the vector passing through 0 which is parallel to e_x. It is clear that the associated principal bundle $\tilde{\xi}$ of ξ (see Chapter VI, discussion after Definition 1) is the bundle with bundle space the Stiefel manifold $V_{n,N}$ (see Chapter VI, discussion after Definition 2). Also $T^+\tilde{\xi}$ is just the associated principal bundle of $\tau(M)$. By the Classification Theorem (see Chapter VI, Theorem 4), the homotopy class of T is uniquely determined independently of the particular imbedding of M used, for N sufficiently large. In particular, T^*, the induced map on cohomology, is an invariant of the associated principal O_n-bundle of $\tau(M)$. Thus, T^* does not depend on the embedding of M^n in E^n, nor does it depend on N (as long as N is sufficiently large).

We now construct a collection of forms on the manifold $G_{n,N}$, in a manner analogous to the construction of the curvature forms on M^n. It will turn out that the curvature forms on M^n can be obtained from this new collection of forms by an application of T' (where T' is the map on forms induced by T).

Let π be the generic element of $G_{n,N}$. We choose an orthonormal basis in π, say $e_1, e_2, \ldots, e_n$ (where $e_i = e_i(\pi)$) and supplement this basis by an orthonormal basis $e_{n+1}(\pi), \ldots, e_N(\pi)$ for $\pi^{\perp}$. We assume the vectors $e_i(\pi)$ vary smoothly on $G_{n,N}$ in a neighborhood wherein we calculate.

Recall that if f is a real valued smooth function defined on $G_{n,N}$ (or for that matter, on any manifold), and if V is a vector field on $G_{n,N}$, then $df(V) = Vf$. If now g is a smooth map from $G_{n,N}$ into E^N, then g can be regarded as a collection of N functions $g_1, \ldots, g_N$ with $g_i : G_{n,N} \to R$ $(i = 1, 2, \ldots, N)$. We then define dg by

$$dg\,(V) = (Vg_1, Vg_2, \ldots, Vg_n).$$

Thus, dg is a mapping

$$dg : D^1(G_{n,N}) \to \underbrace{C^{\infty}(G_{n,N}) \times \cdots \times C^{\infty}(G_{n,N})}_{N \text{ factors}}$$

(Recall the notations $D^1(M)$, $C^{\infty}(M)$ introduced at the beginning of this chapter.)

The vectors $e_i(\pi)$ introduced above can be regarded as maps

$$e_i : G_{n,N} \to E^N.$$

We now define 1-forms $\tilde{\omega}_{\alpha\beta}$ on $G_{n,N}$ $(\alpha, \beta = 1, 2, \ldots, N)$ by

$$\tilde{\omega}_{\alpha\beta} = de_{\alpha} \circ e_{\beta}$$

where $\circ$ is the Riemannian metric on E^N, i.e. the usual dot product. We then define 2-forms $\tilde{\Omega}_{ij}$ on $G_{n,N}$ $(i, j = 1, \ldots, n)$ by

$$\tilde{\Omega}_{ij} = - \sum_{r=n+1}^{N} \tilde{\omega}_{ir} \wedge \tilde{\omega}_{rj}.$$

As before, we introduce forms $\tilde{\Omega}_{(k)}$, $\tilde{\Omega}$ as follows:

(a) $$\tilde{\Omega}_{(k)} = \tilde{\Omega}_{i_1 i_2} \wedge \tilde{\Omega}_{i_2 i_3} \wedge \cdots \wedge \tilde{\Omega}_{i_{k-1} i_k} \wedge \tilde{\Omega}_{i_k i_1}.$$

and

(b) $$\tilde{\Omega} = \varepsilon^{i_1 \cdots i_n} \tilde{\Omega}_{i_1 i_2} \wedge \tilde{\Omega}_{i_3 i_4} \wedge \cdots \wedge \tilde{\Omega}_{i_{n-1} i_n},$$

if n is even.

Remark: In fact, the form $\tilde{\Omega}$ is defined only up to sign on the (nonorientable) manifold $G_{n,N}$. To remove the ambiguity, we may consider $\hat{\Omega}$ as defined on the two-sheeted covering space $\bar{G}_{n,N}$ (see Chapter I, discussion after Definition 7) of $G_{n,N}$. On $\bar{G}_{n,N}$, SO_n acts transitively and in fact, $\bar{G}_{n,N} = SO_N/ SO_n \times SO_{N-n}$. We shall not dwell on this technical point and leave to the reader the task of making rigorous any imprecise statement in the discussion below. Observe that the forms $\tilde{\Omega}_{(k)}$ are already invariantly defined on $G_{n,N}$ since no question of orientation enters in this case.

Observe again that O_n acts transitively on $G_{n,N}$. Thus, if $g \in O_n$, there is induced a smooth map

$$g : G_{n,N} \to G_{n,N}.$$

If ω is an r-form on $G_{n,N}$, we say that ω is invariant under O_n when $g'\omega = \omega$ for all $g \in O_n$, where g' is the induced map on forms.

We assert that the forms $\tilde{\Omega}_{(k)}$, $\tilde{\Omega}$ constructed above are independent of the bases e_i used to define them. As the proof of this assertion very much resembles the proof of Theorems 4 and 5, we leave its details to the reader. It follows very readily from the definition of the forms $\tilde{\omega}_{ij}$ and from the fact that the vectors e_α form an orthonormal basis that $d\tilde{\omega}_{ij} = \sum_{\alpha=1}^{N} \omega_{i\alpha} \wedge \omega_{\alpha j}$. Therefore $d\tilde{\omega}_{ij} = \tilde{\omega}_{ik} \wedge \tilde{\omega}_{kj} - \tilde{\Omega}_{ij}$, where k is summed from 1 to n. Using this formula to replace $(C - 2)$, we may deduce that the forms $\tilde{\Omega}_{(k)}$ and $\tilde{\Omega}$ are closed, in much the same way as the corresponding facts were proved for $\Omega_{(k)}$ and Ω; all additional details are left to the reader.

Finally, we can easily convince ourselves that

$$T'\big(\tilde{\Omega}_{(k)}\big) = \Omega_{(k)}, \quad T'\big(\tilde{\Omega}\big) = \Omega.$$

Hence, we also have

$$T^*\big(\{\tilde{\Omega}_{(k)}\}\big) = \{\Omega_{(k)}\}, \quad T^*\big(\{\tilde{\Omega}\}\big) = \{\Omega\},$$

where T^* is the induced map on cohomology classes and where $\{\ \}$ denotes cohomology class. We now prove

Theorem (8): The curvature cohomology classes of M^n can be expressed as real linear combinations of cup products of the Whitney classes of the associated principal O_n-bundle of $\tau(M)$.

Proof: Let $T_N : M^n \to G_{n,N}$ be a tangential representation of M^n. Let $\Omega_{(k)}^{(N)}$, $\tilde{\Omega}^{(N)}$ be the forms constructed above $\big($where we called them $\tilde{\Omega}_{(k)}, \tilde{\Omega}\big)$. Thus,

$T^*\left(\{\tilde{\Omega}^{(N)}_{(k)}\}\right) = \{\Omega_{(k)}\}$, $T^*\left(\{\tilde{\Omega}^{(N)}\}\right) = \{\Omega\}$. If $i_N : G_{n,N} \to G_{n,\infty}$ is the natural injection, we obtain a map

$$i_N \circ T : M^n \to G_{n,\infty}.$$

Since $i_N \circ T \cong i_P \circ T$ for any N, P which are sufficiently large, the choice of N is immaterial. Moreover, we have

$$(i_N \circ T)^\dagger (\alpha_n) = \widetilde{\tau(M)},$$

where α_n is the bundle introduced in Chapter VI, Definition 5 and $\widetilde{\tau(M)}$ is the associated principal bundle of $\tau(M)$. As the cohomology map i_N^* is onto, there exist elements $\gamma_{(k)}, \gamma \in H^*(G_{n,N})$ such that

$$i_N^*(\gamma_{(k)}) = \{\tilde{\Omega}^{(N)}_{(k)}\}, \; i_N^*(\gamma) = \{\tilde{\Omega}^{(N)}\};$$

whence

$$(i_N \circ T)^* (\gamma_{(k)}) = \{\Omega_{(k)}\}, \; (i_N \circ T)^* (\gamma) = \{\Omega\}.$$

But the elements $\gamma_{(k)}, \gamma$ can be written as linear combinations of cup products of Whitney classes and the theorem follows if we just use the definition of the Whitney classes of the bundle $\widetilde{\tau(M)}$.

Let M^n be an orientable even-dimensional manifold. We have expressed the curvature forms of M^n, originally given in terms of the Riemann tensor on M^n, in topologically invariant form. Let us look, in particular, at the form Ω. Clearly, the integral $\int_{M^n} \Omega$ must also be a topological invariant of M^n.

To find this numerical invariant, one may simply try to compute the integral as it stands. However, by using the relation between Ω and $\tilde{\Omega}^{(N)}$ developed above, we may reduce the problem to a computation of the integral $\int_{T_N(M^n)} \tilde{\Omega}^{(N)}$. Indeed, by the usual change of variable formula, we have

$$\int_{T_N(M^n)} \tilde{\Omega}^{(N)} = \int_{M^n} T_N'\left(\tilde{\Omega}^{(N)}\right) = \int_{M^n} \Omega.$$

Thus, all of the computational burden has been thrown on one particular form $\Omega^{(N)}$ on one particular space $G_{n,N}$. This, of course, reflects the "universal" character of the space $G_{n,N}$. The actual computation of the integral $\int_{T_N(M^n)} \tilde{\Omega}^{(N)}$ can be carried out without too much difficulty (see Pontryagin, loc. cit.). Here, we omit the calculations and content ourselves with stating the final result, as follows.

Theorem (9) (Generalized Gauss-Bonnet Theorem:) If $\chi(M^n)$ is the Euler characteristic of M^n and σ_n is the volume of the n-dimensional unit ball, then

$$\int_{M^n} \Omega = \tfrac{1}{2}\sigma_n \cdot \chi(M^n).$$

CHAPTER VIII

Generalized Cohomology Theories

In the final three chapters of these notes, we continue to develop the cohomology theory of bundles. We shall introduce, for any finite complex X (or, more generally, for any finite cellular pair (X, Y)), a sequence of groups defined in terms of the bundles on X. These groups, together with certain homomorphisms between them, form a system which is very much like a cohomology theory, satisfying all of the Eilenberg-Steenrod axioms except for the dimension axiom. This "bundle cohomology theory" has found many important applications in topology; one of these is discussed in Chapter 10.

This chapter is divided into two parts. In part A, a general notion of "generalized" or "nonstandard" cohomology theory is introduced (having nothing to do with bundles). In part B, we introduce our "bundle cohomology theory", the so-called K-Theory. It is shown that K-Theory is a nonstandard cohomology theory in the sense of part A. A deeper and more detailed study of K-Theory will be carried out in Chapter 9.

Part A: A Nonstandard Cohomology Theory

All the topological spaces we will speak of here will be assumed to be based, i.e. with each space X, some point $x_0 \in X$ will be singled out. Moreover, we shall only consider maps $f: X \to Y$ which are basepoint preserving.

Let T be an arcwise connected space; call T a *test space*. For any space X, we have T^X, the set of all continuous (basepoint preserving) maps of X into T. We let (T^X) denote the set of all homotopy classes of maps of X into T. If T^X is given the compact-open topology, then the elements of (T^X) are just the arc-connected components of T^X. It is easy to check that (T^X) is a functor of two variables; covariant in T, contravariant in X.

If A is a closed subset of X such that the basepoint $x_0 \in A$, we denote by X/A the set obtained by identifying all points of A. X/A becomes a topological space if we define a subset W of X/A to be open iff $p^{-1}(W)$ is open in X (where $p : X \to X/A$ is the natural projection).

We define the *one point union* $X \vee Y$ to be the space obtained from the disjoint union $X \cup Y$ by identifying the basepoints x_0, y_0. We define the *smash product* $X \wedge Y$ by

$$X \wedge Y = X \times Y/X \vee X.$$

Let the basepoint of S^n be ν, the north pole. We put

$$S^n(X) = S^n \wedge X.$$

Then $S^n(X)$ is a covariant functor of X. Indeed, any map $f : Y \to X$ gives rise to a map
$$f' : S^n \times Y \to S^n \times X$$

defined as $f'(p, y) = (p, f(y))$, $p \in S^n$, $y \in Y$. Since $f'(S^n \times y_0) \subseteq S^n \times x_0$, $f'(\nu \times Y) \subseteq \nu \times X$, it is clear that f' induces a map

$$f' : S^n(Y) \to S^n(X).$$

One sees easily that the correspondence $X \to S^n(X)$, $f \to \bar{f}$ is functorial.

We shall now define a non-standard cohomology theory on the class of all pairs (X, Y) with X a cell complex, Y a closed subcomplex. We shall moreover require that the basepoint x_0 be a vertex in Y (provided $Y \neq \phi$). The theory is non-standard in the following senses:

(i) in lowest dimension, the cohomology "groups" are not usually actual groups,

(ii) the dimension axiom is not usually satisfied.

For a pair (X, Y), we set

$$T^{-n}(X, Y) = (T^{S^n(X/Y)})$$

and call $T^{-n}(X, Y)$ the n-th T-cohomology "group" of (X, Y). Although $T^{-n}(X, Y)$ is not actually a group in general, it nevertheless has a "distinguished" element (which is a substitute for a unit). Indeed, if U and V are spaces, with U arcwise connected, we may consider the element of (U^V) which is the class of all mappings homotopic to a constant as the distinguished element.

Having defined $T^{-n}(X, Y)$, we must define for any $f : (X, Y) \to (X', Y')$ a corresponding "homomorphism"

$$f^* : T^{-n}(X', Y') \to T^{-n}(X, Y).$$

This is easily done: f induces a map. $\tilde{f}: X/Y \to X'/Y'$ which in turn induces a map $\hat{f}: S^n(X/Y) \to S^n(X'/Y')$. Since (T^X) is contravariant in X, f induces the desired map.

We must now define a coboundary operator

$$\delta: T^{-(n+1)}(Y) \to T^{-n}(X, Y).$$

Before doing this, we shall list three important properties of the operations $\vee$ and $\wedge$. Their proofs are left as exercises.

(i) $$(X \vee Y) \vee Z = X \vee (Y \vee Z)$$

(ii) $$(X \wedge Y) \wedge Z = X \wedge (Y \wedge Z)$$

(iii) $$S^1 \wedge S^1 = S^2; \text{ in general, } \overbrace{S^1 \wedge \cdots \wedge S^1}^{n} = S^n.$$

Equality above must be interpreted up to homeomorphism.

We shall now state a topological result which is essential in what follows.

Homotopy Extension Theorem: Let (X, Y) be a pair, consisting of a cell complex X and a subcomplex Y. Let $f: X \to T$ be a map and suppose $h_t: Y \to T$ is a partial homotopy of f (i.e. $f|Y = h_0$). Then there exists a homotopy $H_t: X \to T$ such that $H_0 = f$, $H_t|Y = h_t$ $(0 \leq t \leq 1)$.

The proof when (X, Y) is a triangulable pair can be found in Hu—*Homotopy Theory*, p. 14.

Corollary (1): Let A be a subcomplex of the cell complex B. Let t, s denote generic points of $I = [0, 1]$ and let b denote the generic point of B. Let C denote the following subset of $I \times I \times B$:

$$C = \{(0, s, b) \mid s \in I, b \in B\} \cup \{(t, s, b) \mid t \in I, s \in I, b \in A\}.$$

Let $f: C \to T$ be a given map. Then f can be extended to all of $I \times I \times B$.

Proof: Just apply the above theorem (abbrev. HET) to the pair $(I \times B, I \times A)$.

Corollary 1 can be reformulated as follows. Let z be a complex variable ranging over the unit square in the complex plane. Suppose $f(z, b)$ is defined for (a) all z on the bottom of the unit square and all $b \in B$, (b) all z in the unit square and all $b \in A$. Then f can be extended to all z in the unit square and all $b \in B$.

Corollary (2): Suppose $f(z, b)$ is defined for
(a) all z on the left face, bottom face and right face of the unit square and all $b \in B$,

(b) as above. Then f can be extended to all z in the unit square and all $b \in B$.

Proof: Topologically, the bottom face of the unit square is the same as the union of the left, bottom and right faces. Hence, Corollary 2 follows from the reformulation of Corollary 1.

We proceed now to define δ. Let $\alpha \in T^{-(n+1)}(Y) = (T^{S^{n+1}(Y)})$ and let $\phi : S^{n+1}(Y) \to T$ be a representative of α. From (ii) and (iii) above, $S^{n+1}(Y) = S^1(S^n(Y))$. From the definition of smash product, we can easily convince ourselves that ϕ can be regarded as a map

$$\phi : I \times S^n(Y) \to T$$

satisfying $\phi : 0 \times S^n(Y) \to t_0$, $\phi : 1 \times S^n(Y) \to t_0$, $\phi : I \times p_0 \to t_0$, where t_0 is the basepoint of T and p_0 is the basepoint of $S^n(Y)$. We define a family of maps

$$\phi_t : S^n(Y) \to T$$

by setting $\phi_t(p) = \phi(t, p)$, $p \in S^n(Y)$. Thus, ϕ_0 is constant on $S^n(Y)$ and may therefore be extended as a constant to all of $S^n(X)$. (Since $X \supseteq Y$, also $S^n(X) \supseteq S^n(Y)$. Note also that $S^n(X)$ is a cell complex and $S^n(Y)$ is a subcomplex.) Thus, if $f_0 : S^n(X) \to T$ is defined by $f_0(p) = t_0$ for all $p \in S^n(X)$, it follows that ϕ_t is a partial homotopy of f_0. By HET, there is a homotopy

$$f_t : S^n(X) \to T$$

extending ϕ_t. Now $f_1 : S^n(X) \to T$ and since f_1 extends ϕ_1, we see that $f_1 : S^n(Y) \to t_0$. Hence f_1 can be regarded as a map

$$f_1 : S^n(X)/S^n(Y) \to T.$$

An easy check shows that $S^n(X)/S^n(Y) = S^n(X/Y)$. Thus f_1 is a map

$$f_1 : S^n(X/Y) \to T.$$

Let $\{f_1\}$ be the class of f_1 in $(T^{S^n(X/Y)})$ and put

$$\delta\alpha = \delta\{\phi\} = \{f_1\}.$$

We have to show that $\{f_1\}$ is well-defined by α. So let $\phi^{(0)}$ and $\phi^{(1)}$ be two representatives of α. Then $\phi^{(0)}$ and $\phi^{(1)}$ give rise to families of maps $\phi_t^{(0)}$, $\phi_s^{(0)}$ satisfying conditions mentioned above. Moreover, there is a homotopy $\phi_t^{(s)}$ between $\phi_t^{(0)}$ and $\phi_t^{(1)}$ and we have extensions $f_t^{(0)}$, $f_t^{(1)}$ of $\phi_t^{(0)}$, $\phi_t^{(1)}$ to all of $S^n(X)$ which are identically constant for $t = 0$. Define $f_0^{(s)}$ by

$$f_0^{(s)}(p) = t_0, \quad \text{all} \quad p \in S^n(X),$$

and also put

$$f_t^{(s)}(p) = \phi_t^{(s)}(p), \quad \text{all} \quad p \in S^n(Y).$$

We thus have a map f satisfying the conditions of Corollary 2 of the HET and therefore f can be extended to be a map from all of $I \times I \times S^n(X)$ into T. This map in turn gives a map $f_t^{(s)}(p)$ defined for all $t, s \in I, p \in S^n(X)$. Clearly, $f_1^{(s)}$ is a homotopy connecting $f_1^{(0)}$ and $f_1^{(1)}$ and since $f_1^{(s)}$ is constant on $S^n(Y)$, it follows that as elements of $T^{-n}(X, Y)$, $\{f_1^{(0)}\} = \{f_1^{(1)}\}$, i.e. δ is well-defined.

We shall now verify the first six Eilenberg–Steenrod axioms for a cohomology theory. The first three Eilenberg–Steenrod axioms assert the existence and basic properties of the cohomology maps induced by continuous maps and of the coboundary map. They have essentially been proved already; all additional details are left as an exercise.

To prove the exactness axiom, let us consider the sequence

$$\cdots \longrightarrow T^{-n}(Y) \xrightarrow{\delta} T^{-n+1}(X, Y) \xrightarrow{j^*} T^{-n+1}(X) \xrightarrow{i^*} T^{-n+1}(Y) \longrightarrow \cdots$$

where i^* and j^* are induced by the inclusion maps

$$i: Y \to X, \quad j: X \to (X, Y)$$

and δ is defined above.

There are six assertions to check. We shall only do two of them; the others are of the same order of difficulty and are left to the reader.

(1) $\ker i^* \subseteq \text{image } j^*$: Let $\{\phi\} \in \ker i^*$. Then $\phi: S^{n-1}(X) \to T$ and $\phi|S^{n-1}(Y): S^{n-1}(Y) \to T$ is homotopic to the constant map. Call this homotopy ϕ_t. By HET, there is a homotopy $\Phi_t: S^{n-1}(X) \to T$ which extends ϕ_t. Hence $\phi \cong \Phi_1$ and $\Phi_1|S^{n-1}(Y) = \phi_1 =$ the constant map, i.e. $\{\phi\} = j^*\{\Phi_1\}$.

(2) $\ker j^* \subseteq \text{image } \delta$: Let $\{\psi\} \in \ker j^*$. Then $\psi: S^{n-1}(X) \to T$ is the constant map on $S^{n-1}(Y)$ and ψ is homotopic to the constant map. Let ψ_t be the homotopy and for convenience, let $\psi_1 = \psi$, $\psi_0 =$ constant. But then $\psi_t|S^{n-1}(Y)$ is the constant map for $t = 0$ and $t = 1$ and hence induces a map of $S^1(S^{n-1}(Y)) \to T$; call this map Ψ. Then, by definition $\{\psi\} = \{\psi_1\} = \delta\{\Psi\}$, i.e. $\{\psi\} \in \text{image } \delta$.

We now prove the Homotopy Axiom.

Let $f_0, f_1: (X, Y) \to (X', Y')$ be homotopic with homotopy f_t. Then $f_t: (X, Y) \to (X', Y')$ induces $f_t': X/Y \to X'/Y'$ which in turn induces $\bar{f}_t: S^n \wedge (X/Y) \to S^n \wedge (X'/Y')$. Now the map

$$f_i^*: (T^{S^n(X'/Y')}) \to (T^{S^n(X/Y)})$$

is given by $\{h\} \to \{h\bar{f}_i\}$, where $h \in T^{S^n(X'/Y')}$ and $i = 0, 1$. But $h\bar{f}_0$ is homotopic to $h\bar{f}_1$ via the homotopy $h\bar{f}_t$ and hence $\{h\bar{f}_0\} = \{h\bar{f}_1\}$, i.e. $f_0^* = f_1^*$.

We now prove the Excision Axiom. (In fact, in this theory, we have a strong form of excision.) Indeed, let U be any open set in Y and consider the inclusion map
$$f: (X - U, Y - U) \to (X, Y).$$
The fact that
$$f^*: T^{-n}(X, Y) \to T^{-n}(X - U, Y - U)$$
is an isomorphism follows directly from the fact that X/Y is homeomorphic to $X - U/Y - U$.

We note that the dimension axiom is false in general. Indeed, let $\{p, p_0\}$ be the space consisting of two points, with basepoint p_0. Then, since
$$S^n \wedge \{p, p_0\} = (S^n \times p) \cup (S^n \times p_0)/(v \times p) \cup (v \times p_0) \cup (S^n \times p_0),$$
it follows that $T^{-n}(\{p, p_0\}, p_0) = \pi_n(T)$.

We shall now give conditions on T in order that the T-cohomology theory be a genuine generalised cohomology theory.

Definition (1): A space T is said to be a *group-like* space if there exists a continuous map $\eta: T \times T \to T$ (we shall write $t_1 \times t_2 = \eta(t_1, t_2)$) having the following properties.

(i)   There exists an element $e \in T$ such that $e \times e = e$ and such that
   a) the map $t \to t \times e$ is homotopic to the identity map $t \to t$.
   b) the map $t \to e \times t$ is homotopic to the identity map $t \to t$.

(ii) For each $t \in T$, there exists $I(t) \in T$ depending continuously on T such that
   c) the map $t \to I(t)$ is homotopic to the constant map $t \to e$.
   d) the map $t \to I(t) \times t$ is homotopic to the constant map $t \to e$.

(iii) The two maps $(t_1, t_2, t_3) \to (t_1 \times t_2) \times t_3$ and $(t_1, t_2, t_3) \to t_1 \times (t_2 \times t_3)$ are homotopic to each other.

   We say that e is a homotopy unit of T, $I(t)$ is a homotopy inverse of t, and η is homotopy-associative. If, in addition to (i), (ii) and (iii) above, we also have

(iv) The map $\eta': T \times T \to T$ defined by $\eta(t_1, t_2) = t_2 \times t_1$ is homotopic to the map η, we say that T is an *abelian* group-like space.

Note: We take e to be the basepoint of T. Then all the homotopies in the definition must be restricted to be basepoint preserving.

If T is a group-like space, then (T^X) can be given a group structure as follows.

If $\{f\}, \{g\} \in (T^X)$, define $\{f\} \cdot \{g\} = \{f \cdot g\}$ where $f \cdot g$ is given by
$$f \cdot g(x) = f(x) \times g(x).$$

Note that the idempotence of e insures that $f \cdot g$ is basepoint preserving. We define the unit element to be the homotopy class of the map

$$E : X \to T$$

given by $E(x) = e$ for all $x \in X$. If $\{f\} \in (T^X)$, define $\tilde{f} : X \to T$ by $\tilde{f}(x) = I(f(x))$ Then one can see easily that $\{f\} \cdot \{\tilde{f}\} = \{\tilde{f}\} \cdot \{f\} = \{E\}$. The associativity of the multiplication of homotopy classes follows from Definition 1, (iii). Finally, if T is an abelian group-like space, (T^X) is easily seen to be an abelian group.

According to a construction due to Eilenberg and MacLane (see Hu—*Homotopy Theory*, pp. 168–9, 198–204), there exists, for an arbitrary abelian group G, an abelian group-like space T_G such that

$$\pi_1(T_G) \approx G, \quad \pi_n(T_G) \approx 0 \qquad \text{for} \qquad n \neq 1.$$

Consider then the T_G-cohomology theory. If we set $H^n(X, Y) = T_G^{-n+1}(X,Y)$. then, as is easily seen, the dimension axiom is satisfied; in this special case, our general construction leads to normal cohomology theory with coefficients G.

Appendix to Part A

The purpose of this appendix is to point out that, without restricting T in any way, a group structure can be given to $(T^{S^n(X/Y)})$ for all $n \geq 1$. It even turns out that for $n \geq 2$, the group is abelian.

We shall give a rough indication of how this group structure is defined. The reader may consult Bourgin—*Modern Algebraic Topology*, pp. 414–421, for the details. The existence of a group structure in $(T^{S^n}) = \pi_n(T)$ can be deduced from the existence of a map $S^n \xrightarrow{\mu} S_1^n \vee S_2^n$ (which pinches the equator to a point) with certain properties. The fact that $\pi_n(T)$ is abelian for $n \geq 2$ follows from the fact that the two halves S_1^n, S_2^n may be interchanged in a suitable manner. But the map μ naturally induces a map $S^n \wedge W$ $\xrightarrow{\mu'} (S_1^n \wedge W) \vee (S_2^n \wedge W)$ and it turns out that the properties of μ needed to give a group structure (abelian if $n \geq 2$) to (T^{S^n}) are also possessed by μ'.

The reader can now try to decide for himself whether the induced maps in T-cohomology and the coboundary map, both defined in Part A, are group homomorphisms.

Finally, one may ask whether the "natural" group structure outlined here agrees with the group structure defined in Part A in the case where T is an abelian grouplike space. The answer is that they do agree (cf. Bourgin, loc. cit.).

In Part B, we shall introduce a generalized cohomology theory whose test space T can be shown to be an abelian grouplike space. By virtue of the preceding remark, the group structure of the generalized cohomology groups to be introduced can be thought of as being derived from the grouplike structure of the test space. Thus, the remarks made in this appendix are not essential to the reading of the remainder of these notes.

Part B: K-Theory

We begin by describing certain algebraic operations on bundles. We derive from these operations a (commutative) ring $K(X)$. We then show how $K(X)$ relates to the theory developed in Part A.

Whitney Sum of Bundles

1. For $\alpha = 1, 2$, let γ_α be a $U(m_\alpha)$-bundle structure on a space B_α. Let the coordinate neighborhoods be denoted by $\{U_i^{(1)}\}$, $\{U_k^{(2)}\}$ respectively. Also, let $\{U_{b_1}^{(1)}(i,j)\}$, $\{U_{b_2}^{(2)}(k,l)\}$ denote the respective coordinate transformations. Now, the collection $\{U_k^{(1)} \times U_k^{(2)}\}$ covers $B_1 \times B_2$. For $(b_1, b_2) \in (U_i^{(1)} \times U_k^{(2)}) \cap (U_j^{(1)} \times U_l^{(2)})$, we define

$$U_{(b_1, b_2)}(i, k; j, l) = U_{b_1}(i, j) \oplus U_{b_2}(k, l).$$

Here, $\oplus$ denotes the direct sum of matrices. The group $U(m_1) \oplus U(m_2)$ is regarded as embedded in $U(m_1 + m_2)$ via the map which takes $(u, v) \in U(m_1) \oplus U(m_2)$ into the $(m_1 + m_2) \times (m_1 + m_1)$ matrix

$$\begin{bmatrix} u & 0 \\ 0 & v \end{bmatrix}$$

Using the functions $U_{(b_1, b_2)}(i, k; j, l)$ as coordinate transformations, we clearly get a $U(m_1 + m_2)$-bundle structure on $B_1 \times B_2$; we call this bundle structure the *exterior sum* of γ_1 and γ_2 and denote it by $\gamma_1 \circledast \gamma_2$.

If $B_1 = B_2 = B$, then we have the diagonal map $\delta : B \to B \times B$ given by $x \to (x, x)$. Using the notation introduced in Chapter IV, we have the induced bundle structure $\delta^\dagger (\gamma_1 \circledast \gamma_2)$ on the space B. We call this bundle structure the *Whitney sum* of γ_1 and γ_2 and we write

$$\gamma_1 \oplus \gamma_2 = \delta^\dagger (\gamma_1 \circledast \gamma_2).$$

2. Another way of looking at the Whitney sum of bundles (over the same base) is the following:

Let $\xi_\alpha = (E_\alpha, B, F_\alpha, U(m_\alpha), p_\alpha)$ $(\alpha = 1, 2)$ be a complex vector bundle (i.e. a bundle whose fiber F_α is an m_α-dimensional complex vector space) with base B, total space E_α, projection p_α. Let E be the subset $\{(e_1, e_2) \in E_1 \times E_2 \mid p_1(e_1) = p_2(e_2)\}$ of the space $E_1 \times E_2$. Define a projection map

$$p : E \to B$$

by $p(e_1, e_2) = p_1(e_1) = p_2(e_2)$. The fiber is homeomorphic to $F_1 \times F_2$. Since $U(m_1 + m_2)$ acts on $F_1 \times F_2$, we can construct a bundle $\xi = (E, B, F_1 \times F_2, U(m_1 + m_2), p)$ and we call ξ the Whitney sum of ξ_1 and ξ_2.

3. Still another way of viewing the Whitney sum is the following: Let γ_1, γ_2 be bundle structures on B_1, B_2 with groups $U(m_1)$, $U(m_2)$ respectively. By the Universal Classification Theorem, there exist maps

$$\phi_i : B_i \to G_{m_i, \infty} \qquad (i = 1, 2)$$

which induce the bundles γ_i. On the other hand there exists a map N

$$N : G_{m_1, \infty} \times G_{m_2, \infty} \to G_{m_1 + m_2, \infty},$$

defined by $N(\pi_1, \pi_2) = \pi_1 \oplus \pi_2$ where $\pi_i \in G_{m_i, \infty}$ $(i = 1, 2)$. Therefore we have the following diagram:

$$B_1 \times B_2 \xrightarrow{\phi_1 \times \phi_2} G_{m_1, \infty} \times G_{m_2, \infty} \xrightarrow{N} G_{m_1 + m_2, \infty}.$$

The composite map $N \circ (\phi_1 \times \phi_2)$ induces a bundle structure on $B_1 \times B_2$. One can convince oneself that this is the exterior sum $\gamma_1 \oplus\!\!\!\!\# \,\gamma_2$ of γ_1 and γ_2. Again, if $B_1 = B_2 = B$, then we have the composite map

$$N \circ (\phi_1 \times \phi_2) \circ \delta : B \to G_{m_1 + m_2, \infty}$$

and this map induces the Whitney sum of γ_1 and γ_2 on B.

Tensor Product (or Kronecker Product) of Bundles

We given only one version of this construction, corresponding to 3. above. Let γ_i, B_i, ϕ_i be as in 3. The natural bilinear map

$$h : U(m_1) \times U(m_2) \to U(m_1 m_2)$$

given by $(u, v) \to u \otimes v$ induces a map

$$h' : G_{m_1, \infty} \times G_{m_2, \infty} \to G_{m_1 m_2, \infty}$$

and hence we get the diagram

$$B_1 \times B_2 \xrightarrow{\phi_1 \times \phi_2} G_{m_1,\infty} \times G_{m_2,\infty} \xrightarrow{h'} G_{m_1 m_2,\infty} \, .$$

The composite map $h' \circ (\phi_1 \times \phi_2)$ induces a bundle structure on $B_1 \times B_2$. We call this bundle structure the *exterior tensor product* of γ_1 and γ_2 and denote it by $\gamma_1 \circledast \gamma_2$. As before, if $B_1 = B_2 = B$, we can apply the diagonal map δ and get

$$\delta^\dagger (\gamma_1 \textcircled{\#} \gamma_2) = \gamma_1 \otimes \gamma_2 \, .$$

Then $\gamma_1 \otimes \gamma_2$ is called the *tensor product* of γ_1 and γ_2.

Remark: The following statements are easily proved:

(a) $\gamma_1 \oplus \gamma_2 \cong \gamma_2 \oplus \gamma_1$,

(b) $\gamma_1 \oplus (\gamma_2 \oplus \gamma_3) \cong (\gamma_1 \oplus \gamma_2) \oplus \gamma_3$,

(c) $\gamma_1 \otimes \gamma_2 \cong \gamma_2 \otimes \gamma_1$,

(d) $\gamma_1 \otimes (\gamma_2 \otimes \gamma_3) \cong (\gamma_1 \otimes \gamma_2) \otimes \gamma_3$,

(e) $\gamma_1 \otimes (\gamma_2 \oplus \gamma_3) \cong (\gamma_1 \otimes \gamma_2) \oplus (\gamma_1 \otimes \gamma_3)$,

(f) if $f : \hat{B} \to B$, then $f^\dagger (\gamma_1 \oplus \gamma_2) \cong f^\dagger(\gamma_1) \oplus f^\dagger(\gamma_2)$.

(g) if $f : \hat{B} \to B$, then $f^\dagger (\gamma_1 \otimes \gamma_2) \cong f^\dagger (\gamma_1) \otimes f^\dagger(\gamma_2)$.

Lemma (1): Given a principal $U(n)$-bundle ξ over a base X, there exists a principal $U(n')$-bundle $\xi^\perp$ over X (where n' is some suitable integer) such that $\xi \oplus \xi^\perp$ is trivial.

Proof: The lemma is proved first for the case $\xi = \alpha_{n,N} = (V_{n,N}, G_{n,N}, U(n), U(n), p_{n,N})$. Recall that the Stiefel manifold $V_{n,N}$ consists of all orthonormal n-frames at the origin in N-space. Equivalently, we may view V as the set of all pairs $(\pi, v_n) \in G_{n,N}$ and where v_n is an orthonormal basis for π. The projection $p_{n,N}$ is therefore given by

$$p_{n,N} ((\pi, v_n)) = \pi .$$

We define a set $E_{n,N}$ as follows: $E_{n,N} = \{(\pi, v_{N-n}^\perp) \mid \pi \in G_{n,N}, \, v_{N-n}^\perp \text{ is an orthonormal } (N-n)\text{-frame forming an orthonormal basis of } \pi^\perp\}$. We define a projection map

$$p'_{n,N} : E_{n,N} \to G_{n,N}$$

by setting

$$p'_{n,N} ((\pi, v_{N-n}^\perp)) = \pi .$$

We then get a principal bundle $\alpha_{n,N}^\perp = (E_{n,N}, G_{n,N}, U(N-n), U(N-n), p'_{n,N})$. It is clear that $\alpha_{n,N} \oplus \alpha_{n,N}^\perp$ is equivalent to the product bundle $G_{n,N} \times U(N)$, i.e. $\alpha_{n,N} \otimes \alpha_{n,N}^\perp$ is trivial.

To prove the lemma for a general ξ, we choose a "classifying" map for ξ,

$$\phi : X \to G_{n,N},$$

where N is a sufficiently large integer (depending on the dimension of X). Thus,

$$\phi^\dagger(\alpha_{n,N}) = \xi.$$

We define $\xi^\perp$ by setting

$$\xi^\perp = \phi^\dagger(\alpha_{n,N}^\perp).$$

Then, $\xi \otimes \xi^\perp = \phi^\dagger(\alpha_{n,N}) \otimes \phi^\dagger(\alpha_{n,N}^\perp) \cong \phi^\dagger(\alpha_{n,N} \otimes \alpha_{n,N}^\perp)$ by the preceding remark. The lemma now follows easily.

Definition (1): Let ξ_1 and ξ_2 be two principal unitary bundles on a base X. Then ξ_1 and ξ_2 are s-equivalent if there exist trivial bundles τ_1 and τ_2 such that

$$\xi_1 \oplus \tau_1 \cong \xi_2 \oplus \tau_2.$$

It is easy to check that s-equivalence is actually an equivalence relation. We denote it by $\overset{s}{\sim}$ and we denote the s-equivalence class containing the bundle α by $\{\alpha\}$. For the set of all s-equivalence classes, we write $K_0(X)$. Notice that (ordinary) equivalence of bundles implies s-equivalence but s-equivalence does not imply equivalence. E.g., the tangent bundle of S^{2n} is s-equivalent to a trivial bundle but not equivalent to a trivial bundle.

Lemma (2): The set $K_0(X)$ of all s-equivalence classes of principal unitary bundles on X forms an abelian group under the operation induced by the Whitney sum of bundles.

Proof: Let $\{\xi_1\}$ and $\{\xi_2\}$ be any two elements in $K_0(X)$; ξ_1 and ξ_2 are then principal unitary bundles representing the classes $\{\xi_1\}$ and $\{\xi_2\}$. We define

$$\{\xi_1\} \oplus \{\xi_2\} = \{\xi_1 \oplus \xi_2\}.$$

It is easy to check that this operation is well defined. Moreover it is associative and commutative by the remark preceding Lemma 1. The identity of the group is the class $\{\tau\}$ of all trivial bundles τ; this is a well defined object since all trivial bundles are s-equivalent. Moreover,

$$\{\xi\} \oplus \{\tau\} = \{\xi\} = \{\tau\} \oplus \{\xi\}.$$

Let $\{\xi\} \in K_0(X)$, ξ a representation of $\{\xi\}$. Let $\xi^\perp$ be the bundle constructed in the previous lemma, i.e. $\xi \oplus \xi^\perp \cong \tau$ where τ is a trivial bundle. Then

$$\{\xi\} \oplus \{\xi^\perp\} = \{\xi \oplus \xi^\perp\} = \{\tau\}.$$

Thus $\{\xi^\perp\}$ is the inverse element of $\{\xi\}$, and this completes the proof that $K_0(X)$ is an abelian group.

Note: We will see later that $K_0(X)$ can be made into a ring.

Atiyah-Hirzebruch-Grothendieck Functor

Let X be a finite dimensional cell complex, α a principal unitary bundle on X. Denote by (α) the bundle structure equivalence class containing α. We denote by $K_F(X)$ the free abelian group generated by all equivalence classes (α) of principal unitary bundles on X. Let further $K_F^+(X)$ be the subgroup of $K_F(X)$ generated by all elements of the form $(\alpha_1 \oplus \alpha_2) - (\alpha_1) - (\alpha_2)$. We set

$$K(X) = K_F(X)/K_F^+(X).$$

$K(X)$ is called the *Grothendieck Group* of X, or the *A-H-G Functor*. Indeed, $K(X)$ is a contravariant functor from the category of cell complexes and continuous maps to the category of abelian groups and homomorphisms. To see this, note that a map $f: X \to Y$ induces a map $f^\dagger$ from bundles over Y to bundles over X. As $f^\dagger$ carries equivalent bundles into equivalent bundles, we have an induced map, call it $f^\dagger$ again, from $K_F(Y)$ into $K_F(X)$. Now, by the remark preceding Lemma 1, we have

$$f^\dagger((\alpha_1 \oplus \alpha_2)) = f^\dagger((\alpha_1)) \oplus f^\dagger((\alpha_2)).$$

Hence, $f^\dagger$ also maps $K_F^+(Y)$ into $K_F^+(X)$ and thus induces a map, again called $f^\dagger$, from $K(Y)$ into $K(X)$. It is evident that the correspondence $X \to K(X)$, $f \to f^\dagger$ is functiorial.

Again using the above mentioned remark, we see that the tensor product of bundles induces naturally a (commutative) ring structure on $K(X)$. This ring also possesses a multiplicative unit, namely the class of the trivial bundle of dimension one, i.e. the trivial $U(1)$-bundle.

Notation: For a principal unitary bundle α over X, we write $[\alpha]$ for the class of α in $K(X)$. Recall that (α) denotes the equivalence class of α and $\{\alpha\}$ the s-equivalence class of α. We have already observed that $(\alpha) = (\beta) \Rightarrow \{\alpha\} = \{\beta\}$ but not conversely. We also clearly have $(\alpha) = (\beta) \Rightarrow [\alpha] = [\beta]$.

We define a ring homomorphism

$$\dim : K(X) \to Z$$

by setting

$$\dim (\Sigma n_i[\alpha_i]) = \Sigma n_i \cdot \dim \alpha_i.$$

Here, $\Sigma n_i[\alpha_i]$ is an arbitrary element of $K(X)$ so that the n_i are integers and all but a finite number of them are 0. Note carefully that if α_i is a $U(m_i)$-bundle, then by dim α_i is meant the integer m_i and not the dimension of the manifold $U(m_i)$. The integer m_i is also referred to sometimes as the *rank* of $U(m_i)$ and of the bundle α_i. The map dim is called the *dimension homomorphism*. We define

$$\tilde{K}(X) = \ker (\dim).$$

Thus, $\tilde{K}(X)$ is an ideal in $K(X)$. It is clear that $\tilde{K}(X)$, like $K(X)$, is a contravariant functor from the category of finite cell complexes and continuous maps into the category of abelian groups and homomorphisms.

We now try to establish a relationship between $\tilde{K}(X)$ and $K_0(X)$. We define a homomorphism of groups

$$h' : K_F(X) \to K_0(X)$$

by setting

$$h'((\alpha)) = \{\alpha\}$$

and then extending by linearity. Observe that if m is a positive integer, then

$$h'(m(\alpha)) = \{\alpha\} \oplus \{\alpha\} \oplus \cdots \oplus \{\alpha\} \quad (m \text{ factors})$$

while if m is a negative integer,

$$h'(m(\alpha)) = \{\alpha^\perp\} \oplus \{\alpha^\perp\} \oplus \cdots \oplus \{\alpha^\perp\} \quad (m \text{ factors}).$$

Notice also that

$$h'((\alpha_1 \oplus \alpha_2) - (\alpha_1) - (\alpha_2)) = \{\alpha_1 \oplus \alpha_2\} + \{\alpha_1^\perp\} \oplus \{\alpha_2^\perp\}$$
$$= \{\alpha_1 \oplus \alpha_1^\perp \oplus \alpha_2 \oplus \alpha_2^\perp\}$$
$$= \{\tau_1 \oplus \tau_2\}$$
$$= \{\tau\}$$

and $\{\tau\}$ is the identity element of $K_0(X)$. Hence, the subgroup $K_F^+(X)$ of $K_F(X)$ lies in the Kernel of h' and thus h' gives rise to a homomorphism

$$h : K(X) \to K_0(X)$$

which is such that

$$h([\alpha]) = \{\alpha\}, \quad h(-[\alpha]) = \{\alpha^\perp\}.$$

Now, the restriction of h to $\tilde{K}(X)$ is a homomorphism

$$h : \tilde{K}(X) \to K_0(X).$$

We then have the

Lemma (3): The map h is a (group) isomorphism.

Proof: We begin by defining a map

$$i : Z \to K(X)$$

as follows. Let τ_n be the trivial bundle of dimension n. If $m \geq 0$, set $i(m) = [\tau_m]$; if $m \leq 0$, set $i(m) = -[\tau_{-m}]$. The lemma will be proved if we can show that the sequence

$$0 \longrightarrow Z \longrightarrow K(X) \overset{h}{\longrightarrow} K_0(X) \longrightarrow 0$$

is exact. In fact, we shall show that the sequence splits. To do this, we define a homomorphism

$$j : K_0(X) \to K(X)$$

as follows. Let $\{\beta\} \in K_0(X)$ and let β be a representative of $\{\beta\}$. Let $n = \dim \beta$. We set $j(\{\beta\}) = [(\beta) - (\tau_n)]$. If β and β_1 are s-equivalent, there exist trivial bundles $\bar\tau$ and $\bar\tau_1$ such that $\beta + \bar\tau$ and $\beta_1 + \bar\tau_1$ are equivalent. Then, if $n_1 m_1 k_1 l$ are the dimensions of $\beta_1 \beta_1$, $\bar\tau_1 \bar\tau_1$ respectively, we have $\beta \oplus \bar\tau \oplus \tau_m \sim \beta_1 \oplus \bar\tau_1 \oplus \tau_m$, while $\bar\tau_1 \oplus \tau_m$ is clearly the same as the trivial bundle of dimension $n + m + k - m = n + k$, i.e., $\bar\tau \oplus \tau_n$. Thus $\gamma = \beta \oplus \bar\tau \oplus \tau_m \sim \beta_1 \oplus \bar\tau \oplus \tau_n$, and then clearly $[(\beta) - (\tau_n)] = [(\gamma) - (\bar\tau \oplus \tau_m \oplus \tau_n)] \sim [(\beta_1) - (\tau_m)]$. This shows that j is well-defined. Furthermore, the relations

$$\dim \circ i = \text{identity}, \quad h \circ j = \text{identity}$$

$$\dim \circ j = 0, \qquad h \circ i = 0$$

are obvious. Finally, if $[\alpha]$ is an arbitrary generator of $K(X)$ and $\dim \alpha = n$, we can write

$$[\alpha] = [(\alpha) - (\tau_n)] + [\tau_n] = j(\{\alpha\}) + i(n),$$

i.e. $K(X) = \text{im}(i) \otimes \text{im}(j)$. This proves the lemma.

Since $\tilde K(X)$ has a ring structure, $K_0(X)$ can be given a ring structure by using the (group) isomorphism h.

We come now to our main result.

Theorem (1): There exists a space BU such that there is a $1 - 1$ correspondence $K_0(X) \leftrightarrow (BU^X)$.

Corollary (1): There is a $1 - 1$ correspondence $\tilde K(X) \leftrightarrow (BU^X)$.

Proof: This follows immediately from Lemma 3.

Corollary (2): The is a $1 - 1$ correspondence $K(X) \leftrightarrow ((BU \times Z)^X)$ where Z is given the discrete topology.

Proof: $K(X) \cong \tilde{K}(X) \times Z$ and $((BU \times Z)^X) \leftrightarrow (BU^X) \times (Z^X) \leftrightarrow (BU^X) \times Z$. Then, Corollary 2 follows from Corollary 1.

Proof of Theorem 1: We define a sequence of spaces $E^{\infty}_{-n} (n = 1, 2, \ldots)$ as follows. Let E^{∞}_{-n} consist of all sequences of complex numbers $(\ldots, x_{-1}, x_0, x_1, \ldots)$, infinite in both directions, such that

(a) All but a finite number of the x_i are 0.
(b) All the x_i with $i \le -n$ are 0.

We shall regard the infinite Grassmannian $G_{n,\infty}$ as the set of n-planes in the space E^{∞}_{-n} (cf. Chapter III). We then have a sequence of natural inclusions

$$G_{1,\infty} \subseteq G_{2,\infty} \subseteq G_{3,\infty} \subseteq \cdots$$

defined as follows. Let $\pi_n \in G_{n,\infty}$. We have clearly

$$E^{\infty}_{-(n+1)} = E^{\infty}_{-n} \oplus \text{a one-dimensional space.}$$

Let $e_{-(n+1)}$ be a generator of this one-dimensional space and let

$$i_{n,n+1} : G_{n,\infty} \to G_{n+1,\infty}$$

be defined by

$$i_{n,n+1}(\pi_n) = \{\pi_n, e_{-(n+1)}\},$$

i.e. the plane generated by π_n and $e_{-(n+1)}$. We denote the composite inclusion of $G_{n,\infty}$ into $G_{n+k,\infty}$ by $i_{n,n+k}$. We define BU as the union of all the spaces $G_{n,\infty}(n = 1, 2, \ldots)$ taken in the direct limit topology; we write

$$BU = \lim_{n \to \infty} G_{n,\infty}.$$

Recall that each $G_{n,\infty}$ it itself a direct limit space. Thus,

$$G_{n,\infty} = \lim_{m \to \infty} G_{n,m}.$$

Hence, by extracting a "diagonal sequence", we may write

$$BU = \lim_{n \to \infty} G_{n,2n},$$

i.e. as a direct limit of compact spaces.

It follows immediately from this that any compact subset of BU is contained in some $G_{n,2n}$ (and hence in $G_{n,\infty}$). Note also that BU is itself *not* compact.

We now define a map $K_0(X) \to (BU^X)$ as follows: Let $\{\alpha\} \in K_0(X)$, α a representative of $\{\alpha\}$, and let dim $\alpha = k$. (There is then a classifying map

$$\phi_k : X \to G_{k,\infty}$$

which induces α. If $i_k : G_{k,\infty} \to BU$ is the inclusion map, then we define

$$\Phi : X \to BU$$

by $\Phi = i_k \circ \phi_k$. If $\beta \overset{s}{\sim} \alpha$ and dim $\beta = l$, choose a classifying map

$$\psi_l : X \to G_{l,\infty}$$

inducing β. We then have a map

$$\Psi : X \to BU$$

given by $\Psi = i_l \circ \psi_l$. We claim that Φ and Ψ are homotopic. Indeed, since $\alpha \overset{s}{\sim} \beta$, there exist trivial bundles τ_1, τ_2 such that

$$\alpha \oplus \tau_1 \cong \beta \oplus \tau_2.$$

Let dim $(\alpha \otimes \tau_1) = $ dim $(\beta \otimes \tau_2) = r$. Then $r \geq k, l$ and we have maps

$$\phi_r, \psi_r : X \to G_{r,\infty}$$

given by $\phi_r = i_{k,r} \circ \phi_k$, $\phi_r = i_{l,r} \circ \psi_l$. It is easy to see that

$$i_{k,r}^\dagger(\alpha_r) \cong \alpha_k \oplus \tau_1, \quad i_{l,r}^\dagger(\alpha_r) \cong \alpha_l \oplus \tau_2$$

where, in general, α_n is the standard principal $U(n)$-bundle over $G_{n,\infty}$ (see Chapter VI, Definition 5). But then

$$\phi_r^\dagger(\alpha_r) \cong \alpha \oplus \tau_1, \quad \psi_r^\dagger(\alpha_r) \cong \beta \oplus \tau_2$$

and hence

$$\phi_r^\dagger(\alpha_r) \cong \psi_r^\dagger(\alpha_r).$$

By Chapter VI, Theorem 4, we obtain

$$\phi_r \simeq \psi_r$$

and since $\Phi = i_r \circ \phi_r$, $\Psi = i_r \circ \psi_r$, it follows that

$$\Phi \simeq \Psi,$$

as claimed. Thus, the correspondence

$$\{\alpha\} \to [\Phi],$$

where $[\Phi]$ is the homotopy class of Φ, is well-defined. The fact that this correspondence is $1 - 1$ follows immediately from the converse of the theorem just referred to. We prove finally that the correspondence is onto. Pick any $\Phi : X \to BU$. As X is a finite cell complex, X is compact and so also is $\Phi(X)$. From a remark made above, this means that $\Phi(X) \subseteq G_{n,\infty}$ for sufficiently large n. Thus, Φ can be factored in the form

$$\Phi = i_n \circ \phi_n$$

where ϕ_n is a map from X into $G_{n,\infty}$. We set

$$\alpha = \phi_n^\dagger(\alpha_n).$$

The reader can check that α is uniquely determined by Φ up to s-equivalence. Even more, α is uniquely determined by $[\Phi]$ up to s-equivalence. This can be proved by using the compactness of $X \times I$. Thus, the correspondence $\{\alpha\} \to [\Phi]$ is indeed invertible and we are finished.

Remark (1): It can be shown that BU is an abelian grouplike space. If (BU^X) is endowed with its natural group structure (see Part A and the appendix to Part A), it turns out that $\tilde{K}(X)$ and (BU^X) are group isomorphic.

Remark (2): Let $U = \lim_{n \to \infty} U(n)$ be the direct limit of the unitary groups. U is called the infinite unitary group. Then BU can be regarded as the universal classifying space for U; hence the notation BU.

Definition (2): Let (X, Y) be a cellular pair, i.e. Y is a subcomplex of the finite cell complex X. If $Y = \phi$ and if X has no a priori basepoint, we replace X by the disjoint union $X \cup \{p\}$ of X with a point p which becomes the basepoint. For each $n \geq 0$, we set

$$K^{-n}(X, Y) = \tilde{K}(S^n(X/Y)).$$

By the results of Part A, the groups $K^{-n}(X, Y)$ form a generalized cohomology theory, the so-called K-theory. In the next chapter, we examine the particular features of this cohomology theory in more detail.

CHAPTER IX

Continuation of K-Theory

In this chapter, we shall examine in more detail the structure of the groups $K^{-n}(X, Y)$ defined at the end of the last chapter. As a reference for the material in this chapter, we suggest Atiyah and Hirzebruch—*Vector Bundles and Homogeneous Spaces*, Proceedings of Symposia in Pure Mathematics, Vol. 3, Differential Geometry, pp. 7–38, American Mathematical Society, 1961.

1. Product Theory

First of all, let us consider an arbitrary generalized cohomology theory, based on some grouplike space T. In Chapter 8, we used the notation $T^{-n}(X, Y)$ for $(T^{S^n(X/Y)})$. We look at the exact sequence of the pair $(X \times Y, X \vee Y)$. Using the facts that $T^{-n}(X, Y) = T^{-n}(X/Y, *)$ (where $*$ means the basepoint) and $X \times Y/X \vee Y = X \wedge Y$, we arrive at $(E) \cdots \xrightarrow{\delta} T^{-n}(Y \wedge Y) \xrightarrow{\pi^*} T^{-n}(X \times Y) \xrightarrow{i^*} T^{-n}(X \vee Y) \xrightarrow{\delta} \cdots$ Here, $i : X \vee Y \to X \times Y$ and $\pi : X \times Y \to X \wedge Y$ are the natural maps and i^*, π^* are the induced maps.

Lemma (1): The exact sequence (E) breaks up into short split exact sequences

$$0 \longrightarrow T^{-n}(X \wedge Y) \xrightarrow{\pi^*} T^{-n}(X \times Y) \xrightarrow{i^*} T^{-n}(X \vee Y) \longrightarrow 0.$$

Proof: First, we make some preliminary remarks. If (S, s_0) is any based space, let ΩS be the space of loops on S which begin and end at s_0. Inductively, we set $\Omega^n S = \Omega(\Omega^{n-1} S)$. We observe two properties of the operation Ω^n: (a) $\Omega^n S$ is grouplike for $n > 0$ regardless of whether or not S is grouplike, (b) there is a natural $1 - 1$ correspondence between $(S^{S^n W})$ and $((\Omega^n S)^W)$ (W any space) which can be described as follows. Suppose $n = 1$, the general case following inductively. A map $f : S^1 \wedge W \to S$ can be viewed simply as a map $f : I \times W \to S$ such that $f(0 \times W) = s_0, f(1 \times W) = s_0, f(I \times w_0) = s_0$. A map $f' : W \to \Omega S$ is defined by letting $f'(w)$ be the loop, which evaluated at time t, is just $f(t, w)$; $f'(w)(t) = f(t, w)$. The restrictions on f guarantee that f' is a basepoint preserving map from W to ΩS. The correspondence $[f] \to [f']$ (where $[\ ]$ means homotopy class) is the desired correspondence.

Returning to the proof of the lemma, we begin by showing that the map $((\Omega^n T)^{X \times Y}) \xrightarrow{i^*} ((\Omega^n T)^{X \vee Y})$ is onto. So let $[f] \in ((\Omega^n T)^{X \vee Y})$, $f : X \vee Y \to \Omega^n T$ a representative of $[f]$. Let $f_1 = f | X \times y_0$, $f_2 = f | x_0 \times Y$. Define a map $F : X \times Y \to \Omega^n T$ by setting $F(x, y) = f_1(x, y_0) \cdot f_2(y, x_0)$, the product arising from the grouplike structure of $\Omega^n T$. Clearly, F extends f up to homotopy, i.e. $i^*([F]) = [f]$. It is even easier to see that the map $((\Omega^n T)^{X \wedge Y}) \xrightarrow{\pi^*} ((\Omega^n T)^{X \times Y})$ is $1 - 1$. Hence, the short sequence described in the lemma is indeed exact. To see that the sequence splits, we observe first that $T^{-n}(X \vee Y) \cong T^{-n}(X) \oplus T^{-n}(Y)$. (This assertion is clear if we appeal to the very definition of T^{-n}.) Now, the natural projections $\pi_1 : X \times Y \to X$, $\pi_2 : X \times X \to Y$ induce maps $\pi_1^* : T^{-n}(X) \to T^{-n}(X \times Y)$, $\pi_2^* : T^{-n}(Y) \to T^{-n}(X \times Y)$ and hence $\pi_1^* \oplus \pi_2^* : T^{-n}(X) \oplus T^{-n}(Y) \to T^{-n}(X \times Y)$ is defined. Identifying $T^{-n}(X \vee Y)$ with $T^{-n}(X) \oplus T^{-n}(Y)$, we see then that $\pi_1^* \oplus \pi_2^*$ provides the desired splitting.

Let us now return to K-Theory. The (external) tensor product of bundles induces naturally a multiplication

$$K(X) \oplus K(Y) \xrightarrow{\mu} K(X \times Y).$$

Recall that $\tilde{K}(X) = Ker \, (\dim)$, where $\dim : K(X) \to Z$ is the homomorphism defined in Chapter 8. dim may be thought of as the homomorphism induced by the inclusion map $x_0 \to X$ (where x_0 is the basepoint of X). Now, if $a \in \tilde{K}(X)$, $b \in \tilde{K}(Y)$, then, as can easily be seen,

$$\mu(a, b) \in Ker \, [\tilde{K}(X \times Y) \to \tilde{K}(X \vee Y)].$$

By Lemma 1, it follows that $\mu(a, b) \in \tilde{K}(X \wedge Y)$. Thus, μ induces a multiplication, call it $\tilde{\mu}$

$$\tilde{K}(X) \oplus \tilde{K}(Y) \xrightarrow{\tilde{\mu}} \tilde{K}(X \wedge Y).$$

For $m, n \geq 0$, it is now possible to define a multiplication

$$K^{-m}(X, X_0) \oplus K^{-n}(Y, Y_0) \to K^{-(m+n)}(X \times Y, (X_0 \times Y) \cup (X \times Y_0)).$$

This is done as follows:

$$K^{-m}(X, X_0) = \tilde{K}(S^m(X/X_0)),$$

$$K^{-n}(Y, Y_0) = \tilde{K}(S^n(Y/Y_0)),$$

$$K^{-(m+n)}(X \times Y, (X_0 \times Y) \cup (X \times Y_0)) = \tilde{K}(S^{m+n}(X \times Y/X_0 \times Y \cup X \times Y_0)).$$

But
$$X \times Y/(X_0 \times Y) \cup (X \times Y_0) = X/X_0 \wedge Y/Y_0$$
and
$$S_m (X/X_0) \wedge S^n (Y/Y_0) = S^{m+n} (X/X_0 \wedge Y/Y_0).$$

Thus, we have only to a multiplication
$$\tilde{K}(S^m (X/X_0)) \oplus \tilde{K}(S^n (Y/Y_0)) \to \tilde{K}(S^m (X/X_0) \wedge S^n (Y/Y_0)).$$

And such a multiplication, namely $\tilde{\mu}$, has just been defined. For simplicity, we shall denote this multiplication by juxtaposition. Using the natural homeomorphism between $X \times Y$ and $Y \times X$, we get a product
$$K^{-n} (Y, Y_0) \oplus K^{-m} (X, X_0) \to K^{-(m+n)} (X \times Y, (X_0 \times Y) \cup (X \times Y_0)).$$

Lemma (2): If $a \in K^{-m} (X, X_0)$, $b \in K^{-n} (Y, Y_0)$, then $ab = (-1)^{mn} ba$.

Proof: We have the homeomorphisms $S^m \wedge S^n \leftrightarrow S^{m+n}$, $S^n \wedge S^m \leftrightarrow S^{m+n}$ and the composition
$$S^{m+n} \to S^n \wedge S^m \to S^m \wedge S^n \to S^{m+n}$$
is a map of degree $(-1)^{mn}$. The lemma follows easily from this (see Atiyah-Hirzebruch, loc. cit.).

Let now (X, X_0) be a cellular pair with basepoint $x_0 \in X_0$. We have diagonal maps
$$X \xrightarrow{d} X \times X, \quad X_0 \xrightarrow{d} (x_0 \times X) \cup (X \times X_0).$$

Passing to the quotient, we obtain a map
$$X/X_0 \xrightarrow{d} (X/x_0) \wedge (X/X_0).$$

By considering the composition
$$K^{-m}(X) \oplus K^{-n} (X, X_0) \longrightarrow K^{-(m+n)} (X \wedge (X/X_0)) \xrightarrow{d^*} K^{-(n+m)} (X/X_0)$$
we see that $\sum_{n \geq 0} K^{-n} (X, X_0)$ is a $\sum_{m \geq 0} K^{-m}(X)$-module. Summing up, we have the following theorem.

Theorem (1): $\sum_{m \geq 0} K^{-m}(X)$ is a graded anticommutative ring. There is a product mapping of degree 0
$$\left(\sum_{m \geq 0} K^{-m}(X)\right) \oplus \left(\sum_{n \geq 0} K^{-n} (X, X_0)\right) \to \sum_{p \geq 0} K^{-p} (X, X_0)$$
turning $\sum_{n \geq 0} K^{-n} (X, X_0)$ into a graded $\sum_{m \geq 0} K^{-m}(X)$-module.

Addendum: The multiplications defined above have evident functorial properties. As an example, let $f: (X, X_0) \to (X', X_0')$, $g: (Y, Y_0) \to (Y', Y_0')$ be mappings of pairs. Then the diagram

$$K^{-m}(X', X_0') \oplus K^{-n}(Y', Y_0') \longrightarrow K^{-(m+n)}(X' \times Y', (X_0' \times Y') \cup (X' \times Y_0'))$$

$$\downarrow f^* \oplus g^* \qquad\qquad\qquad\qquad\qquad \downarrow (f \times g)^*$$

$$K^{-m}(X, X_0) \oplus K^{-n}(Y, Y_0) \longrightarrow K^{-(m+n)}(X \times Y, (X_0 \times Y) \cup (X \times Y_0))$$

is easily seen to be commutative. Notice also that a map $f: X \to Y$ induces a homomorphism

$$f^*: \sum_{m \geq 0} K^{-m}(Y) \to \sum_{m \geq 0} K^{-m}(X)$$

which is a ring homomorphism.

Remark: Observe that in the above discussion we have used the particular properties of K-Theory only once, namely in deducing the existence of a map $\mu: K(X) \oplus K(Y) \to K(X \times Y)$. The rest of the development merely made use of the fact that K-Theory is a generalized cohomology theory. Thus, a product theory as above can be established for any T-cohomology theory which admits a map

$$\mu: T^0(X) \oplus T^0(Y) \to T^0(X \times Y).$$

2. The Bott Theorem and its Consequences

The special properties of a generalized cohomology theory depend entirely on the structure of the test space T of the cohomology theory. The homotopy structure of the space BU, which is the test space in K-Theory, has been completely determined by Bott. We present here Bott's results (in a formulation due to Bott and Atiyah) without proof. These results are then used to deduce some of the main results in K-Theory. For a proof of Bott's Theorem, see Milnor-*Morse Theory* and J. Schwartz—*Nonlinear Functional Analysis*, Gordon and Breach 1968, as well as Bott's original papers.

Theorem (2) (Bott-Atiyah-Hirzebruch): $\tilde{K}(S^1) = 0$, $\tilde{K}(S^2) = \mathbf{Z}$. The generator of $\tilde{K}(S^2)$ can be described as follows: Let S^2 be represented as $P_1^{\mathcal{C}}$ and let η be the canonical line bundle (the Hopf bundle) over $P_1^{\mathcal{C}}$, i.e. over each point $[z_1, z_2] \in P_1^{\mathcal{C}}$ ($[z_1, z_2]$ means projective class of the pair (z_1, z_2)), the fiber is the complex line consisting of all pairs $(\lambda z_1, \lambda z_2)$, $\lambda \in C$. Let 1 denote the trivial 1-dimensional bundle over S^2 and set $\mu = \eta - 1$. Then

$g = [\mu] \in \tilde{K}(S^2)$ (because dim $g = 0$) and g is a free generator of $\tilde{K}(S^2)$. Finally, let $a \in K^{-m}(X, X_0)$. Then the map

$$\beta : K^{-m}(X, X_0) \to K^{-(m+2)}(X, X_0),$$

given by $\beta(a) = ag$, is an isomorphism, the so-called Bott isomorphism.

Proof: The assertion concerning $\tilde{K}(S^2)$ made in Theorem 2 is elementary and may be proved as follows. Since S^2 may be covered by two coordinate discs P^+ and P^- intersecting in a circle C, and since any $U(n)$-bundle structure over P^+ or P^- is trivial, a $U(n)$-bundle structure over S^2 is determined by a coordinate change mapping h on C, which is a mapping $h : C \to U(n)$. Two such mappings h and h' determine equivalent bundle structures if and only if there exists maps $g_+ : P^+ \to U(n)$ and $g_- : P^+ \to U(n)$ such that $g_+ h g^{-1} = h'$. (Cf. the Remark preceding Definition 2 of Chapter 4.) It is trivial to verify that this is the case if and only if h and h' are homotopic. In this way, we established a correspondence between $U(n)$-bundle structures on S^2, and homotopy classes in $\pi_1(U(n))$. Since, as is developed in more detail below, any map $h : C \to U(n)$ can be deformed into a map $h : C \to U(1) \subseteq U(n)$, it follows that any $U(n)$-bundle structure over S^2 is equivalent to the direct sum of a $U(1)$-bundle structure and a trivial bundle. Thus the structure of $\tilde{K}(S^2)$ is determined by the $U(1)$ bundles which it contains. If a $U(1)$-bundle μ corresponds in the above sense to a given map $h : C \to U(1)$, then $\mu \otimes \mu$ corresponds to $h^2 : C \to U(1)$. Since it is easy to see that the Hopf bundle η corresponds to a generator h of the group $\pi_1(U(1))$, it follows that every $U(n)$-bundle structure on S^2 is s-equivalent either to a Kronecker power of η or to the inverse of one of these bundles. From this, verification of the asserted structure of $\tilde{K}(S^2)$ is easy.

We sketch the proof of the remaining assertion of Theorem 2. Let X be any finite-dimensional complex. Then, according to Theorem 1 of the preceding section, and its proof, the elements of $\tilde{K}(X)$ are in 1–1 correspondence with the homotopy classes of maps $\phi : X \to G_{n,2n}$ for any sufficiently large n. Examination of the details of the proof of the Bott periodicity theorem (Cf. J. Schwartz, Nonlinear Functional Analysis, Lemma 7.22, Corollaries 7.23, 7.24, Lemma 7.27, and Corollary 7.28) shows that there exists an imbedding of $G_{n,2n}$ into the loop space $\Omega(U(2n))$ which induces an isomorphism of $(G_{n,2n}^X) \to (\Omega(U(2n))^X)$ for low-dimensional spaces X. This imbedding may be described as follows. If p is an n-plane in E^{2n}, let E_p be the orthogonal projection onto p. Then $c_p(t) = \exp(2\pi i (I - E_p) t)$, $0 \leq t \leq \frac{1}{2}$; $c_p(t) = \exp(2\pi i t) I$, $\frac{1}{2} \leq t \leq 1$, defines a closed loop in $U(2n)$, whose end-points are both the identity map; $p \to c_p(t)$ is the desired imbedding.

For n large, $V_{2n,4n} = U(4n)/U(2n)$ is simply connected in all low dimensions, and is a bundle with fiber $U(2n)$ over $G_{2n,4n} = U(4n)/U(2n) \times U(2n)$. Thus, any map $\phi: Y \to U(2n)$ is homotopic in $V_{2n,4n}$ to a constant, and the resultant homotopy ϕ_S, projected by the natural map $V_{2n,4n} \to G_{2n,4n}$, defines an element of $((\Omega(G_{2n,4n}))^Y)$. The map $(U(2n)^Y) \to ((\Omega(G_{2n,4n}))^Y)$ defined in this way is an isomorphism of homotopy classes for low dimensional Y. (See below for a more familiar algebraic representation of this isomorphism.) Composing our two isomorphisms, and using the trivial identity $(\Omega(Z_1)^{Z_2}) \cong (Z_1^{S^1 \wedge Z_2})$, we obtain an explicit isomorphism $(G_{n,2n}^X) \to (U(2n)^{S^1 \wedge X}) \to (G_{2n,4n}^{S^2 \wedge X})$ for any X of dimension low compared with n. This composite isomorphism is the Bott isomorphism β of Theorem 2.

Finally, Theorem 2 identifies the isomorphism β as the product operation $a \to ag$. We omit the proof of this identification, noting however that it is used only occasionally in what follows, and that it may be derived from the explicit form of β as given above. The reader interested in additional details is referred to the cited papers of Bott and Atiyah-Hirzebruch Q.E.D.

Corollary (1): $K^{-s}((p_1, p_2), p_2) \cong Z$ if s is even, $\cong 0$ if s is odd.

Remark: Corollary 1 shows that the homotopy groups $\pi_s(BU)$ are periodic of order 2. The usual Bott Periodicity Theorem asserts that the homotopy groups $\pi_s(U)$ of the infinite unitary group are periodic of order 2, with $\pi_s(U) \cong Z$ if s is odd, $\cong 0$ if s is even. Actually, this assertion is equivalent to Corollary 1 as we now show.

We shall prove 3 statements, which together will readily establish our claim.

(1) For given s and for k sufficiently large,

$$\pi_{s-1}(U(k)) \cong \pi_{s-1}(U(k+1)) \cong \cdots \cong \pi_{s-1}(U).$$

(2) For given s and for k sufficiently large,

$$\pi_s(G_{k,2k}) \cong \pi_{s-1}(U(k)).$$

(3) For given s and for k sufficiently large,

$$\pi_s(G_{k,2k}) \cong \pi_s(G_{k+1,2k+1}) \cong \cdots \cong \pi_s(BU).$$

Proof of (1): $U(k)$ is a bundle over $U(k+1)/U(k) = S^{2k+1}$ with fiber $U(k)$. By the exact homotopy sequence of a bundle (see Chapter 6), we obtain

$$\cdots \longrightarrow \pi_s(S^{2k+1}) \xrightarrow{\partial} \pi_{s-1}(U(k)) \longrightarrow \pi_{s-1}(U(k+1)) \longrightarrow \pi_{s-1}(S^{2k+1}) \longrightarrow \cdots$$

But for $2k + 1 > s$, $\pi_s(S^{2k+1}) = 0$ and we find

$$0 \to \pi_{s-1}(U(k)) \to \pi_{s-1}(U(k+1)) \to 0$$

to be exact. That is, $\pi_{s-1}(U(k)) \cong \pi_{s-1}(U(k+1))$; moreover, the isomorphism is induced by the inclusion map $U(k) \to U(k+1)$. Using the same kind of compactness argument that has been given before, we conclude easily that the inclusion $U(k) \to U$ also induces an isomorphism $\pi_{s-1}(U(k)) \cong \pi_{s-1}(U)$. Thus, (1) is proved.

Proof of (2): We know that $V_{k,2k}$ is a bundle over $G_{k,2k}$ with fiber $U(k)$. Again by the exact bundle sequence,

$$\cdots \longrightarrow \pi_s(V_{k,2k}) \longrightarrow \pi_s(G_{k,2k}) \overset{\partial}{\longrightarrow} \pi_{s-1}(U(k)) \longrightarrow \pi_{s-1}(V_{k,2k}) \longrightarrow \cdots$$

By Lemma 2' of Chapter 6, $\pi_s(V_{k,2k}) = 0$ for $2k + 1 > s$. The conclusion (2) follows.

Proof of (3): The inclusion maps $U(k) \to U(k+1)$, $U(2k) \to U(2k+1)$ give rise to maps

$$\phi : V_{k,2k} = U(2k)/U(k) \to U(2k+1)/U(k+1) = V_{k+1,2k+1}$$

$$\psi : G_{k,2k} = U(2k)/U(k) \times U(k) \to U(2k+1)/U(k+1) \times U(k) = G_{k+1,2k+1}.$$

Clearly, ϕ is a bundle map which covers ψ. Therefore we have the following commutative diagram:

$$\cdots \longrightarrow \pi_s(V_{k,2k}) \longrightarrow \pi_s(G_{k,2k}) \overset{\partial}{\longrightarrow} \pi_{s-1}(U(k)) \longrightarrow \pi_{s-1}(V_{k,2k}) \longrightarrow \cdots$$
$$\downarrow \qquad\qquad \downarrow{\scriptstyle\psi_*} \qquad\qquad \downarrow{\scriptstyle i_*} \qquad\qquad \downarrow$$
$$\cdots \longrightarrow \pi_s(V_{k+1,2k+1}) \longrightarrow \pi_s(G_{k+1,2k+1}) \overset{\partial}{\longrightarrow} \pi_{s-1}(U(k+1)) \longrightarrow \pi_{s-1}(V_{k+1,2k+1}) \longrightarrow \cdots$$

It follows from (1) and (2) that for $2k + 1 > s$, ∂ and i_* are isomorphisms. But then ψ_* is also an isomorphism. The fact that the inclusion $G_{k,2k} \to BU$ also induces an isomorphism $\pi_s(G_{k,2k}) \to \pi_s(BU)$ follows again by a conpactness argument.

Combining (1), (2) and (3), we see that $\pi_s(BU) \cong \pi_{s-1}(U)$. This establishes our original claim.

We now proceed to obtain some more information about the groups $K^{-n}(X, X_0)$ from the Bott Theorem.

Lemma (3): Let $f: (X, X_0) \to (X', X_0')$ be a mapping of pairs. Then the diagram

$$K^{-n}(X', X_0') \xrightarrow{\beta} K^{-n-2}(X', X_0')$$
$$\downarrow f^* \qquad\qquad \downarrow f^*$$
$$K^{-n}(X, X_0) \xrightarrow{\beta} K^{-n-2}(X, X_0)$$

is commutative.

Proof: This follows immediately from the diagram in the addendum to Theorem 1 and from the definition of β.

Lemma (4): If (X, X_0) is a pair, then the diagram

$$K^{-n-1}(X_0) \xrightarrow{\delta} K^{-n}(X, X_0)$$
$$\downarrow \beta \qquad\qquad \downarrow \beta$$
$$K^{-n-3}(X_0) \xrightarrow{\delta} K^{-n-2}(X, X_0)$$

is commutative.

Proof: This follows from Lemma 3 by the following rather standard argument. Let $X \cdot X_0$ be the space $(X \cup X_0 \times [0, 1])/X_0 \times \{1\}$, wherein we identify $X_0 \times \{0\}$ with X_0. Write CX_0 for the subspace $(X_0 \times [0, 1])/X_0 \times \{1\}$ of $X \cdot X_0$. Then CX_0 is easily seen to be deformable to a point. The natural identification map $X \cdot X_0 \to X/X_0 = (X \cdot X_0)/CX_0$ is therefore easily seen to induce an isomorphism $j: K^{-n}(X/X_0) \to K^{-n}(X \cdot X_0)$. On the other hand, $(X \cdot X_0)/X \times \{0\} = S^1 \wedge X_0$, so that the identification map $X \cdot X_0 \to S^1 \wedge X_0$ induces a homomorphism $k: K^{-n-1}(X_0) = K^{-n}(S^1 \wedge X_0) \to K^{-n}(X \cdot X_0)$. Comparison with the definition of the coboundary map δ (cf. Chapter 8, part A, paragraph following Corollary 2) will show that $\delta = j^{-1}k$. Thus $\beta\delta = \beta j^{-1}k = j^{-1}k\beta$ by Lemma 4. Q.E.D.

Theorem (3): Let (X, X_0) be a pair and let $X_0 \xrightarrow{i} X$ and $(X, \phi) \xrightarrow{j} (X, X_0)$ denote the natural inclusions. Consider the diagram

$$\cdots \longrightarrow K^{-2}(X) \xrightarrow{i^*} K^{-2}(X_0) \xrightarrow{\delta} K^{-1}(X, X_0) \xrightarrow{j^*} K^{-1}(X)$$

with the maps β, $\delta \circ \beta$, i^*, $K^0(X_0)$, $K^{-1}(X_0)$, i^*, δ, and

$$K^0(X) \xleftarrow{j^*} K^0(X, X_0)$$

where the top row is the exact sequence of the pair (X, X_0). Then the hexagonal part of the diagram is exact.

Proof: Exactness at $K^{-1}(X)$, $K^{-1}(X_0)$, $K^0(X, X_0)$ and $K^0(X)$ being obvious, we have only to check exactness at $K^0(X_0)$ and $K^{-1}(X, X_0)$. Exactness at $K^{-1}(X, X_0)$ is also obvious, because β is an isomorphism. We check exactness at $K^0(X_0)$:

(a) By Lemma 4, $\delta\beta \circ i^* = \beta\delta \circ i^*$. But since $\delta \circ i^* = 0$, it follows that $\beta\delta \circ i^* = 0$, i.e. Im $i^* \subseteq$ Ker $\delta\beta$.

(b) Suppose $\delta\beta(a) = 0$, $a \in K^0(X_0)$. Then $\beta(a) \in$ Ker δ, and therefore $\beta(a) = i^*(a')$, $a' \in K^{-2}(X)$. Since β is onto, $a' = \beta(a'')$, $a'' \in K^0(X)$. Thus, $\beta(a) = i^*\beta(a'') = \beta i^*(a'')$ (by Lemma 3). Since β is $1 - 1$, $a = i^*(a'')$, i.e. Ker $\delta\beta \subseteq$ Im i^*.

Definition (1): If $n \geq 0$ is any integer and (X, X_0) a pair, we put

$$K^n(X, X_0) = K^0(X, X_0) \quad \text{if } n \text{ is even,}$$

$$K^n(X, X_0) = K^{-1}(X, X_0) \quad \text{if } n \text{ is odd,}$$

$$K^*(X, X_0) = K^0(X, X_0) \oplus K^1(X, X_0).$$

The following theorem is an immediate consequence of the above definitions and results.

Theorem (4): $K^*(X)$ is a Z_2-graded anticommutative ring, i.e. $K^0(X) \cdot K^0(X) \subseteq K^0(X)$, $K^0(X) \cdot K^1(X) \subseteq K^1(X)$, $K^1(X) \cdot K^1(X) \subseteq K^0(X)$. Moreover $K^*(X, X_0)$ is a Z_2-graded $K^*(X)$-module. Finally, we have an exact hexagon

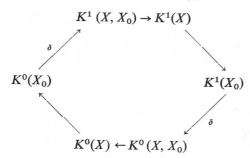

3. The Chern Character

This section will be devoted to constructing a certain ring homomorphism between $K(X)$ and the ordinary (e.g. singular) cohomology ring of X with rational coefficients. This homomorphism, the so-called Chern character, plays a very important role in the study and calculation of the ring $K(X)$. We shall, for example, perform such a calculation in the next chapter, in the case that X is projective space.

The Chern character is defined using the Chern classes. Thus, to begin with, we establish a fundamental theorem on Chern classes.

Theorem (5) (The Whitney Product Theorem): Let ξ_1, ξ_2 be complex bundles on complexes X_1, X_2. The following relation between Chern classes holds:
$$c\,(\xi_1 \,\textcircled{\#}\, \xi_2) = c(\xi_1) \times c(\xi_2); \quad \text{(see Chapter 8).}$$

If $X_1 = X_2 = X$, we may apply the diagonal map to this relation and obtain
$$c\,(\xi_1 \oplus \xi_2) = c(\xi_1) \cup c(\xi_2).$$

Proof: Let us denote by c_j, $c_k^{(1)}$, $c_l^{(2)}$ the Chern classes of $G_{n_1+n_2,\infty}$, $G_{n_1,\infty}$, $G_{n_2,\infty}$ respectively. We have a mapping
$$\tilde{N} : G_{n_1,\infty} \times G_{n_2,\infty} \to G_{n_1+n_2,\infty}$$

defined as follows: $G_{n_i,\infty}$ is regarded as the set of n_i-planes in E_i^∞, an infinite dimensional Euclidean space and $G_{n_1+n_2,\infty}$ is regarded as the set of $(n_1 + n_2)$-planes in $E^\infty = E_1^\infty \oplus E_2^\infty$. $\tilde{N}$ is given by $\tilde{N}(\pi_1, \pi_2) = \{\pi_1, \pi_2\}$, i.e. the plane generated by π_1 and π_2. We know that there exist classifying maps of ξ_1, ξ_2, i.e. maps
$$\phi_1 : X_1 \to G_{n_1,\infty}, \quad \phi_2 : X_2 \to G_{n_2,\infty}$$

such that $\phi_i^\dagger(\alpha_{n_i}) = \xi_i\,(\alpha_{n_i})$ is the universal bundle over $G_{n_i,\infty}$. Evidently, the bundle $\xi_1 \,\textcircled{\#}\, \xi_2$ is induced by
$$\tilde{N} \circ (\phi_1 \times \phi_2) : X_1 \times X_2 \to G_{n_1+n_2,\infty}.$$

Since the cohomology rings $H^*(G_{n_i,\infty}; Z)$ are torsion-free (see Chapter 3), it follows from Künneth's Theorem that
$$\tilde{N}^*c_j = Q_j(c_k^{(1)}, c_l^{(2)})$$

where Q_j is a homogeneous polynomial of degree j. Now,
$$c_j\,(\xi_1 \,\textcircled{\#}\, \xi_2) = [\tilde{N} \circ (\phi_1 \times \phi_2)]^* \, c_j = (\phi_1 \times \phi_2)^* \circ \tilde{N}^*(c_j)$$
$$= (\phi_1 \times \phi_2)^* \, Q_j\,(c_k^{(1)}, c_l^{(2)}).$$
Therefore,
$$c_j\,(\xi_1 \,\textcircled{\#}\, \xi_2) = Q_j\,(c_k^{(1)}(\xi_1), c_l^{(2)}(\xi_2)).$$

It remains to determine the polynomial Q_j. To do this, let $X_i = P_n^{(1)} \times \cdots \times P_n^{(n_i)}$ and let $X_{12} = X_1 \times X_2$. Here, n is chosen so large that $n\,(n_1 + n_2)$

$\geq j$. In Chapter 3 (cf. the proof of Theorem 3 of that chapter), we have defined maps

$$N_i : P_n^{(1)} \times \cdots \times P_n^{(n_i)} \to G_{n_i, \infty}$$
$$N : X_{12} = P_n^{(1)} \times \cdots \times P_n^{(n_1 + n_2)} \to G_{n_1 + n_2, \infty}.$$

Recall that N_i is defined as follows: An element $v_j \in P_n^{(j)}$ determines a one-dimensional subspace of a Euclidean space E_j^n. Putting $E^{n_i \cdot n} = E_1^n \oplus \cdots \oplus E_{n_i}^n$, we define $N_i((v_1, v_2, \ldots, v_{n_i}))$ as the plane π in $E^{n n_i} \subseteq E^\infty$ spanned by the one-dimensional spaces $v_1, \ldots, v_{n_i}$. Clearly,

$$N = \tilde{N} \circ (N_1 \times N_2).$$

Therefore, using Theorem 3 of Chapter 3, we find that if σ_j (resp. $\sigma_k^{(1)}$, resp. $\sigma_l^{(2)}$) is the j-th (resp. k-th, resp. l-th) elementary symmetric polynomial on $n_1 + n_2$ (resp. n_1, resp. n_2) generators, then

$$\sigma_j(t_1, \ldots, t_{n_1 + n_2}) = Q_j(\sigma_k^{(1)}(t_1, \ldots, t_{n_1}), \sigma_l^{(2)}(t_{n_1 + 1}, \ldots, t_{n_1 + n_2})).$$

But we also have

$$\sum_{j=1}^{n_1 + n_2} z^j \sigma_j(t_1, \ldots, t_{n_1 + n_2}) = \prod_{j=1}^{n_1 + n_2} (z - t_j) = \prod_{j=1}^{n_1} (z - t_j) \cdot \prod_{j = n_1 + n1}^{n_1 + n_2} (z - t_j)$$
$$= \left(\sum_{k=1}^{n_1} z^k \sigma_k^{(1)}(t_1, \ldots, t_{n_1}) \right) \cdot \left(\sum_{l=1}^{n_2} z^l \sigma_l^{(2)}(t_{n_1 + 1}, \ldots, t_{n_1 + n_2}) \right).$$

Thus,

$$Q_j(\sigma_k^{(1)}, \sigma_l^{(2)}) = \sigma_j = \sigma_j^{(1)} + \sigma_{j-1}^{(1)} \cdot \sigma_1^{(2)} + \cdots + \sigma_1^{(1)} \cdot \sigma_{j-1}^{(2)} + \sigma_j^{(2)}.$$

Since $c(\xi) = 1 + c_1(\xi) + c_2(\xi) + \cdots$, Theorem 5 follows. Q.E.D.

Our next aim is to show the existence of a very important homomorphism $K(X) \to H^*(X, \emptyset)$, where $\emptyset$ is the field of rational numbers, called the *Chern character* of a virtual bundle. Before defining this homomorphism, however, we prepare some technical lemmas concerning unitary bundles, which we will need in order to establish that the map to be defined is in fact a homomorphism. The object of these lemmas is to show that any algebraic relation between Chern classes that holds for all Whitney sums of U_1-bundles holds for all U_n-bundles generally (cf. Lemma 5 below). To establish this basic fact, we show that, given any U_n-bundle ξ over a base X, there exists a space Y and a mapping $\varrho : Y \to X$ such that

a) $\varrho^\dagger(\xi)$ is reducible to the torus subgroup T_n of U_n, i.e., is a direct sum of U_1-bundles. (This is the point of Theorems 6 and 7 below, and of their corollaries.)

9 Schwartz, Differential

b) $\varrho^*: H^*(X) \to H^*(Y)$ is a 1–1 mapping (this is the point of Theorems 8 and 9 below).

The space Y is constructed from the space E of the principal bundle ξ by an elementary general procedure, which it is the aim of the next few paragraphs to describe. Let $\alpha = (E, X, G, G, p)$ be a principal G-bundle, G a topological group. By definition, G acts on itself by *left* translations. We observe that there is a natural action of G on the total space E. In fact, E may be regarded (see Chapter 4) as the set of triples (x, g, U) with $x \in X$, $g \in G$, and U an open neighborhood of x, divided out by the equivalence relation $(x, g, U) \sim (x, g', V) \Leftrightarrow g' = g_{uv}(x) \cdot g$ (where g_{uv} is the coordinate transformation). Then G acts on E on the *right* by

$$[(x, g, U)] \cdot g_0 = [(x, g \cdot g_0, U)]$$

where [ ] means equivalence class. One checks easily that this is a well-defined action.

Suppose now Y is a space on which G acts on the left. We can define an action of G on the Cartesian product $E \times Y$ on the right,

$$\phi : (E \times Y) \times G \to E \times Y$$

by setting

$$\phi((e, y), g) = (eg, g^{-1} y).$$

Therefore we may also form identification space, denoted by $(E \times Y)/G$ and endowed with the identification topology. We denote the equivalence class of (e, y) in $(E \times Y)/G$ by $\{(e, y)\}$. If we define the map

$$p' : (E \times Y)/G \to X$$

by setting

$$p'(\{(e, y)\}) = p(e)$$

then we get a bundle $((E \times Y)/G, X, Y, G, p')$.

Let $\beta = (E, X, J, J, p)$ be a principal J-bundle where J is a closed subgroup of a Lie group G. Let $i: J \to G$ denote the injection map. One defines a left action of J on G in the obvious way. Using the construction of the preceding paragraph we get a bundle $((E \times G)/J, X, G, J, p')$. It is easy to see that this bundle initially defined as a J-bundle, can also be viewed as a principal G-bundle $((E \times G)/J, X, G, G, p')$. (Just observe that G acts on $(E \times G)/J$ on the right by acting on the second factor.) We will denote this latter bundle by $i_+(\beta)$. Thus $i_+(\beta)$ is a G-bundle which, from its definition, is clearly reducible to a bundle with respect to the subgroup $J \leq G$.

Now let $\xi = (E, X, G, G, p)$ be a principal G-bundle, G a Lie group. Let J again denote a closed subgroup of G, $i : J \to G$ the injection. Since J acts on E on the right, we can form E/J. One checks that $\beta = (E, E/J, J, J, \sigma)$ is a principal J-bundle over E/J where the projection σ is defined by

$$\sigma(e) = \{e\}.$$

In the preceding paragraph, we have defined the G-bundle $i_+(\beta)$. Let $\{e\} \in E/J$ and let e, e' be 2 representatives of $\{e\}$. Then e and e' are equivalent modulo J and therefore, a fortiori, equivalent modulo G. Hence the map

$$\varrho : E/J \to X$$

given by

$$\varrho(\{e\}) = p(e)$$

is well-defined and the diagram

is commutative. It is clear that the collection $(E/J, X, G/J, G, \varrho)$ is a bundle. On the other hand, the map ϱ induces a principal G-bundle $\varrho^\dagger(\xi)$ over the base E/J. The total space of $\varrho^\dagger(\xi)$, as we have seen in Chapter 4, consists of all pairs $(\{e\}, e')$ (with $\{e\} \in E/J$; $e, e' \in E$) such that $\varrho(\{e\}) = p(e)$. Let $\bar{E}$ denote this total space and let $\bar{p}$ be the corresponding projection

$$\bar{p}\,((\{e\}, e')) = \{e\}.$$

The following theorem now identifies the induced bundle $\varrho^\dagger(\xi)$ with the reducible bundle $i_+(\beta)$.

Theorem (6): $\varrho^\dagger(\xi)$ is equivalent to $i_+(\beta)$.

Proof: We shall construct a map j' such that the diagram

$$(E \times G)/J \xdashrightarrow{\;j'\;} \bar{E} \subseteq E/J \times E \qquad E$$

becomes commutative, this is done as follows. We first define a map

$$j : E \times G \to (E/J) \times E$$

by setting $$j((e, g)) = (\sigma(e), e \cdot g).$$

Using the facts that $\varrho\sigma = p$, $p(e \cdot h) = p(e)$ for any $h \in G$, and $\sigma(e \cdot k) = \sigma(e)$ for any $k \in J$, we see easily that j induces a map

$$j' : (E \times G)/J \to \bar{E}.$$

It is readily seen that j' is $1-1$ and onto.

It is also clear that j' covers the identity map of E/J into itself, i.e. $p' = \bar{p} \circ j'$. This proves the theorem.

Taking G to be the unitary group U_n and J a "maximal torus" T_n of U_n (e.g. the (closed) subgroup of all diagonal matrices in U_n), we get the following theorem.

Theorem (7): Let $\xi = (E, X, U_n, U_n, p_n)$ be a principal U_n-bundle. Let T_n be the subgroup of diagonal matrices of U_n, $i_n : T_n \to U_n$ the inclusion map. Let $\beta = (E, E/T_n, T_n, T_n, \sigma_n)$, $(i_n)_+(\beta) = ((E \times U_n)/T_n, E/T_n, U_n, U_n, p'_n)$ and $\varrho_n^\dagger(\xi) = (\bar{E}, E/T_n, U_n, U_n, \bar{p}_n)$ be as above (where $\sigma_n, p_n\bar{p}_n$ have the same meaning as $\sigma, p', \bar{p}$ above). Then $(i_n)_+(\beta) \cong \varrho_n^\dagger(\xi)$. Moreover, E/T_n is the total space of a U_n-bundle over X with fiber U_n/T_n and projection ϱ_n; the diagram

$$
\begin{array}{ccc}
E & \xrightarrow{\ \sigma\ } & E/T_n \\
& \searrow{\scriptstyle p_n} & \downarrow{\scriptstyle \varrho_n} \\
& & X
\end{array}
$$

is commutative.

Recalling the definition of bundle reducibility (see Chapter 4, Definition 3), we have

Corollary (1): The U_n-bundle $\varrho_n^\dagger(\xi)$ is reducible to T_n.

Since $T_n = U_1 \times U_1 \times \cdots \times U_1$ (n factors), we have

Corollary (2): $\varrho_n^\dagger(\xi)$ is a (Whitney) sum of n U_1-bundles.

This completes the first step of the argument outlined in a), b) above. Next we specialize still further, taking E in Theorem 7 to be a classifying bundle $V_{n,\infty}$, and studying the relation between $H^*(G_{n,\infty})$ and $H^*(V_{n,\infty}/T_n)$.

Let $\alpha_m = (V_{m,\infty}, G_{m,\infty}, U_m, U_m, \varrho_m)$ be the universal U_m-bundle (see Chapter 6, Definition 5). We set $\alpha_1 = \alpha$. Recall that $G_{1,\infty} = P_\infty$, infinite dimensional (complex) projective space, while $V_{1,\infty} = S^\infty$, the infinite dimensional (complex) sphere. We define

$$\alpha^n = (S^\infty \times \cdots \times S^\infty, P_\infty \times \cdots \times P_\infty,$$
$$U_1 \times \cdots \times U_1, U_1 \times \cdots \times U_1, p_1 \times \cdots \times p_1),$$

where each Cartesian product has n factors. Since the space $S^\infty \times \cdots \times S^\infty$ is homotopically trivial in all dimensions and since $U_1 \times \cdots \times U_1 = T_n$, it follows from Chapter 6, Theorem 3 that α^n can be considered as a universal T_n-bundle. Thus, the space $P_\infty \times \cdots \times P_\infty$ is a universal classifying space for T_n-bundles. Instead of the cumbersome notation above, we write

$$\alpha^n = (E_{T_n}, X_{T_n}, T_n, T_n, p_{T_n}).$$

Recall the result proved in Chapter 2:

$$H^*(X_{T_n}; Z) = H^*(P_\infty \times \cdots \times P_\infty; Z) \cong Z(t_1, \ldots, t_n),$$

the polynomial ring in n indeterminates.

We now apply Theorem 7 to the U_n-bundle α_n, setting

$$\beta = (V_{n,\infty}, V_{n,\infty}/T_n, T_n, T_n, \sigma_n)$$

in Theorem 7. It follows that there exists a communitative diagram

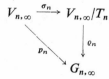

and that $(i_n)_+(\beta) \cong \varrho_n^\dagger(\alpha_n)$. Since $V_{n,\infty}$ is homotopically trivial in all dimensions, we can consider β as a universal T_n-bundle with base $V_{n,\infty}/T_n$. In what follows, we write β_n for this universal bundle β. By the universality property, the spaces $V_{n,\infty}/T_n$ and X_{T_n} are homotopically equivalent and we get

$$H^*(V_{n,\infty}/T_n; Z) \cong H^*(X_{T_n}) \cong Z[t_1, \ldots, t_n].$$

Again by Theorem 7, $V_{n,\infty}/T_n$ is the total space of a U_n-bundle over $G_{n,\infty}$ with fiber U_n/T_n. We then have the following theorem, which we state without proof. See Husseini—*Topics in the Algebraic Topology of the Classical Groups*, University of Wisconsin lecture notes, Chapter 2, page 14.

Theorem (8): The sequence of graded rings

$$1 \longrightarrow H^*(G_{n,\infty}) \xrightarrow{\varrho_n^*} H^*(V_{n,\infty}/T_n) \xrightarrow{j_n^*} H^*(U_n/T_n) \longrightarrow 1$$

is exact. Here, $j_n : U_n/T_n \to V_{n,\infty}/T_n$ is the inclusion of the fiber into the total space.

Now let $\xi = (E, X, U_n, U_n, p)$ be any principal U_n-bundle. We have then bundles $\beta = (E, E/T_n, T_n, T_n, \sigma_n)$ and $(E/T_n, X, U_n/T_n, U_n, \varrho)$. By the Classification Theorem, there exists a map

$$f : X \to G_{n,\infty}$$

such that $f^{\dagger}(\alpha_n) = \xi$. If we let $\bar{f}$ be the map

$$\bar{f}: E/T_n \to V_{n,\infty}/T_n$$

induced by the bundle map $\tilde{f}: E \to V_{n,\infty}$ covering the map f, then it is easily seen from the above definitions that $\bar{f}^{\dagger}(\beta_n) = \beta$. The following diagram is then seen to be commutative, where j and j_n are inclusions of fibers in total spaces:

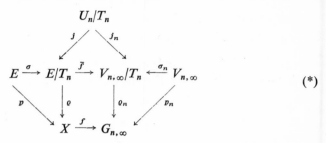

$$(*)$$

We look at the top triangle of diagram (*) and take its induced cohomology diagram:

$$H^*(U_n/T_n)$$

$$H^*(E/T_n) \xleftarrow{\;\bar{f}^*\;} H^*(V_{n,\infty}/T_n)$$

with maps j^* and j_n^*.

Theorem 8 tells us that j_n^* is surjective. It follows immediately that j^* is also surjective. A nontrivial argument (see Husseini, loc. cit.) then establishes the following result.

Theorem (9): The map $\varrho^* : H^*(X) \to H^*(E/T_n)$ is injective.

After these preliminaries we are prepared to give the definition and derive the properties of the Chern character:

Let $c_1, c_2, \ldots, c_n$ be the Chern classes of $G_{n,\infty}$, i.e. the elements of $H^*(G_{n,\infty})$ corresponding to the elementary symmetric polynomials $\sigma_1, \ldots, \sigma_n$ on n indeterminates $t_1, t_2, \ldots, t_n$. The Chern classes of ξ (see diagram (*)) are $c_i(\xi) = f^*(c_i), i = 1, \ldots, n$. The total Chern class of ξ is $c(\xi) = 1 + c_1(\xi) + \cdots + c_n(\xi)$.

The function $G(t_1, \ldots, t_n) = \sum_{i=1}^{n} e^{t_i}$ is a power series in the indeterminates t_i, with rational coefficients and symmetrical in these indeterminates. Thus we may write $G(t_1, \ldots, t_n) = R(\sigma_1, \ldots, \sigma_n)$, where R is a power series in the elementary symmetric functions $\sigma_1, \ldots, \sigma_n$. We define the Chern character of ξ by $ch(\xi) = R(c_1(\xi), \ldots, c_n(\xi))$. Since any sufficiently high power of a

Chern class (for a bundle over a finite complex X as base) vanishes, the expression $R\left(c_1(\xi), \ldots, c_n(\xi)\right)$ reduces to a finite sum, and $ch\,(\xi)$ is a well-defined element of $H^*(X) * \varnothing = H^*(X; \varnothing)$.

The fundamental fact that $ch\,(\xi)$ induces a homomorphism of the ring $K(X)$ into $H^*(X, \varnothing)$ may be deduced as follows. We showed above that

$$H^*\left(V_{n,\infty}/T_n\right) \cong Z\left[t_1, \ldots, t_n\right].$$

Let us regard the indeterminates t_i as being the ring generators of $H^*(V_{n,\infty}/T_n)$; $t_i \in H^2\left(V_{n,\infty}/T_n\right)$. We set

$$\gamma_i = \bar{f}^*(t_i), \quad (i \leq i \leq n).$$

Then $\gamma_i \in H^2\left(E/T_n\right)$ and are called the *roots* of the principal U_n-bundle ξ. Now, setting $c_0(\xi) = 1$, we have

$$\varrho^* c\,(\xi) = \varrho^*\left(\sum_{i=0}^n c_i(\xi)\right) = \varrho^* f^*\left(\sum_{i=0}^n c_i\right)$$

By the commutativity of the square in (*), we deduce

$$\varrho^* c\,(\xi) = f^* \varrho_n^*\left(\sum_{i=0}^n c_i\right).$$

By Theorem 9, $\varrho_n^* : H^*(G_{n,\infty}) \to H^*(V_{n,\infty}/T_n)$ is a $1-1$ map of the subring of $Z\left[t_1, \ldots, t_n\right]$ consisting of all symmetric polynomials into the full ring $Z\left[t_1, \ldots, t_n\right]$. Thus,

$$\varrho_n^*\left(\sum_{i=0}^n c_i\right) = 1 + \sum_{i=1}^n \sigma_i.$$

But by the definition of elementary symmetric polynomials,

$$1 + \sum_{i=1}^n \sigma_i = \prod_{i=1}^n (1 + t_i).$$

Therefore,

$$\varrho^* c\,(\xi) = f^*\left(\prod_{i=1}^n (1 + t_i)\right) = \prod_{i=1}^n (1 + \gamma_i).$$

Now, $\sum_{i=1}^n e^{\gamma_i}$ is an element of the ring $H^*(E/T_n : \varnothing)$. (Note again that at this point, we must assume that for some integer m_0, the cohomology groups $H^m(E/T_n)$ are 0 for $m \geq m_0$; of course, this follows automatically if $\bar{t}/T_n$ is a finite dimensional complex. If this condition is not satisfied then the power series $\sum_{i=1}^n e^{\gamma_i}$ may not degenerate into a finite sum and will then represent an element in $H^{**}(E/T_n; \emptyset) = \prod\limits_{j \geqq 0} H^j(E/T_n; \emptyset)$, the unrestricted direct product.) Moreover, $\sum\limits_{i=1}^{n} e^{\gamma_i}$ is a symmetric polynomial in the roots γ_i, and is therefore a polynomial in the elementary symmetric functions on the roots γ_i. In other words,

$$\sum_{i=1}^{n} e^{\gamma_i} = R\left(\bar{f}^*(\sigma_1), \ldots, \bar{f}^*(\sigma_n)\right),$$

where R is as above.

Notation: If z is an indeterminate, we define the *Chern polynomial* by

$$c(\xi, z) = 1 + c_1(\xi) z + \cdots + c_n(\xi) z^n.$$

Recalling the equation $\varrho^*c(\xi) = \prod\limits_{i=1}^{n} (1 + \gamma_i)$, we will allow ourselves to write formally

$$c(\xi, z) = \prod_{i=1}^{n} (1 + \gamma_i z).$$

If $\xi \cong \eta$, then evidently $ch(\xi) = ch(\eta)$. Thus, the map

$$(\xi) \to ch(\xi)$$

is a well defined map. (Recall that (ξ) is the equivalence class of ξ.) Let K_F and K_F^+ be as in the paragraph following the proof of Lemma 2, Chapter 8. We may now extend by linearity to get a homomorphism

$$ch: K_F(X) \to H^*(X; \emptyset).$$

We shall now investigate the behavior under Whitney addition of ch on $K_F^+(X)$, and also its behavior for tensor products. We have

Theorem (10): If ξ is a principal U_n-bundle on X and η is a principal U_m-bundle on X, then

(a) $\qquad\qquad ch(\xi \oplus \eta) = ch(\xi) + ch(\eta).$

(b) $\qquad\qquad ch(\xi \otimes \eta) = ch(\xi) \cdot ch(\eta).$

Proof:

(a) It follows from the Whitney Product Theorem that

$$c(\xi \oplus \eta, z) = c(\xi, z) \cdot c(\eta, z).$$

But this means that if $\{\gamma_1, \ldots, \gamma_n\}$ are the roots of ξ and $\{\gamma_1', \ldots, \gamma_m'\}$ are the roots of η, then $\{\gamma_1, \ldots, \gamma_n\} \cup \{\gamma_1', \ldots, \gamma_m'\}$ are the roots of $\xi \oplus \eta$.

Hence,

$$\varrho^* ch\,(\xi \oplus \eta) = \sum_{i=1}^{n} e^{\gamma_i} + \sum_{j=1}^{m} e^{\gamma'_i} = \varrho^* ch\,(\xi) + \varrho^* ch\,(\eta),$$

from which (a) follows immediately.

(b) Since

$$\left(\sum_{i=1}^{n} e^{\gamma_i}\right) \cdot \left(\sum_{j=1}^{m} e^{\gamma'_i}\right) = \sum_{i=1}^{n} \sum_{j=1}^{m} e^{\gamma_i + \gamma'_i},$$

it is sufficient, in order to establish (b), to show that the set of roots of $\xi \otimes \eta$ consists of $\{\gamma_i + \gamma'_j; 1 \leq i \leq n, 1 \leq j \leq m\}$. We shall now prove this:

Case 1: ξ and η are U_1-bundles.

Proof: We have $c_1\,(\xi \otimes \eta) = c_1(\xi) + c_1(\eta)$. The proof of this fact is left as an exercise. Since $c\,(\xi \otimes \eta, z) = 1 + c_1(\xi \otimes \eta) \cdot z$, $c\,(\xi, z) = 1 + c_1(\xi)\,z$, $c\,(\eta, z) = 1 + c_1(\eta) \cdot z$, the result follows immediately from the definition of the quantities γ_i.

Case 2: $\xi = \xi_1 \oplus \cdots \oplus \xi_n, \eta = \eta_1 \oplus \cdots \oplus \eta_m$, where the ξ_i's and η_j's are U_1-bundles.

Proof: We have

$$\xi \otimes \eta = \sum_{i,j} \xi_i \otimes \eta_j.$$

Hence, by the Whitney Product Theorem,

$$c\,(\xi, z) = \prod_{i=1}^{n} (1 + c_1(\xi_i)\,z)$$

$$c\,(\eta, z) = \prod_{j=1}^{m} (1 + c_1(\eta_j)\,z)$$

$$c\,(\xi \otimes \eta, z) = \prod_{i,j} (1 + c_1(\xi_i \otimes \eta_j)\,z) = \prod_{i,j} [1 + \{c_1(\xi_1) + c_1(\eta_j)\}\,z].$$

Hence, the assertion follows in Case 2.

Case 3: ξ and η are arbitrary.

Proof: This will follow from

Lemma (5): Any algebraic relation between Chern classes that holds for all sums of U_1-bundles holds generally.

Lemma 5 will in turn be a consequence of

Lemma (6): Let $\xi_1, \ldots, \xi_r$ be principal unitary bundles over X (not necessarily of the same dimension). Then there exists a space Y and a map

$$\phi : Y \rightarrow X$$

such that the induced map

$$\phi^* : H^*(X) \to H^*(Y)$$

is injective and such that each of the induced bundles $\phi^\dagger(\xi_i)$ $(1 \leqq i \leqq r)$ over Y is a sum of U_1-bundles.

Proof: The proof is divided into 2 parts;

(1) $r = 1$: Let $\xi_1 = (E_1, X, U_{m_1}, U_{m_1}, p_1)$. We define Y to be the space E_1/T_{m_1} and ϕ to be the map ϱ (see Theorem 7). The fact that ϕ^* is injective follows from Theorem 9 and the fact that $\phi^\dagger(\xi_1)$ is a sum of U_1-bundles follows from Corollary 2 of Theorem 7.

(2) $r > 1$: Using part (1), we find a space Y_1 and a map

$$\phi_1 : Y_1 \to X$$

such that ϕ_1^* is injective and such that $\phi_1^\dagger(\xi_1)$ is a sum of U_1-bundles. Again by part (1), we find a space Y_2 and a map

$$\phi_2 : Y_2 \to Y_1$$

such that ϕ_2^* is injective and such that $\phi_2^\dagger \phi_1^\dagger(\xi_2)$ is a sum of U_1-bundles. Observe also that $\phi_2^\dagger \phi_1^\dagger(\xi_1)$ is still a sum of U_1-bundles. By defining

$$\psi : Y_2 \to X$$

as $\psi = \phi_1 \circ \phi_2$, we see that

$$\psi^* = \phi_2^* \circ \phi_1^* : H^*(X) \to H^*(Y_2)$$

is injective and that $\psi^\dagger(\xi_1)$ and $\psi^\dagger(\xi_2)$ are sums of U_1-bundles. This proves the lemma in case $r = 2$. The general case is done inductively using the above procedure.

Thus, Lemma 9 and with it Lemma 8 and Theorem 10 are proved. Q.E.D.

We now note an important corollary of Theorem 10.

Corollary: Let K_F and K_F^+ be as in the paragraph following the proof of Lemma 2, Chapter VIII. $ch|K_F^+(X) = 0$. Thus, $ch : K_F(X) \to H^*(X; \varnothing)$ induces a hommorphism

$$ch : K(X) \to H^*(X; Q),$$

which is a ring homomorphism.

In the situation of Theorem 10, we dealt with bundles ξ, η over the same space X. More generally, we may suppose ξ is a bundle over X and η is a bundle over another space Y. Then, statements analogous to those of Theorem 10 and its corollary hold. For example, we have a commutative diagram

$$
\begin{array}{ccc}
K(X) \otimes K(Y) & \xrightarrow{\;\mu\;} & K(X \times Y) \\
\downarrow{\scriptstyle ch \otimes ch} & & \downarrow{\scriptstyle ch} \\
H^*(X; \varnothing) \otimes H^*(Y; \varnothing) & \longrightarrow & H^*(X \times Y; \varnothing)
\end{array}
$$

The map on the bottom line is just the Künneth isomorphism.

If we look at $ch|\tilde{K}(X)$, we obtain the following commutative diagram:

$$
\begin{array}{ccc}
\tilde{K}(X) \otimes \tilde{K}(Y) & \xrightarrow{\;\tilde{\mu}\;} & \tilde{K}(X \wedge Y) \\
\downarrow{\scriptstyle ch \otimes ch} & & \downarrow{\scriptstyle ch} \\
\tilde{H}^*(X; \varnothing) \otimes \tilde{H}^*(Y; \varnothing) & \longrightarrow & \tilde{H}^*(X \wedge Y)
\end{array}
$$

Here $\tilde{H}^*(X; \varnothing)$ means reduced cohomology, i.e. $\tilde{H}^*(X; \varnothing) = H^*(X, x_0; \varnothing)$. The map in the bottom line is again an isomorphism by the Künneth tensor formula.

We introduce additional notation as follows: First, let $H_G^*(X)$ denote the ordinary cohomology ring of X with coefficients in G. We set

$$
H_G^e(X) = \sum_{i \geq 0} H^{2i}(X; G), \quad H_G^\sigma(X) = \sum_{i \geq 0} H^{2i+1}(X; G).
$$

Then evidently,

$$
H_G^*(X) = H_G^e(X) \oplus H_G^\sigma(X).
$$

We have the following

Lemma (7): ch maps $K(X)$ into $H_Q^e(X) \subseteq H_Q^*(X)$. Moreover, if X is connected, ch maps $\tilde{K}(X)$ into $\tilde{H}_Q^e = \sum_{i \geq 1} H^{2i}(X; \varnothing)$.

Proof: The proof follows easily from the fact that the roots of a bundle are 2-dimensional cohomology classes.

We shall now define a map

$$
ch : K^{-n}(X, X_0) \to H^*(X, X_0; \varnothing).
$$

To do this, we begin by defining the suspension isomorphism

$$
\sigma^n : \tilde{H}_Q^*(W) \to \tilde{H}_Q^*(S^n(W)).
$$

We put

$$
\sigma^n(x) = x \otimes s^n,
$$

where s^n is the canonical generator of $H^n(S^n; \mathbf{Z})$ and where W is any complex. The fact that σ^n is an isomorphism follows from the Künneth tensor formula. Now let $a \in K^{-n}(X, X_0) = \tilde{K}(S^n(X/X_0))$. Then, $ch(a) \in \tilde{H}_Q^*(S^n(X/X_0))$ by Lemma 7 and $(\sigma^n)^{-1} ch(a) \in \tilde{H}_Q^*(X/X_0) \cong H_Q^*(X, X_0)$. The map

$$a \to (\sigma^n)^{-1} ch(a)$$

is then the desired map (by abuse of notation)

$$ch : K^{-n}(X, X_0) \to H_Q^*(X, X_0).$$

To stress the analogy with Theorem 2, we shall set

$$s^2 = \hat{g}, \quad \sigma^2 = \hat{\beta}.$$

Thus, we have an isomorphism

$$\hat{\beta} : \tilde{H}_Q^*(X/X_0) \to \tilde{H}_Q^*(S^2(X/X_0))$$

given by

$$\beta(a) = \hat{a} \otimes \hat{g}.$$

Lemma (8): The diagram

$$\tilde{K}(X) \xrightarrow{\beta} \tilde{K}(S^2(X))$$

$$\tilde{H}_Q^*(X)$$

with maps ch

is commutative.

Proof: Let g, β be as in Theorem 2, and let $\hat{g}$, $\hat{\beta}$ be as above. The result would follow immediately from the second commutative diagram in the discussion after the corollary to Theorem 10 if we knew that $ch(g) = \hat{g}$. But $g = [\eta - 1]$ where η is the canonical line bundle over P_1^C, i.e. η is induced by the inclusion map $P_1^C \xrightarrow{i_1} P_\infty^C$. Thus,

$$c_1(\eta) = i_1^*(c_1),$$

i.e. $c_1(\eta)$ is a generator of $H^2(P_1^C)$. Now,

$$ch(\eta) = e^{c_1(\eta)} = 1 + c_1(\eta) + \tfrac{1}{2}c_1^2(\eta) + \cdots$$

But $c_1^2(\eta) = c_1^3(\eta) = \cdots = 0$ and therefore

$$ch(g) = ch(\eta) - ch(1) = 1 + c_1(\eta) - 1 = c_1(\eta).$$

Q.E.D.

If now $a \in K^n(X, X_0)$, we define

$$ch(a) = ch(\beta^{-m}a)$$

where m is so chosen that $n - 2m \leq 0$. (Note again the abuse of notation.) Lemma 8 shows that this definition is legitimate. We have thus defined

$$ch : K^n(X, X_0) \to H_Q^*(X, X_0)$$

for all integers n. Moreover (see Lemma 7), it follows that

(a) ch maps $K^0(X, X_0)$ into $H^e_Q(X, X_0)$,

(b) ch maps $K^1(X, X_0)$ into $H^\sigma_Q(X, X_0)$.

To complete the picture, recall that in Theorem 4, we constructed an exact "K-hexagon". Similarly, we have an exact "H-hexagon" as follows:

$$\begin{array}{ccc}
& H^\sigma_Q(X, X_0) \longrightarrow \tilde{H}^\sigma_Q(X) & \\
\nearrow & & \searrow \\
\tilde{H}^e_Q(X_0) & & \tilde{H}^\sigma_Q(X_0) \\
\nwarrow & & \swarrow \\
& \tilde{H}^e_Q(X) \longleftarrow H^e_Q(X, X_0) &
\end{array}$$

Exercise: Prove that ch is a natural transformation of the K-hexagon to the H-hexagon.

(Hint: By virtue of Theorem 4, it suffices to show that ch is a Q-cohomology invariant of bundles, i.e. $ch \circ f^\dagger = f^* \circ ch$, where f is a continuous map of spaces. The latter is most conveniently proved by first proving it for sums of U_1-bundles, in which case it is practically trivial, and then extending to the general case by using the line of argument established above.)

Remark: When we defined ch on $K^{-n}(X, X_0)$ and $K^n(X, X_0)$ above, we required the image to lie in $H^*_Q(X, X_0)$. Alternatively, we could have proceeded as follows. Define

$$ch : K^{-n}(X, X_0) \to H^*_Q(S^n(X/X_0))$$

in the obvious way. Then put

$$\mathscr{H}^{-n}(X, X_0) = H^e_Q(S^n(X/X_0)).$$

We claim that the groups $\mathscr{H}^{-n}(X, X_0)$ form a generalized cohomology theory. In fact, for any integer n, there exists a space $\mathscr{E}_n$ (a so-called Eilenberg-MacLane space; the usual notation found in the literature for such a space is $K(Q, n)$) such that for any finite complex X,

$$H^n_Q(X) \cong (\mathscr{E}^X_n).$$

We define

$$\mathscr{E} = \mathscr{E}_2 \times \mathscr{E}_4 \times \mathscr{E}_6 \times \cdots$$

Then clearly

$$(\mathscr{E}^X) \cong \sum_{i \geq 1} H^{2i}(X; Q) = \tilde{H}^e_Q(X).$$

This shows that $\mathscr{E}$ is a test space and our contention that the groups $\mathscr{H}^{-n}(X, X_0)$ give a generalized cohomology theory is proved. Finally, we can construct an

"$\mathscr{H}$-hexagon" just as for K-Theory (using $\hat{\beta}$ instead of β) and then show that ch is a natural transformation from the K-hexagon to the $\mathscr{H}$-hexagon.

4. The Atiyah-Hirzebruch Spectral Sequence

In this section, we describe a spectral sequence relating the ordinary cohomology of a cellular pair with its K-cohomology. The spectral sequence will allow us to obtain some useful information about the K-groups. The spectral sequence in question is essentially that derived in Chapter 5. We shall, however, reformulate and generalize the spectral sequence described in that chapter, casting the results derived into the general algebraic form set forth in Cartan and Eilenberg—*Homological Algebra*, Chapter 15. This generalized formulation is as follows.

We first define the notion of a *group table*. By a *pair* we shall mean a pair of integers (p, q) with $-\infty \leqq p \leqq q \leqq +\infty$; by a *triple* we shall mean a triple of integers (p, q, r) with $-\infty \leqq p \leqq q \leqq r \leqq +\infty$. A group table is then a collection as follows:

(a) For each pair (p, q), there is an abelian group $H(p, q)$.

(b) Given 2 pairs such that $(p, q) \leqq (p', q')$ (i.e. $p \leqq p'$, $q \leqq q'$), there is a homomorphism $H(p', q') \to H(p, q)$.

(c) For each triple (p, q, r), there is a homomorphism $H(p, q) \xrightarrow{\delta} H(q, r)$.

These groups and homomorphisms will be required to satisfy the following set of axioms:

(0) $H(p, q) = 0$.

(1) $H(p, q) \to H(p, q)$ is the identity map.

(2) If $(p, q) \leqq (p', q') \leqq (p'', q'')$, then the triangle

$$H(p'', q'') \longrightarrow H(p, q)$$
$$\searrow \qquad \nearrow$$
$$H(p', q')$$

is commutative.

(3) If $(p, q, r) \leqq (p', q', r')$, then the square

$$\begin{array}{ccc} H(p', q') & \xrightarrow{\delta} & H(q', r') \\ \downarrow & & \downarrow \\ H(p, q) & \xrightarrow{\delta} & H(q, r) \end{array}$$

is commutative.

(4) For each triple (p, q, r), the triangle

$$H(p, q) \xrightarrow{\delta} H(q, r)$$

$$H(p, r)$$

is exact.

(5) The groups $H(p, q)$ stabilize for small values of p or for large values of q.

Examples:

(i) Let (X, A) be a pair of spaces and let

$$X = X_N \supseteq X_{N-1} \supseteq \cdots \supseteq X_0 = A$$

be a finite filtration of (X, A). We define X_m for arbitrary m by setting

$$X_m = A \quad \text{if} \quad m \leq 0, \qquad X_m = X \quad \text{if} \quad m \geq N.$$

We define a group table by putting

$$H(p, q) = \sum_{n \geq 0} T^{-n}(X_q, X_p),$$

for an arbitrary T-cohomology theory (T grouplike). The homomorphism $H(p, q) \to H(p', q')$ is just the homomorphism

$$\sum_{n \geq 0} T^{-n}(X_{q'}, X_{p'}) \to \sum_{n \geq 0} T^{-n}(X_q, X_p),$$

induced by the inclusion map

$$(X_q, X_p) \subseteq (X_{q'}, X_{p'}).$$

The homomorphism $H(p, q) \to H(q, r)$ required in (c) above is the composition

$$\sum_{n \geq 0} T^{-n}(X_q, X_p) \longrightarrow \sum_{n \geq 0} T^{-n}(X_q) \xrightarrow{\delta} \sum_{n \geq 0} T^{-n}(X_r, X_q).$$

The axioms are all seen to be verified.

(ii) As a particular case of (i), we may replace $\sum_{n \geq 0} T^{-n}(X_q, X_p)$ by $K^*(X_q, X_p)$ (see Definition 1), or $H_Q^*(X_q, X_p)$ (with its usual Z-grading or with the Z_2-grading defined above).

(iii) As a special case of (i) in another sense, let (X, A) be a pair of finite complexes. Then we obtain a canonical filtration of (X, A) by using the skeleta of X. In other words, let X_p be defined as the union of A with the p-skeleton of X.

The most important fact about group tables is the following theorem.

Theorem (11): Given a group table, there exists a spectral sequence $\{E_r^p\}$, $r \geq 1$, such that (a) $E_1^p = H(p, p+1)$, (b) the first differential ∂^1 coincides with $H(p, p+1) \xrightarrow{\delta} H(p+1, p+2)$, (c) the groups E_∞^p are the factors of a filtration of $H(-\infty, \infty)$.

This theorem has essentially been proved in Chapter 5 of these notes. In fact, what we proved there was the existence of a spectral sequence with the desired properties in case the group table is the one described in Example (i) above. However, we observed that the construction of the spectral sequence does not depend in an essential way on the topological structure of (X, A). In fact, the same proof goes through for any group table.

We shall now restrict our attention to the situation described in Example (iii) above. In particular, we want to analyze the terms E_1 and E_2 in more detail in this case. Let us make the abbreviation

$$T^* (X, A) = \sum_{n \geq 0} T^{-n}(X, A).$$

Recall that we have

$$E_1^p = H(p, p+1) = T^* (X_{p+1}, X_p).$$

Notice that X_{p+1}/X_p is a grape bunch (or a bouquet of spheres), that is,

$$X_{p+1}/X_p = S_1^{p+1} \vee S_2^{p+1} \vee \cdots \vee S_{\alpha_{p+1}}^{p+1}$$

where α_{p+1} is the number of $(p+1)$-cells in (X, A). Let

$$f_i : (D_i^{p+1}, \partial D_i^{p+1}) \to (X_{p+1}, X_p) \qquad (1 \leq i \leq \alpha_{p+1})$$

be the attaching maps for the $(p+1)$-cells of (X, A) (see Chapter 2). Define

$$I_{p+1} : T^* (X_{p+1}, X_p) \to \sum_{i=1}^{\alpha_{p+1}} T^* (D_i^{p+1}, \partial D_i^{p+1})$$

by setting

$$I_{p+1}(a) = (f_1^*(a), \dots, f_{\alpha_{p+1}}^*(a)).$$

I_{p+1} is evidently an isomorphism. We shall describe the inverse isomorphism I_{p+1}^{-1} explicitly. We set

$$\theta_i^{p+1} = f_i(\mathring{D}_i^{p+1}), \qquad (1 \leq i \leq \alpha_{p+1}).$$

Evidently,

$$\theta_i^{p+1} \subseteq X_{p+1} - X_p,$$

or equivalently

$$X_p \subseteq X_{p+1} - \theta_i^{p+1}.$$

Consider the composition map g_i,

$$X_{p+1}/X_p \to X_{p+1}/X_{p+1} - \theta_i^{p+1} \to D_i^{p+1}/\partial D_i^{p+1},$$

defined as follows. The first map is induced by the inclusion

$$(X_{p+1}, X_p) \subseteq (X_{p+1}, X_{p+1} - \theta_i^{p+1}).$$

The second map can be described by taking θ_i^{p+1} to $\overset{\circ}{D}_i^{p+1}$ by means of f_i^{-1} and by taking $X_{p+1} - \theta_i^{p+1}$ to a point. We then have a map

$$J_{p+1} : \sum_{i=1}^{\alpha_{p+1}} T^* (D_i^{p+1}/\partial D_i^{p+1}) \to T^* (X_{p+1}/X_p)$$

given by

$$J_{p+1}(a_1, \ldots, a_{\alpha_{p+1}}) = g_1^*(a_1) + \cdots + g_{\alpha_{p+1}}^*(a_{\alpha_{p+1}})$$

Clearly, J_{p+1} is the inverse of I_{p+1}. Using the fact that $E_1^p = H(p, p+1)$, we obtain easily

$$E_1^p = C^p \left(X, A; \sum_{n \geq 0} T^{-n-p-1}(x_0) \right),$$

where C^p is the cochain group. We now examine the differential ∂^1, i.e. the coboundary map

$$\delta : \sum_{n \geq 0} T^{-n}(X_{p+1}, X_p) \to \sum_{n \geq 0} T^{-n}(X_{p+2}, X_{p+1}).$$

We shall define a map

$$h* : \sum_{i=1}^{\alpha_{p+1}} T^* (D_i^{p+1}/\partial D_i^{p+1}) \to \sum_{j=1}^{\alpha_{p+2}} T^* (\partial D_j^{p+2}),$$

where α_{p+2} is, of course, the number of $(p+2)$-cells of (X, A). To do this, we consider the $(p+2)$-cells of (X, A) and the attaching maps

$$f_j : (D_j^{p+2}, \partial D_j^{p+2}) \to (X_{p+2}, X_{p+1}), \qquad (1 \leq j \leq \alpha_{p+2}).$$

(Note that we are overworking the symbol f_j.) For any i such that $1 \leq i \leq \alpha_{p+1}$, we have the composed map

$$\partial D_j^{p+2} \xrightarrow{f_j} X_{p+1} \longrightarrow X_{p+1}/X_{p+1} - \theta_i^{p+1} \longrightarrow D_i^{p+1}/\partial D_i^{p+1},$$

where the latter two maps have been defined previously; we call this composed map h_{ij}. We then have the induced map

$$h_{ij}^* : T^* (D_i^{p+1}/\partial D_i^{p+1}) \to T^* (\partial D_j^{p+2}).$$

We now define a map

$$h_j^* : \sum_{i=1}^{\alpha_{p+1}} T^* (D_i^{p+1}/\partial D_i^{p+1}) \to T^* (\partial D_j^{p+2})$$

by setting

$$h_j^* (a_1, \ldots, a_{\alpha_{p+1}}) = h_{1j}^*(a_1) + \cdots + h_{\alpha_{p+1},j}^*(a_{\alpha_{p+1}}).$$

Finally, we define the desired map h^* by

$$h^*(a_1, \ldots, a_{\alpha_{p+1}}) = (h_1^*(a_1, \ldots, a_{\alpha_{p+1}}), \ldots, h_{\alpha_{p+2}}^*(a_1, \ldots, a_{\alpha_{p+1}})).$$

We see easily that the following diagram is commutative:

$$
\begin{array}{ccc}
\displaystyle\sum_{i=1}^{\alpha_{p+1}} T^*(D_i^{p+1}/\partial D_i^{p+1}) & \xrightarrow{\;I_{p+1}^{-1}\;} & T^*(X_{p+1}/X_p) \\
\end{array}
$$

$$
\begin{array}{c}
\displaystyle\sum_{j=1}^{\alpha_{p+2}} T^*(\partial D_j^{p+2}) \\[2mm]
\end{array}
$$

$$
\begin{array}{ccc}
\displaystyle\sum_{j=1}^{\alpha_{p+2}} T^*(D_j^{p+2}/\partial D_j^{p+2}) & \xleftarrow{\;I_{p+2}\;} & T^*(X_{p+2}/X_{p+1})
\end{array}
$$

with maps labeled h^*, δ, δ.

We have at this point almost shown that the differential ∂^1 is precisely the "formal coboundary" operator $\tilde{\delta}$ of the cell complex (X, A) (cf. Chapter 2, Lemma 11). To complete the proof that $\partial^1 = \tilde{\delta}$, we make use of the following statement: The map h_{ij} defined above can be viewed as a map of a $(p+1)$-sphere into itself. As such, h_{ij} belongs to a homotopy class characterized by its degree, say D_{ij}. If we can show that

$$h_{ij}^*(a) = D_{ij} \cdot a$$

for any $a \in T^*(S^{p+1})$, then we will have completed the proof that $\tilde{\delta} = \partial^1$. We state the needed assertion as

Lemma (9): Consider an arbitrary generalized cohomology theory, based on a test space T. Let

$$\phi : S^m \to S^m$$

be a map of degree D. Then the induced map

$$\phi^* : T^{-n}(S^m) \to T^{-n}(S^m)$$

takes an element $a \in T^{-n}(S^m)$ into the element $D \cdot a$.

Proof: a is represented by some map

$$f : S^n \wedge S^m \to T,$$

or, by means of the usual identification (see the proof of Lemma 1 above), by a map

$$f' : S^m \to \Omega^n T.$$

But then $\phi^*(a)$ is represented by the map

$$f' \circ \phi : S^m \to \Omega^n T.$$

If I^m is the m-cube and we identify S^m with $I^m/\partial I^m$, then ϕ is homotopic to the map $S^m \to S^m$ obtained by setting n copies of I^m next to each other to make a "pile" J, and taking the composite map $I^m \to J \to I^m$, where the map $I^m \to J$ multiplies a coordinate of $x \in I^m$ by n, and $J \to I^m$ maps this stretched coordinate back to $[0, 1]$ by periodicity. Since precisely the same construction is used to define addition of homotopy classes, it is clear that $[f' \circ \phi] = D \cdot [f']$. Q.E.D.

Since ∂^1 is the formal coboundary operator, it follows that

$$E_2^p = H^p\left(X, A; \sum_{n \geq 0} T^{-n-p-1}(x_0)\right),$$

where H^p is the formal cohomology group. By virtue of Lemma 11 of Chapter 2 (more precisely, by virtue of the dual assertion of this lemma), H^p is isomorphic to the ordinary cohomology group of (X, A).

Remark: The proof of Lemma 11 was not given in Chapter 2. However, the proof of the lemma can easily be obtained by using the results of Chapter 5. Indeed, let us consider the spectral sequence of Chapter 5, with $H(X, A)$, etc. taken as ordinary homology. By looking at the definition of the differential ∂^r (see the first line of the proof of Theorem 1 of Chapter 5), we see immediately that $\partial^r = 0$ for $r \geq 2$. Thus, it follows that

$$E_2^j \cong E_3^j \cong \cdots \cong E_\infty^j.$$

But, we have

$$E_\infty^j = \frac{\text{Im } [H(X_j, A) \to H(X, A)]}{\text{Im } [H(X_{j-1}, A) \to H(X, A)]}$$

and this quotient group is readily seen to be $H_j(X, A)$, the ordinary j-homology group of (X, A).

Note: The fact that the differentials ∂^r ($r \geq 2$) are zero in case T^* is ordinary cohomology theory will be of great importance to us in what follows.

Let us sum up the results we have obtained so far.

Theorem (12): Let (X, A) be a cellular pair. There exists a spectral sequence such that

$$E_1^p = C^p\left(X, A; \sum_{n \geq 0} T^{-n-p-1}(x_0)\right)$$

$$E_2^p = H^p\left(X, A; \sum_{n \geq 0} T^{-n-p-1}(x_0)\right)$$

and such that the E_∞^p are the graded groups of a suitable filtration of the generalised cohomology group $T^*(X, A)$.

Corollary: Let (X, A) be a cellular pair. There exists a spectral sequence such that

$$E_1^p = C^p(X, A; Z)$$

$$E_2^p = H^p(X, A; Z)$$

and such that the E_∞^p are the graded groups of a suitable filtration of the group $K^*(X, A)$.

Proof: We have only to use the fact that

$$K^*(x_0) = K^0(x_0) \oplus K^1(x_0) \cong Z \oplus 0. \quad \text{Q.E.D.}$$

We have now the following situation. We have a cellular pair (X, A) and two group tables associated with it. Namely, we have

$$H(p, q) = K^*(X_q, X_p) \tag{1}$$

$$\hat{H}(p, q) = H_Q^\$(X_q, X_p). \tag{2}$$

We use the notation

$$H_Q^\$(X_q, X_p) = H_Q^e(X_q, X_p) + H_Q^\sigma(X_q, X_p)$$

to distinguish from the usual Z-grading

$$H_Q^*(X_q, X_p) = \sum_n H_Q^n(X_q, X_p).$$

We have shown in Section 3 the existence of a natural transformation, namely ch, from the K^*-Theory to the $H_Q^\$$-Theory. In other words, we have a natural transformation from one group table to the other. We propose to study the relationships between the resulting spectral sequences E_r^p, $\hat{E}_r^p$ which can be obtained by virtue of this natural transformation. We look first at the abstract algebraic situation.

Lemma (10): Let $\{H(p, q)\}$, $\{\hat{H}(p, q)\}$ be two group tables and let $\phi : \{H(p, q)\} \to \{\hat{H}(p, q)\}$ be a natural transformation which is a homomorphism, i.e. ϕ consists of a collection of homomorphisms

$$\phi^{p,q} : H(p, q) \to \hat{H}(p, q)$$

which commute in an obvious way with induced homomorphisms and coboundary homomorphisms of the group tables. Then there exists a collection $\Phi = \{\Phi_r^p\}$ of homomorphisms of the spectral sequence $\{E_r^p, \partial^r\}$ into the spectral sequence $\{\hat{E}_r^p, \hat{\partial}^r\}$. In other words, we have homomorphisms

$$\Phi_r^p : E_r^p \to \hat{E}_r^p$$

such that $\Phi_r^{p-r} \circ \partial^r = \hat{\partial}^r \circ \Phi_r^p$. Moreover, the mapping

$$\Phi_1^p : E_1^p \to E_1^p$$

coincides with the mapping

$$\phi^{p,p+1} : H(p, p+1) \to \hat{H}(p, p+1).$$

Proof: The intermediate groups E_r^p are defined by

$$E_r^p = \frac{\text{Im } [H(p-1, p+r-1) \to H(p-r, p+r-1)]}{\text{Im } [H(p, p+r-1) \to H(p-r, p+r-1)]},$$

and similarly for $\hat{E}_r^p$. (In fact, we have observed that the case of a general group table is essentially no different than the case of Example (i) above, treated in Chapter 5 where essentially the above formula is given.) Since the ϕ's commute with induced homomorphisms, it is clear that they induce a homomorphism from $\text{Im } [H(p-r, p+r-1) \to \hat{H}(p-r, p+r-1)]$ into $\text{Im } [\hat{H}(p-1, p+r-1) \to \hat{H}(p-r, p+r-1)]$, and similarly for the "denominators" of E_r^p and $\hat{E}_r^p$. We then have the required induced map from E_r^p to $\hat{E}_r^p$ which we denote by Φ_r^p. The fact that the Φ's commute with the differentials of the spectral sequences follows from the fact that the differentials are defined by using induced homomorphisms and coboundary homomorphisms and the ϕ's commute with these. The assertion about Φ_1^p is plain. Q.E.D.

Lemma (11): Suppose that Φ is a collection of homomorphisms of $\{E_r^p, \partial^r\}$ into $\{\hat{E}_r^p, \hat{\partial}^r\}$ as above. Suppose that for some r_0,

$$\Phi_{r_0}^p : E_{r_0}^p \to \hat{E}_{r_0}^p$$

is injective for all p. If the $\hat{\partial}^r$ are zero for all $r \geq r_0$, then also the ∂^r are zero for all $r \geq r_0$ and

$$\Phi_r^p : E_r^p \to \hat{E}_r^p$$

is injective for all $r \geq r_0$. If, in addition, $\Phi_{r_0}^p$ is surjective, then all the Φ_r^p $(r \geq r_0)$ are surjective.

Proof: We show that $\partial^{r_0} = 0$. In fact, let $a \in E_{r_0}^p$. Then

$$\Phi_{r_0}^{p-r_0}(\partial^{r_0}a) = \hat{\partial}^{r_0}\Phi_{r_0}^p(a) = 0$$

since $\hat{\partial}^{r_0} = 0$. As $\Phi_{r_0}^{p-r_0}$ is injective, $\partial^{r_0}a = 0$; whence $\partial^{r_0} = 0$. But then, by the Leray relation, $E_{r_0+1}^p = E_{r_0}^p$, $\hat{E}_{r_0+1}^p = \hat{E}_{r_0}^p$ and the map $\Phi_{r_0+1}^p : E_{r_0+1}^p \to \hat{E}_{r_0+1}^p$ coincides with the map $\Phi_{r_0}^p : E_{r_0}^p \to \hat{E}_{r_0}^p$. In particular, $\Phi_{r_0+1}^p$ is injective and we may use induction to complete the proof.

We now return to the concrete group tables $H(p, q) = K^*(X_q, X_p)$, $\hat{H}(p, q) = H_Q^\$ (X_q, X_p)$. We have

Theorem (13): Let (X, A) be a cellular pair such that $H^*(X, A; Z)$ is torsion-free. Then,

$$ch : K^*(X, A) \to H_Q^\$ (X, A)$$

is injective. Consequenty $K^*(X, A)$ is free abelian of finite rank.

Proof: Letting $\phi = ch$ and using Lemma 10, we find homomorphisms Φ of $\{E_r^p, \partial^r\}$ into $\{\hat{E}_r^p, \hat{\partial}^r\}$. For $r = 1$,

$$\Phi_1^p : E_1^p \to \hat{E}_1^p$$

coincides with

$$ch : K^* (X_{p+1}, X_p) \to H_Q^\$ (X_{p+1}, X_p),$$

again by Lemma 10. But we have calculated $K^*(X_{p+1}, X_p)$ and $H_Q^\$(X_{p+1}, X_p)$, and we have

$$ch : C^p(X, A; Z) \to C^p(X, A; Q)$$

(see Theorem 12 and its corollary) where ch is just the map induced by the coefficient homomorphism $Z \to Q$. For $r = 2$, we have

$$\Phi_2^p : H^p(X, A; Z) \to H^p(X, A; Q)$$

and Φ_2^p is again the map induced by the homomorphism $Z \to Q$ (because ∂^1 coincides with the formal coboundary operator and the Φ's commute with the differentials). Since $H^*(X, A; Z)$ is torsion-free, Φ_2^p is injective. Moreover, we have observed that the differentials $\hat{\partial}^r$ ($r \geq 2$) vanish. By Lemma 11,

$$\Phi_r^p : E_r^p \to \hat{E}_r^p$$

is injective for $r \geq 2$. But for r large enough, say $r \geq R$, $E_r^p = E_\infty^p$ (because the skeleta of (X, A) stabilize) and hence

$$\Phi_\infty^p : E_\infty^p \to \hat{E}_\infty^p$$

is injective. Using the remark following Lemma 9 (applied to cohomology rather than homology), we see finally that

$$ch : K^*(X, A) \to H_Q^\$ (X, A)$$

is injective. This proves Theorem 13.

Theorem (14): Let (X, A) be any cellular pair. Then

$$ch \otimes 1 : K^*(X, A) \otimes Q \to H_Q^\$ (X, A) \otimes Q \cong H_Q^\$ (X, A)$$

is an isomorphism and maps $K^0(X, A) \otimes \mathcal{Q}$ into $H^e_{\mathcal{Q}}(X, A)$ and $K^1(X, A)$ $\otimes \mathcal{Q}$ onto $H^o_{\mathcal{Q}}(X, A)$.

Proof: In place of the group table $H(p, q) = K^*(X_q, X_p)$, we consider the group table $\bar{H}(p, q) = K^*(X_q, X_p) \otimes \mathcal{Q}$, and argue as in Theorem 13. The Chern character induces a homomorphism Ψ of $\{\bar{E}^p_r, \bar{\partial}^r\}$ into $\{\hat{E}^p_r, \hat{\partial}^r\}$ and

$$\Psi^p_1 : \bar{E}^p_1 \to \hat{E}^p_1$$

coincides with the identity homomorphism

$$ch : C^p(X, A; \mathcal{Q}) \to C^p(X, A; \mathcal{Q}).$$

By Lemma 11, Ψ^p is an isomorphism for all r and the theorem is proved. Q.E.D.

Corollary: Let (X, A) be any cellular pair. Then $K^0(X, A)$ (resp. $K^1(X, A)$) is a finitely generated abelian group whose rank is equal to the sum of the even-dimensional (resp. odd-dimensional) Betti numbers of (X, A).

5. Cohomology Operations in K-Theory

In this section, we shall define a sequence of maps

$$\Psi^k : K(X) \to K(X).$$

These maps will be ring homomorphisms which commute with induced homomorphisms, i.e. cohomology operations. The operations Ψ^k play a fundamental role in the proof of Adams' Theorem on vector fields. See Adams— *Vector Fields on Spheres*, Ann. of Meth., Vol. 75, 1962.

We now begin the construction of the Ψ^k. First, we need some preliminaries on representations of compact topological groups. As a reference for unproved results, see Pontryagin—*Topological Groups*. Recall that a unitary representation ϱ of a compact group G is a continuous homomorphism

$$\varrho : G \to U^n$$

for some n; n is called the degree of ϱ. (Of course, the concept of representation can be defined for any topological group, but our only interest later will be in compact groups G.) Representations ϱ_1 and ϱ_2 of G, having the same degree n, are called equivalent (we write $\varrho_1 \sim \varrho_2$) if there exists a $u \in U(n)$ such that $\varrho_1(g) = u^{-1}\varrho_2(g)u$ for all $g \in G$. We denote the equivalence class of ϱ by (ϱ). The notions of direct sum and tensor product of representations are defined in the evident manner. Note that if $\deg(\varrho_i) = n_i$ $(i = 1, 2)$, then $\deg(\varrho_1 \oplus \varrho_2) = n_1 + n_2$ and $\deg(\varrho_1 \otimes \varrho_2) = n_1 \cdot n_2$. We say that a representation ϱ of degree n is reducible if the representation space E^n (on which $U(n)$ acts in the usual way) has a proper subspace left invariant by all the transformations $\varrho(g)$, $g \in G$. By classical properties of the unitary group, any unitary representation is completely reducible, i.e. can be written as a direct sum of irreducible representations. The character of a representation ϱ is the complex-valued function

$$\chi_\varrho(g) = tr\,(\varrho(g)).$$

Clearly, $\varrho_1 \sim \varrho_2$ implies $\chi_{\varrho_1} = \chi_{\varrho_2}$. Moreover, we have

$$\chi_{\varrho_1 \oplus \varrho_2} = \chi_{\varrho_1} + \chi_{\varrho_2}, \qquad \chi_{\varrho_1 \otimes \varrho_2} = \chi_{\varrho_1} \cdot \chi_{\varrho_2}.$$

Finally, we shall need a few deeper results of representation theory. We can define a group-invariant integral (the Haar integral) on G. With respect to this integral, the notion of orthogonality of functions may be defined. If

$$f_1, f_2 : G \to \mathbb{C}$$

are complex-valued functions, f_1 is said to be orthogonal to f_2 if

$$\int_G f_1(g)\,\overline{f_2(g)}\,dg = 0.$$

We then have the following propositions:

1) Let ϱ_1, ϱ_2 be two nonequivalent unitary irreducible representations of G. Then the characters χ_{ϱ_1} and χ_{ϱ_2} are orthogonal functions. If ϱ is a unitary irreducible representation of G, then χ_ϱ has length, i.e.

$$\int_G \chi_\varrho(g)\,\overline{\chi_\varrho(g)}\,dg = 1.$$

As an immediate corollary of 1), we have

2) Two unitary representations of a compact group G are equivalent if and only if their characters are equal.

We now wish to define an analogue of the Atiyah-Hirzebruch-Grothendieck functior $K(X)$ for compact groups G. We begin by defining $\hat{K}_F(G)$ as the free abelian group generated by equivalence classes of representations of G. (By representation we will always mean unitary representation of some degree.) We denote by $\hat{K}_F^+(G)$ the subgroup of $\hat{K}_F(G)$ generated by elements of the form $(\varrho_1 \oplus \varrho_2) - (\varrho_1) - (\varrho_2)$ and we put

$$\hat{K}(G) = \hat{K}_F(G)/\hat{K}_F^+(G).$$

We denote by $[\varrho]$ the class of ϱ in $\hat{K}(G)$. The elements of $\hat{K}(G)$ may be called *virtual representations*. (Similarly, the elements of $K(X)$ may be called *virtual bundles*.) Observe that an arbitrary element θ of $\hat{K}(G)$ may be written as

$$\theta = \Sigma\, n_i[\varrho_i]$$

with the representatives ϱ_i of $[\varrho_i]$ being irreducible. This follows from the fact that all representations are completely reducible and we are dividing out by $\hat{K}_F^+(G)$. By analogy with the dimension homomorphism of $K(X)$ onto Z, we may define the degree homomorphism

$$\deg : \hat{K}(G) \to Z$$

in the obvious way. Thus $K(G)$ is a commutative ring with unit (the product in $\hat{K}(G)$ being induced by tensor product of representations, the unit being induced by the trivial representation of degree 1) together with an augmentation deg. A continuous homomorphism $\varrho : G \to H$, with H another compact group, gives rise in a natural way to a map

$$\varrho^* : \hat{K}(H) \to \hat{K}(G)$$

which has evident functorial properties.

Let ξ be a G-bundle structure on X. Thus ξ is determined by an open covering $\{U\}$ of X together with functions

$$g_{UV} : U \cap V \to G$$

which satisfy certain properties (see Chapter 4). If ϱ is a continuous homomorphism from G into H, we define an H-bundle structure $\varrho(\xi)$ on X as follows. The open covering $\{U\}$ of X remains the same. We define the functions

$$h_{UV} : U \cap V \to H$$

by setting

$$h_{UV}(x) = \varrho\,(g_{UV}(x)), \quad x \in U \cap V.$$

The function h_{UV} satisfy the requirements for a bundle structure, as is easily seen.

Let now θ be a virtual representation of $U(n)$, so that

$$\theta = \Sigma\, n_i[\varrho_i].$$

If ξ is a $U(n)$-bundle on X, we define a virtual bundle $\theta(\xi)$ by setting

$$\theta(\xi) = \Sigma\, n_i[\varrho_i(\xi)],$$

where $\varrho_i(\xi)$ has the meaning described in the last paragraph.

Suppose that for each n we have an element $\theta_n \in \hat{K}(U(n))$. We shall call $\Theta = \{\theta_i\} = \{\theta_1, \theta_2, \ldots,\}$ simply a *sequence*. Let

$$\pi_1 : U(n) \times U(m) \to U(n),$$

$$\pi_2 : U(n) \times U(m) \to U(m)$$

be projection maps.

Definition (2): Θ is called an additive sequence if

$$\theta_{n+m}(\pi_1 \oplus \pi_2) = (\theta_n \circ \pi_1) + (\theta_m \circ \pi_2)$$

for all n, m. In other words, for all $u \in U(n)$, $v \in U(m)$, we have

$$\theta_{n+m}(u \oplus v) = \theta_n(u) + \theta_m(v).$$

Lemma (12): Let ξ be a $U(n)$-bundle on X, η a $U(m)$-bundle on X and Θ an additive sequence. Then

$$\theta_{n+m}(\xi \oplus \eta) = \theta_n(\xi) + \theta_m(\eta).$$

Proof: The proof is easy and its details are left to the reader.

Definition (3): Let Θ be an additive sequence and $a \in K(X)$. We write a as

$$a = \Sigma\, n_i[\xi_i]$$

and we define

$$\Theta(a) = \Sigma\, n_i \theta_{d_i}(\xi_i),$$

where ξ_i is a $U(d_i)$-bundle. It follows from Lemma 12 that this definition is consistent.

Definition (4): Let Θ be an additive sequence. Θ is called multiplicative if

$$\theta_{nm} \circ (\pi_1 \otimes \pi_2) = (\theta_n \circ \pi_1) \cdot (\theta_m \circ \pi_2)$$

for all n, m. In other words, for all $u \in U(n)$, $v \in U(m)$, we have

$$\theta_{nm}(u \otimes v) = \theta_n(u) \cdot \theta_m(v).$$

Lemma (13): Let ξ be a $U(n)$-bundle on X, η a $U(m)$-bundle on X and Θ a multiplicative sequence. Then

$$\theta_{nm}(\xi \otimes \eta) = \theta_n(\xi) \cdot \theta_m(\eta).$$

Proof: The proof is similar to that of Lemma 12 and is also omitted.

Theorem (15): If Θ is a multiplicative sequence, then

$$\Theta : K(X) \to K(X)$$

(see Definiton 3) is a ring homomorphism which is natural with respect to maps of X, i.e. Θ is a cohomology operation.

Proof: The first part follows from Lemmas 12 and 13. The second part is easy to prove and its details are left to the reader.

We are now ready to define the cohomology operations Ψ^k. Let V be a (complex) vector space, V^* the dual space of V. Let V_r be the set of multi-linear maps

$$V^* \times \cdots \times V^* \to \mathcal{C} \qquad (r \text{ factors of } V^*)$$

which are skew-symmetric; V_r is then the Grassmann space associated with V^*. A unitary map

$$u : V \to V$$

induces a unitary map

$$u^{(r)} : V_r \to V_r$$

defined by

$$u^{(r)} (v_1 \wedge \cdots \wedge v_r) = uv_1 \wedge \cdots \wedge uv_r.$$

The map

$$u \xrightarrow{K_V^{(r)}} u^{(r)}$$

is a unitary representation of the group of unitary transformations on V. If $V = E^n$, a Euclidean space, we write

$$K_{E^n}^{(r)} = K_n^{(r)}.$$

Thus $K_n^{(r)}$ is a unitary representation of the unitary group $U(n)$.

Let $x_1, \ldots, x_n$ be n formal variables. $\sum_{i=1}^{n} x_i^k$ is a symmetric function of the variables and can therefore be written as $Q_n^k(\sigma_1^{(n)}, \ldots, \sigma_n^{(n)})$, where Q_n^k is a polynomial with integral coefficients and where $\sigma_j^{(n)}$ is the j-th elementary symmetric function of the variables. We set

$$\psi_n^k = Q_n^k (K_n^{(1)}, K_n^{(2)}, \ldots, K_n^{(n)}),$$

where addition and multiplication are to be taken in the sense of direct sum and tensor product of representations. Thus, ψ_n^k is a virtual representation of $U(n)$ for each k, and we can form the sequence

$$\Psi^k = \{\psi_1^k, \psi_2^k, \ldots\}.$$

Lemma (14): Ψ^k is a multiplicative sequence for each k.

Before proving this, we establish the following

Formula: If $u \in U(n)$, then $\chi_{\psi_n^k}(u) = tr\,(u^k)$.

Proof: With respect to a suitable basis, u is in diagonal form. Let the eigenvalues of u be $\lambda_1, \ldots, \lambda_n$ and the corresponding eigenvectors be $e_1, \ldots, e_n$. The vectors $e_{i_1} \wedge \cdots \wedge e_{i_r}$ $(1 \leq i_1 < i_2 < \cdots < i_r \leq n)$ form a basis for the space E_n^r. These vectors are eigenvectors of $u^{(r)}$ with corresponding eigenvalues $\lambda_{i_1} \lambda_{i_2} \cdots \lambda_{i_r}$. By the classical trace formula,

$$\chi_{K_n^{(r)}}(u) = \sum_{1 \leq i_1 < \cdots < i_r \leq n} \lambda_{i_1} \lambda_{i_2} \cdots \lambda_{i_r} = \sigma_r^{(n)}(\vec{\lambda}),$$

where $\sigma_r^{(n)}(\vec{\lambda})$ is the r-th elementary symmetric function of the numbers $\lambda_1, \ldots, \lambda_n$. By the way characters behave with respect to direct sums and tensor products, we obtain

$$\chi_{\psi_n^k}(u) = Q_n^k \left(\sigma_1^{(n)}(\vec{\lambda}), \ldots, \sigma_n^{(n)}(\vec{\lambda}) \right)$$
$$= \lambda_1^k + \lambda_2^k + \cdots + \lambda_n^k = tr\,(u^k).$$

Q.E.D.

Proof of Lemma 14: We have to prove two things:

(a) $\qquad\qquad \psi_{n+m}^k (u_1 \oplus u_2) = \psi_n^k(u_1) + \psi_m^k(u_2),$

(b) $\qquad\qquad \psi_{nm}^k (u_1 \otimes u_2) = \psi_n^k(u_1) \cdot \psi_m^k(u_2).$

Proof of (a): We shall show that the trace of both sides of (a) are equal. Applying proposition 2) above will yield the result. We have, using the formula just established, $tr\,(\psi_{n+m}^k(u_1 \oplus u_2)) = tr\,((u_1 \oplus u_2)^k)) = tr\,(u_1^k)$ $+ tr\,(u_2^k) = tr\,(\psi_n^k u_1) + tr\,(\psi_m^k u_2)$.

(b) is proved similarly.

Theorem (16): $\Psi^k : K(X) \to K(X)$ is a cohomology operation for each positive integer.

Proof: This follows directly from Theorem 15.

If Θ and Θ' are additive sequences, we shall define a composed sequence $\Theta \circ \Theta'$ as follows. The n-th term $(\Theta \circ \Theta')_n$ of the sequence $\Theta \circ \Theta'$ shall be the virtual representation $\Theta(\theta_n')$. This latter element is defined in a manner completely analogous to the situation in Definition 3. We have then the following theorem.

Theorem (17): $\Psi^k \circ \Psi^l = \Psi^{kl}$.

Proof: As in Lemma 14, it will suffice to show that

$$tr\,(\Psi^k \circ \psi_n^l(u)) = tr\,(\psi_n^{kl}(u))$$

for all $u \in U(n)$. Using the formula established above,

$$tr\ (\Psi^k \circ \psi_n^l(u)) = tr\ (u^{kl}) = tr\ (\psi_n^{kl}(u)). \quad \text{Q.E.D.}$$

Let $a \in K(X)$ and let $ch_q(a)$ denote the $2q$-dimensional component of $ch\ (a)$. We have then the following

Lemma (15): $ch_q\ (\Psi^k a) = k^q \cdot ch_q\ (a)$.

Proof: First of all, let z be a complex number of modulus 1, regarded as a unitary matrix of degree 1. Then $tr\ (\psi_1^k(z)) = z^k$. It follows that if ζ is a $U(1)$-bundle, then

$$\Psi^k(\zeta) = \zeta^k.$$

Let $\xi = \xi_1 \oplus \cdots \oplus \xi_n$ be a sum of $U(1)$-bundles. Then

$$ch\ (\xi) = e^{c_1(\xi_1)} + \cdots + e^{c_n(\xi_n)}.$$

Since $\Psi^k(\xi) = \Psi^k(\xi_1) + \cdots + \Psi^k(\xi_n)$, it follows that

$$ch\ (\Psi^k(\xi)) = ch\ \Psi^k(\xi_1)) + \cdots + ch\ (\Psi^k(\xi_n)) = e^{c_1(\xi_1^k)} + \cdots + e^{c_n(\xi_n^k)}.$$

Looking at the proof of part (b) of Theorem 10, we see that

$$c_1(\xi_i^k) = k \cdot c_1(\xi_i), \qquad 1 \leq i \leq n.$$

Therefore,

$$ch\ (\Psi^k(\xi)) = e^{k \cdot c_1\ (\xi_1)} + \cdots + e^{k \cdot c_1\ (\xi_n)}.$$

This, together with the formula for $ch\ (\xi)$, implies the result for ξ. The result for general bundles now follows from Lemma 5. Finally, the passage from bundles to elements of $K(X)$ offers no difficulties.

Let us observe now that the virtual representation ψ_n^k has degree n. This follows directly from

$$\sum_{i=1}^{n} x_i^k = Q_n^k\ (\sigma_1^{(n)}, \ldots, \sigma_n^{(n)})$$

upon making the substitution $x_1 = 1, x_2 = 1, \ldots, x_n = 1$.

If X is a space with basepoint x_0, then

$$K(X) \cong K(x_0) \oplus \tilde{K}(X).$$

It follows from the preceding remark that the cohomology operations Ψ^k respect this direct sum decomposition. In fact, $\tilde{K}(X)$ is characterized by the condition that its elements have dimension zero and Ψ^k acts like the identity on $K(x_0)$. (Just look at what Ψ^k does to the line bundle over x_0.) We have now the following

Theorem (18): The operation $\Psi^k : \tilde{K}(S^{2q}) \to \tilde{K}(S^{2q})$ is given by

$$\Psi^k(a) = k^q \cdot a.$$

Proof: Recall that $\tilde{K}(S^{2q}) = K^0(S^{2q})$. Since $H^*(S^{2q}; Z)$ is torsion-free, it follows from Theorem 13 that

$$ch : K^0(S^{2q}) \to \tilde{H}_Q^e(S^{2q})$$

is injective. It even follows that ch maps $K^0(S^{2q})$ isomorphically onto $\tilde{H}^e(S^{2q}; Z) \subseteq \tilde{H}_Q^e(S^{2q})$. But

$$\tilde{H}^e(S^{2q}; Z) = H^{2q}(S^{2q})$$

so that actually

$$ch_q : K^0(S^{2q}) \to H_Q^{2q}(S^{2q})$$

is an injective map, taking $K^0(S^{2q})$ isomorphically onto $H^{2q}(S^{2q}; Z)$ $\subseteq H_Q^{2q}(S^{2q})$. Applying ch_q to $\Psi^k(a)$, we get, by Lemma 15,

$$ch_q(\Psi^k a) = k^q \cdot ch_q(a).$$

The theorem follows because of the injectivity of ch_q.

Corollary: Let $\beta : \tilde{K}(X) \to \tilde{K}(S^2 X)$ be the Bott isomorphism. Then

$$\Psi^k \circ \beta = k \cdot (\beta \circ \Psi^k).$$

Proof: Let g be the generator of $\tilde{K}(S^2)$. By Theorem 18,

$$\Psi^k(g) = k \cdot g.$$

Therefore,

$$\Psi^k \circ \beta(a) = \Psi^k(a \cdot g) = \Psi^k(a) \cdot \Psi^k(g) = \Psi^k(a) \cdot kg = k \cdot \beta \circ \Psi^k(a)$$

or any $a \in \tilde{K}(X)$. This proves the corollary.

CHAPTER X

Vector Fields on Spheres

In this chapter, we shall outline the determination of the maximum number of linearly independent vector fields on the sphere S^{n-1}. We shall denote this integer by $M(n-1)$. For every integer $n \geq 1$, we define an integer $\varrho(n)$ as follows: Write n as a product of a power of 2 and an odd number

$$n = (2a(n) + 1) \cdot 2^{b(n)}$$

and then divide $b(n)$ by 4 to obtain

$$b(n) = c(n) + 4d(n).$$

Thus, $a(n)$, $b(n)$, $c(n)$, $d(n) \geq 0$ and $0 \leq c(n) \leq 3$. Finally, set

$$\varrho(n) = 2^{c(n)} + 8d(n).$$

We shall then outline the proof of the following theorem.

Theorem: $M(n-1) = \varrho(n) - 1$.

A manifold M^n is called *parallelizable* if it admits n linearly independent vector fields. As an immediate application of the above theorem, we have the

Corollary: The only parallelizable spheres are S^1, S^3, S^7.

The inequality $M(n-1) \geq \varrho(n) - 1$ is established in Part A of this chapter. This part of the proof involves no algebraic topology whatsoever; it is due to Hurwitz, Radon and Eckmann. See Eckmann—*Gruppentheoretischer Beweis des Satzes von Hurwitz-Radon über die Komposition quadratischer Formen*, Comment. Math. Helvet., Vol. 15, 1942. The inequality $M(n-1) \leq \varrho(n) - 1$ is sketched in part B. The proof makes use of K-Theory, as well as some recent work of Atiyah and James; it is due to J.F.Adams. See Adams—*Vector Fields on Spheres*, Ann. of Meth., Vol. 75, 1962.

Part A: $M(n-1) \geqq \varrho(n) - 1$

The desired result follows from the following theorem. See Eckmann, loc. cit.

Theorem (1): Let G_p be the abstract group generated by p elements ε, a_1, $a_2, \ldots, a_{p-1}$ and subject to the defining relations $\varepsilon^2 = 1$, $a_j^2 = \varepsilon$ ($j = 1, \ldots, p-1$), $a_k a_l = \varepsilon a_l a_k$ ($k \neq l$; $1 \leqq k, l \leqq p - 1$). Then if and only if $p \leqq \mathrm{p}(n)$ does there exist an orthogonal representation

$$\phi : G_p \to O_n$$

such that $\phi(\varepsilon) = -I$.

Corollary: $M(n-1) \geqq \varrho(n) - 1$.

Proof of Corollary: Let $\phi : G_{\varrho(n)} \to O_n$ have the properties described in Theorem 1. Put $A_i = \phi(a_i)$ ($1 \leqq i \leqq \varrho(n) - 1$). Plainly, $A_k^2 = -I$, $A_k A_l = -A_l A_k$ ($k \neq l$). Now, to define $\varrho(n) - 1$ linearly independent vector fields on S^{n-1}, it suffices to define maps $V_i : S^{n-1} \to R^n$ ($1 \leqq i \leqq \varrho(n) - 1$) such that

(a) $(V_i(x), x) = 0$ ($1 \geqq i \geqq \varrho(n) - 1$; all $x \in S^{n-1}$).

(b) $(V_i(x), V_j(x)) = \delta_{ij}$ ($1 \leqq i, j \leqq \varrho(n) - 1$; all $x \in S^{n-1}$).

We define $V_i(x) = A_i x$. A direct calculation, using the above properties of the A_i, shows that (a) and (b) are indeed satisfied.

Q.E.D.

In order to carry out the proof of Theorem 1, we shall quote a series of results on the theory of representations of finite groups. We remark that statements 1), 2), 3), 5) below generalize to arbitrary compact groups. For proofs, see Hall—*The Theory of Groups* and Pontryagin—*Topological Groups*.

By representation, we mean representation in $Gl(n, \mathbb{C})$ (or $Gl(n, R)$).

1) Every representation ϱ of G is equivalent (notation: $\sim$) to a direct sum of irreducible unitary representations. Moreover, the irreducible parts of ϱ are unique up to $\sim$.

2) Let ϱ_1, ϱ_2 be representations of G. Define $\chi_{\varrho_1} : G \to \mathbb{C}$ by $\chi_{\varrho_1}(g) = tr(\varrho_1(g))$. Then $\varrho_1 \sim \varrho_2$ iff $\chi_{\varrho_1} = \chi_{\varrho_2}$. If, moreover, ϱ_1 and ϱ_2 are irreducible, then $\varrho_1 \sim \varrho_2$ iff $\Sigma_{g \in G} \chi_{\varrho_1}(g) \chi_{\varrho_2}(g) \neq 0$.

3) Let $g \in G$ be an arbitrary element, different from 1. Then there exists an irreducible representations R_g of G such that $R_g(g) \neq I$.

4) The number of inequivalent irreducible representations of G is equal to the number of conjugacy classes in G.

5) If G is abelian, all the irreducible representations of G are one-dimensional.

6) $\Sigma_R \{\deg R\}^2 = \# (G)$, where $\# (G)$ is the order of G and where we sum over the set of all inequivalent irreducible representations of G.

7) For any irreducible representation R of G, $\deg R \mid \# (G)$.

8) (Schur's Criterion): Let R be an irreducible representation of G and let $\bar{R}$ be the representation of G defined by $\bar{R}(g) = \overline{R(g)}$ (i.e. the complex conjugate of the matrix $R(g)$). Then,   (i) R is $\sim$ to a real representation of G iff $\Sigma_{g \in G} \chi_R(g^2) > 0$; (ii) $R \sim \bar{R}$ but R is *not* $\sim$ to a real representation of G iff $\Sigma_{g \in G} \chi_R(g^2) < 0$; (iii) R is not $\sim \bar{R}$ (in which case R cannot be $\sim$ to a real representation of G) iff $\Sigma_{g \in G} \chi_R(g^2) = 0$.

9) (Special case of Schur's Lemma): Let Ω be an irreducible set of $r \times r$ matrices and let B be an $r \times r$ matrix which commutes with each element of Ω. Then $B = \beta I$, where $\beta \in \mathcal{C}$.

We now proceed to the proof of Theorem 1: We have

$$G_p = (\varepsilon, a_1, \ldots, a_{p-1}; \varepsilon^2 = 1, a_j^2 = \varepsilon, a_k a_l = \varepsilon a_l a_k \ (k \neq l)).$$

Using the defining relations, we see immediately that every element in G can be written as either $a_{i_1} \cdots a_{i_s}$ or $\varepsilon a_{i_1} \cdots a_{i_s}$ $(1 \leq i_1 < \cdots < i_s \leq p-1)$. In particular, $\#(G) = 2^p$. Let H be the subgroup of G_p generated by ε. As ε lies in $\zeta(G_p)$, the center of G_p, H is normal. Clearly, G_p/H is a direct sum of $p-1$ copies of $\mathbf{Z}_2$ and is thus abelian. Hence, $H \supseteq [G_p, G_p]$ and it follows that for all g, h in G, $ghg^{-1}h^{-1} = 1$ or ε, i.e. $ghg^{-1} = h$ or εh. Therefore, the conjugacy class of h consists of h and εh unless h lies in $\zeta(G_p)$.

We now find $\zeta(G_p)$. If $\{i_1, i_2, \ldots, i_s\} \neq \{1, 2, \ldots, p-1\}$, (i.e. if $s < p-1$; recall that $i_1, i_2, \ldots, i_s$ are arranged in ascending order), pick an index j not in $\{i_1, i_2, \ldots, i_s\}$. Then, $a_j^{-1}(a_{i_1} \cdots a_{i_s}) a_j = \varepsilon^s a_{i_1} \cdots a_{i_s}$. Now pick j in $\{i_1, \ldots, i_s\}$. Then, $a_j^{-1}(a_{i_1} \cdots a_{i_s}) a_j = \varepsilon^{s-1} a_{i_1} \cdots a_{i_s}$. Thus, since either ε^s or $\varepsilon^{s-1} \neq 1$, the element $a_{i_1} \cdots a_{i_s}$ is not in $\zeta(G_p)$ if $i_1, \ldots, i_s \neq \{1, \ldots, p-1\}$. Moreover, $a_j (a_1 a_2 \cdots a_{p-1}) a_j^{-1} = \varepsilon^{p-2} a_1 a_2 \cdots a_{p-1}$. Hence, $a_1 a_2 \cdots a_{p-1}$ lies in $\zeta(G_p)$ iff p is even. Similarly, $\varepsilon a_{i_1} \cdots a_{i_s}$ lies in $\zeta(G_p)$ iff $\{i_1, \ldots, i_s\} = \{1, \ldots, p-1\}$ and p is even. We have then $\zeta(G_p) = \{1, \varepsilon\}$ if p odd, $\zeta(G_p) = \{1, \varepsilon, a_1 a_2 \cdots a_{p-1}, \varepsilon a_1 \cdots a_{p-1}\}$ if p even.

Now, the number of conjugacy classes in G_p is equal to the number of elements not in $\zeta(G_p)$ divided by 2, plus the number of elements in $\zeta(G_p)$. Using 4) above, we find:

(1–o) For odd p, the number of inequivalent irreducible representations of G_p is $\dfrac{2^p - 2}{2} + 2 = 2^{p-1} + 1$.

(1–e) For even p, this number is $\dfrac{2^p - 4}{2} + 4 = 2^{p-1} + 2$.

Using 5) above, we see that G_p/H has 2^{p-1} one-dimensional irreducible representations. Hence G_p has at least 2^{p-1} one-dimensional irreducible representations. In fact, if $R: G_p/H \to U_1$, then $R \circ \pi: G_p \to U_1$ (where $\pi: G_p \to G_p/H$ is the natural map) and R not $\sim R$ implies $R \circ \pi$ not $\sim R' \circ \pi$. Thus, there are at least 2^{p-1} irreducible representations $R_1, \ldots, R_{2^{p-1}}$ of G with $\varepsilon \to +I$. We now find, using (1–o) and (1–e):

(2–0) For odd p, there is exactly one irreducible R^* not included in the collection $R_1, \ldots, R_{2^{p-1}}$. Using 6) above, we have $2^{p-1} \cdot 1^2 + (\deg R^*)^2 = 2^p$; then $\deg R^* = 2^{(p-1)/2}$.

(2–e) For even p, there are exactly 2 irreducible R_1^*, R_2^* not included in the collection $R_1, \ldots, R_{2^{p-1}}$. Again by 6), $2^{p-1} \cdot 1^2 + (\deg R_1^*)^2 + (\deg R_2^*)^2 = 2^p$, i.e. $(\deg R_1^*)^2 + (\deg R_2^*)^2 = 2^{p-1}$. By 7), $\deg R_i^* = 2^{\alpha_i}$, $\alpha_i \leq p$ $(i = 1, 2)$. In order for $(2^{\alpha_1})^2 + (2^{\alpha_2})^2 = 2^{p-1}$, we must have $\alpha_1 = \alpha_2$. It follows that $\deg R_1^* = \deg R_2^* = 2^{(p-2)/2}$.

By the irreducibility of R^*, R_1^*, R_2^* and by 1), 3), 9) above, we find

(3–0) R^* maps $\varepsilon \to \beta I$, where $\beta \in \mathbb{C}$, $|\beta| = 1$ and $\beta \neq 1$.

(3–e) Either R_1^* or R_2^* (or both) maps $\varepsilon \to \beta I$, where β has the same property as in (3–0). For definiteness, assume $R_1^*(\varepsilon) = \beta I$.

Recall that Theorem 1 asks for the existence of *real* orthogonal representations of G_p. Up to now, we may only assert, by virtue of 1) above, that R^*, R_1^* are complex unitary representations of G_p. But now, in general, if R is a complex irreducible representations of a finite group G and if R is not $\sim$ to a real representation, then $R \oplus \bar{R}$ is $\sim$ to a real irreducible representation. Thus, if necessary, we may replace R^*, R_1^* by $R^* \oplus \bar{R}^*, R_1^* \oplus \bar{R}_1^*$ respectively. Using 8) above, we shall now find the exact values of p for which R^* and R_1^* are $\sim$ to real representations. Let $g \in G_p$ be arbitrary; then $g = a_{i_1} \cdots a_{i_r}$ or $\varepsilon a_{i_1} \cdots a_{i_r}$ as we have already observed. In either case, $g^2 = \varepsilon^r \cdot \varepsilon^{r-1} \cdot \ldots \cdot \varepsilon = \varepsilon^{r(r+1)/2}$. Thus, $g^2 = 1$ if $r \equiv 0, 3 \pmod 4$ and $g^2 = \varepsilon$ if $r \equiv 1, 2 \pmod 4$. Now, let $R = R_1$ if p is odd, $R = R_1^*$ if p is even and let $d = \deg R^* = 2^{(p-1)/2}$ if p is odd, $d = \deg R_1^* = 2^{(p-2)/2}$ if p is even. Then $\chi_R(g^2) = d$ if $r \equiv 0, 3 \pmod 4$ and $\chi_R(g^2) = -d$ if $r \equiv 1, 2 \pmod 4$. Summing over G_p, we get

$$\Sigma_{g \in G_p} \chi_R(g^2) = 2d \left\{ \binom{p-1}{0} - \binom{p-1}{1} - \binom{p-1}{2} \right.$$
$$\left. + \binom{p-1}{3} - \cdots \right\}. \tag{†}$$

Let $(1 - i)^{p-1} = x + iy$. Expanding by the binomial theorem, we see that $x + y$ is equal to the expression in the brackets on the right hand side of (†). It now remains to determine the sign of $x + y$ for the various values of p. An easy check, (using the Argand Diagram), shows that $x + y > 0$ if $p \equiv 0, 1, 7 \pmod 8$, $x + y = 0$ if $p \equiv 2, 6 \pmod 8$, $x + y < 0$ if $p \equiv 3, 4, 5 \pmod 8$.

Put $\hat{R} = R$ if p is such that $x + y > 0$ and put $\hat{R} = R \oplus \bar{R}$ otherwise. We define $k(p)$ by deg $\hat{R} = 2^{k(p)}$. Then it follows from (2–o), (2–e) and the results of the last paragraph that

$$
k(p) = \begin{cases}
\dfrac{p-2}{2} & \text{if } p \equiv 0 \pmod 8 \\[2mm]
\dfrac{p-1}{2} & \text{if } p \equiv 1, 7 \pmod 8 \\[2mm]
\dfrac{p}{2} & \text{if } p \equiv 2, 4, 6 \pmod 8 \\[2mm]
\dfrac{p+1}{2} & \text{if } p \equiv 3, 5 \pmod 8.
\end{cases}
$$

It follows from (3–0), (3–e), 8) that $\hat{R}$ is (up to $\sim$) a real orthogonal representation of G taking $\varepsilon \to -I$ (i.e. $\beta = -1$).

Now let $n \geq 1$ be given. Using 1), (2–0), (2–e), we see that there exists a real orthogonal (not necessarily irreducible) representation $\phi : G_p \to O_n$ iff $2^{k(p)} | n$. Writing $n = (2a(n) + 1) \cdot 2^{b(n)}$, we see that $2^{k(p)} | 2^{b(n)}$. Theorem 1 will be proved if we can show that the largest value of p satisfying $k(p) \leq b(n)$ is just $\varrho(n)$. Having calculated $k(p)$ in the last paragraph, we have thus reduced Theorem 1 to a purely number-theoretic verification. Substituting for $k(p)$, we see that we must find the largest p for which

$$
p \leq \begin{cases}
2b(n) + 2 & \text{if} \quad p \equiv 0 \pmod 8 \\
2b(n) + 1 & \text{if} \quad p \equiv 1, 7 \pmod 8 \\
2b(n) & \text{if} \quad p \equiv 2, 4, 6 \pmod 8 \\
2b(n) - 1 & \text{if} \quad p \equiv 3, 5 \pmod 8.
\end{cases}
$$

From this calculation, it is clear that the maximum p is of the form $2b(n) + \delta$, where δ depends only on the congruence class of $b(n)$ mod 4. We calculate δ explicitly as follows: Consider the table

Value of $b(n)$	Value of $2b(n) + \delta$			
0	2	①	0	−1
1	4	3	②	1
2	6	5	④	3
3	⑧	7	6	5
	$p \equiv 0$ (mod 8)	$p \equiv 1, 7$ (mod 8)	$p \equiv 2, 4, 6$ (mod 8)	$p \equiv 3, 5$ (mod 8)

In each of the four rows of the table, we have encircled the largest number consistent with the restriction on p on the bottom. Thus, in the first row, 2 is greater than 1, but $2 \not\equiv 0$ (mod 8) while $1 \equiv 1$ (mod 8). We have thus found that the maximum p is of the form

$$
p = \begin{cases}
2b(n) + 1 & \text{if} \quad b(n) \equiv 0 \ (\text{mod } 4) \\
2b(n) + 2 & \text{if} \quad b(n) \equiv 1 \ (\text{mod } 4) \\
2b(n) + 4 & \text{if} \quad b(n) \equiv 2 \ (\text{mod } 4) \\
2b(n) + 8 & \text{if} \quad b(n) \equiv 3 \ (\text{mod } 4).
\end{cases}
$$

Finally, to see that these values give $\varrho(n)$, write $b(n) = c(n) + 4d(n)$ and note that by definition, $c(n) = i$ iff $b(n) \equiv i \ (\text{mod } 4)$, $0 \leq i \leq 3$.

Part B: $M(n - 1) \leqq \varrho(n) - 1$

Lack of time prevents us from entering into the details of the proof. We shall therefore content ourselves with giving an outline of the main ideas of the proof, referring the reader to Adams' very lucid paper (hereafter denoted by (VF)) for most of the details.

The starting point for Adams' investigation is the following theorem.

Theorem (2): Let $n \geq 1$. If there exist $\varrho(n)$ linearly independent vector fields on S^{n-1}, then there exists an integer $m \geq 1$ with $\varrho(m) = \varrho(n)$ such that the truncated real projective space $P^R_{m+\varrho(m)}/P^R_{m-1}$ has the following property: there exists a map

$$
f: P^R_{m+\varrho(m)}/P^R_{m-1} \to S^m
$$

such that the composite map

$$S^m = P_m^R/P_{m-1}^R \xrightarrow{\ i\ } P_{m+\varrho(m)}^R/P_{m-1}^R \xrightarrow{\ f\ } S^m$$

is of degree 1.

Note: For any integers $p > q$, there is a natural embedding of P_q^R into P_p^R. P_p^R/P_q^R is therefore a well-defined object. The mapping i in the above theorem is of course induced by the mapping of pairs

$$(P_m^R, P_{m-1}^R) \to (P_{m+\varrho(m)}^R, P_{m-1}^R).$$

Adams proves Theorem 2 by making extensive use of James' work on the homotopy of Stiefel manifolds and Atiyah's work on the so-called Thom complexes. The ideas used in proving this theorem require the introduction of a whole collection of concepts, including the Spanier-Whitehead S-Theory. We will not discuss these concepts here, referring to the papers of James and Atiyah cited in (*VF*).

By virtue of Theorem 2, the inequality $M(n-1) \le \varrho(n) - 1$ is reduced to the following theorem.

Theorem (3): There does not exist a map

$$f\colon P_{m+\varrho(m)}^R/P_{m-1}^R \to S^m$$

satisfying the condition mentioned in Theorem 2.

Thus, the problem of proving the nonexistence of a certain number of vector fields is reduced to the problem of proving the nonexistence of a certain map. There is a familiar method in algebraic topology of attacking such a problem. Namely, if $g\colon X \to Y$ is a hypothetical map whose existence we are trying to disprove, then g induces a map $g^*\colon H^*(Y) \to H^*(X)$ in cohomology. If g is assumed to posses some topological property which we wish to show is impossible, we attempt to deduce that g^* has some simple algebraic property incompatible with the properties of the rings $H^*(X)$, $H^*(Y)$, thus contradicting the existence of g^*, hence of g. (For simple examples illustrating this method, see Hu—*Homotopy Theory*, Chapter 1.) Even if the ring structure of the cohomology rings is insufficient to contradict the existence of g^*, it may be possible to contradict the existence of g^* by introducing cohomology operations into the cohomology rings of spaces. For an account of this theory, together with several applications (including a partial solution to the vector field problem), we refer the reader to Epstein and Steenrod— *Cohomology Operations*.

In (*VF*), Adams uses K-theory instead of ordinary cohomology theory in order to contradict the existence of f (see Theorem 3). That is, he considers the induced map

$$f* : K_R(S^m) \to K_R(P^R_{m+\varrho(m)}/P^R_{m-1}).$$

Here, K_R is the functor, analogous to K of Chapter 9, but with real vector bundles in place of complex vector bundles. (We should then write $K = K_C$.) Using the notation of Theorem 2, we see that $f \circ i \simeq$ ident. (the topological property of f). It follows that $i* \circ f* =$ ident. (the algebraic property of $f*$). Thus, $K_R(P^R_{m+\varrho(m)}/P^R_{m-1})$ splits as a direct sum ker $i* \oplus$ im $f*$. Although the ring structure of $K_R(P^R_{m+\varrho(m)}/P^R_{m-1})$ does not rule out the possibility of such a splitting, it turns out that the operations Ψ^k discussed in Chapter 9 do in fact disallow such a splitting.

The work to be done therefore consists of explicit calculations of the rings $K_R(P^R_p/P^R_q)$ $(p > q)$ and of the operations $\Psi^k : K_R(P^R_p/P^R_q) \to K_R(P^R_p/P^R_q)$. Actually, Adams calculates the rings $K_\Lambda(X)$ in the following order:

a) $\Lambda = C,$ $X = P^C_p/P^C_q$

b) $\Lambda = C,$ $X = P^R_p/P^R_q$

c) $\Lambda = R,$ $X = P^R_p/P^R_q.$

Since the spaces P^Λ_p/P^Λ_q are quite simple cell complexes, the necessary calculations, using the methods of Chapter 9, are very manageable. (In particular, the ordinary cohomology groups of these spaces can be calculated trivially, using the method of Chapter 2.)

Simply for the purpose of illustrating the results of Chapter 9, we shall close this chapter by carrying out step a) above. Before stating the result, we introduce a bit of notation. First of all, we allow ourselves to write K, P_p instead of K_C, P^C_p in the next few paragraphs. Let η be the canonical line bundle over P_p, i.e. over each projective class $[z_1, z_2, \ldots, z_{p+1}] \in P_p$, the fiber of η is the complex line consisting of all $(p + 1)$-tuples $(\lambda z_1, \lambda z_2, \ldots, \lambda z_{p+1})$, $\lambda \in C$: (cf. Chapter 9, Theorem 2). If 1 is the trivial line bundle over P_p, we put $\mu = \eta - 1$. Then $[\mu] \in \tilde{K}(P_p)$.

We now observe that the Chern class $c_1(\eta)$ is a generator y of the cohomology group $H^2(P_p; Z)$. In fact, the standard inclusion

$$i : P_p \to P_\infty$$

serves as a classifying map for the bundle η and therefore, if $c_1 \in H^2(P_\infty)$ is the universal Chern class,

$$c_1(\eta) = i*(c_1),$$

from which our assertion follows immediately.

We now prove the following result.

Theorem (4): The ring $K(P_p)$ is a truncated integral polynomial ring with a single generator $[\mu]$ and a single defining relation $[\mu]^{p+1} = 0$. The natural projection $P_p \to P_p/P_q$ sends $\tilde{K}(P_p/P_q)$ isomorphically onto the ideal of $K(P_p)$ generated by $[\mu]^{q+1}$. Finally, the cohomology operations Ψ^k satisfy the relation $\Psi^k([\mu]^s) = ((1 + [\mu])^k - 1)^s$.

Proof: The additive structure of $K(P_p)$ is easily deduced from Chapter 9, Theorem 13 and corollary to Theorem 14. In fact, since $H^*(P_p; Z)$ is torsion-free, it follows that (with the notation of Chapter 9) $K^r(P_p) \cong Z^p$ if r is even, $\cong 0$ if r is odd (where, in general, Z^f means direct sum of f copies of Z). In particular, $\tilde{K}(P_p) = K^0(P_p) \cong Z^p$ and therefore

$$K(P_p) \cong \tilde{K}(P_p) \oplus Z \cong Z^{p+1}.$$

We claim that the elements $1, [\mu], [\mu]^2, \ldots, [\mu]^p$ actually form a set of group generators for $K(P_p)$ (from which it follows that $[\mu]$ is a ring generator for $K(P_p)$). We shall show that the elements $1, [\mu], [\mu]^2, \ldots, [\mu]^p$ form a Q-basis for the Q-linear space $K(P_p) \otimes Q$. To see this, we observe first that

$$ch\,(\eta) = e^{c_1(\eta)},$$

and since $c_1(\eta)$ has been identified with a generator y of

$$H^*(P_p; Z) \cong Z[y]/(y^{p+1}),$$

$$ch\,(\mu) = ch\,(\eta) - 1 = e^y - 1 = y + \frac{y^2}{2!} + \cdots. \qquad (*)$$

To prove the Q-basis property of the powers of $[\mu]$, is clearly enough to show that the elements $1, [\mu], [\mu]^2, \ldots, [\mu]^p$ are Q-linearly independent. Suppose then that we have a linear relation

$$a_0 \cdot 1 + a_1 \cdot [\mu] + \cdots + a_p \cdot [\mu]^p = 0.$$

Applying the Chern character to this equation, we get

$$a_0 + a_1 \left(y + \frac{y^2}{2!} + \cdots \right) + a_2 \left(y + \frac{y^2}{2!} + \cdots \right)^2 + \cdots = 0.$$

But it follows from the known properties of y that then

$$a_0 = a_1 = \cdots = a_p = 0,$$

which is what we wanted. We omit the additional calculations needed to show that $\{1, [\mu], [\mu]^2, \ldots, [\mu]^p\}$ actually forms a "Z-basis" of $K(P_p)$) (cf. Atiyah and Hirzebruch, *Vector Bundles and Homogeneous Spaces*, p. 19, Corollary 3, (iii)).

Since $y^{p+1} = 0$, it follows easily that

$$ch(\mu^{p+1}) = 0.$$

But ch is injective (see Chapter 9, Theorem 13) whence $\mu^{p+1} = 0$. Thus, we have established the first assertion of Theorem 4. To obtain the second assertion, we consider the exact sequence of the pair (P_p, P_q):

$$\cdots \longrightarrow K^{-1}(P_q) \overset{\delta}{\longrightarrow} K^0(P_p, P_q) \overset{j^*}{\longrightarrow} K^0(P_p) \overset{i^*}{\longrightarrow} K^0(P_q)$$

(Here, i^* and j^* are induced by the standard inclusions.) We have observed above that $K^r(P_q) = 0$ if r is odd. Hence, j^* embeds $\tilde{K}(P_p/P_q) = K^0(P_p, P_q)$ into $K^0(P_p)$. By exactness, im $j^* = \ker i^*$, and $\ker i^*$ is clearly generated by $[\mu]^{q+1}, \ldots, [\mu]^p$. This establishes the second assertion.

Finally, we calculate the operations Ψ^k in $K(P_p)$. Since η is a line bundle, we have

$$\Psi^k(\eta) = \eta^k$$

(see the first paragraph of the proof of Lemma 15, Chapter 9). By the definition of $[\mu]$,

$$\Psi^k(1 + [\mu]) = (1 + [\mu])^k.$$

Since Ψ^k is a group homomorphism,

$$\Psi^k([\mu]) = (1 + [\mu])^k - 1.$$

Finally, since Ψ^k is a ring homomorphism,

$$\Psi^k([\mu]^s) = ((1 + [\mu])^k - 1)^s.$$

Q.E.D.

The calculations corresponding to b) and c) above may be carried by similar but technically slightly move complicated methods. Finally, as indicated above, the structural properties of these rings can be shown to preclude the existence of the map f of Theorem 3.

Subject Index

WELCOME
TO MY
WORLD

WELCOME TO MY WORLD

Johnny Weir

Gallery Books

New York London Toronto Sydney

I dedicate this story to the lovers and iconoclasts

who never stop the world from spinning,

and to the two people who have taught

me the beauty of life and love—

my mother, Patti, and my father, John

Gallery Books
A Division of Simon & Schuster, Inc.
1230 Avenue of the Americas
New York, NY 10020

First Gallery Books hardcover edition January 2011

GALLERY BOOKS and colophon are trademarks of Simon & Schuster, Inc.

For information about special discounts for bulk purchases, please contact Simon & Schuster Special Sales at 1-866-506-1949 or business@simonandschuster.com.

The Simon & Schuster Speakers Bureau can bring authors to your live event. For more information or to book an event contact the Simon & Schuster Speakers Bureau at 1-866-248-3049 or visit our website at www.simonspeakers.com.

Designed by Jaime Putorti

Manufactured in the United States of America

10 9 8 7 6 5 4 3 2 1

Library of Congress Cataloging-in-Publication Data

Weir, Johnny, 1984–.
  Welcome to my world / Johnny Weir.
    p.   cm.
    1. Weir, Johnny, 1984–. 2. Figure skaters—United States—Biography. I. Title.
GV850.W45 A3 2011
796.91'2092 B—dc22   2010044198

ISBN 978-1-4516-1028-4
ISBN 978-1-4516-1137-3 (ebook)

Contents

Prologue

I get more messages than Jesus. Actually, make that Santa.

My BlackBerry and iPhone won't stop their incessant buzz-
ing. First it's my best friend Paris (and no, not the heiress) on the
personal line, then a very hot and very young, supposedly
straight guy who attended my weekly *Weeds* night fête and com-
plimented my cupcake selection. *What could he want?* Not the
time to find out. Ditto for the calls and texts on my professional
line: record producer, ice show producer, reality show producer.
It'll all have to wait.

Right now the only distraction that matters is the wailing intercom in my manager Tara's Manhattan apartment. Our driver

has been angrily trying to get us downstairs and into the car for the last forty-five minutes.

Just a few more seconds for a last look in the mirror. Other than a black Viktor & Rolf jacket over a stunning emerald green chiffon Pucci blouse, the rest of my outfit is pretty much the Johnny Weir uniform: black skinny jeggings and pointy black Christian Louboutins. Joey, my makeup artist, has gone way over the top with my eyes to match the magnitude of tonight's event. A final turn to check out my mullet, newly dyed magenta (an absurd little touch that lands me on both People.com and PerezHilton.com the next day), and we're off.

The Town Car races just a few blocks east through Hell's Kitchen and over to Sixth Avenue, where a mad jumble of photographers and gawkers gather in front of Radio City Music Hall. We could have taken a cab the short distance. But celebrities don't take cabs, Tara says, they take cars.

"I'm not a celebrity," I say to her as the driver opens our door. "Just an ice skater."

Instantly we are enveloped in craziness. On the red carpet of the *Sex and the City 2* movie premiere, where it's names, names, names, I have to keep my jaw from dropping open (I don't want to look bad in photos, after all). Chris Noth walks by, then Donald Trump, quickly followed by *Ugly Betty*'s Becki Newton. All the Gossip Girls bring up the rear.

Anyone who is famous and in New York City is on that carpet.

"Johnny! Johnny!"

My name is being shouted from every angle. Photographers want me to give them flair and TV reporters want the crazy quotes. But even more surreal are the stars trying to get ahold of me. Gabourey Sidibe, an Oscar nominee, stops to tell me she's a fan, right before I get a big hug from the French actor Gilles Marini. I can't believe people whose lives are splashed in the pages of *Us Weekly* or *People* know my name.

I can't even believe I'm *at* this premiere, but I received my invitation from the star of *Sex* herself—my icon Sarah Jessica Parker. Daytime talk-show host Kelly Ripa (who has been a longtime supporter of mine but became an überfan after the 2010 Olympics) and her husband, Mark Consuelos, had me and Tara over to their gorgeous, two-story penthouse for dinner, where we were sipping wine when in walked SJP escorted by Bravo exec and on-air personality Andy Cohen.

I had a mini heart attack deep down inside. A fan of *Sex and the City* since the show started, I have always wanted to be Carrie Bradshaw. The character informed a lot of my youth and fashion daring; she inspired me to be a New York–style single lady.

She held out her hand to me and said, "I'm Sarah Jessica."

"Of course you are," I said, awestruck. "I'm Johnny Weir."

"I know exactly who *you* are," she said with a Bradshaw-esque glimmer in her eye.

Sarah Jessica was everything I imagined she'd be: sweet, tiny, beautiful, good smelling, kind of like a fairy-god celebrity. We all sat around under the stars on Kelly and Mark's roof deck, enjoying delicious food, talking about projects and kids. I felt just like one of the ladies.

Before Sarah Jessica left, we exchanged contact information and she invited me to her big premiere. I was still on cloud nine and already crafting an outfit in my head when an hour and a half later, I received an email from her with the subject line: "This Eve." "Such an honor to meet you," she wrote. "Look forward to seeing you at the premiere."

So tonight, thanks to Sarah Jessica, I'm having a true Cinderella-cum-Carrie-Bradshaw moment. Inside Radio City's theater, there seems to be a star in every other seat. Tara spots Jennifer Love Hewitt wearing the same Hervé Leger dress as she, completely making her night (especially after I tell Tara she wears it best).

As we slowly make our way down the aisle, someone taps me on the back. Turning around, I realize it's Vera Wang. As the famed bridal designer turned designer of everything including mattresses, she is a legend in her time. But she was also part of my competition, having designed the 2010 Winter Olympic costumes for my archrival Evan Lysacek. As if that weren't bad enough, she decided to trot out some nasty comments about *my* Olympic costumes in the press. She tells me she'd been misquoted in the press and wants to bury the hatchet. Vera Wang doesn't have to apologize to me. She's Vera Wang. But I accept.

Glancing to Vera's right, I notice Anna Wintour, a sight that sends my heart into palpitations. To me, Ms. Wintour is everything. Not only is she the ultimate dominatrix of style, but I love how she runs her magazine and how brutal she'll be to get ahead. Even if you don't respect fashion, you have to respect her for being on top of her industry for so long.

Vera must have seen my eyes darting in the *Vogue* editor-in-chief's direction because she decides to introduce us. "This is my friend Anna," she says in the way of only the very rich.

For me, this is on par with meeting Lady Gaga or Christina Aguilera, a big, big moment. I don't know how to make my approach. Usually I like to hug and kiss on both cheeks (I'm like a mobster and hug everyone I meet, even businessmen). But Anna is already sitting in her seat, so I don't want to climb over Vera to hug and kiss her, risking the possibility of my tripping and squashing the tiny fashionista to death and ending her reign at *Vogue*. No, I definitely don't want that to happen.

So I have to settle for extending a very well-manicured hand to take hers. It just doesn't seem proper, though. So while she's holding my hand, I curtsy as if she's the Queen Mother and say, "It truly is an honor." Then I beat a hasty retreat lest I start to stutter like a fool.

As we continue down the aisle, Tara leans in to me and asks, *"Who was that?"*

"Are you fucking kidding me?"

After deciding to never ever speak to Tara again because she doesn't know who Anna Wintour is, I take another look at our tickets. Where are our seats? We are still walking toward the front of the theater, past Anna Wintour and Vera Wang, past Suzanne Somers and Donald Trump. We even pass Liza Minnelli and we're still going. All these bigwigs and legends have worse seats than me? When we find our seats—down front and dead center—I feel absolutely gorgeous and successful. I think to myself, *This is exactly where I like to be.*

The *Sex* premiere comes and goes, swirling among the countless events, meetings, awards, and obligations that make up the whirlwind I call my life. Ever since the Olympics, that spectacularly individual moment on the ice when my fate as an athlete was finally sealed in artistry and controversy, I have done anything and everything under the sun.

Here's an abridged list:

—Went to the Kentucky Derby in a giant black Chanel sun hat decorated with a white rabbit carcass

—Toured the Fashion Institute of Technology to decide whether I should attend design school

—Judged Miss USA Pageant in a multipastel Chris Benz feather coat because I didn't want the beauty queens showing me up

—Hired a stylist

—Accepted an award from GLAAD

—Landed a book deal

—Filmed an episode of *The Rachel Zoe Project*

—Filmed an episode of *The Soup*

—Did a voice-over as a waiter on *American Dad*

—Appeared on *The Wendy Williams Show*

—Held meetings about a fashion line

—Did a photo shoot for MAC Cosmetics

—Skated in a benefit in Harlem hosted by Donald Trump

—Wore headbands to everything

—Taught a skating seminar to children to Indianapolis

—Met Cher after attending her concert

—Commentated on the World Championships for TV

—Got snapped by paparazzi while birthday shopping for my mom with my brother in SoHo

—Recorded a single called "Dirty Love"

—Appeared on *The Joy Behar Show* twice in one week

—Appeared on the *George Lopez* show twice in one week

—Covered Elton John's Oscar party for the E! network

—Met Kelly Osbourne, love of my life

—Took meetings about a perfume and skincare launch

—Appeared as a judge on *RuPaul's Drag Race*

Friends and family think I'm crazy to run myself ragged on the heels of a soul-wrenching, medal-less Olympics. "Take it easy and give yourself some time," they say. But at this point I'll take almost anyone's call, because I have to figure out the next chapter of my life. I want to explore all the opportunities being handed to me because I know they won't last for long.

Plus, quiet reflection and waiting is not my way. For the past thirteen years, it's been beaten into me to never look back.

As a figure skater, sitting in the kiss and cry area—that little box at a competition where we wait alongside our coaches with TV cameras trained closely on our faces for our scores—everything you have worked so hard and so long for comes down to a few numbers. You kill yourself and give everything to be ready for an event, and then in a flash it's over, leaving nothing in its wake but a profound emptiness. Whether you have achieved a medal or failed miserably, loved or hated the process of getting there, in that second you fall to the pit of your existence.

You feel tired. No, you feel dead. And in that state of utter depletion, you have to immediately start building yourself up for whatever's next. The job of a champion is to leave the moment behind as soon as it's happened in order to get back on the ice and start the process all over again.

For so long I stripped my life down to nothing but skating to become one of the best in the world. Despite my many attempts at rebellion, I was constantly ruled by my coaches, training, the United States Figure Skating Association ("the federation"), and other strictures of my sport. And then, in what felt like a heartbeat, it was done.

With all the astonishing adventures and staggering catastrophes of my competitive skating career behind me, I'm in the kiss and cry of my life.

1

A Very Weird Child

Above the bed where I slept as a child, a small hexagonal window let in a vision of the dark woods outside our home. I'd often lie awake at night as the shadows danced across my bedroom wall. The trees would shake back and forth in the wind, a tense crackling noise accompanying their ominous listing. I was sure one of them would crash through the roof, instantaneously and tragically ending my life at the tender age of seven.

My flair for drama, or melodrama anyway, came early.

But as much as I hated that window in the darkness, when the sun shined I loved its view onto the outside world. I was pretty divided about my entire bedroom: a torture chamber by night, my showpiece by day. When my parents built their dream house in Quarryville, Pennsylvania, they involved me in the planning so that I could have exactly the room I wanted. The result included lacy white curtains, a small wooden desk for drawing, and a bright apple-red carpet (my mother, a huge fan of red who even chose it as the color of our kitchen sink, was my inspiration).

I also picked a water bed, just like my parents had. Water beds don't come in kid's sizes, so every night I'd climb into this gigantic bed, my tiny frame rolling on the seductive waves that were beyond my comprehension at the time. Our cat Shadow always slept beside me. I loved that cat, but his incessant kneading filled my mind with visions of the bed popping and drowning us both in a geyser of water. To paraphrase Oscar Wilde, there's heaven and hell in each of us. That described pretty much my whole childhood, including my cat.

The duality was a product of my hyperactive imagination. In the waking hours, it was my biggest asset. A quiet child who loved to play alone, I dreamed up new and fantastic scenarios each day. Sitting in the middle of the forest, mounds of earth became lions in the African veldt and flowers turned into exotic birds. Jumping over fences and tree stumps, I turned into a horse competing dressage at Devon.

But at night my mind turned on me. The hexagonal window was just one example of many, including the horse farm display on the far side of my room. My father had built the wooden stable to house my prized collection of beautiful Breyer horses.

At fifteen dollars a pop, the horses were expensive but I was addicted to them, so every holiday I'd get a new one to add to my pastoral tableau. It wasn't playing I did so much as meticulous art direction. And it got me through the day. Come nightfall, however, the horses betrayed me, their regal faces grimacing like something out of Satan's stable.

Given my troubled relationship with the dark, I needed not one night-light to fall asleep, but three. For good measure, my mom would also put on the radio. She tuned it to a soft rock station, the kind of music she liked to listen to, hoping that the sounds of Eric Clapton and Amy Grant would lull me to sleep.

One particular night, the undertones of '80s synthesizers began to work its calming magic and I felt myself drifting off to sleep. But when the song ended, a commercial came on the air. I don't know what it was for—car insurance, Mothers Against Drunk Driving—but the most terrifying noise of shattering glass and crunching bone filled my room. I lunged for the radio to make it stop and began searching for another station with less drama.

Scanning the dial, I moved past late-night preachers talking about what Jesus wants and classic rock with its whining guitars until something totally unexpected and foreign rose up from the speaker: notes on a piano, then a flute in the background. The ethereal sound, although heavy and somber, made me feel very light. Blue skies and plains with long, green grass broke through the gloom of my room. The music transported me to another world of my own design by giving me the space to make up my own stories.

At the end of the song, I leaned in close to learn from the announcer that the piece was from Chopin and the station classical. A vast and magical world opened up where I could imagine whatever I wanted. I kept the dial glued to the classical station from then on, unaware of the very real places music would one day take me.

———————

The truth is, you had to have an active imagination to not go crazy where I grew up. A speck on the map in the middle of rural Pennsylvania, Quarryville's most exotic feature is its Amish people. The isolated subdivision where we lived sat in the middle of seven Amish farms. Kids could walk down the street late at night by themselves, and people put away the locks for their doors long ago.

Town itself consisted of one gas station and one traffic light. An Amish store called Goods sold socks and camouflage gear for hunting, a popular pastime in the area. There was one video store, a Chinese takeout place, and an ice cream stand that only stayed open in the summer. The most extraordinary thing that happened during my childhood was a hot air balloon crashing down in a nearby cul-de-sac. When its shaken riders knocked on our door to ask for help I thought I would die from excitement.

My parents, John and Patti, moved the family to Quarryville

from nearby Oxford, where they had gown up. They've known each other since kindergarten. Dad, a football player, and Mom, a cheerleader, began dating after high school, married, had me four years later and my brother, Boz, four years after that. Jobs at a nuclear power plant in Peach Bottom brought them to Quarryville. For as long as I can remember, they both rose at dawn each day to go to the plant, where my mother had a desk job and my father was an engineer, and returned at night for a family dinner.

Despite the fact that my parents led conventional lives and didn't stray far from their roots, they had an energy that compelled them to do things their own way. Especially Mom. While everyone in her family made chicken and dumplings by rolling out the dough into flat noodles, she made little balls. But her independence went well beyond dumplings. She's someone who says whatever's on her mind to anyone, including me. When I was a little kid people often mistook me for a girl because I liked to wear my hair long. But if anyone ever suggested I cut it, my mom always had the same reply, "If that's how Johnny likes his hair, that's all that matters."

She likes nice things, too, and taught me about taste. Walking into a store, she'd turn to me and say, "Okay, Johnny, I'm telling you, I'm going to pick out the most expensive thing here. And then we're going to have to downsize and pick something different." And we always did.

Many nights I'd watch from the edge of her bathtub as my mom got ready to go out to a party. She'd spritz herself with

Estée Lauder's Youth Dew (a scent that she started wearing religiously at the age of thirteen and is indelibly marked on my olfactory memory) and brush back her short, dark brown hair. Her wide-set eyes, high forehead, and square chin, which she had inherited from her father, were almost an exact replica of my own.

I'd play with the lipsticks and eye shadow until she left the bathroom to pick out an outfit, then watch as she perused her vast leggings collection (it was the '80s after all) for a pair to wear that night. A tiny woman, five foot three and very thin, my mother loved fashion. She had polka-dotted dresses, leggings in every color under the sun, and a lot of hot heels. She was crazy, crazy, crazy for shoes.

While my dad slapped on his Old Spice, she settled on a pair of black leggings, pink pumps and an oversized cream top with shoulder pads. I thought her outfit was so glamorous. "Yes, Mommy, that looks good," I said, offering my unsolicited stamp of approval.

I liked that my mom was different from the other moms. Her short, slick hair was a far cry from the long, flowing bouffant that was the 'do du jour back then. She had a rebellious streak and didn't care what anyone thought about her.

My dad shared my mother's independent spirit, but in a quieter way. A strong guy with a big, thick neck, my father built tree houses and forts, whatever my brother and I asked for. As a kid, I thought my father was fearless. Once he decided to burn a huge pile of leaves he had raked in the yard. But he put a little bit too much gasoline on it, so when he threw the match on the pile, flames shot up and his arm caught on fire. Wearing only a T-shirt, he scooped up my brother and me in the nonburning arm and ran away from the leaping flames. After throwing us into the neighbor's yard, he rolled to the ground and put himself out.

My dad's toughness extended to his parenting style. When he gave my brother and me chores, they had to be done perfectly. After I weeded the flower bed and in between the brick walkway, he would inspect and, sure enough, finding a few tiny, missed seedlings, make me do it again. And again. And again. He wouldn't tolerate anything half-finished. I hated him for his meticulousness when I was little, but now I get it. As much as my mother gave me my free spirit and love of special things, my dad taught me to balance that with an appreciation for discipline. You need to get everything done and done the right way before you can enjoy yourself.

Mom taught me about style, Dad about effort. What they gave me together was respect—for other people, but also for myself. My parents never made me feel odd, even though I definitely didn't act like all the other kids. When I spent hours lining up my toy animals in neat rows only to put them away again, they applauded my power of concentration. My mom didn't mind when I played with her shoes, and my dad got me riding lessons simply because I asked him. That's why I believed in myself a lot.

While most kids get awkward if their friends make fun of them for something, I never changed my behavior because of what anyone else thought. Even as a seven-year-old boy, proudly showing off my new bike with streamers on the handlebars (my mom had bought it for me; Dad was against it) I didn't let the other boys' taunts ruin my ride.

"That's for girls," they all laughed.

"Well, *I* like it," I said.

Heckling only eggs me on, making me want to become more of whatever it is that people are mocking. So the next day I returned to the boys' hangout, riding my new bike, only this time I had braided the streamers to make them even prissier. So what if what I liked didn't match up with that of others? Life was whatever I wanted to make of it or make it into.

The boys didn't respond and left me alone from then on. I wasn't always right in my choices—maybe the streamers were a bit silly—but I needed to figure that out on my own terms.

2

The Natural

As a child, my mercurial imagination was matched only by my boundless energy. I hated to sleep when I thought about all the activities I could be doing. During the day, I ran the soles of my sneakers down from my various obsessions: track, roller skating, gymnastics, anything that wasn't a team sport (which I despised because I'm simply not a team player, and never will be).

My parents did their best to accommodate my every interest. During my gymnastics craze, my father built me a set of balance beams in the backyard where I practiced the dips, turns, and hops I'd seen on TV, not allowing myself to progress to the next level of beams until I had fully mastered the moves on the shorter one without falling. I pursued all my hobbies with the zeal and seriousness of a pro, even if I had no real idea what I was doing. When I got to the highest beam, I completed my routine by jumping off, then raising my arms in an Olympic salute, thousands of adoring fans in my head cheering for me.

So it was that my parents ended up buying me a pair of beat-up black leather skates from Play It Again Sports, our local used sporting goods store, after the images of Kristi Yamaguchi winning gold for her country in the 1992 Winter Olympics in Albertville, France, sparked my fancy.

My family always got Olympic fever during the winter games. It must be the Norwegian blood from my dad's side coursing through us like an icy bobsled track. We knew the names of all the top athletes, their hometowns, even the cheesy made-for-TV backstories. My dad loved the skiers and bobsledders, but for my mom and me it was all about the skating. That year Kristi was a revelation, all steely confidence and extravagant costumes.

With Kristi in mind, I laced up my new used skates, the blades as dull as butter knives, and flung open the big French doors that led onto the deck and out to the cornfields behind our house in Quarryville. The cold air blasted me full force. I had never been so happy to feel ice and wind in my life. The area had been hit by a blizzard and for the last five days my mother, father, brother, and I had been trapped inside with six-foot-tall snowdrifts blocking the doors and windows. It's a miracle my brother and I didn't kill each other—or that my parents didn't kill the both of us.

The sun was out and shining over the vast white landscape. My destination was in sight: a snow-cleared patch of ice in the middle of the cornfield. I took off, running down the stairs in my skates, through the yard and out to the field. The cold filled my lungs and the sun warmed my cheeks as I sped across the yard. All that was missing was the theme song to *Chariots of Fire*. But then out of nowhere I caught a blade on a frozen tree root and went flying face-first into a snow bank. Not exactly an Olympic moment.

But eventually I reached the ice. Although it was my first time on ice skates, I'd logged considerable hours on roller skates in our home's sprawling unfinished basement. The gray cement was the perfect surface for figure eights to various classical music cassettes my parents bought me for holiday gifts, and I used the steel support pole in the center of the room to practice turns.

I was pretty sure these moves would translate to my rock-covered ice patch in the middle of a cornfield. In my mind's eye, I was gliding smoothly and effortlessly in a sleek sparkling costume, the crowd of adoring fans chanting my name. Of course, anyone who saw me that day must have wondered who the crazy kid was in the beat-up blades, hopping over small stones and pumping his arms like he'd just landed a triple axel.

———

definitely caught the skating bug that winter afternoon in the cornfields. The feeling of speeding from one place to another so quickly was amazing. And that might have been the start of my career on ice if not for a certain dapple gray Arabian horse-cross Shetland pony named Shadow (no relation to my cat). My parents had bought him for me after my love of equestrianism grew way past the meticulous Breyer display on my bedroom shelf and into a serious commitment to competitive horseback riding. I'd been around horses since I was a baby, but shortly after turning nine, something inside of me clicked—probably the fact that my dad had competed in horse shows as a kid and had a small chest filled with pretty ribbons to prove it. I told him I wanted to learn to ride the way he had.

I started taking lessons in English saddle and fell in love instantly. I've always been intensely competitive—if another kid could climb up a tree in two minutes, I wanted to be able to do it in one—so with the framework of instruction to channel my innate ability to focus, success came quickly. When my trainer Sue said, "You have to work on your posture," I went home and sat perfectly straight for two hours until my back was shaking. In school, when all the other kids were sleeping on their desks during a moment of quiet, I practiced making my ankles stronger by lifting and lowering my feet for a beautiful line in stirrups.

I won my very first show and within a year was close to making the national team, despite the fact that I was young—and small for my age. It was clear I had a future in horseback riding, so much so that my parents uprooted the entire family from our dream home when I was ten so that I could be closer to my training facilities. The old leather skates wouldn't be making the journey.

As much as I appreciated my family's sacrifice, I wasn't thrilled to be the newest resident of Little Britain. Quarryville hadn't exactly been a thriving metropolis, but compared to Little Britain it felt like Paris in the springtime. The exotic Amish had been supplanted by lonely and desolate land.

I was on the horse seven hours a week, but that still left plenty of time to kill. My parents, perhaps worried that I might find devil's play to pass the time, continued to look for activities to occupy me. Nearly two years had passed since my foray in the cornfields, but I still talked about ice skating, and I still busted out the roller skates every chance I got. And so, Christmas morning in 1994, several months after we moved to Little Britain, found me unwrapping my first pair of real figure skates— black beauties with blades so sharp they could cut skin. And that wasn't all. The gift also came with a package of group lessons at the University of Delaware's professional skating rink, about a forty-five-minute drive from our new home.

The ice rink was littered with kids flailing around on skates. My group name, the Orange Triangles, said it all. I'd signed on for lessons to jump and spin like the beautiful skaters I had seen on TV, not trudge around the ice being called by the shape of a construction sign.

The shapes were a necessity. They were the only way the teachers could keep track of the hordes of kids on the ice during lesson time. Blue Circles, Green Squares, and Orange Triangles separated fifteen different groups of at least twelve kids. It was a veritable Grand Central Station on ice. At eleven, I was the oldest kid by far in my group and the only boy to wear figure skates. The other lads in their hockey skates gave me a few weird looks but I had absolutely no interest in being a hockey brute.

The hour-long lesson almost over, I couldn't wait for the hour of free skating that came in the package price. The teacher had spent most of her time on falling and getting up on the ice (the first thing anyone learns in figure skating). Decked out in my favorite black tracksuit made out of windbreaker material with big green and purple triangles on the shoulders, I was ready to let it rip. The University of Delaware Ice Arena, as big as a small stadium, fueled my imagination.

So did Oksana Baiul, whom I had been transfixed by while watching the 1994 winter Olympics (the first to be played separate from the summer games). Along with the rest of the universe, my family had been glued to the TV watching to see if Nancy Kerrigan, the favored American, would take home gold. But my heart belonged to Oksana. She was *so* much more fun to watch. Her skinny body, adorned in a pink costume with marabou trim on the sleeves, moved fluidly and musically. She

was exotic, from a far-off land called Ukraine, which I'd proceeded to do book reports on (I loved to trace the Cyrillic alphabet from a book I found about the Soviet states, imagining
myself wrapped in fur and riding a large sleigh through a mysterious and snow-swept city). When she won the Olympics, I
wasn't surprised. And the uproar after—that she didn't deserve
it and the competition had been fixed—made me love her even
more.

As soon as I was released from the gulag of my group, I took
off. No longer a novice with two lessons under my belt, I was a
champion skater like Oksana with imaginary fans who began to
fill the seats of the arena. But to be a real skater, you had to
jump. Any idiot knew that. So that's what I had planned for
today—to do a jump like I had seen on TV.

I didn't know it at the time, but I had been unconsciously
training myself to be a figure skater. Through the movement of
roller skating and the rigor of horseback riding, I was very aware
of my body and its different functions. On a trampoline in back
of our house, I had spent the summer practicing rotating like
the skaters on TV, jumping up, spinning, and landing.

I headed for a small opening in between a girl tottering in
bright pink pants and two boys pushing each other hockey style.
Once in the clear I pushed off on one leg and jumped forward,
flying in the air as I rotated around one and a half times, and
landing backward. It felt just as great as I had imagined, and I
planned to spend the next fifty-two minutes doing them again
and again while my adoring fans cheered me on.

But my group teacher interrupted me.

"Johnny, do you have any idea what you just did?" she said, pulling me aside.

I had no idea she had been watching me.

"Yeah, I jumped."

"You did an axel. That usually takes someone at least two years to learn. You just did it in two hours."

———

I wasn't too sure about this lady. Priscilla Hill, my new skating teacher, showed up to our first lesson wearing a snowsuit . . . in the summertime. It wasn't even a cute girl's snowsuit but rather a big puffy gray one from the U.S. Air Force, for which her husband flew planes. She also called me Johnny, which I hated. Although my family called me that to differentiate me from my dad, at school and in my professional life I went by John. I tried correcting her a bunch of times, but she seemed not to take notice. Very happy and smiling all the time, Priscilla had an extremely childlike aspect that made me feel like she was younger than me. Her accessory of choice was a backpack in the shape of a panda bear.

The teacher who had noted my axel brought me to Priscilla not only because she had won national medals during her competitive skating career and now coached a lot of good skaters but also because she was a "lefty" like me. Those who rotate counterclockwise when they skate only account for about 20 percent of people, and it's important to have a coach not confused by the difference.

After one lesson, Priscilla gave me her opinion: I had a lot of talent but I needed more time on the ice. A lot more time. At eleven years old, I was practically middle-aged for a figure skater. My skills weren't nearly up to par, she said. Just as you have to practice a foreign language, I would have to work every day to become fluent. Once a week certainly wasn't going to cut it. We needed to move to Delaware because Priscilla didn't want to work with me after "he's been in the car for a long commute and exhausted," she told my mom and me.

Move to Delaware? I was floored. We had just moved for my horseback riding, plus I didn't want to live in a totally different state, away from all my family and friends. From the minute the first teacher pulled me from the crowd, I knew I wanted to be in the Olympics. But I didn't realize everything that it entailed. I didn't realize that I wouldn't be able to live a normal life or keep riding.

I definitely didn't understand the financial strain of paying for all my activities. I had a good riding pony, which costs the same as a car and is expensive to maintain. Now my parents were faced with paying for a skating coach and renting time on the ice.

My mom, however, understood I couldn't continue to ride horses and skate at equally intense levels. The money issue aside, I wouldn't have been able to keep both up, plus go to school. The next day she sat me down at the breakfast bar facing our kitchen and said, "Johnny, you have to make a choice. Are you going to ride or are you going to skate? Because we can't afford for you to do both, and your body can't handle doing all this stuff."

It was such a big decision, one that would affect not only my future but that of our entire family. We would have to move again if I chose skating, and to a totally different kind of environment. But my mom was content to leave it up to me. Even when we were little, she respected her kids and let us make up our minds about pretty much everything.

She left me at home to "sit and figure out what you're going to do" while she went to the grocery store. For the next three hours I stayed glued to my stool, staring at the white tiles with blue flowers of the bar and contemplating what would be the right choice for my life. I kept alternating between the image of myself as an Olympian in horseback riding versus figure skating.

My mom finally returned and, after putting the groceries away, asked if I wanted a sandwich. "Please," I said. She made me my favorite—roast beef with tomatoes—and sat down next to me. "Okay, Johnny. You've been alone long enough; did you make a decision?" I immediately started crying because I had made a decision, and it was a hard one: "I'm going to skate."

"Are you sure?" my mom asked because she'd say "Are you sure?" about everything. "Are you sure, Johnny?"

We were both crying by this point.

"Yes, Mom. I'm going to be a skater."

In the spring of 1996, after only about ten months of living in Little Britain, my family packed up again to move to Delaware. Other than the trauma of my having to say good-bye to my pony Shadow, none of us shed too many tears about leaving the house in the middle of nowhere.

My extended family, however, was pretty shocked and upset. A number of them came down hard on my parents about moving not once but twice for the fancy dreams of a kid who hadn't even hit puberty. "What the hell are you thinking?" one aunt said. "Why are you leaving Pennsylvania, everything you know, and your big beautiful house to move to a shit box in Delaware? It's a cesspool down there."

But my parents didn't listen to any of it. As kids, both of them had a lot of dreams smashed before they could even start—whether because of strict parents, too many kids in the house and not enough money, or simple small-mindedness. They never wanted to regret having said no, so they did everything within their power to help me achieve whatever fantastical notion I set for myself.

I had to agree with my extended family on one point: our new house was kind of a shit box. At least compared to what we were used to back home. No more rolling hills, cornfields, forests, or quiet cul-de-sacs. Now we looked right into our neighbors' windows and it really creeped me out. I kept my blinds shut tightly at all times; I've always put a high premium on privacy.

Luckily, there wasn't too much time to dwell on Delaware and its shortcomings because I got swept up immediately in the ice rink. During that first summer program, I spent almost all day at the arena, five days a week, without ever stepping outside, even though the arena wasn't more than eight minutes from our house by car.

My parents and I got up at four o'clock in the morning, early enough for them to drop me off and get to work at the power plant in Pennsylvania on time. By five o'clock I was out on the ice training with Priscilla. Because she didn't want me to acquire bad habits, I wasn't allowed to skate without her supervision. So by seven o'clock I was off the ice with about ten hours to kill before I could get back on the ice at five for one last hour of practice.

The rink—where I ate my packed lunch from home at a makeshift table using one of the chairs from an administrator's office and took naps on a stretching mat in an open area above the stands—became my babysitter.

Because Priscilla had decided I would do pairs skating, as well as skate on my own, I had to do weight training in order to become strong enough to lift my partner. The trainer at the rink had his work cut out for him: I was a tiny, skinny kid for the longest time. At four foot nine and seventy pounds, people used to ask my mom all the time if she was feeding me.

I was fine with the weight training, but I really hated the dance classes that were also part of the summer program. There were five different teachers, one for every day of the week, including the un-jazziest jazz teacher on Mondays and a fat lady who taught modern dance Thursdays, and I despised all of them for boring me—except for Yuri on Wednesdays.

Originally from Saint Petersburg, Yuri Sergeev had danced with the Kirov Ballet and had a strange accent not unlike my idol Oksana. While he taught us Russian, Greek, and Moldovan folk dances, I had the same thrill as when I used to trace the Cyrillic alphabet from my book on the Soviet Union. Except that Yuri was alive and able to return my excitement.

He took me under his wing, offering me ten extra minutes after class to privately coach how to hold my arms or head in ways that would look good on the ice. I was built in a way that Russians favored when looking for kids to train as skaters, so Yuri knew the best positions for my body, and I loved the extra attention.

For the most part, though, I spent my time watching other kids practice and train. Seeing the skaters at the junior and senior levels go through their programs, get tangled in frustration, and work it out with their coaches was my greatest lesson during that period. I began to differentiate the styles from little clues like a straightened arm or tilt of the head. I was a sponge drinking up anything and everything that would make me a better skater.

The ice rink was a haven where I made friends who were equally passionate about skating and so made me feel comfortable expressing myself through music and movement. It stood in stark contrast to life outside, which was foreign, and not in a good way. Living in a new state, my parents, brother, and I were away from all our friends and family in what seemed like a big city filled with traffic lights, noise, and dirt.

As the temperature outside the rink dipped with the arrival of fall, I faced yet another terrifying aspect of my new life: school. I showed up the first day totally unprepared for the experience of eight hundred kids in an unruly urban middle school. My first mistake was my outfit. A small, pale kid, all eyes and lashes, I had chosen to wear jeans that hit a little above my ankle and a big, brightly colored polo shirt and my backpack with the straps on both shoulders. It's like I wanted to be killed.

I couldn't believe my eyes. Rocking big baggy jeans and ripped apparel were kids, if that's what you could call them, in all colors and sizes. There were Asians and Jews, Muslims in head scarves and lots of African Americans. I had never been so close to black people and now they were knocking into me, big boys with as much facial hair as my dad.

It didn't take long for the other students to find out that I was a skater—I only went to school half days to accommodate my training schedule—and begin calling me a "homo" or "faggot" when I walked down the hallway. They would sing aggressively anti-Johnny raps. But I was always strong enough to take that sort of thing. Especially now that I had skating to wrap myself in: it was my art and nobody could take it from me.

"So where did your son skate before this," one of the other mothers asked my mom at the rink.

I was working on my double jumps, rotating twice in the air and coming down with a haughty flourish I'd developed with Yuri. Priscilla was yelling at me to stop jumping around and concentrate on my footwork. All I wanted to do was jump and have the arena whirling around me. I didn't care at all about technique, but Priscilla beat it into me. She discovered my inner talents, the edge quality I became known for, and forced them out.

"This is the first place Johnny's skated at," my mom answered. "He's only been skating for six months."

"No way; he's too good," another mom said. "You have to be lying."

Nobody believed my mother, Priscilla, or me that I had just started because I could already do a lot of the spins and jumps that the older kids were struggling with. I could do them without thinking, while they were falling and falling and falling. On the ice, it was clear that I had something special, but the other parents gossiped that I was keeping a secret. My mom hated it, but I love it when people talk about me.

I never wanted to do something that I was going to be mediocre at, even as a kid. So if I wasn't a star, I would still pretend I was one. But when Priscilla would talk about me ("Oh, I have this wonderful boy I'm training") or I would notice the other coaches coming to watch me while I practiced, I knew it wasn't all in my head.

But I still had to prove myself in competition. My first big trial was the qualifying competition for the Junior National Championships in Pittsburgh. My training up to that point had been fast and furious to the point of dizzying. In order to get to the qualifiers that September, I had less than three months to pass a total of eight tests required by the U.S. Figure Skating Association (USFSA) for competing on an official level. I had already participated in a bunch of small, local competitions to get ready for battle. Although I had always won these contests by a landslide, I didn't know how I would do on a much larger stage.

At my rink and even in the local competitions, I was in a safe nest where I was coddled by all the coaches and the other kids around me. Because I was one of the only boys in my age group, everyone rooted for me to keep pushing. If I learned a new jump or new program, they told me how great it was. But would I skate as well surrounded by an arena full of strangers?

When we all piled into the car to make the drive from Delaware to Pittsburgh, the cool fall air smelled faintly of burning leaves. My skating partner Jodi Rudden and I had worn coordinated orange (me) and red (her) turtlenecks in homage to the season. She and I were similarly opinionated, driven, and outspoken, and we even looked alike with our pale skin, dark hair, and tiny bodies. The matching turtlenecks drove home the effect. In the car with my mom and Jodi's mom, Janice, we were bouncing off the walls. It was the first time that I'd really been away. I couldn't wait to stay in a hotel and eat in restaurants like a real grown-up.

Pulling up to the arena, the number of kids who had come to Pittsburgh to compete was bewildering. The South Atlantic region we were part of extended from Pennsylvania all the way down to Florida. I was up against twenty-two boys in my division of the singles skate, more than double the number of any of my previous competitions. Plus, the South Atlantic region has always been known as the strongest, the hardest, and the most talented group on the East Coast. Scanning the boys in my group, many of whom had the shoulders of miniature linebackers, I suddenly found the prospect of eating at T.G.I. Friday's not all that appealing.

I competed in singles first. The rink was smaller than the University of Delaware's arena, but family and skating fans packed the stands because my group, juvenile boys, were young and cute, a real crowd pleaser. We were divided into groups of six and thanks to the Weir family luck, which is not good, I drew to skate last in the last group. Waiting for boy after boy to complete his program, listening to the thunderous applause or, horror, the gasps of falls, proved utter torture.

By the time my group got on the ice for our six-minute warm-up period, I felt sick to my stomach. Those minutes ticked by as slowly as a century, but when they were over I made a beeline, still wearing my skates, for the lobby. Standing in my costume, I found my mom and said, "I want ice cream."

I don't know if I thought I was on death row ordering my last meal, or if the dairy would soothe my bubbling stomach, but I just needed something to calm me down. My mom rushed and got me a vanilla cone from a nearby stand that wasn't doing too much business. I took a few licks and stoically returned to the rink.

Priscilla, who had traded her snowsuit for a big fur coat in honor of the event, guided me to the ice. I had gone about six shades paler than my already translucent skin. I felt awful. *Why did I want to do this in the first place? I am a horrible person for selling Shadow and now I am going to pay. I'm not ready. What was Priscilla thinking, sending me out after only six months of training?* A piercing shriek from the crowd broke my spiraling thoughts.

"Go, Johnny!"

It was my partner, Jodi. I looked up and saw her in her red turtleneck screaming for me. A whole group of people that I trained with—all the big kids and their parents—surrounded her. They pumped their fists and made catcalls.

Then my music started, and I did the only thing I could do: I went out and skated. After a whirlwind of jumps, spins, and footwork, I had earned all first place scores from the judges. Not too long after, Jodi and I killed in pairs, earning all first place votes, too.

We qualified for the Junior National Championships, which would be even harder than this competition and require a lot of training between then and April to be prepared. But more astounding than qualifying was the realization that, yes, I was as good as everyone said I was. It wasn't all in my head. I floated home on the assumption that my entire future would come just as easily and naturally, but I was in for a rude awakening.

3

A Star Is Born

I sized up the other boys on the ice and thought, *I've got this locked up.* Not knowing what to expect at the Junior National Championships, I initially approached the biggest contest of my life so far with a fair share of trepidation. But during the practice right before the competition, I figured out that no one else could do a triple jump. In the five months since the qualifying championships in Pittsburgh, I had learned *two* different ones and had incorporated both into my program. A boy to my left landed with a thud during a double axel. Oh, yeah, I had this.

So far the trip out to Anaheim, California, had been a fantasy come to life. My partner, Jodi, and I traveled together—we were also competing in the pairs—and because it was spring and the West Coast, we ditched the turtlenecks for matching shirts: purple, the color of royalty. On my first long flight, I played a *Wheel of Fortune* video game my mom had bought me. This was heaven.

Bright, beautiful California felt like a different planet from dour Delaware. The sun shined all the time and people sold tropical fruit on the side of the road. Our hotel was big and comfortable, just how I like them. Young skaters from all over the country filled the elevators, rushed through the lobby, and caught up with old friends in the lounge. Because I was very shy, I didn't make it a point to mix with the rest of the skaters but I shared in the excitement of our common goal.

During the warm-up, I felt extremely confident. But just like in my old bedroom, when my happy impressions would flip once the sun went down, my peace of mind vanished in the moments before the competition. As I waited for the announcer to call my name, my previously positive assessment of my chances of winning turned on its head. Suddenly I became convinced that I *wouldn't* win. This was the first time I was performing the triple jumps in front of people at a competition. The best skaters in the world fell while doing them on TV all the time, and I hadn't even been skating a year yet. Everything that had given me confidence became negative.

I couldn't turn the worrying thoughts off. I knew they were my nerves flaring up and assumed they would sort themselves out once I settled into my program. But they followed me onto the ice and flew alongside me like harpies while I skated. I had grown a couple of inches in the last several months and my long legs suddenly felt as if they belonged to someone else.

The real problem, though, was my head. During my program, I made five or six mistakes and finished up with a curious mix of bewilderment, anger, and fear. However, nothing could prepare me for the shock about to come. When the judges presented their placements, there were all these different numbers I had never seen before: 14, 5, 6, 2, 13. I was used to seeing all ones. "What does this mean?" I asked. Well, what it meant was that I placed fourth in the men's competition when I should have won it and experienced my first major loss. I was shocked. Even though I had been nervous, I hadn't imagined not winning. I'd never truly contemplated failure.

———————

Forget Jodi. Panic was my most trusted companion for the next two years as I went from a kid to an Olympic-level athlete. After my first taste of losing at the National Championships, I discovered another part of myself that couldn't be controlled simply with hard work and talent. I was never sure who would show up on competition day—confident Johnny or the guy who choked. Just like the vivid thoughts in my head as a child that made my environment delightful during the day and conversely paralyzed me at night, the force of my personality worked both for and against me.

Very often I did well. After moving from juvenile up two levels to novice, I won the regional and sectional championships and then placed third in the National Championships in 1998. Right after turning fourteen, I won a Junior Grand Prix event in Slovakia, beating a lot of high-level junior skaters who were older than me.

But just as often, I didn't do well. In 1999, the year I learned to do a triple axel, the jump necessary to compete at the Olympic level, I completely psyched myself out during my first competition of the Junior Grand Prix in the Czech Republic and suffered a humiliating defeat, coming in seventh.

I was all over the place. On the one hand, I decided I wanted to go to the 2002 Olympics in Salt Lake City, Utah. I knew I wouldn't be a champion, but I thought I could make the team after only five years of skating, which was ludicrous. On the other, I was completely out of my comfort zone while competing. It didn't matter that I trained every single day, going through the exact same routine perfectly without problems. As soon as I stepped on the ice for a competition, I started sweating and my heart raced. Every imaginable bad thought worked its way into my head: *you're ugly, you're lazy, you're just not good enough*. I was my harshest critic.

My big problem—one that stayed with me for a long time in my career—was that I didn't know how to compete. Unlike most kids who start on the ice at three years old, getting their makeup done, wearing costumes, and learning to compete against other kids, I went right from zero to national-level competition. I didn't get that comfortable kiddie period to learn how to react in different situations, how to deal with stress, and, most important, how to keep nerves under control. Going from zero to sixty, I was crashing left and right.

I was also becoming a teenager. What a combo. When you're an angst-ridden hormonal mess, that's a *wonderful* time to undergo constant scrutiny.

As I started to grow hair in places where I didn't think people should have hair, I sprang up from my long-standing height of four foot nine to five six while barely tipping the scales at a little over one hundred pounds. I was still a beanpole, but a bigger beanpole. With my body changing, I not only had to deal with normal anxieties but also keep adjusting my techniques.

By the 2000 National Championships, I had a full-on career crisis at the ripe old age of fifteen. Even though I fell on my triple axel in the short program, none of the other skaters tried one, so the judges still put me in first. But then, with the expectation of winning that I found crippling, I had a complete meltdown in the free program. Obsessed with trying not to fall, of course I fell. It was my first competition against Evan Lysacek, a then skinny waif from Illinois. Until my debacle during the free program, Evan had been in fifth place. Ultimately he won and I took fifth.

Everything changed as I climbed the ranks of competitive skating. My body, my technique, my ability, my emotions, my surroundings, all in turmoil and flux. The one constant, however, was that I sucked at competing. People from around the world were saying the same thing: "Johnny's wonderful. He can do triple axels and is great in practice. But in any contest, he falls apart."

Struggling with my mental stability, I asked myself, *Can I do this?*

———————

The Chinese skaters, in their government-issued costumes, accepted their scores grimly. This was the last place on earth I wanted to be. I had told the USFSA flat out I didn't want to go to the Chinese Junior Grand Prix, but they sent me anyway. And when the federation says go, you go. They wanted me there because I was the only person from the States at the junior level who could do a triple axel. Like Russia's junior skaters, the Chinese were a group that everyone feared because they could all do really difficult jumps. They were a bitch to contend with.

Seven months after the Nationals, those embarrassing falls still hurt. I hadn't forgotten what a rotten job I had done and still didn't know how to beat down my nerves. And here I was, facing skaters who didn't seem to have any emotions, only perfect technique. I was also a bit wobbly, having subsisted for the prior couple of days on nothing but black coffee and energy bars I had carried with me from home (I don't do Chinese food).

All I had going for me was the fact that this competition didn't really matter. In all the years competing in the Junior Grand Prix circuit, I had never made the finals because of my terrible track record. Winning some competitions and losing others, I never gained enough points to make it all the way and this year was no different.

So I hit the ice without inhibition despite it being the first time I chose to include two triple axels in my long program. No matter how many mistakes I made, Priscilla's philosophy was to make everything harder. Never step back, always step forward, even if it hurts. But the pressure of hard programs never bothered me, only the pressure I put on myself, and that was completely gone in China. I skated perfectly in both programs and took second place to a Chinese boy, which exceeded everyone's expectations, including my own.

My personal victory in China set off a winning streak that restored my confidence and that of those around me—crucial since I was moving to the next and highest group in skating, the senior level. These are the skaters who are on TV and go to the Olympics; these are the ones who really count. Three weeks later, back in the States, I moved from the regional competition to the larger sectional, defeating everyone on the East Coast. People started to whisper about me doing well in the next National Championships, a totally unexpected rumor for a newly minted Olympic-level skater.

I felt a new and odd sensation: calm. Even as the months flashed by quickly and I arrived in Boston for the 2001 National Championships, *the* event that dictated who went to the World Championships and the Junior World Championships (and helped define early favorites for the following year's Olympic team), I remained comfortable in my skating. I didn't know if I was learning or simply getting over a phobia, but I prayed my new Zen state stayed.

I should have been scared. At sixteen, I was the youngest competitor in the senior level by four years. On top of that, the week before I had sustained a bad hip flexor injury, which required a cortisone shot three inches from my naughty bits that left me without much feeling in my hip while I skated. But being the underdog is where I flourished. On top, I needed to worry. I really didn't think I was going to do anything but show up— maybe get tenth place if I was lucky. After my short program, to my astonishment, I placed sixth, which meant I was in the group of skaters who performed their free program live on ABC Sunday afternoon. For the first time, I was going to be on national TV.

When I got on the ice to warm up the next day, I couldn't believe the men skating around me. They were the best six skaters in the country, and I was part of it. Watching the big American champions like Timothy Goebel and Michael Weiss, whom I had followed for years on television, spin and stretch in the flesh didn't feel real. *What am I doing here?* I thought before remembering that I had to stop staring and start practicing.

Before I even touched the ice to compete, I had already won. As part of "the group," the best six, I would get my pick of Grand Prix events that fall and a shot at the 2002 Olympics. After all my personal issues, I was so honored to be there and returned the honor by skating my ass off. The big tassels on my costume's shoulders shook as I shimmied and danced to my raucous Hungarian music. I rocked it so hard and clean. Although I placed last in the group, I couldn't have been happier: sixth in the country was not a bad place to be.

Sofia, Bulgaria, in March is not pretty. I arrived in the Eastern European city as the highest-ranked U.S. skater competing in the Junior World Championships after my performance in Boston. Spring was nowhere to be found among the crumbling smog-stained buildings and empty streets. Even though morning was fully under way when the taxi spewing exhaust picked my mom, Priscilla, and me up from the airport, a gray mist filled the deserted vista. Occasionally a person, bundled head to toe from the cold, popped up looking like a walking cocoon.

The Junior Grand Prix series takes skaters to really obscure places like Banská Bystrica, Slovakia, and Hamar, Norway, because it lacks the funding of the senior series. Although it's a European capital, Sofia came as a shock to our little traveling band. I stared out the window of the taxi, marveling at the desolation. My anxiety mounted as the bleakness extended. I was a pretty finicky traveler who always felt uncomfortable abroad. Just dialing a different area code was enough to freak me out. Surveying the alien landscape, I knew I was going to feel *very* uncomfortable here.

I was jolted out of my reverie by the taxi lurching to a halt in the middle of the street. There wasn't another car or person on the road as far was we could see, so why had the driver stopped all of a sudden? My mom, clearly suspecting a scam, glared at the driver while Priscilla, as she was known to do in any uncomfortable situation, began laughing loudly like an overgrown kid.

"What's going on?" I asked the driver in my faltering Russian.

Because of my interest in Russia, I had taught myself some simple phrases and figured he might understand me since Bulgarian is very close. Unfortunately, I had no idea what he said back to me. My mother was able to surmise his meaning when the driver jammed his finger at the windshield.

"Johnny! Dogs!" she said.

Right outside the cab, a pack of wild dogs snarled at us. The twenty or so mangy, wolflike canines bared their teeth and howled before taking off for a dowdy Soviet-style municipal building. Oh, no, I was definitely not comfortable here.

My surroundings weren't the only reason for my discomfort (although it didn't help when the people at the hotel registration said, "You can turn right out of the hotel during the day, but only right; never go left. And at night, don't leave the hotel at all.") I had trained hard for the event and was skating well, but the pressure was on like never before. Every single person knew who I was.

At the arena the day of the event, one of the USFSA officials came up to me, accompanied by a few of his foreign counterparts. The white-haired official, in a Brooks Brothers blue blazer and khaki pants that made him look like he had just stepped out of a Florida golf club, gave me a big scary smile.

"This is our next great skater," he announced as he patted me hard on the back. "Watch him now. Soon he's going to be our next champion."

He might as well have jabbed a blade into my leg. I entered my short program with the needling sense that I was going to be a big failure. I blindly made my way through a routine, which included a triple axel–triple toe loop combination, the hardest thing that anybody was doing on the ice during the event. But that's not where I fell. It was during my last jump, a triple flip, that I landed on the ground. A jump I had learned three years earlier! Trudging off to the kiss and cry box to await my scores, I was so disappointed. The judges didn't see it that way, though. They kept me in first place, despite my fall, firmly sticking behind their choice for the next generation of Olympic skater. One of the first things you learn as a figure skater is that the judges give special treatment to their favorites. Going into the competition, they always have an idea of who the best skaters are, and that guides them in their scoring.

The weight of number one crushed me as I readied myself to compete in the long program the following day. It was more of an unraveling, really. When I looked in the mirror of my locker room, I saw a fraud. A big, ugly, stupid fraud. With bad hair. In the reflection, the short spikes were clearly crooked. Great, I hadn't even done my hair well.

As the second-to-last skater in the event, I was forced to sit backstage like a caged animal ready for the slaughter. Listening to the raucous audience reactions for the other skaters, like

Evan, who was second to me after the short program, and the scores being read on the loudspeaker as they reverberated through the massive building, I was a dazed and crying mess.

Panicking like never before, I couldn't stop sobbing. Priscilla sat nearby, helplessly silent. While she was a good friend and a great coach, constantly pushing me past my limits and always expecting more, she wasn't good at the raw emotion thing. So I just sat there and wept until she stood and said, "Okay. It's time to go."

I got up and wiped my face. Chin up, jacket slung over my shoulders, I let Priscilla walk me out as the boy before me, who hadn't done very well, finished his program to anemic applause. Junior-level competitions don't draw a big crowd, so the stands were sparsely filled with random, glum-looking Bulgarians and American supporters in their various brightly colored windbreakers.

When I stepped on the ice, the audience began a slow clap that steadily got faster and faster in anticipation of my performance. The increasing tempo made my heart race with terror. Shaking, I couldn't look at the stands for fear that I'd faint and I couldn't look at Priscilla, because I'd start crying again. So I just started skating around in little circles.

I needed some kind of release. There was too much emotion coursing through me. The panic became physical discomfort, an illness corroding an otherwise healthy body. I needed to snap out of it, but I didn't know how.

"Next on the ice, representing the United States: Johnny Weir," the announcer said over the loudspeaker.

Nothing was right. The fans were strangers and the rink decrepit. I hadn't eaten properly in this Eastern Bloc country for an entire week. Everything around me was foreign and uncomfortable.

And then I heard the first few bars of my music, a synthesizer's ominous imitation of balalaika accordion music.

An amazing thing happened: the rink dropped away and the faces receded as "The Heart of Budapest" enveloped me like an old friend. The only thing that I knew in that building at that moment was my music, and I let myself fly upon the normalcy offered up by its folk harmonies. That song and I had spent a lot of time together.

It guided me through my program perfectly. I got off the ice to excited screams from the crowd and hugged Priscilla. After the judges read my scores and named me the new Junior World Champion, I started crying and so did Priscilla. Looking up into the stands, I found my mom and she was tear-streaked, too.

The pain of fear had given way to a burst of accomplishment. The first time in my career that I relied on my muscle memory and let my body do what it was trained to do, the moment marked a huge milestone in my life as an athlete. Music's ability to move me, something that had alleviated my fear of the dark as a child, inspired me to become an artist and then returned to teach me how to become a competitor.

4

Enfant Terrible

Adrenaline coursed through my body as I pushed across the ice. And this was only practice. My first time in Russia—Moscow, no less—marked a homecoming of sorts. Ever since my earliest connections tracing the Cyrillic alphabet and finding a kindred spirit in Yuri the dance teacher at my rink in Delaware, I had continued to develop a love for the country and its dramatic skating style. No matter that my Russia was a mythical one of sable furs, vodka shots, and tsars that had little to do with secret police, bread lines, and bureaucracy. It got to the point where the Russians came to think of me as one of their own, making this a golden place for me to skate.

The pressure was on during my first trip to the real country in the fall of 2002 to compete in the Cup of Russia, the Russian Grand Prix. The judges, officials, and coaches eagerly anticipated my arrival: they had been waiting to see this American who skated like a Russian since I had won the Junior World Championships a year and a half before. "Johnny looks like a Russian on the ice, so we're excited for him to compete," an official told Priscilla and me on our arrival. "He'll be accepted well."

The high expectations of how I would do (something I never felt comfortable absorbing) wasn't the only thing making me nervous. Despite the way I entered the ice like I owned the place, the deep dark truth was I had no idea whether I could get through my whole program. My condition wasn't where it should have been because my training wasn't what it should have been. I just needed some space. Eighteen years old, I was entering my adolescent rebellion on the late side. In truth, I was completely sick of hanging out with Priscilla and my mom.

But this wasn't the time to start doubting myself. I had a big competition tomorrow and right now I was practicing . . . in Moscow . . . for the Russian Grand Prix . . . in my beautiful new costume. I couldn't wait to warm up the sparkly onesie since it was the very first I ever designed. Performing to music from Cirque du Soleil, I had been going for a deranged circus look. The black velvet pants traveled up into a turquoise Lycra top layered with black fishnet (I'm a sucker for netting). To show off my lithe but fully mature body, a turquoise string snaked up my sides and around my waist, ending in a rip at one of the shoulders. I looked like I had just fallen off a trapeze and was very proud of the overall effect.

The American judges walked into the arena and over to my coach while I ran through my program to see what this tight little number could do. I was deep into my impression of a tragic Weimar circus performer when one of the judges ordered me over to him with an angry wave of his hand. As I skated closer, I saw Priscilla's face had gone white and she had the awkward smile she always had when we were in trouble.

"What is *that*?" the judge said as he pointed at my outfit. "This is totally a slap in the face to us."

"He looks like one of them, a Russian!" another judge said. "We can't let him go out there like that."

I couldn't believe what the U.S. skating officials were saying about my perfect costume. Yes, I preferred the more form-fitting, one-piece costumes favored by male Russian skaters to the big pirate blouses and cheap tuxedo pants that the American men wore. But this was a completely original design created by me. They hadn't seen anything like it before.

"You are going to have to change your costume," the first judge ordered.

I started to make my way off the ice as my tears turned the arena into one big blurry white prison. I couldn't simply "change my costume." My costume, like my choice of music, helped create the mood and character of the program. It offered another dimension to consider, aside from landing all the jumps and completing all the spins. In short, it helped me compete.

Much like A-List actresses who won't hit the red carpet unless they're dripping in five million dollars' worth of diamonds, I can't skate unless I feel beautiful. When I perform, my hair and makeup have to be done and I need a costume with a story. That's why I've always had a big say in what I wear on the ice, even when I was younger and wanted things that were unrealistic for my size. Skating to classic Russian balalaika music when I was thirteen, I had demanded a full Cossack costume with big, billowing pants, boots, and a little vest. But because I was so tiny I looked like a child survivor of a pogrom wearing a dead soldier's uniform and had to admit I couldn't really pull it off.

Still, I always had an opinion. When I moved from junior level to senior level skating, Stephanie Handler, my faithful costume designer, put in shoulder pads to chunk me up a little bit because I was a wispy fifteen-year-old kid competing against guys who were in their mid- to late twenties. I freaked out, finding the padding not only cheesy but also distracting since they sort of flew around in the wind when I was skating.

Once I went through my growth spurt around seventeen and got my man body, I was ready to act like a man—and design my own costume. After seeing the Cirque du Soleil show in Philadelphia, I was inspired to sit down and sketch different silhouettes and color schemes. I knew I wanted a Russian-style skating costume: they all wore one-piece catsuits with the whole story of their performance written out on the design. Flamboyant and over the top, Russian men weren't afraid to wear really tight things that showed off their line.

Stephanie said yes to my sexy circus freak immediately. She had been waiting for me to have that moment when I was old and big enough to wear something crazy. My mom and Priscilla approved, knowing that I needed some freedom in my life and preferring it be through costume than other, more destructive venues that tempted me.

When Stephanie finally translated my drawing into the actual costume, I felt a deep thrill wearing it on the ice. I knew I had done something special, something unique.

As it turned out, though—according to the officials from my country telling me I couldn't wear it—the costume was a little *too* unique. Before I could make my dramatic exit off the ice, the first judge caught me by the arm. "One more thing," he said. "Your hair is also disrespectful. Please change it before tomorrow."

I tore out of his grip, out of my costume and skates, and out of the arena. Back in my room, I flopped on my bed, sobbing my eyes out and listening to Christina Aguilera on my earphones. The singer had been the inspiration for my hair, which I had dyed pieces of white blond and fire-engine red, just little pieces. Mostly it was brown. I thought I was making a statement, like Christina, and that it looked good (which, of course, looking back, it did not).

I had been planning on changing it before I went to the

competition, but the geezers from the federation had been so insulting by adding my hair on top of the awful things they said about my costume. Now there was no way I was going to change—my hair, my costume, anything. Maybe they could push me around when I was sixteen but not anymore.

I was ready to leave the quiet Johnny of the Junior World Championships behind and go out on a limb. My new out-there, artistic side clearly came as a shock to some people in skating because they hadn't seen that aspect of me (no one had except my closest friends). But my federation saw my costume, my program, and maybe even me as an affront to American skating tradition.

I was in a jam: if I wore my costume, it would be a big fuck-you to my country. But if I didn't wear it, I wasn't being true to myself. So I did what any self-respecting artist would do—I lied.

I pretended I was sick and withdrew from the competition. I lied to my mother, Priscilla, everyone. Each time a doctor tried to get into my hotel room to check me out, I feigned sleep. I was so terrified—knowing somewhere deep down that my duplicity was costing people a lot of money and possibly also my career if caught—that I practically made myself sick. Despite the fear of lying on all fronts, I couldn't go through with the competition. Who were these people to tell me what to do? No American skater had been accepted in Russia the way I had been and they wanted to ruin it. In the countless hours of hard work I put into creating my costume and program, all they could find was something twisted. Well, I refused to be suppressed.

How did I go from a sweet, skating child to a crazy bitch who tells lies because he can't wear what he wants? My transformation was a gradual one, but my burgeoning divadom had started as soon as I'd returned home from Sofia a year and a half earlier. My ego grew a couple of sizes when I walked into the rink in Delaware to find a huge banner that read "Johnny Weir: Junior World Champion. Congratulations!" and a crowd that began cheering upon my arrival. The skating community crowned me the next big thing, and I was ready for the title. This year Junior World Champion, next the Olympic team. I was finally headed in the right direction. Or so I thought.

The federation treated me like royalty, sending me to the Goodwill Games in Australia in August of 2001, a huge televised event where I competed against the top ten skaters in the world. I was paid ten thousand dollars just to show up—incredible, considering I would have probably shelled out to be in the company of my idols like Irina Slutskaya, Michelle Kwan, Evgeni Plushenko, and Alexei Yagudin. Initially overwhelmed to be part of such an elite group, I skated well enough to earn ninth place and back pats from the rest of the men. I wasn't yet the best, but I belonged.

My becoming a celebrity (at least in the skating world) had the unfortunate timing of coinciding with my late-bloomer's adolescence. Although I was nearly eighteen, I displayed all the signs of rebellion that kids who lead less sheltered lives than a competitive skater go through much earlier. Now that I was a star, I decided I had to dress the part. I tossed the timid polos and practical track pants of my youth, taking my fashion cues from the boy bands popular at the time. *NSYNC had it going on as far as I was concerned. I waltzed into my ice rink in a thin tank top with "Rock Star" blazoned across it in sparkles and my hair colored with various shades of store-bought dye.

I didn't experiment with drugs but rather my identity. My new favorite catchphrase was "Fabulous!" and absolutely everyone in the world became "honey" as I became freer with my personality. Now that I was a grown-up, I wanted to do as I pleased (although looking back, there is nothing more immature than declaring yourself a grown-up, and no life less free than that of a competitive skater). While before it would have been rare for me to stay out past dark, now I began spending a lot of time away from home with friends from the rink. We would watch movies late at night at a friend's house and then head to a diner afterward. When that got boring, we would sit in one of our cars and watch drunk people make fools of themselves outside the 7-Eleven. Either way, I often didn't get home until 2 a.m. But hanging out—that's what adults did! However tame my rebellion sounds, it was pretty unusual behavior for a training athlete.

The only people not giving me the respect I deserved were my mom and Priscilla. They weren't treating me like a man, or a star, but rather like a big baby. Was I eating properly? Did I get enough sleep? Where had I been so late the night before? These were questions for a kid, not a champion skater about to turn eighteen years old.

Yes, I started to enjoy having a drink with friends on occasion and I didn't watch my diet as closely as I should (meaning I ate more than a tomato for dinner). Other American skaters might have been horrified: that wasn't top athlete behavior. But it wasn't like I was skipping practice or anything. I showed up, on time, for every session.

Priscilla and my mom might have been on my ass about my new "bad" attitude, but I wasn't too worried. I had gotten this far without paying too much attention to what other people had to say and I intended to keep it that way. My whole career up until this point had come easy—well, except for competing. So what if I wasn't inspired to work hard? My success would continue to happen, just like it always had.

Like most teens and authority figures, Priscilla and I fought constantly. Our biggest battle was over my doing run-throughs, practicing the program with all the elements from the beginning to the end. She wanted me to do them to prepare mentally and physically for competitions. I felt that doing lots of jumps for stamina and conditioning was plenty. "The Russians don't do run-throughs," I told her with a dismissive wave of my hand. "So I'm not going to do run-throughs, either."

I had dedicated the previous six years of my life to catching up to skaters my own age. Having caught up and passed most of them by, I thought I had earned the right to glide on talent for a little while.

However, figure skating is an unforgiving sport where no one gets a pass for talent alone. After I withdrew from the Grand Prix in Russia in a big-time diva fit over my costume, the USFSA dealt a harsh blow by withdrawing me from my other Grand Prix event in Japan. I wouldn't have enough points to make it to the Grand Prix Final, even if I won the event, the federation reasoned, so they didn't want to waste the money sending me there.

Even though it was of my own doing—I had made an incredibly stupid mistake by lying to get out of the event—I was angry at the world for mistreating me. Everyone was so busy putting me in my place when all I wanted was to be an adult, which I thought meant the freedom to do whatever I wished.

I was still fuming over the federation's decision the following day when I showed up for practice. Priscilla, in her snowsuit, stood with her arms crossed like two fat cigars battling each other. I could tell something was up because she normally greeted me with an overly cheerful hello that irritated the hell out of me.

"What's with you?" I asked, lacing up my skates.

Silence.

"I'm not happy about the Grand Prix thing, either. In fact, I'm sure I'm more upset than you," I said.

"That's not what's bothering me," she said.

"Well, out with it."

"You smoked a cigarette!"

"Who told you that?"

"It's not important who told me."

"Then I'll tell you it's not true."

"Kristi told her mom that you were at a party smoking a cig-arette. And Sara told Jeff, who told me yesterday while he was coaching."

"Snitch!"

"So it's true."

I just glared at Priscilla in her stupid snowsuit. God, I hated that thing. It was summer, for heaven's sake.

"You're the only student I have who's going to go someplace, and you don't even care about it," she said. "So I'm going to quit teaching, and you may as well quit skating."

Her version of a scared straight speech needed a lot of work. If she wanted to quit teaching, she should go ahead and be my guest. I would find another coach. I didn't need her or anybody else for that matter.

"Fuck you," I said, and left.

———————

I apologized to Priscilla eventually. My mother made me do it ("Tell her you'll never smoke again and it will be fine," she said) after a long week of not speaking to each other. But I didn't fall in line. I continued to practice as I saw fit, running roughshod over my coach's demands, and having fun with my friends at night.

When I arrived in Dallas in January of 2003 for the National Championships, the cracks in my plan of doing things only my way grew instantaneously from tiny fractures to huge fault lines. Because I had withdrawn from the last couple of competitions, nobody had seen me skate practically all year. My condition remained shrouded in mystery, which allowed the skating world's imagination to fill in the question marks with big expectations. A few of the top skaters had withdrawn from the event because of injuries and people predicted I would do great things. They needed at least one showstopper and I fit the bill.

God, was I in bad shape. I had trained every day but I was nowhere near showstopper condition. At least I looked good, I tried to tell myself. For my short program to the Cirque du Soleil music, I decided to wear the deranged trapeze artist costume the officials had demanded off my back in Russia. "Screw everyone," I said. "I'm going to wear what I want." Priscilla, normally a total conformist, was so terrified of me by this point, she didn't argue.

Waiting to go on the ice, I put all my confidence into that costume, as if it could carry me through the program instead of the other way around. I also put a little in a higher power. And apparently He listened. Through some act of God I skated a perfect short program. A private miracle, unbeknownst to the judges and audience, landed me in second place and a shot at competing in the World Championships. No one was more surprised than me.

But a short program is only two and a half minutes long. A long program is four and a half minutes, and facing those two extra minutes the next day brought me to my knees. It's a long exertion time for skaters in the best condition. My mind ran to black as it had so many times before. Why hadn't I done my run-throughs? Right before I was set to compete, I faced the bleak fact: I wasn't prepared. "I can't do this. I can't do this," I murmured softly to myself.

With every TV camera trained on me, I put myself on the ice and delivered a half-hearted pep talk: *you are going to try.* My music from *Dr. Zhivago* started, and I began skating. But hope didn't last long; ten seconds into the program my blade got stuck in between the wall and the ice while I was doing a simple cross-over.

I went tumbling onto the ice in a tangle of confusion and embarrassment. It was so crazy I didn't know what to do with myself. I got up very quickly, and then, even though I wasn't injured, put my hand on my back, pretending that there was something wrong. Lying seemed to have become my default.

Now what should I do? Out of instinct, I had pretended to be hurt. There was nothing to do but go through with it. I stopped my program and skated over to the referee.

"Ugh, I hurt my back so bad," I said.

"Well, can you continue?" the referee asked.

Could I? "Yes, I can continue."

Okay, Johnny. Get your shit together. Let's go.

I started skating again and I could feel my audience, the collective anticipation, as I went up into the air. It's the same sensation as when somebody's staring at you from across the room and you can feel it before you even turn around. When you're on the ice, you feel all of these eyes, and you can feel, through their eyes, their emotions. At that moment, it was pure hope.

I landed the first jump. Excited that I wasn't injured, the audience cheered me on. I did the first jumping pass through their slow, rhythmic claps . . . good. The second jumping pass . . . great. I had another triple axel planned and went into the air. It was huge. I felt this is my shot to really rock. My last thought before I came down was *God's going to help me again*.

Then I came down very hard, literally. On my landing, I popped my kneecap out of place and couldn't get up. Finally, this was no lie. After what seemed like an eternity, I rose from the ice and hobbled over to the boards. "I can't continue," I said, and withdrew from the competition.

People's genuine concern for me after the fall made me feel worse because I knew I had brought this on myself. I had wanted to be treated like an adult, but instead had acted like a child. I had wasted the once-in-a-lifetime opportunities presented me and thrown away what should have been the most important season in my career. Now truly injured, I had no idea what it would take for me to get back on track.

A few minutes after I withdrew from the National Championships, an elderly woman, Helen McLoraine, who helped fund my skating career and had traveled from Colorado to watch me compete, fell while she was getting up to leave the rink. I found out a few days later that my benefactress—the lady who had sent my mother money here and there through the years to help with a costume or some extra for music editing simply because she loved my skating—had passed away in the hospital.

Up until that point, I had been the next golden child of U.S. figure skating, and now it was done after I completely ruined the whole season in which I was supposed to make a name for myself. After the event in Dallas, the federation took me out of Envelope A, which assured the top-tier athletes consideration for international events and a little bit of money for training. I could no longer compete at the biggest senior level events such as the World Championships or in the Grand Prix series. My stupidity and hubris had landed me in skating purgatory, cast out from the mainstream and any kind of official track. I knew I had earned my karma and deserved everything that was happening, but that didn't make it any easier to deal with.

I don't do things halfway. As spectacularly as I had risen up the skating ladder, I fell just as hard and fast. In one quick year, I went from an alternate for the Olympics, Goodwill Games athlete, and the next favorite of U.S. figure skating to a complete and utter write-off.

5

Embracing the Starving Artist

My ankles swelled into a war zone of black, blue, and bloody red from the countless footwork passes I'd run through. My hip flexors were slack with overuse from millions of jumps and difficult spins. Every muscle in my body ached. Even my brain throbbed from an entire day of having directives in Russian hurled at me as rapidly and forcefully as machine-gun fire. In a temporary break from my regular training with Priscilla, I spent the summer of 2003 in a program with one of the world's best Olympic coaches. During the insane, grueling summer camp for skaters, I subsisted on coffee and slept in a stranger's extra bedroom—and I had never felt luckier.

I had been so disheartened by the fiasco at the National Championships in Dallas and my subsequent relegation to a skater's no-man's-land by the USFSA that I briefly considered quitting the sport altogether. I didn't think I had the head for it anymore. Resting on talent alone, I had turned last season (when I should have proved myself Olympic-level material) into a total disaster. The skating world didn't believe I had what it took to be a serious competitor, proving that with my new low ranking.

Their harsh voices berated me in my head until I came to my senses. I had never listened to those people before, so why would I now? I wanted to keep skating. I *needed* to. After all my family had sacrificed, personally and financially, for me to pursue this dream, I couldn't give up after encountering a bump in the road (even if the bump was the size of Mount Everest). Plus, I hated when people told me what to do. If the entire federation signaled that I should quit, then I would do the opposite—even if it killed me.

But if I planned on reviving my career after taking a blowtorch to it, a real change of pace was in order. Last year had been a failed experiment in stretching my wings, but the original impetus hadn't been totally wrong. I did need to be away from Priscilla and my mom so that I could learn how to stand on my own two skates. I needed to be inspired.

That inspiration came in the form of a fur-swathed, Dior-toting Russian woman named Tatiana Tarasova. In the obscure town of Simsbury, Connecticut, the world-famous skating coach and choreographer spent summers training an elite group of athletes including Olympic champions such as Alexei Yagudin and Ilia Kulik and my friend, the skating star Sasha Cohen. After Sasha helped me get a foot in the door, I skated for Tarasova. Her only comment, to my mother, was, "Yes, I will take Johnny." Normally she charged in the double-digit thousands for one program, but Tarasova let me train with her all summer for free since I didn't have a penny to my name. Waiving her fee proved she believed in me and offered encouragement before I took even a single lesson. I had been given a second chance and resolved not to blow it.

At the International Skating Center of Connecticut, we skated for about six hours a day, so much more than I was used to, after which I would fall, practically paralyzed, into the bed in the bedroom I rented from a random woman. No matter how stiff or sore I felt, I hit the ice the next morning with the kind of energy fueled by inspiration. Unlike the University of Delaware's crowded rink, here only five truly great skaters trained together.

In the classic Russian style, Tarasova taught us in groups, as opposed to one-on-one, so that we fought each other to be the best. The dynamic brought out the competitive spark still smoldering from my childhood. I definitely responded to all the skaters trying to one-up each other as we vied for Tarasova's attention. The edge of my footwork got sharper and my jump technique stronger.

Entering the session late one day, she began barking in a choppy, aggressive Russian and finding fault everywhere she looked. Although I was far from fluent, I had taught myself enough Russian that I could communicate and understand when others spoke.

Suddenly Tarasova stopped and clapped her bejeweled hands together.

"Umnitza," she said, which was Russian slang for "perfect boy."

I had just come out of a spin in the new short program Tarasova had created for me and decided to extend my leg with a little more bravado than perhaps was necessary. At first I had no idea she was talking to me.

"You look like a young Baryshnikov," she said, giving me a big smile before launching into a list of a million things I had done wrong.

Attracting Tarasova's attention, I felt very special. And surprised. She had praised me for the kind of thing that Priscilla, trying to follow direct orders from the federation, constantly told me to tone down during my normal training life. Skate more like a man; watch your fingers so that they aren't balletic; not so much movement in your hips, please!

But Tarasova appreciated everything that made me me, including my artistic side. She liked my body, which mimicked those of Russian ballet dancers, and provided choreography that enriched the way I moved on the ice. *"Umnitza,"* she applauded me throughout the summer, nurturing the healthy side of my ego and transforming Simsbury into a special hideaway where nothing was too artistic, nothing too over the top. With Tarasova I found my first opportunity to express myself fully and freely.

Not eager to leave this incubator, I didn't take any breaks from the group's training regimen apart for a necessary one to compete in a little local event back in Delaware. It was July and I had been training with Tarasova for less than a month when Priscilla told me at the last minute that I was expected at the Liberty Open at The Pond Ice Arena in Newark, Delaware. The call instantly dealt my ego, which Tarasova had been vigorously massaging, a brutal blow.

In the skating world, there's an unspoken standard: once you compete in the National Championships on television and fight for a spot on the World Championship team, you don't participate in small, local open events like the one in Newark. Those were the competitions where I blew everyone away at the juvenile level when I was just starting out at twelve years old. My entering the event at The Pond was as if Madonna were to try out for *American Idol*. But when Priscilla asked the federation how I could fix my reputation and get things back on track after last season, they responded firmly that I had to return to square one and prove myself all over again. "We need to make sure he's training," an official had told Priscilla, "and doesn't do anything like he did last year again."

So it was I found myself outside the small rink, steeling myself for a humiliating trial. The worst part was that I didn't even feel prepared for this tiny event. July was extremely early to compete. I had just started working with Tarasova and the new short program she created for me was still in process. Meanwhile, we had been so focused on the new choreography that I hadn't yet started doing run-throughs of the long program that I intended to hold over from the previous season.

With my heavy equipment bag slung over my shoulder, I registered myself at the foldout card table near the entrance and after writing my name, the elderly woman distributing the makeshift badges looked up from my signature with her mouth in a little shocked O.

In the skating world I was famous, for good and for bad. So my appearance turned heads in surprise as people wondered why I was there.

After changing into a simple gray and white costume, still a tight onesie that unabashedly showed off my thin frame but reflected my humble status in its lack of adornment, I waited near the ice. The other low-ranked senior level skaters with no chance at a national title sneaked furtive glances in my direction.

"Well, well, well, Johnny Weir," said a judge in a Team USA windbreaker, hair dyed a slightly bluish tint. "What the hell are you doing here?"

The tips of my ears turned red with shame. I stared straight ahead and muttered, "Skating," thinking about how much my mother hated when my brother and I mumbled as kids.

"Oh, you're going to skate for us today?" another judge said, sipping from a large Dunkin' Donuts coffee that smelled sickeningly of blueberries.

"Yes, ma'am."

"Did you hear? He's training with the great Tarasova. Well, I can't wait to see this. That is, if he can stand on his skates long enough."

The judges cackled mercilessly while I burned with my own thoughts. Before the cruel comments, I had felt deeply embarrassed. Now I choked with rage.

Training with Priscilla had been all about the problems with my skating; ours was a nuts and bolts operation. Whenever I headed out onto the ice during an event, I concentrated on my mistakes, which I knew well from hours of having them pointed out, and implored myself not to make them. Although the stage in Newark was tiny, this was the first time I had competed since the Dallas National Championships, the culmination of every single mistake I had made thus far in my career. My history weighed heavy.

But in this small place and moment, something shifted. After the announcer unceremoniously called my name and I took to the ice, the problem child found himself replaced by another one: *umnitza,* perfect boy. Tarasova's voice played in my head, egging me on to remember the art and beauty and forget the pettiness of scores. The power of an Olympic coach telling me day in and day out how good I was fortified me. *Just go out and skate,* I told myself.

And I did. Cleanly, beautifully, perfectly.

Afterward, I took off my skates, changed into my regular clothes, and left without waiting to see my scores printed on the little pieces of white paper. I didn't need to see the proof: I knew I had won.

In Simsbury the next day, I went right back to work, trying to outjump, spin, and sparkle the other skaters in my group. Tarasova, who blustered into our session just as I was completing a triple axel with joyful exuberance flying out of my overly balletic pinkies, clapped her hands in delight. She never asked me how the competition went or uttered one single word about it. This, another of her lessons, programmed me to know that nothing matters but the moment. Whatever happens at an event, good or bad, dissipates when you train on a clean slate of ice.

———————

I stood on the bed and taped a piece of paper to my bedroom ceiling. Then I lay down to make sure I could see the words when I woke up in the morning and before I went to sleep at night. They read: "Johnny Weir National Champion." Clear as day.

Having returned to Delaware at the end of the summer, I refused to lose the drive or inspiration I had achieved with Tarasova and the other skaters in Simsbury. If I were going to be a national, or even international, champion, I needed to strip my life down to nothing but skating. Back home, however, I was surrounded by temptations that knocked me on my ass last season. Friends beckoned with parties or just one quick cocktail. Fried or sugary food appeared particularly tasty after my long workouts.

So I taped the mantra to my ceiling to keep myself in check. "No, I can't come to the party. I have to go to bed early so I can be the National Champion," I said to friends. I did Priscilla's drills like a good boy and chose black coffee over cheesecake because I was dieting to be the National Champion.

Being dirt poor also helped keep me in line. I had a lot of trouble with money because, well, I didn't have any. The federation had cut off my official funding and anyone who had previously given me money had either died or decided I was washed up. I didn't merit a spot on any of the ice tours, where skaters typically make cash to fund their lives, and couldn't get a job like a normal person because my training occupied all of my days.

I love money and, as my mother taught me, nice things, but through my experience that summer with Tarasova, I got in touch with my inner Russian-ness. And Russians, in general, don't have money. So I was fine with not having it, either. I wore my poverty as a badge of a prideful club. I was a member of a romantic long-suffering sect, the Starving Artist. As part of my destitute chic period, I never dressed up for anything and hardly showered. If my hair was greasy from a workout the day before, I simply put it back in a headband. That's what we artists, concentrating solely on the work before us, did. It was inspiring to feel like you had nothing.

The only time I got really fancy and dressed up was when I had my costumes on to compete. Sparkly, tight, colorful, and expressive, they transformed my drab, unwashed persona like a glorious drag queen who only comes alive to put on a show. For my long program, I had re-created the bland gray and silver two-piece, puff-blouse costume from my *Dr. Zhivago* program last season to look like an icicle. Baby blue Lycra covered in white fishnet, paint, and Swarovski crystals, the result was totally razzle-dazzle, much more Russian, and much more me.

The costume for my new short program showed my sensitive side (the depth behind all that glitter). The choreography Tarasova created to "Valse Triste" by Jean Sibelius, a slow, melodic march, had me tell the story of a man who arrives home from war in a suit he hasn't worn since before he left to fight. Waiting for him in his duffel for over a decade, the suit has been ruined by dirt and shredded by time. My costume reflected that image with jagged rips and tears throughout the cloth, an oversized burnt and floppy rose on the lapel. Sorrow that would read on the ice.

Sectionals was another stop on the Johnny Weir shame tour that year. Competing in regional or sectional events is another one of those things a skater at the level of International Grand Prix events just doesn't do. But I did. Because I didn't finish in the top six in the previous National Championship, I had to requalify. Even though I had taken about ten steps backward, my only choice was to keep moving forward.

On the drive to the event, I popped Christina Aguilera's *Stripped* into the CD player and pumped up the volume to liven up the deadly ride. The lyrics to "Make Over" filled up the inside of Priscilla's massive SUV, providing some necessary color to the gray winter landscape. Christina helped me steel myself. Although I had no money or idea what the future would hold, a terrific group of friends supported me. My mom was still my best friend and even Priscilla and I were getting along better than ever. I had no fear heading into quad jumps or driving to an event where I would be something of a laughingstock, because I was in control of my life.

Still, by the time I arrived at Art Devlin's Olympic Motor Inn, where I was staying in Lake Placid, my relentless spirit had begun to relent, just a little. What started as a tickle in my throat turned into a full-blown cold, a fitting tribute to the dreary iced-over town. I have always felt uneasy in Lake Placid. In close proximity to nothing more than cold, dark mountains and miles of trees and townies, the tiny town is horror-movie material. My motel, little more than polyester bedspreads and ugly carpeting, provided no comfort. This wasn't the official hotel of the sectionals where all the other skaters were staying. No, that was down the street and more than I could afford. I had to settle for serial killer lodging. Wrapping myself up in my own sheet so that I wouldn't have to touch the dubious bedding, I took solace in my thriftiness and hoped this Starving Artist might get at least a few hours of sleep.

Though I felt sick and tired the next day, my confidence going into the event soared off the charts. My costumes were unique and gorgeous; I had a short program created by a world-class choreographer; and I was skinny as a rail. Nobody at this two-bit competition could touch me. A few of my friends had generously driven up to watch me skate, which reminded me that although I felt totally alone at times, I wasn't really.

I skated my short program flawlessly, but during my long program, I fell down on a jump. Unlike in years past, however, I didn't unravel at the first hint of a mistake. Because I was far and away going to win, the fall wouldn't hurt me. I stopped for a second on the ice, caught my breath, skated around in a little circle to gather myself, and then gestured to my friends before finishing. A little impertinent perhaps, but eight hours was a long way to drive to watch me skate.

I won and, more important, earned my place at the National Championships. I still had a lot ahead of me to prove that I could be good again, but for the moment I basked in the relief of accomplishment. I knew it was short-lived since, as I had learned from Tarasova, tomorrow I would be back on the ice starting from zero.

However, my moment of glory was even more short-lived than expected. Right after the competition, while I made my way to the locker room to change, a judge approached me.

"You know you're never going to be able to work yourself back from this," he said.

"Excuse me?" I said, although I had heard him perfectly.

"Johnny, just don't expect anything at Nationals. You shot yourself in the foot last year," he said. "You're looking better, and you can obviously skate well. But all I'm saying is you're not going to get any favors from us."

I waited to see if he was finished and then turned to the locker room without offering a reply. There was nothing I could say to him, at least nothing that wouldn't get me in deeper trouble with the federation.

If he or any of his cronies who didn't believe in me had seen the mantra taped to my ceiling—Johnny Weir National Champion—they would have laughed me out of the arena. But his remarks, instead of eroding my confidence, only stoked the fire in my belly. I *would* be the next national champion, not only to prove something to myself but also to shove it down the throat of anyone who counted me out.

———

Not a single skater who needed to qualify at the sectional championships had won a national title in nearly a decade, but that's what I set out to do when I arrived in Atlanta for the Nationals in January of 2004. I had a goal, but I wasn't an idiot. It would be a miracle if I could pull it off. A lot of famous people were competing, such as Timothy Goebel and Michael Weiss, two of the big mainstays of figure skating at that time. So I had a long list of fierce challengers and skating favorites, plus a panel of judges who practically hated my guts. A miracle, indeed.

I looked good on the ice during practice—boom, boom, boom, landing every jump—and impressed a few stragglers who had come to watch me, probably by mistake. Any pressure I felt going into the competition came from within since, frankly, nobody else paid me any attention. The press wasn't writing about me, fans weren't clamoring for my autograph, and the officials weren't monitoring my practices. As I said, I was a complete write-off.

Flying under the radar, I entered into the short program by psyching myself up with the idea that I had something special to bring to skating in the States—if I could just keep it together. I was a hybrid of Russian and American skating, two very different schools of thought. With coaches from both countries, I had married the artistic with the athletic, the passion with technique. My costumes were different and so was the way I moved my body. I was an American boy with a Russian soul, and nobody else skated anything like me.

Armed with this knowledge, I did what I had done since Tarasova gave me the program—skate clean and perfect and beautiful. I got off the ice and waited for my scores, not knowing what kind of numbers I would receive. I had skated well, but judging isn't a cut-and-dry operation. A whole mess of things go into deciding what kind of number to put to a performance. Technique is a factor but so are subjective notions of skating as an art and the kind of skater who *should* win. Needless to say, politics plays a huge role. The judges consider who they want to be the face of the sport when making their decisions.

When my scores came up they reflected the federation's ambivalence toward me. My numbers were all over the place. For my artistic score, they ranged from 4.9, which was horrible for a senior level skater, to a stellar 5.8 out of a perfect score of 6.0. Because none of the judges expected me to be prepared or skate well, it was like they didn't know what to do with me when I did. After both the technical and artistic scores were posted, I'd received a majority of the judges' votes for first place.

It was a real shock, not just to me, Priscilla, and my mom, but to everyone at the event. In one short program, I went from outcast to first place. The press needed to rewrite the story lines to include me: the skater who had "imploded" in a "disastrous" last season had turned into a "contender."

Suddenly all the skaters and officials who hadn't given me the time of day only a few hours before were patting me on the back.

"You did so amazing!"

"You're skating like the champion we always knew you'd be."

"What happened?"

Just as I had ignored the mean remarks by the judge at sectionals, so I did the same with the praise. Good, bad, whatever, I wasn't going to listen to it because it was all fake. I had my blinders on and reminded myself that every single one of those backslappers had been equally ready to send me home.

I needed that fire and aggression the next day to get me through the long program, which is hard enough to get through without the pressure of being number one. This time, however, I refused to buckle under my virtuosity. After a year of training my mind to believe I deserved the title of champion and following up with the behavior to prove it, I was ready for a repeat performance. I was strong enough now. I could do it.

Unfortunately, I drew to skate last, a horrible, horrible place for someone with my history of nerves to be in. I didn't know if I'd be able to keep up my tough attitude as one by one, the best American skaters performed before me. Michael Weiss, my fiercest rival at this event, skated second to last. A big hulking and classless idiot with three national titles, two world medals, and two Olympic teams under his wide belt, he was a huge star and everything that the U.S. Figure Skating Association wanted at the helm. I sat huddled in the dressing room, listening to every torturous moment, when the crowd erupted into applause for some fantastic jump he landed cleanly. His scores also came through loud and clear. They were great numbers: 5.7's, 5.8's, and 5.9's. Just great. For him.

I left my bravado in the dressing room when it was time for me to compete. Skating around in a little dazed circle, I had my eyes wide open but couldn't see anything. Priscilla tried to talk to me, but I couldn't hear what she was saying, either. I had come down with hysterical blindness and deafness. I fought to stay calm and got into my starting position.

Which Johnny was it going to be?

Good? Or bad?

I started out feeling shaky and too aware of my body. A loose sequin at my neck scratched and the nail on my left big toe pressed slightly into the skate. My breath caught in my chest, flittering about like a caged bird. Then I started to pick up speed in my program. The sound of shearing ice and the visual whirl of the arena drowned out the small discomforts my nerves had produced. The speed, music, and flow combined to give me that rush of great skating. Suddenly I was flying and before I hit the last forty seconds of the program, the crowd had started clapping and hollering.

When I finished, the entire audience leaped to its feet. I couldn't even hear the announcer say, "And again, ladies and gentlemen, Johnny Weir," because people were screaming so much. Everyone was excited over this comeback, me included. A year before I had been lying in the center of the ice with television cameras broadcasting my fraudulent, injured self to countries across the globe. Now I stood in the center, healthy and whole. I didn't care what place I was going to get; this was my victory.

Even though I was clearly the emotional favorite of the audience, sitting in the kiss and cry area waiting for my scores I didn't think I actually had a chance at winning the title. The judge at sectionals had put it plainly: "We aren't going to do anything for you, Johnny." I had said I wanted to win, but the truth was I felt happy to the point of tears at the prospect of earning my first senior national silver or bronze medal.

My technical scores came up, and they were all 5.9's, and 5.8's, higher than Michael's. My pulse raced. Then the second round of scores for artistic merit came up, and I had a perfect 6, 5.9's and one 5.7. All but two judges gave me first place. Now I was really crying. I had won my first national title just as I'd promised myself and everyone else I would.

When you go on the ice to do anything, you're totally alone. You can have the best, most expensive coaches in the world and an entire team of people behind you, but once you're actually out there, it's you that has to do it. I had done everything myself, and I did it my own way.

6

Razzle-Dazzle

I hadn't felt anything even close to love at first sight since watching Richard Gere in *Pretty Woman* at the tender age of six. That's when I first realized there was something different about me. Seeing Julia Roberts get swept off her feet by her rich and handsome client, I wanted to be her so badly because *he* did something so special to me. Kissing seemed like a weird thing to do, but I knew if I were going to do it, it would be with Richard Gere.

As a small child without many inhibitions, I immediately quizzed my friends about the movie. Had they seen it? Did they want to be Julia Roberts like I did? All I got were a lot of funny looks. Nobody understood where I was coming from—especially the boys. "That's just weird," one of them said.

At that age, you have no idea what gay or straight is or any of the ramifications of being different. By puberty, however, I started to get a clearer picture. I came to understand what gay meant, and that many people didn't like it. I also knew that sexually I was gay. But I didn't worry about it much. Perhaps realizing the core truth so young made it easier to accept as I went along in life.

I also didn't feel the need to make my sexuality much of an issue, since at thirteen, I was nowhere close to having any kind of physical contact with anyone, other than hugging my best girlfriends. I didn't wrestle with being gay or let it change my life in the slightest; it simply became a fact of nature, albeit a private one.

Being a serious ice skater was a big part of the reason my "way of life" didn't trouble me too much. I had a job and objective upon which no entanglements could infringe. When you are that young and driven, life isn't a series of random occurrences. Rather, it is a single track shooting toward one thing, and for me that was the Olympics. I didn't bother talking to my friends or family about my feelings, not because I was ashamed, but because it wasn't important to me. Skating was the only thing that had any meaning. And I talked about that *all* the time.

When I did think about sex, which (and this will probably shock a lot of people) wasn't that often, my ideas were very much formed by *Pretty Woman,* hold the prostitution. I have been a romantic forever and even as a young teenage boy knew I wanted sex to be special. I didn't want to be one of these people you read about in sex ed, getting disgusting-looking diseases from casual encounters. I wanted to wait to be in love to have sex. I figured I would be old, say seventeen or eighteen, by the time I gave it up and by then life would sort itself out.

It took me a long time to actually feel really physical. Sure, there were those late nights when, staying up to watch *Oz,* I would feel a strange stirring. But in general, I didn't have any interest in fulfilling my sexual urges. I was way too busy.

Then I had my first kiss with a boy.

I was sixteen at the time, and he was twenty-one—really, there was nothing boyish about him. A pairs skater I knew from the rink, he was very tall and strong, manly aspects I found sexually attractive. But the thought of the two of us hadn't crossed my mind because I didn't scope out guys, plus he was dating a girl at the time.

Late one night he IM'd me and the chat went in a surprising direction.

"Have you ever kissed a boy?" he wrote.

"No, I don't know if I'll have time to," I responded.

My flirting style needed a little work.

"Maybe it's time that you did. I'm having a party. Come and practice."

I got all dolled up for the party, which was filled with older kids from the rink. It wasn't my first drinking party, but I was feeling it. In the few parties I had attended in the past, I would walk in and watch the other kids, guzzling beers or wine coolers in various corners of a house, slowly getting trashed as if I were a chaperone noting everyone's bad behavior. I wasn't a tattle, but I've always felt much older than my peers. Tonight, however, what would normally have seemed stupid to me became exciting.

At six feet tall, my friend usually towered over me, but that night he leaned down close to my face so that I could smell from his hot breath that he'd been drinking.

"It's time to practice," he said, pulling me into a dark corner.

In the darkness of some den, he put his big hands on my narrow hips.

"This is just so I can teach you how to kiss," he said.

Whatever. I was kissing someone for real and it was sexual, dirty and naughty and French. I loved every second of our twenty minutes in heaven. It totally and unexpectedly lit me up.

It might sound naive, but I was surprised by how much I liked exploring the sexual side of myself. With my complete focus narrowly trained on skating, I hadn't given myself much latitude to daydream, let alone experiment with the real thing. Now I had a man, with hair on his chest, no less, who wanted to "practice" with me on a regular basis.

Even though our situation was far from romantic, the pairs skater became my first real crush. The guy was so at war with himself that he would barely talk to me or even look me in the eye, unless it was "practice time." But I was always up for practice.

About once a week he would pick me up at my house under the ruse that we were going to the movies. Instead, we would just make out in his car. Then he would disguise the whole event to himself so he didn't have to face facts. I knew our relationship didn't have a future, but I enjoyed the make-out sessions. I had no trouble divorcing the sexual from the emotional because I wasn't looking for this guy to validate my existence. I was so overly confident in my future: that I would be a champion, make money, be a success. I didn't care what anyone else thought of me. If I had discovered I wasn't too busy for kissing, I was still too busy for a boyfriend, or a girlfriend, for that matter.

———

After I turned eighteen years old and had officially become an adult, I decided to tell my mother about these feelings. It just seemed like the adult thing to do and I'd vowed that I would be an open and honest adult with the people who mattered to me.

I waited until late one night after my dad had already gone to sleep (my dad is a cool guy but homosexuality is completely foreign to him and not something I was ready to throw in his face). My mom had fallen asleep, curled up on the couch with the cats, while watching *Law & Order*. I shook her awake and looked her in the eyes.

"Mom, I have been eighteen for a week. Adult to adult, I need to tell you something. I'm gay."

Although I knew full well that she had nosed around the rink for years, trying to find out the very information I was telling her, she still seemed shocked to hear it. She couldn't speak and her shoulders went way up around her ears. Suddenly it felt like I was sitting in the room with a stranger, and this was my mom, my best friend. The energy around us dropped as she started to cry.

I wasn't angry. In fact, I had a *Freaky Friday* moment with my mom where I was suddenly filled with maternal impulses. No mother wants to hear her son say he's gay, no matter how wonderful his life is and how well he treats her. Those two little words rip the picture of a daughter-in-law and grandchildren into a million little pieces. I felt sorry for my mom and wanted her to know everything was going to be all right.

But of course, my mom, the superhero, didn't give up her role just because I'm gay.

"I don't really care, Johnny, as long as I know that you are going to be happy," she said. "I want you to be healthy and I want you to have someone in your life."

My mother's reaction, rare coming from a parent, showed me something I already knew: she loves me unconditionally. It doesn't matter what I do; she would never love me more or less. While I continued to maintain that being gay was such a small part of me, it was still a part. So I was greatly relieved that my mother accepted it, because she is one of the few people whose opinion of me truly matters.

Suddenly I felt this great freedom to be out there now that my mom knew I was gay (she was the only person I have ever come out to officially in my family. It's not an issue for the rest of them and they don't ask any questions, which I consider a blessing). For my entire life up until that point, my best friends were all women. But now that I could flounce around and have limp wrists if I wanted to, I began to make friends with a few other gay guys whom I met through skating.

It wasn't easy for me. I am a solitary person who does well in family units and small groups of people. In large groups, like at parties, I shut down and get extremely bashful and cold. The problem is that in general I don't trust anyone, but especially not strangers. As a kid I always thought someone was going to try to kidnap me. As an adult I always think someone is trying to use me.

I definitely didn't trust Paris when I first encountered him. In fact, we hated each other for a long time. Paris was a recent implant to the University of Delaware training facility and to the university itself. Aside from skating, I felt like I had nothing in common with this creature from the dirty South. On the ice, we would exchange nasty looks—two bitchy queens locking crowns.

So when one of my girlfriends invited Paris to the movies with us, I was deeply offended. Not only was he my workplace nemesis (even though I didn't know him), but as den mother of our group, I was the one who made our plans and extended invitations.

After the movies, we were all hanging out, and Paris sat down next to me to make small talk. His rapprochement went off awkwardly at first—he loved Madonna, while I loved Christina Aguilera—but we eventually found common ground in an unlikely subject: the Hilton sisters. Yes, we bonded over Paris and Nicky Hilton. We both thought they were incredibly tacky yet oddly enthralling. He and I fell deep into a discussion of entitlement and the existential meaning of being famous for absolutely nothing. That kind of conversation was totally refreshing. When you come from a small place, a lot of people don't have big dreams or aspirations (like when I'd mention a Birkin bag, not a lot of people got it). But Paris got it, and by the end of the evening nicknames had solidified our friendship: he became Paris, as he was the fun, sociable one, and I became Nicky, the subtle fashionista.

We never called each other by our real names again (Paris's nickname took so well that when the paparazzi shoot him, he's labeled "Paris" in the photo). In Paris, I found a kindred spirit, someone cold, rude, and abrupt on the outside but soft and shy on the inside. After our second time hanging out, Paris was family. In college, away from home for the first time and running all over the place and partying, he needed taking care of, and I love going into that mother hen role. Beyond our love of the Hiltons, that's how we jelled: I found fun in his world and he found stability in mine.

Paris fit into the worldview I had developed in my short and inexperienced life that the physical and emotional were completely separate realms—at least for me. Paris became my closest confidant and constant companion but I wasn't in the least attracted to him. When I came out to my mom, I told her I might still marry a woman. I wasn't talking about sex. Forever and ever and happily ever after doesn't necessarily pertain to sex. I have loved so many women in the way that every husband should love his wife. And you can have sex with a total stranger. I just didn't know if I would ever find sex and love in one person.

Then, a month into working with Tatiana Tarasova in my attempt to undo the mistakes I had made the previous season, I met Alex at a small party after the Liberty competition in Delaware. He was gorgeous—a pairs skater (yes, another one) with clear blue eyes—but I didn't go right to sex in my mind. I'm not an overly sexual person and the possibility of it is never my main attraction. Instead, I was drawn to his mysterious combination of contradicting qualities. He was at once warm and a concrete wall. He gave me his entire life story, but it didn't include the fact that he was gay—which of course he was. He was forthright but uncomfortable with himself. I became immediately infatuated with this sweet, awkward, and fashionably unfashionable boy.

Unfortunately as a skater trying to claw my way back to the Olympic level, I could only pursue one thing at that point: skating. We texted each other a lot of innocuous messages the first twenty-four hours after meeting, but the flame quickly died out. He lived in New England, and I was way too young and naive to know the meaning of long distance.

Still, when Alex sent me a text that he was going to be at the Eastern sectionals in Lake Placid where I was competing to qualify for the Nationals, those small characters, which appeared on my phone, lit my heart on fire.

After the event, I got dolled up in my room at Art Devlin's

Olympic Motor Inn and picked my way through the quiet, dark streets covered in snow and ice to the official hotel where a couple of skaters were hosting a party in their room. At the sectionals, the room parties were way more exciting than the actual competition. Skaters packed themselves into one room like sardines and filled the bathtubs with liquor and ice. This was their well-earned time to get loose. I had gotten all decked because I knew Alex would be one of the warm bodies there.

Outside the hotel room, I could hear the muffled but distinctive sound of drunken voices. When I opened the door, the muted fun turned into the kind of full-on din that normally had me turning on my heels and heading for my pajamas. But tonight adrenaline, some left over from winning the sectionals and more in anticipation of seeing Alex, coursed violently through me in an Incredible Hulk moment.

Almost as soon as I set foot in the room, Alex appeared right in front of my face. His eyes were bluer than I remembered and staring directly into mine with a level of anticipation that matched my own. I had turned this moment over and over in my mind, but now that we were here, I froze. How should I greet him? Alex and I hadn't touched each other before. I couldn't shake his hand—that would be ridiculous. But was a hug too much? I remained frozen, caught between a hug and a shake.

Alex moved in and relieved me of the tension with a big hug. It seemed that someone had become more comfortable with his sexuality in the past few months. When he came in close, I could smell a special mixture of vodka and Gucci's Envy cologne. Why not? Having won his competition, he had his own celebrating to do. Or perhaps he was looking for a little liquid courage.

We sat down with the rest of his friends, but pretty much all my attention went to Alex and reading the signals coming from him. He sat so close to me that our thighs pressed together—*that had to be a sign, right?* Then there was the faux drunken move where he went kind of boneless and draped himself near me.

The greatest sign, though, appeared to me when Alex went up to get another drink. There was something different about him, which I couldn't pinpoint at first. Then I realized: his clothes! When we first met in Delaware I teased him (kind of how the boy in elementary school pulls the hair of the girl he likes) because none of his clothes fit. All of it was in Extra Boy size, that horrible boxy look usually favored by straights. In Lake Placid, my heart leaped when I saw his fitted pants contoured his legs and his shirt didn't blouse out: he hadn't forgotten me and I didn't forget him.

When he returned, I gave him a few signals of my own.

"Come with me," he said.

Alex led me out of the bustle of the party and into another hotel room, this one quiet and dark. The boldness of this previously shy boy surprised me. But as soon as we got inside, his confidence seemed to disappear into the darkness. Our first moment of true physical connection was clumsy and tense in the way of most meaningful encounters where both parties want so much for everything to go right. The pressure of hoping this might turn into something added weight to every part of my body. When we kissed, I felt the vaguely familiar physical warmth from previous explorations, but layered below was a tenderness that squeezed my heart so hard I thought it would pop. The physical and emotional parts of me collided for the first time.

I've never been a good whistler, but after I deposited Alex back at the party and said my good nights to the rest of the crowd (with exultant winks from friends and dirty looks from a few jealous types), I whistled and pranced all the way down the icy path to my room.

———————

I wasn't sure it was possible, but Johnny Weir could in fact fall in love. All it took was a kiss for me to fall for Alex—the kind of descent where your blood sugar dips to the bottom and you get overly excited for no reason. Nineteen years old, skating phenomenally again, and setting my sights on the national title, I felt like I was on top of the world. Adding love to the list gave me confidence on steroids.

For the first time in my life I was tingling from the tips of my fingers to my toes. Puppy love. Lust. True romance. I wasn't sure of the label but I did know this is what these things are supposed to feel like. This is what everyone sings about in pop songs or writes about in books.

We talked almost every night on the phone, but my training made the time in between our visits unbearably long. By the time Paris and I made our first of many visits to New England,

Alex and I were bursting with pent-up energy. We lasted about ten minutes hanging out with the crowd at a skating party before I found myself in a dark room, alone with my very first heartthrob. On a stranger's bed, we made out and played Twenty Questions the way teenagers do.

"We are obviously really into each other, but I want to know what your thoughts are," I said.

"I want to be happy and I don't want you to hurt me," Alex responded.

In figure skating there were a lot of rumors about me—stuff like I had wild threesomes with judges and skaters—all of which were completely false. The skating world is a catty place filled with backstabbing, but because I had been a bitch to so many people during my diva period, it was easy for them to make up stories about me. I wanted to put Alex at ease but didn't know if I could.

"I want to tell you that the majority of rumors about me are false. But if you have a question, you should just ask me directly and I will tell you exactly what went down. I'm not ashamed or afraid and promise to tell you the truth."

"I don't really have many questions," Alex said shyly.

"I want to tell you something anyway," I said.

"What?"

"I'm a virgin."

"Me, too."

"And I really like you."

"I really like you, too."

Revealing deep secrets to each other in the dark, Alex and I both knew whatever we had started that night after sectionals *was* special. We had found love.

As our relationship quickly turned into a committed one, I discovered the unbelievable power in having someone (other than your mother) supporting and loving you in all moments. I also discovered the prickly underside of that bond: other people's envy.

Figure skating, where jealousy runs as rampant as rhinestones, is a fucked-up place to find your romantic future. Still, most of us seek it there, believing that no one else but another skater can understand us. Who else but another skater wouldn't laugh at the fact that I had to go to bed every night at nine in the year leading up to the Nationals? On my first real date with Alex, I ate only a tomato at dinner. A civilian probably would have dialed an anorexia hotline on the spot, but he didn't even blink because he understood that is what you do to get in fighting shape.

It is a human thing to want to bond with someone who understands you, but skating is a small world, making the pool of available love-interests unfairly small to choose from. It's harder to find a decent guy in the skating scene than it is to get into Harvard. Competition gets fierce, to put it mildly.

When Alex and I hooked up, he hadn't really been out. So this sweet and kind kid with clear blue eyes and a very wealthy family represented an untapped and enticing resource in this world of boys who wanted to bang like bunnies. A few skaters in his area pined hard-core over Alex.

Having a bad reputation at the time, I seemed like an easy

target for sabotage. Once we went exclusive, the rumors about my so-called slutty behavior ramped up. However, nobody knew (other than Paris, Alex, and a few others) how big a prude I was in reality. So when one guy with a crush on Alex forced his way into a bathroom while I was using the facilities during a party so he could put the moves on me, he was surprised that I pushed him so hard he knocked his head against the wall. He had hoped to run directly to Alex with news that we had made out. But I don't like shifty games or people barging into the bathroom.

None of that silly stuff ever posed a threat to Alex and me. Raised by two parents who truly love each other, I knew a relationship wasn't a game where you played a part to win the other over. All that mattered was our connection, deepened by expressing our true feelings, no matter what they were. With the strength of that example at home, I was fearless when it came to telling and showing Alex how much I loved him. For Alex, whose parents went from having a home and three kids to going through an ugly divorce, loving someone presented a more terrifying challenge, like bungee jumping off the Grand Canyon.

But together we took the leap of saying I love you and eventually losing the Big V together. Although I had wanted to wait until I was in love, my virginity had never been much of an issue for me. So when I finally had sex, I was surprised at how fulfilled I felt. Staring at each other with smiles from ear to ear, I remember thinking, no matter what, we would always be a part of each other's lives because of this moment.

Of course, a lot of that had to do with the fact that both of us waited for the right person with whom to share that intimate experience.

It is not often that people wait for quality. It makes no difference that I like to have sex with men; my value system is very old-fashioned. I believe there is nothing sexier than knowing one's self-worth. As eccentric and flamboyant as I appeared, I waited until I was almost twenty to lose my virginity, because I wanted it to mean something. I wanted to be in love. I inherited that belief from my mother, who taught me to never settle for less than the best. And in my book, Alex was hands down the best.

While out-of-control has never been my preferred state, I felt crazy alive—"crazy" being the operative word. I would burst out hysterically crying for no apparent reason because I was deeply, madly, passionately in love. That kind of strong emotion made me at once insane and content. It was all brand-new and confusing as hell.

Add to that the new and euphoric peak I reached in my skating career after my win at the Nationals, and honestly I don't think there has ever been another time in my life when I was happier.

Right after I won the title in Atlanta, Alex visited me in my hotel room.

"A lot of people are going to propose marriage to me, so you'll have to stay on your toes," I teased him.

A few days after the biggest skating moment in my life, Alex sent a whole cheesecake to my house with a card that read, "I'm staying on my toes . . . and making sure you eat."

7

Almost Famous

Photos of famous people from around the world covered the tasteful gray walls of the media consultant's sleek Upper East Side office where I sat waiting. Most of them were signed with little notes, like "You're the best" and "I couldn't have done it without you," to this woman my skating federation had charged with reining in me and my big mouth.

After winning the National Championships, I was immediately thrust into the spotlight with every major press outlet wanting to interview the new, and very surprising, top U.S. skater. But in the very first moment of my media blitz, I got in trouble. During the press conference after the competition, a reporter asked me about my "unusual" free skate costume. Inspired by *Dr. Zhivago,* my gorgeous blue and silver sparkly onesie, snowy and icy in a modern way, required a description to do it justice.

"It's like an icicle on coke," I said.

The statement just came out naturally, inspired by the muse. The astonished reporters looked at me as if *I* were on coke and tried to make sense of a skater who said more than just "I'm so happy to have won." I *was* so happy to have won the event, so much so that I didn't think about the import of my words. But the truth is I never do. Whether it's in a public forum or in my bedroom with friends, I never filter myself.

Almost as soon as it came out of my mouth, the comment was everywhere: television, newspapers, and the Internet, in America and abroad. Drugs! It really freaked everyone out. The big impact of my tiny comment and the number of people I offended startled me. Only on day one of my newfound stardom, I wasn't used to anyone paying too much attention to what I said. My then agent lamely tried to backtrack by saying that what I really meant was that my costume looked like Coke flowing down the side of a frosty can. Did he really think people were that stupid?

Well, I sure didn't and quickly vowed to keep my foot-in-mouth disorder, a Weir family trait, no matter how famous I got. There's always going to be someone who has an issue with something you've said no matter how fake you try to be, so what's the point in bottling up your feelings and thoughts?

Having separate public and private personas was way too complicated for my taste.

The USFSA begged to differ. Livid that their national champion was talking about drugs (plus a few little comments about how bad they were at their jobs), they signed me up for media training the day before I was scheduled to appear on the *Today* show. Everyone worried about how ridiculous I'd be, given the massive exposure on morning television. And I'm not saying they weren't right to worry.

When the woman, a small New York City successful type in a pencil skirt and heels who clearly came from the Barbara Walters school of hair and makeup, introduced herself I knew instantly this was not my people. Sitting behind an enormous desk covered in awards, she threw me a toothy smile that cracked the foundation around her eyes and mouth. Everything about this lady was studied, from her framed credentials to her French manicure. I was so agitated I left my sunglasses on: I had my first World Championships in a few weeks and would have much preferred spending this time training rather than getting spokesperson tips.

"As an athlete, you need to appear centered and focused," she said.

"Why?"

"You're a role model now to lots of younger kids. You have to maintain that image."

This was going to be a long three hours. Instead, I wished she would give me tricks for getting dewy-looking skin on television.

"Can't a role model be funny and clever?" I asked.

"Sure," she said, perking up. "Humor's a terrific way to break the ice on TV. Try a joke, but stick to sports. Only sports. Like, 'I almost put on the wrong skates before I got on the ice.'"

"I don't get it."

The next morning when I arrived on the *Today* show set, I had just enough information from media training to make me very uptight but not enough to be charming. In the car at 4:30 a.m. on the way to midtown, I came down with a case of the jitters. It's rare that figure skaters get the chance to talk in front of the entire country—apart from small sound bites. This was an opportunity for me to present myself through words.

I was also nervous because I had to skate on Rockefeller Center's really small outdoor rink—during a torrential downpour. The last thing I wanted to do was fall on my ass in front of millions of TV viewers. I couldn't wear my costume, which really upset me, because it was too cold and I might get sick. So there I was, in decidedly boring white track pants and a warm-up jacket, with no one to cheer for me around the rink because of the freezing rain. But as they say, the show must go on, so I skated in two inches of rain and by some miracle landed all my jumps.

By the time I finished, I was soaked to the bone but tried to smile for the cameras as rain dripped from my hair and nose. What a TV debut. But the *Today* show anchors were so impressed that I'd skated through the rain without slamming into Rockefeller Center that they invited me to sit on the couch instead of doing my interview rinkside (a coup that maybe also had to do with them not wanting to get wet). I behaved myself like a national champion—well, almost. When Matt Lauer asked me how I was preparing for the upcoming World Championships, I gave a nod to my media trainer. "I'm trying to stay centered," I said. "And not let *Today* show interviews make me jaded."

Today was just the first stop on my new life as a real international skating star. A few weeks later at the World Championships in Germany, I proved my win at the Nationals was no fluke. After flawless short and free skate programs, both of which earned me standing ovations, I finished in fifth place overall. Losing to the Russian firecracker and my skating hero Evgeni Plushenko, the event champion, and beating Michael Weiss, I was thrilled by how the competition went. Tatiana Tarasova, with whom I planned to create new world-class programs for the upcoming season, had worked it for me before my arrival, raving to all the Russian officials about how great I was. Each member of the Russian team, normally standoffish to foreigners, shook my hand, patted me on the back, and said, "Good job." I felt like part of the gang.

Immediately after the competition, I was on a plane with the biggest names in skating, including Plushenko, Irina Slutskaya, Elena Sokolova, and Sasha Cohen, to start rehearsals for the

Champions on Ice tour. Landing a spot on one of the two major ice skating tours in America meant I would be making a steady, and good, income for the first time in my life. In addition to its financial advantages, the tour built up its skaters' egos by touting them as the best and brightest stars (or, in my case, the sparkliest). Touring with Champions on Ice was something every skater, seasoned or not, dreamed of getting to do. From March to May, we toured the country, where every night I soaked up the enthusiastic reception from fans who came to watch me, the country's new champion, skate.

As one of the top six skaters in the world, I was given three Grand Prix events when the assignments came out in June. My first time back on the senior Grand Prix since I had withdrawn in shame three years before, I returned in high style. I was selected to compete in Nagoya, Japan, at the NHK Trophy, in Paris at the Trophée Eric Bompard, and in Moscow's Cup of Russia. All three potentially meant great prize money and more opportunities to make a name for myself. Three top competitions within the span of five weeks presented a heady world tour, but I was ready.

What I wasn't prepared for was the crowd waiting for me when I stepped off the plane in Japan that October. After a twenty-four-hour journey from Philadelphia to Nagoya, I looked more like cargo than human in sweatpants, a loose T-shirt, rumpled cardigan, and baseball cap hiding the hair matted to my head. My skin had the sheen of the great unwashed. So I was shocked and horrified when a group of twenty young Japanese women began snapping my picture after I walked through the sliding glass doors of customs. Luckily I had the presence of mind to wear sunglasses, but I made a permanent note to self to bring a change of clothes, hair product, and makeup on the plane so I'd be camera ready forever after.

At first I was more confused than surprised: why were these people here? Then I saw the handmade signs plastered with hearts, Hello Kitty stickers, and my name. They were here for me. These were *my* fans.

Figure skating fans are a very unique breed of people. These are the folks who watch skating every time it's on TV and not just during the Olympics. They fill the seats of touring ice shows and comment online about every aspect of the sport. They feel like they are part of skaters' lives.

My fans—a core group of ladies called Johnny's Angels (they voted on the name themselves)—are überfans who always go above and beyond. What makes them particularly incredible is that I don't make it easy to be a fan of me. I wear outlandish outfits and say even more outlandish things. Like everyone else in my life, they need to have a thick skin.

Still, if anyone wrongs me, there'll be a battle. And I love my fans for that. Their emotional support is a huge part of my success—so is their financial support. I literally wouldn't be able to afford to skate if I didn't have fans: they have paid for costumes and on occasion coaching bills. That's why I never feel like I give my fans enough, although I work very hard to keep them happy.

Apart from those throwing flowers or holding signs for me at competitions, the airport in Japan was my first time coming face-to-face with regular individuals who loved and supported me—from across the world, no less.

I stopped to sign autographs and take pictures. In return, the fans offered me beautifully wrapped presents of handmade soaps, a fur collar, and anime notebooks—all things they knew I would like from reading interviews with me in the press. One girl had made me a special cell-phone holder covered with rhinestones and little Chanel logos (I told any reporter who would print it how much I loved Chanel, even though I couldn't afford the real thing at the time). I was so touched by the thought and effort.

"How did you know what plane I was on?" I asked her.

"Competition in four days. We wait at airport for two days already," she said.

For me? I was stunned. My own mother wouldn't wait half an hour for me in the car.

"Where Johnny luggage?" another girl said, pointing to the one little bag I held.

"Oh, the airline can't find it. Not even my skates," I said.

The women gasped, a few putting their hands to their mouths in polite horror.

"Don't worry!" I said, trying to put out the alarm. "It should come in a few days . . . I'm in very good shape . . . not a problem if I miss one or two practices . . . I will be fine."

I waved good-bye to them merrily and hopped onto the bus that took me and my mom to our hotel. But that wasn't the last I heard from my fans in Japan. The next day they were waiting for me in the lobby of my hotel (the official hotel of the Grand Prix was posted on the Internet) with bags of socks, underwear, T-shirts, toothpaste, and anything else someone who lost his luggage might need.

I thanked all of them for the thoughtful and helpful gesture. Amid the group of bowing women, I saw the fan who had made me the bedazzled cell-phone cover. She and I bowed a couple of times before she approached me.

"Johnny, it would be my honor to give you special gift," she said.

"You've already given me more than enough," I said, starting to feel a little worried.

"No, please," she said, guiding me to a small seating area off the lobby.

I wasn't sure what was happening but reasoned that she probably wouldn't come on to me, or chop me into little pieces, in front of the hotel staff. What happened next astonished me more than if she had actually wielded a machete.

She handed me a beautifully wrapped box that I tentatively opened, upset about messing up the perfect paper, ribbon, and paper flower. I fished around the tissue for a second before I hit upon something cool and delicate. I pulled out the breathtaking object as if it had just been born. It was a gold and blue enamel Fabergé egg. As she had explained in her faltering English, she had flown to Moscow to purchase one in an authentic shop after reading about my love of Fabergé eggs in a magazine article. I did love the precious eggs but never imagined I'd actually own one. Not even counting the travel expenses, the gift must have cost her a small fortune. And in exchange for that treasure, she asked nothing in exchange except my happiness.

Being a "celebrity," albeit in a very specific world, was pretty wonderful. It was a bit strange to have my photo taken by strangers while walking out of the hotel or buying my fourth Starbucks coffee of the day, but I wasn't complaining. I enjoyed being adored.

The love fest continued when I arrived at the competition and went through the process of accreditation. The Japanese skating officials in charge greeted me warmly and said that coaches in their country were teaching young kids to skate like me—the biggest compliment I could imagine receiving. My porcelain skin and big eyes appealed to Japanese tastes for sure. But the way I skated—into myself and quiet—also resonated with their culture. The realization of my popularity in the country gave me quite a boost going into the event.

When I got on the ice for my long program, a new one created by Tarasova to "Otoñal" by Raul Di Blasio, it was so quiet you could have heard a program rustling. I had already skated well with my new short program to "Rondo Capriccioso" by Camille Saint-Saëns for the pleased and respectful audience. But by the time I had finished the free skate, people were standing and screaming. I even saw women crying. In a country that prides itself on being calm and quiet, the audiences usually barely clap. So this kind of raucous appreciation at the end of the program, very rare for Japan, marked a tremendous debut.

My scores were announced, and I was far and away the winner, beating the runner-up, Timothy Goebel, by more than twenty points. That night, exhausted and elated in my hotel bed, I called Alex to say good night (or maybe it was good morning for him). "It's starting to happen," I said. "I can't believe this. Everything's coming together."

That was pretty much the extent of my celebration, since a few days later I arrived in Paris, where I had to forget the gold medal I had just won and start training for the next Grand Prix a week later.

I'd been to France but always to compete in little towns. Paris was completely new to me and, living in Delaware, a complete treat that I planned to enjoy. Every day after practice I walked the crooked streets, enjoying the intoxicating aroma of buttery croissants and fluffy baguettes (that stuff didn't exactly fit into my skating diet) and lots of luscious dark coffee.

But far and away my favorite cultural delight in Paris was the fashion. Beautiful clothes have always been something I adored and followed like a moth to a flame. But I previously had to relegate my passion to reading fashion magazines since I wasn't able to afford anything much nicer than a pair of designer jeans. But since the Champions on Ice Tour, I had been saving my pennies for this very moment—a shopping trip in the fashion mecca that is Paris.

I walked down the Champs-Élysées and skipped on the Rue Saint-Honoré. It was everything I had imagined. Each boutique window screamed beauty and luxury with clothes by Gaultier,

Lacroix, Galliano, Christian Dior, Chanel, and Hermès. Inside the hushed stores, I joined the ranks of chic ladies in fur-trimmed tweed coats with delicate "CC" buttons and men in slick suits that screamed European glamour. I'll never forget my first big purchase: a pair of caramel-colored Yves Saint Laurent ankle boots with little heels, aptly called the "Jonny." I never dreamed my feet could look so beautiful and almost danced back out onto the street where the scent of cigarette smoke, Chanel No. 5, garlic, and apple napoleon mingled in the air with the angst-ridden soundtrack provided by a lonely violinist and decrepit accordion player. As a fashion addict on his first binge, it was the most erotic time of my life.

I returned to my hotel room laden down with those crisp, life-affirming shopping bags from the world's most beautiful stores, ready to put everything away properly and perhaps try on a few incredible pieces again. Opening the door, I discovered to my abject horror that someone, who had strewn his clothes all over the small room, was showering in the bathroom. It wasn't an intruder but simply another skater. In my mind, the two were equally upsetting.

By this point, I understood some things about myself. Number one: I didn't eat in the cafeteria the organizing committee created for these events, preferring to venture out to the cafés or restaurants of the host city, because everyone would stare at me while I consumed lunch. And number two: I didn't have roommates. These competitions are expensive for federations, so they require skaters to bunk together in order to save costs. But one thing I can't abide is sleeping in the same room as somebody else, especially a stranger. I need my space, and when I'm competing, I definitely need my space.

After enough whining to my reluctant federation (and enough medals around my neck), they let me buy out the other half of the room when I traveled the circuit. It wasn't like I was asking them to pay for it. I had enough extra money to make myself comfortable. I knew other skaters would be jealous and call me a diva, but I didn't really care what they thought. I wanted to get a good night's sleep and win.

Although I had paid to have the small, spartan room with two single beds pushed together to myself, the federation had booked somebody else in there while I was out. My luggage barely fit in there (I do not travel lightly). So I started collecting the stranger's underwear, socks, T-shirts, and pants and stuffing them back into his duffel bag until he emerged from the shower with a towel around his waist.

"I'm really sorry," I said, folding his things a little more neatly. "But I've paid for this room myself. You can't stay here."

"Johnny, when they put me in this room, I knew I shouldn't be here. But there's no other place for me to go. I just had to get a shower and need a little sleep."

"You had your shower, but you can't sleep here. I've packed your luggage again. Please get out."

The poor guy, a pairs skater from Connecticut, threw on jeans and a shirt and fled the room, still soaking, to avoid the effects of my full-on tantrum.

Having a diva fit wasn't my finest moment, but if my federation wanted me to be a star, they would have to start treating me like one. Or at least giving me a room to myself when I had paid for it. The federation found the pairs skater another home, and I held up my end of the bargain, winning the gold a few days later at the French Grand Prix, much to the chagrin of local fans who whistled (the French form of booing) at my victory over their champion Brian Joubert. Beating the world silver medalist from the year before in his own country signaled my ascendancy on the international stage.

Having conquered Paris, it was directly on to Russia. The only problem: I still didn't have my tourist visa to get into the country.

Priscilla and my mom, who traveled with me wherever I went, had dutifully gone to the Russian consulate the day after we arrived in Paris with my official letter stating that I was set to skate in the Russian Grand Prix two weeks later. Because Russians are big figure skating fans, a lot of the people that worked in the consulate knew who I was. It seemed like we would have the visa well before the typical weeklong waiting period.

But we quickly found ourselves caught up in red tape. Every day my mother, who didn't speak a syllable of French, took the Paris metro to the Russian consulate, where she would line up at eight o'clock in the morning and wait for hours until they told her the visa still wasn't ready. We steadily got more nervous until the situation turned into full-on panic when I still didn't have a visa the day before I was supposed to leave for Moscow.

Priscilla, my mom, and I heard rumors the Russians were engaged in a game of payback for what happened to Evgeni Plushenko at the World Championships, held in Washington, D.C., two years earlier. The Americans had held up his visa (perhaps because they had a champion threat with Timothy Goebel) so that Evgeni had to come to the competition a day late. I had no idea of it was true, but my visa process was going so slowly, we weren't sure if I'd make the Russian Grand Prix at all.

Although the entire U.S. team and the rest of the international skaters had already left, I continued to train in Paris, trying not to let geopolitics divert me from my run-throughs, until finally, two days before the Grand Prix, my mother came tearing into the hotel as if she were being chased by a couple of gendarmes: she had our visas!

We were ready to go—our bags had been packed and waiting for two days. Now we just needed a flight. The U.S. Figure Skating Association travel agent could book us on a direct flight the next morning from Charles De Gaulle for Sheremetyevo on Aeroflot, but at the time the Russian airline's fleet of old planes had more than its fair share of crashes. So we took a pass and opted instead for a Lufthansa flight that connected in Frankfurt.

When we landed in Frankfurt the following day after a little hopper flight, Team Johnny was a little weary from the drama. Priscilla, my mom, and I sat silently in our own little world as we waited on the tarmac for the plane to debark. We sat and sat and sat and sat until eventually the pilot got on the intercom to say that our gate had experienced some sort of mishap and it would take hours for us to get off the plane.

We missed our flight to Moscow.

After a night in a hideous airport hotel in Frankfurt, where terrorist cells were certainly forming and I didn't sleep a wink, we left for Russia, landing (after a snow delay, of course) just in time for me to make the draw party that decided the order of skaters the next day. I wasn't on the official ice in Russia until the practice hour the morning before the competition, which left me feeling totally unprepared and terrified. Already a control freak who likes to have his skates laced and tight half an hour before I perform, I wanted everything to be absolutely perfect since this was my first time returning to Russia since 2002, when I'd withdrawn from the same event, claiming I was "sick."

The scheduling screwup was the last thing I needed for an event that would take all my confidence to win. Russia is a rough place for foreigners to compete. Not only is figure skating one of the country's most popular sports, but in general their nationalism is off the charts and makes American pride look downright unpatriotic. From a very early age, Russians are taught that they are the best. Representing America, I was already at a severe disadvantage and the lack of practice time didn't help.

But when I got on the ice, a small weary speck in the middle of this massive Soviet-built stadium called Luzhniki filled to the last row, I was treated to a wholly unexpected surprise. Huge banners with "Johnny We Love You" and "We've Been Waiting for You" written in Cyrillic letters waved in time to chants of support. The Russians welcomed me like one of their own. Tarasova, the grand doyenne of the skating world and a living legend in her native land, waited at the boards in her large fur poncho, physical proof that she stood by me.

The audience pushed me through a few mistakes and, before the last run of the straight-line footwork sequence in my long program, screamed and clapped to the music. Just like in Japan, I was floored by the fan response, although in Russia the experience was even more special because after all these years of trying to speak Russian, understand the culture, and take the best from their history of skating, its people, in a rare show of affection, accepted my performance. I wasn't perfect and got second, by a wide margin, to Evgeni Plushenko, world champion, Olympic silver medalist, and not a bad person to lose to.

The night after the Russian Grand Prix exhibition skate, I was ready to celebrate. I had the highest point total of any skater on the circuit, which meant going into my first Grand Prix Final, two weeks later in China, I was number one in the world. But first I needed to get my drink on. The Ukraina Hotel, where all the skaters were staying, one of seven famous Stalinist buildings known as the Seven Sisters, was incredibly high, incredibly old, and incredibly rundown. It didn't have computer access, the TV only received two channels, and you had to shower on your knees in the bathtub. But the grand hotel, with twenty-foot ceilings in every room including the bathrooms, was tailor-made for debauchery.

Sitting in one of the hotel's many bars, surrounded by friends I had made during summers training with Tarasova, I treated everyone, including myself, to champagne. A heavy cloud of smoke hung over the room's thick red curtains and red velvet chairs as the drink went immediately to my head. I was rail thin, hadn't touched alcohol since the Grand Prix started, and was already giddy from my current standing on the circuit. The combination made for a pretty cheerful evening.

At a certain point I spotted Evan Lysacek with a few other Americans sitting in the corner and decided to approach him in a moment of good sportsmanship.

"Having a good night, Evan?" I asked.

He wasn't a fan of Russia and had placed fifth in the event, so I didn't imagine it was the time of his life.

"Yeah, great," he said.

"I think it would be a good idea to have a handstand contest," I said out of the blue. I was pretty tipsy.

"You're on."

Upstairs in the hallway on the floor where all the Americans were staying, Evan and I competed in handstands. I was losing terribly when I came down wrong on one of my very pointy gray leather boots (I enjoy a pointy shoe because I've got small feet, and I think pointy shoes make them look bigger). In retrospect, it wasn't the most practical footwear in which to carry on a handstand contest. With a sprained ankle, I decided to call it a night and hobbled back to my room.

Getting on the bus to the airport at four o'clock the next

morning, I winced at the pain in my ankle. I was still a little tipsy from the night before and reasoned the pain, which I kept to myself, wasn't all that bad. I'd be fine by the time we landed in the States. But the tipsy feeling wore off during a deep sleep on the bus ride. And when I awoke, my ankle was so stiff I couldn't put any weight on it. Trying to get off the bus with my two giant suitcases, a small rolling bag, a purse, *and* my throbbing ankle, I ended in a jumble on the snowy street. The injury was so bad I knew I would never make it to the Grand Prix finale in China.

"Mom, I'm out. I can't. I can't," I said, covered in snow like an idiot. "I hurt my ankle . . . doing handstands."

My mom just looked at me and said, "Oh, Johnny."

———————

Waiting for my turn in the exhibition skate after the 2005 World Championships in Moscow, I sucked fiercely on a cough drop to try to rid myself of the taste of bitter disappointment. I had worked so hard to create a special Russian number for the exhibition—the gala of champions where the top five finishers from every event performed one last time for the crowd—because I went into the competition thinking I would earn gold and become the best skater in the world. In the end, I hadn't even earned a medal.

I had returned to Moscow for the event in March cockier than ever, having just won my second national title, which firmly crowned me the best skater in America. Going into the National Championships in Portland, Oregon, as the favorite, the pressure was intense. Winning a national title is one thing, but defending it is quite another. The stress was two hundred times greater than anything I had ever experienced. The media hounded me, hoping, praying, and waiting for me to say something stupid like I had the year before.

I just kept my head down, training harder and harder and harder every day. It paid off: I beat Timothy and Evan to become the first person in several years to win two national titles in a row, and I was only twenty years old.

Going to the World Championships, in one of my adopted home cities, no less, everything was amazing. A few people waited for me at the airport, which is really rare for Russia. And some of my fans from Japan traveled to Moscow to watch me compete. Skinny from months of hard dieting and even harder workouts and fortified by my clear international support, I was ready to be world champion.

And then, a few days before the competition, my body decided to rebel.

I've always had trouble with the bottom of my foot where a calcium deposit flares up on occasion. The condition, known as sesamoiditis, is unpredictable and embarrassingly painful. As an ice skater, there is so much pressure on your body when you land that everything has to work properly or it hurts like hell. Even a toenail that's a tiny bit too long can kill.

By the third day of practices, I just couldn't pull myself together and the pain had shot up into my knee. I considered withdrawing but couldn't stand cutting short the best season of my life because of a goddamn calcium deposit. So I said, "Fuck you, foot," and tried to forget the hurt and just do my job.

I was so nervous because, if nothing else, I didn't want to let my audience down. After Evgeni withdrew because of a bad back, the Russian media told me, "Johnny, you're the highest 'Russian' right now." No pressure. Apart from the American doctor, Priscilla, and my mom, nobody knew about my sesamoiditis—it's not exactly a sexy injury—plus in figure skating, people could care less if you are hurt. If you make excuses for bad skating, you just come off as a whiner. You might have suffered a concussion or your dog just died, but all that matters is your performance on the ice.

And mine did not total up to world champion material. Skating on what felt like knives plunging into my left foot, I made some sad mistakes (like falling on my ass during a triple axel) during the short program. Though I tried to claw my way back during the free skate, with the entire Soviet stadium clapping along to the beat of my music, I couldn't pull off a world medal. Evan bumped me out of third place.

As fourth in the world, I was still able to perform my exhibition number conceived as a thank-you to the Russian people for all their support and kindness. I had decided to skate to Russian music, a radical choice since even Russian athletes wouldn't skate to their own country's music, preferring to bow to the English-speaking world in this one regard.

I chose the famous song *"Ya Tebya Ne Kogda, Ne Zabudu"* from Russia's first rock musical, *Yunona I Avos,* which told the story of Conchita, a Mexican princess, and Nikolai, a Russian naval officer who falls in love with her. Although Conchita has an arranged marriage planned, the two people from very different worlds enter into a crazy love affair. Nikolai, eventually choosing duty over love, returns to the navy, where he promptly dies in a storm, and his soul enters the body of a seagull. A hopeless romantic, I love these sad stories where one lover dies and the other one never gets over it.

The packed crowd was already in a great mood when I got on the ice, screaming and clapping for the terrific skating that made them love the sport in the first place. Their boisterous energy invigorated me: it was time to put on a show.

A hush descended while the first few melancholy chords of the sad slow song started up, and I could tell nobody grasped what the music was. They never expected an American to skate to a Russian song, so even though they had heard the song a million times, in those beginning seconds, they didn't get it.

Then the first word of the song floated over the stadium.

"Tiy."

As soon as the audience comprehended the Russian word for "you," the entire building erupted.

They loved it. Hundreds of Russian people were on fire—on their feet, screaming, cheering, crying, yelling "Bravo!" I had wanted to make a connection but the emotion was far more than I could have ever anticipated. What I didn't know at the time was the singer, Nikolai Karachentsov, a really famous artist in Russia, had just been in a bad car accident and lay in a coma at the hospital while I skated. The tragedy gave meaning and pathos to my performance.

For me, the moment had meaning of an entirely different sort. With goose bumps traveling the length of my body, I no longer cared that I was fourth. I felt so good on the ice, because people related to what I was saying with my music and movements. *"Ya tebya ne kogda, ne zabudu,"* Karachintsev sang, "I will never forget you." The reaction from the audience—which understood my artistry on the ice and desire to bridge cultural divides—was worth gold to me.

My dad, John Weir, pushing me around in diva fashion, circa mid-'80s.

My all-time favorite Halloween look—Baby Bird, handcrafted by Patti Weir, circa mid-'80s, Pennsylvania.

Ballet fingers at eighteen months, 1985, Pennsylvania.

Celebrating with
Shadow, 1990s,
Pennsylvania.

With my pairs partner, Jodi,
enjoying virgin daiquiris,
1997, California.

Family portrait, 2002,
Pennsylvania.

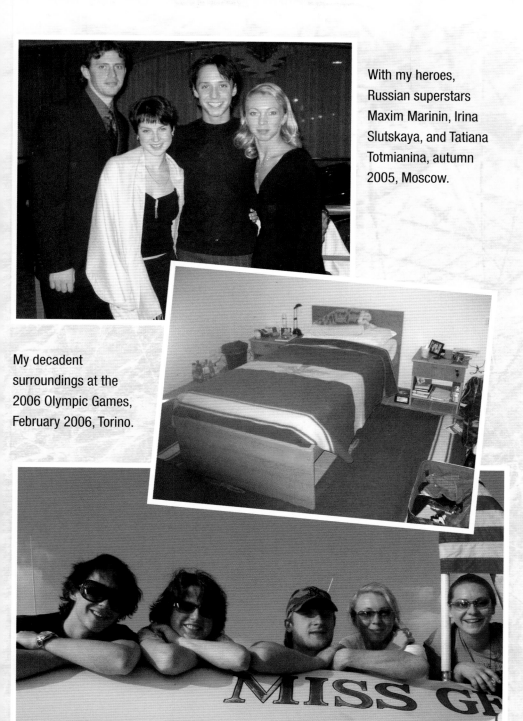

With my heroes, Russian superstars Maxim Marinin, Irina Slutskaya, and Tatiana Totmianina, autumn 2005, Moscow.

My decadent surroundings at the 2006 Olympic Games, February 2006, Torino.

In the midst of the Champions on Ice tour with my friends Irina Slutskaya, Evgeni Plushenko, Tatiana Totmianina, and Marina Anissina, July 2006, Minnesota.

With my Ukrainian family, Nina Petrenko and Galina Zmievskaya, autumn 2007, Washington.

Patti and I in Red Square, November 2007. The Moore side of my family doesn't believe in dressing warm!

My favorite place in this world: Saint Basil's Cathedral in Red Square, November 2007.

One of my dearest friends,
Alexander Uspenski, and I,
October 2007, Everett.

Paris and I having a
moment, August
2009, New York City.

With my mama at the first screening of my film, *Pop Star on Ice,* June 2009, New York City. *(Courtesy of Shane O'Neill Photography)*

A quiet moment with my agentress, Tara Modlin, February 2010.

My official badge for 2010
Olympic team selection,
January 2010, Washington.

The tunnel leading
to the opening
ceremony of the
2010 Olympic
Winter Games,
February 2010,
Vancouver.

An unlikely duo:
me and Evan
Lysacek at the
Vancouver
Olympic Games,
February 2010.

The first meeting with a man my parents brought me up listening to, Sir Elton John, March 2010, Los Angeles.

Costume fitting in New York, summer 2010.

The original album cover for my single, "Dirty Love."
(Courtesy of John Paul Tran and MAC Cosmetics)

8

Birdbrain

Harp chords, gentle as raindrops on a placid pond, and a lofting soulful cello resonated over the tinny loudspeakers of a no-wheresville ice arena. A Russian legend sang *"tak krasivo, moy lebed"* ("so beautiful, my swan," as a young American skater soared and spiraled across a giant sheet of mirrored ice, re-imagining the iconic performance of Maya Plisetskaya as the Dying Swan.

I was back in Simsbury, Connecticut, that June, creating programs with Tatiana Tarasova for my first Olympic season as an actual contender, the dream I'd had since stepping on the ice at age twelve. I finally agreed to a radical idea she had been proposing since the first year we started working together. I would skate a short program to "The Swan," by Saint-Saëns, a classical piece traditionally reserved for women.

A strict and aggressive coach, Tarasova is an artist before she's anything else and sees things in a very different light than most other coaches. She relishes the over-the-top and theatrical in everything from choreography to costuming. Driven by an idealized art form in her head, she comes up with concepts that are off-the-chart crazy for skating. And my skating to "The Swan" was one of them. To her, it made perfect aesthetic sense; my naturally quiet and delicate way on the ice mirrored the mellow cello piece.

Before, I had hesitated to play the part of a dancing female swan. My public image at that point, while not exactly that of a choirboy, still retained a purity and classiness. I was a young, fragile, porcelain-looking American who stood out because I skated more like a ballet dancer. But that's where it ended. Gender bending would take me into a whole new and very taboo arena, where I would stand totally alone.

It's kind of funny, but although everyone on the outside thinks of figure skating as the gayest sport in the universe, those who wield power within it rail against that image. Female or male, skaters are supposed to represent a sanitized ideal, like a figurine atop a child's birthday cake. The result is that homosexual skaters are terrified of announcing or showing any signs of their sexual orientation since the judges, many of whom are gay themselves, will hold it against them. No American skaters were out, in public anyway, and hadn't been since U.S. champion Rudy Galindo came out publicly in 1996 after intense media pressure. The U.S. Figure Skating Association wanted it to stay that way, and even skating in a "feminine" way was tantamount in their rule book to declaring yourself gay. One had to act like a man. On skates and in sparkles.

When Tarasova initially broached the subject, I worried that skating to a piece of music traditionally reserved for women might hurt my reputation with the judges. For the Olympics, I had to release something great and memorable, so when she brought up the idea again, I reconsidered: the short program would be subtle and at the same time shocking. Four years before, Tarasova had created revolutionary programs that helped Alexei Yagudin win the Olympics. *This woman knows how to make an Olympic moment,* I thought. Putting my future in her bejeweled hands, I dove into the part of a lady swan.

As soon as we started to choreograph *The Swan,* I knew I had made the right decision. The experience was complete magic. There were times where I seemed to be running across the ice for hours on my toe picks, my arms fluttering like the feathers of a wounded swan. Tarasova stripped me down to the basest, most animalistic elements of a bird, and on that freeing journey, we were so pleased with ourselves we began calling the program a "masterpiece." Perhaps a little cocky, but swans aren't known for their humility.

I spent all summer preening my new feathers and giving interviews in which I talked about *The Swan*'s great beauty and originality. By its debut at my first Grand Prix event of the year in Canada that October, however, I had shed a lot of my initial certainty. There was big pressure at Skate Canada, the first real international event of the Olympic season, and *The Swan* had gone through drastic choreography changes from the original to conform to new amendments to the judging system the International Skating Union had voted on late that summer. They altered the parameters of acceptable spins and step sequences in a way that forced skaters to jam in more technique (and leave behind any art) in order to rack up points. My poor swan aside, the season leading up to the Olympics was a pretty stressful time to be changing the rules.

At the practice for the Grand Prix, I could already feel the first blush of Olympic fever. In Canada, they're crazy about skating, and fans, who had paid for tickets just to watch the practices, packed the building. I wore my swan costume (I always like to warm up in my costume before the real event) under a jacket but was unabashedly excited to let this beauty free. Feathers delicately etched from sequins and stitching extended across my torso, a few floating freely and dramatically down my black pant leg. One arm, representing the long neck of a swan, cleverly ended in a red glove that looked like a swan's beak. The other arm, covered in sparkling netting, was an avant-garde nod to the under layer in the construction of a swan costume and the deep ballet tradition of this piece.

Before I had a chance to ditch the jacket, a few of the Russian officials came up to Priscilla and me, kissing us warmly on both our cheeks and slapping our backs with loving roughness. They were especially keen on seeing me do well at the Grand Prix.

"Everyone's looking to you to carry America at the Olympics," they said. "Evgeni Plushenko, Stéphane Lambiel, and you are the favorites."

Their words thrilled like a juicy piece of surprising gossip. But then their high praise was quickly supplanted with an opposite reaction. Was *my* country looking to me to carry our men's team at the Olympics? The news came as a shock since my federation had never shown me anything close to that sentiment. It was confusing. But no matter my federation's plan for the future, the Russians had jolted me back into excitement to show in this moment what I could do as The Swan.

I took off my warm-up jacket with hundreds of pairs of eyes watching my every move and cast my glance downward to get deep into the mind-set of a demure and sensitive bird. The audience had no idea what a treat they were in for—a real artiste on the ice. But just then I heard a strange sound, which I didn't recognize at first. It was the crowd laughing at me.

A gaggle of reporters crowded around me after an event, waiting for a famous Weir sound bite and, well, I aimed to please. Still in my swan costume, one of them asked about my one red hand. When addressing the press, I always tried to avoid the obvious and add a little something unexpected. So I didn't want to simply answer, "It's the swan's beak, dummy." Then it hit me, out of nowhere, true inspiration.

"Well, his name is Camille—two *l*'s," I said, thinking about the music's genius composer Camille Saint-Saëns. "I think he's my evil side. When I skate poorly, I blame it on my glove."

I thought it was funny, and so did the reporters. They thought a lot of stuff I said those days was funny. Since I first performed *The Swan* at Skate Canada, something in me had shifted. The moment I appeared on the ice in my swan costume was a near catastrophe that wound up spinning into a huge success. I pushed past the snickering and skated *The Swan* so well the crowd went crazy. People were initially uncomfortable with the spectacle, but the intense emotion that built and unfurled slowly, just like emotions in real life, really resonated. It foreshadowed the reality that *The Swan* would become one of my most popular programs and completely change the world's perception of me.

Unfortunately, the rest of the event didn't go nearly as well. During the free skate, I made a long series of mistakes that ended with me badly spraining my ankle. They pulled me off the ice and put my leg in a cast as I watched the hideous scores that put me in a humiliating seventh place.

Still, it was as if the bird's spirit had untethered me from my last remaining inhibitions. Both my personality and persona were in serious flux. *The Swan* took my natural inclination for poetic license and launched it into the realm of pure camp. Freeing my artistic side in a way that flew in the face of my federation's ideals transformed me from the innocent to seriously sassy in what I had to say.

I stood out all the more because most skaters limit themselves to a very boring script in the hopes of not offending anyone. In sports, there's a clear line of what you can and can't discuss. While you're supposed to bring attention to your sport, it should be in a very rah-rah American way that won't offend a Republican or Christian rights group. The federation wants little robots that all spout the same message. And I was anything but that. I refused to stick to the script: "I hope I skate well. I just want to do my best, and I've worked really hard with my coach." This boosted my popularity with people outside skating's microcosm. Regular kids watching at home adored me because I clearly didn't give a shit about what others thought. That's universal appeal.

The one irritating by-product of my liberation, however, was the media's new moniker for me: flamboyant. Whereas before they had described me as artistic and elegant, now I was "over-the-top" and, of course, "flamboyant." The sexual connotations of the word annoyed me because sex, as much as I might enjoy it, has nothing to do with how I skate. But even more than that, it implied a lack of seriousness and I was as serious as any skater out there, just not as boring. Still, there wasn't a single article about me that didn't use the f-word, and there were a lot of articles about me.

I couldn't complain too much since I was complicit in my new "flamboyant" image. It was like a drug: the more outrageous I sounded, the more attention I got. I gave the people what they wanted with loose comments like:

—declaring myself a "country bumpkin"

—describing my outfit as a "Care Bear on acid"

—calling skating judges "furry old women sitting there with grimaces on their faces"

My colorful language made me the clear press, and public, favorite. But my federation was not pleased. The Loose Cannon had become a fey loose cannon. I was basically their worst nightmare.

By the National Championships in January (the biggest deciding event of my career to that point because of its direct impact on the Olympic team), they let it be known that Evan Lysacek, my main American rival, was the favorite of U.S. Figure Skating Association officials. They spread the word at the event held in Saint Louis that it was Evan's time to win. Their claim wasn't baseless; his Grand Prix season had been stellar, whereas mine had not. But his skating was less of a factor than his persona. For figure skating people, he was easier to get their heads around. Straitlaced, he did everything they told him to. Meanwhile, I was out there wearing a swan carcass.

Although the press loved me because I was open and entertaining, and the public was ready to crown me the star of the upcoming Olympics, as the federation promoted Evan as skating's newest angel, I could feel myself getting pushed out. And I didn't like it.

My only weapon in the war for the halo was a performance that nobody could quibble with. Fueled by the fire of a scorned skater, I performed one of the best programs of my career. My *Swan* at the Nationals was stunning, with not one move or element out of place, earning me a personal best score of 83.28, the highest recorded for a short program in the United States under the new judging system at that time. Evan and Michael Weiss both fell, so I finished the night with a huge lead ahead of second place.

I celebrated by making a really off-color drug reference to the crowd of reporters waiting for me when I got off the ice that compared my performance to another skater's speedier program.

"For [mine], they kind of sat back and had their cognac and their cigarettes and they were relaxing and watching," I said. "His was like a vodka-shot-let's-snort-coke kind of thing."

The federation was fuming the next morning when my comment popped up in countless newspaper articles and Internet postings. While I practiced in the day off between the short and long program, one of the federation's biggest bosses pulled me aside.

"The other skater's mother is very upset and wants you to make a public apology to him," he said. "You have completely disrespected U.S. figure skating, and you need to fix it."

"Really?"

Of course, I didn't fix it. I didn't care. I mean, it was just a little comment, not a big life-or-death issue. This wasn't a communist country; I was free to say what I liked.

Going into my long program with that defiant, and naive, stance, I quickly lost my eleven-point lead to a bunch of technicalities (and my big mouth). Although I had the crowd on its feet, I had done too many combinations according to the new rules, so I received no points for one jumping pass.

After a few nail-biting moments of watching the guys behind me skate, I won the National Championship for the third year in a row, something nobody had done since Brian Boitano in the '80s. But I considered the win tarnished by what I saw as an unjustly small margin. Still, no one outside the skating world cares about points, only winners and losers. With three national titles under my belt and a direct pass to the Olympics, it appeared to the public like I was forever dominant over U.S. figure skating. Far from the truth, I was more than happy to let that image prevail.

My win at the Nationals immediately launched me into the frenzy of the Olympic season, when the whole world, which hasn't paid attention to skating for four years, suddenly tunes in. My name was everywhere, and everyone started calling and coming out of the woodwork. Suddenly we needed a security guard at the front of my rink (which blacked out all of its windows because of the attention) because people were sneaking in to watch me or get on-ice interviews. In between training every day, I was on the phone with different media outlets like *Sports Illustrated* and the *New York Times* so that when people discussed U.S. figure skating at the Olympics, it wasn't the great ice dancers Tanith Belbin and Ben Agosto they talked about, or even Sasha Cohen. It was Johnny Weir. Despite what my federation thought, the press and public had crowned me the next princess of the Olympic Games.

9

Golden Boy

Priscilla and I prepared to go through a third security checkpoint to get into the Olympic Village in Torino, which was more secure than an army base. I hoisted my enormous Rimowa suitcases onto a table for an Italian policeman to inspect. He dexterously maneuvered around the cases and started rifling through the furs, black jeans, boots, and colorful scarves I had brought for my first trip to the Olympics.

When he finished, a few national police waved us forward with their large machine guns. Then we boarded a bus that would finally take us into the Village, but not before the policemen checked underneath, using long sticks with mirrors on the ends, to make sure there were no bombs. Because of the atrocity against the Israeli team by Black September, a Palestinian terrorist organization back during the Munich games of 1972, the Olympics had become something of a militarized zone.

The alarming experience of entering the fortified gate exacerbated my prior reservations about staying in the Olympic Village. When competing, I'm one to be very alone, and in the Olympics it's typical to have four roommates per bedroom. My biggest fear was being housed in a room with four other skaters that I'd be competing against. We would bump into each other on the way to the single shower and pass the flu around, another common occurrence at the games.

But as soon as we made it past the guards, the heaviness lifted. I saw the flags with the Olympic rings flutter against Torino's mellow rolling landscape. Fresh-faced athletes from around the world walked along little pathways to the various buildings, and instinctively I felt the sheer joy and excitement of being part of this elite group.

My happiness only increased upon learning of my housing assignment: a single room in the same condo as the curling team's doctors and coaches. My federation had granted me my wish by putting me far away from the other skaters. Priscilla and I split up (she was staying with the female skating team), and I entered the curling house, hauling my heavy, heavy luggage up three flights to my own private floor.

I opened the door onto the sad little scene. Despite the European obsession with thread count and hand tailoring, I always find their accommodations pretty mean. There was a twin-sized wooden bed frame, with a thin mattress covered by a blue fleece blanket on it. Next to it, a little brown stool functioned as a side table. The only closet was a small wardrobe that wouldn't even house the furs I had brought along. A tile floor with no rugs added the final chilling detail.

Because I spend so much of my time on the road, there's nothing I hate more than checking into a hotel room and having it feel very foreign. I need my home base to have a security-blanket feel in order to withstand the harsh realities of training and competing. This monastic chamber as it stood would not do as my lodging for the next three weeks.

I walked over to Priscilla's room to check out her living space, but when I arrived she was nowhere to be found. The building was empty since the women's skating team didn't arrive for another week and a half. So I started poking around and a lightbulb went off in my head. I grabbed a bunch of fleece blankets, two lamps, a bedside table, and a few extra towels for good measure. Laden down with all my loot, I shimmied across the Olympic Village and into the curling quarters.

Back in my room, I set to work decorating my space. I lifted the bed up, which only took about two fingers because it was so light, and I spread out two of the blue fleece blankets as a rug that almost covered the entire floor space. I unpacked, staging my luggage for a touch of glamour. I hung my fur coats on the door handles for coziness and my official accreditation on the wall for inspiration. I arranged framed photos of me, my family,

Alex, and my dog and lastly lit a few candles. By the time I got into bed, I felt at home.

"Johnny, the smalls were running out but we put some aside because we knew you were coming," an Olympic official said before handing me three enormous bags of Team USA paraphernalia. In the team processing area, where I received my information and uniforms for the Olympics, I wondered how I was going to fit all this stuff into my already cramped room.

Me being me, I knew I wasn't really going to wear any of the uniforms the smiling woman handed me. I don't believe in them and for years had gotten in trouble for it. That whole tracksuit look; it's just not me. Simply put, they're tacky. I'm very proud to be American but I don't feel the need to rub it in everyone's face with an ugly jacket. I wear what I want, which is usually black and fun. Isn't freedom as American as apple pie and football?

Although I didn't like to wear team uniforms, the processing was a proud moment. As soon as the woman handed me my bags that she had held especially for me, I felt like a real part of the U.S. team. And that was something I hadn't felt before, either, because of my federation's slights or because I had excluded myself. I threw myself into the Olympic spirit and into the entire uniform to the delight of the photographers who snapped my picture. I had worked long and hard for this goal; it was time to enjoy it.

That first photo op and subsequent press conference was a continuation of the love affair between me and the press. During the media event with the rest of the men's team, Evan Lysacek, Matthew Savoie, and myself, nearly every single question was directed at me.

"Johnny, how are you preparing for the Olympics?"

"Ambien and espresso."

Laughs.

"How are you enjoying the Olympic Village?"

"It's dirty. I had to do a lot of cleaning."

More laughs.

I was more than pleased to be the ringleader of this American team of young, talented, first-time Olympians. However, the microscope I was under didn't lose its focus after the press conference. Lots of media showed up for every official practice held for the male single skaters. In addition to the judges and other skaters watching, it made for a tough training situation. I didn't want people to see me sweat or breathe heavily. And I certainly didn't want to fall on my ass and have it appear in every newspaper the next day with the headline: "Weir Not Olympic Ready!" So for a week and a half, I didn't push myself in an effort to appear perfect, and my condition started to go down.

To blow off steam in this pressure-cooker environment, I engaged in massive retail therapy in downtown Torino. I let the conversion rate unnecessarily confuse me into thinking everything was cheaper than it was and made very good friends with the people at Louis Vuitton. I went to their boutique practically every day even if I just got a wallet or a little brace-let. Personally imitating a housewife working out her emotions with her credit card at the mall, I spent way too much money that Olympics.

There weren't enough monogrammed LVs in the world, however, to soothe my nerves the day I finally had to compete in the short program. My anxiety scared me (I hadn't felt crazy like that since I was a junior skater) even though my expectations were tempered going into the competition. With Evgeni Pluskenko and Stéphane Lambiel skating, I wasn't sure I would even place. But this was the Olympics. Billions of people would be watching and that alone sent me spinning.

I pushed through my day, practicing and then heading into the city for a simple plate of salad that I ate by myself. Then I re-turned to my room where I watched *Will & Grace* (God, I love that Karen) on my portable DVD player before taking a nap. Not wanting to be rushed, I began putting on my makeup and doing my hair two hours before it was time to catch the bus to the arena.

Right before I left my room, I said a little prayer asking who-ever is up there to help me: *give me power, put air in my lungs, and just help me push.* I blew my candles out and went down-stairs to meet Priscilla.

Backstage at the rink, it was dark and crammed with people. I frantically searched for a place to hide and collect my thoughts, but every nook seemed occupied with skaters, coaches, press, and volunteers. Although newly built for the Olympics, the place stunk of sweat, leather, ammonia, and fear. I felt like I couldn't breathe.

Then time ran out. I walked out of the tunnel and into light so bright it was blinding. There were so many people, so many TV cameras, so many photographers. Dark circular lenses almost ringed the entire rink.

As my eyes adjusted to the light, the announcer said my name and I thought the roof would blow off the building with the American, Russian, and Japanese fans all cheering for me.

I knew it was this Olympic moment for which I had created the *The Swan,* and a lot of things were going to happen in the next ten minutes.

Although my feet were on the ice, my mind floated up to the fans in the seats and returned backstage. Then it settled on the issue of my less-than-perfect condition. In my attempt to maintain a perfect image during practices for the past couple of weeks, I hadn't done full run-throughs of either my short or long program. For as good a shape I was in going into the Olympics, I hadn't kept it up in the period right up to the event.

I had to snap myself back into the moment, right here, right now, on the ice. So I moved toward the boards and punched the wall so hard my knuckles went red and hurt like hell. That did the trick. As I moved onto the ice, the arena went completely quiet. Nobody was screaming; nobody was talking. All I could hear were the shutters on all the cameras around the rink going off. I stood, in the middle of the sporting world, alone on a giant sheet of white ice.

My music started and I completely zoned out the camera shutters, bright lights, flags, and people. Concentrating on the chords of the harp that began the piece, I just started to skate the way that I knew I could. I let the music carry me through my first jump, a triple axel—flawless. Then my second, triple lutz-triple toe—also flawless. I followed it with a perfect sit spin, and people began to cheer. For a spin! I nailed the footwork sequence and began skating full speed toward my last jump.

I was making eye contact with the judges—trying to pick out the ones I knew so I could give them an extra-soulful dying-swan look before going into the jump—when suddenly I realized that—*Oh, my God!*—I was doing the wrong footwork. At that time, I trained with Priscilla each morning by doing different entrances into jumps and had mixed myself up.

With the wall rapidly approaching, I had to do something, so I just jumped. *The Swan* provided, and I landed the triple flip perfectly, did one more beautiful spin into a balletic step sequence and my final combination spin. The crowd roared while I tucked into my last I'm-a-dead-swan pose.

I shrugged as I got off the ice. It had been a clean performance, but the botched footwork left me wanting something more from myself. It certainly wasn't as good as the National Championships. What an inane mistake at the end! I waited for disappointment.

Then the marks came up. Up until that point, my highest international score had been around 75, a pretty average sum. For my Olympic performance of *The Swan*, I earned a total of 80 points, putting me in second place behind Plushenko and ahead of Lambiel and the Canadian skater Jeffrey Buttle. I literally couldn't believe it.

If the hard numbers didn't do it, the excitement from everyone backstage drove home the reality that I was the only American in a position to win a medal. Evan had placed tenth by the end of the night and the next American was a few behind him. My whole team patted me on the back, congratulating me for carrying our country. Every reporter, even ones that I'd had some friction with in the past, were there, too, smiling and proud. They lobbed me softball questions, which were basically all different forms of "How does it feel to be so awesome?"

It felt great, and it only got better when I returned to my room. Emails from fans in the United States and around the world filled my account. They had come in almost as soon as I finished the competition. "Johnny, you are America's bright star." "We love you, Johnny!" "I want you to marry my daughter—you two even look alike!" Okay, some of them were a little off, but the incredible outpouring of love and support covered me like a warm blanket as I drifted off to a contented sleep.

The night before the long program, I couldn't sleep at all. I couldn't come down from the idea that by the end of tomorrow, less than ten years into my skating career, I might have my first Olympic medal. Tossing and turning on the paper-thin mattress,

I was having heart palpitations. So many people were waiting for me to win it. What if I let them down? I couldn't; I was too close. But of course I could—I had choked for much less before. As the first light of morning filtered in through the window, the ceiling and walls seemed to close in on me.

It was going to be a very long and lonely day. After my morning practice, attended by every person with press credentials and a pulse, I had a hideous amount of time to kill before the competition, which wasn't until late at night so that it could be televised live in the States.

To get away from my panicky thoughts, I watched a *Will & Grace* marathon, letting the narcotic of TV lull me into a much-needed nap in which I slept harder than I had in months. When I awoke, I started in slowly on the routine that had proved successful for the short program, spending an inordinate amount of time on my hair and makeup, saying my prayer, blowing out my candles, and walking downstairs to meet Priscilla and the bus that would take us to the competition.

Priscilla and I, both bundles of nerves wrapped in heavy furs, didn't speak as we stood waiting at the bus stop. The only other sign of life in the dark, quiet, cold and completely dead Olympic Village was the president of the Japan Skating Federation, who waited next to us for the bus. The three of us watched our breath make little silent clouds against the sky for a while. Then Priscilla pulled her hand out of her coat to check her watch. The Japanese president and I gave her a sideways glance but stayed silent. A few seconds later Priscilla checked her watch again.

"Do you know where the bus is?" Priscilla asked the president.

"No. It's supposed to be now," she answered.

After checking her watch once more, Priscilla startled the small Japanese woman with her loud, nervous laugh. The bus, scheduled to be here at half past the hour, was now ten minutes late and we officially started to freak out. How were we going to get to the rink? It wasn't like there were cabs or subways in the Olympic Village.

"Oh, well. I guess nobody wants me to skate," I joked nervously.

Nobody laughed. Priscilla walked out into the middle of the deserted street while the president wrung her hands. All of a sudden Priscilla began flapping her arms like a crazy duck. A pair of headlights appeared in the distance.

A volunteer, on call for emergencies, pulled up in a tiny Smart car. While the emergencies were supposed to be things like slipping on the ice or suicide bombers, we begged her to take us to the rink. We piled into the minuscule automobile, skating equipment, furs, limbs, and all, and drove like bats out of hell to get there on time.

When we arrived, every TV camera was waiting for me because I was supposed to be on the bus that had emptied out twenty minutes earlier (apparently we were the only ones who hadn't received the memo that the bus schedule had changed that day). They all quickly cut to my awkward extrication from this clown car, but I could have cared less. I ran into the building so I could get my spot in the dressing room and start getting ready.

There is nothing I hate more than being rushed—but I really hated it at the Olympics. Everything was go-go-go from that moment on. I got into my costume, laced up my skates, and prepared to walk out of the chute and into the warm-up. If I found the crowd during the short program loud, it was nothing compared to the deafening noise that night. In the final group, there were six men skating from six different countries: Russia, America, Switzerland, Japan, Canada, and France. The result was an international cacophony that defied comprehension. The Swiss had cowbells, the French had horns, and everyone had guttural or high-pitched screams in their native languages.

As a performer, you love to hear the audience cheering. But this was aggressive to the point of overwhelming. It was so loud Priscilla had to yell things to me while we stood face-to-face. In this most important moment of my life, I couldn't hear my coach; I couldn't even hear myself.

I didn't hear them call my name, but when the third skater finished I knew it was my time to compete. The lighting was dimmer than it had been for the short program, almost like relaxing mood lighting. But I was so tight that I couldn't feel the ice. It's important to me that my feet are one with the ice, but in that moment I was keenly aware of being on top of it.

I moved on full autopilot to the piano in "Otoñal." After completing three jumping passes and a spin perfectly, I started getting into the groove and enjoying the audience's amplification with each element.

There was a bit of a breather in my program before skating into my second triple axel, and in that momentary void of activity, I lost focus. I looked around and remembered my stiffness, bringing that quality to the next jump. I didn't finish the rotation and landed on two feet. My incomplete triple axel set me off for a shaky footwork sequence. Before the next element, a combination jump of a triple lutz and a triple toe loop, I tried to snap myself back into my performance. But because I was so nervous I wouldn't make it, I just did the triple lutz and left more points on the table.

The next couple of jumps were fine, and running through my head was the thought: *Okay, Johnny, you've definitely fucked up enough. Get it together.* I skated toward the judges for the last jump, but as I was setting up I tripped and had to skate right through. I was so shocked by the whole situation that I couldn't remember what mistakes I had made already in the four-and-a-half-minute program. Like a goldfish swimming around in a circle, I forgot what I'd done and where I'd been. I knew, however, I couldn't leave all those points from a second missed jump, so in that second I changed my program. I turned around, heading in completely the wrong direction, and tried to jump again. And I did it, although it was really ugly, and I barely landed it.

I moved to the kiss and cry area in a daze. Devastated that I hadn't fought for the program and instead let myself and everyone down, all I wanted to do was cry. But with three billion people watching me around the world, I had to keep the tears bottled up. A few did escape when the number five popped up next to my name on the monitor in front of me. That was it. No suspense. No second chance. I flat out didn't have a medal.

In the mix zone, where the media interviews the athletes, the press eagerly awaited my arrival. But for a different reason than I was used to.

"How do you feel now that you've lost America's medal?" a reporter shouted.

I had lost an Olympic medal, the only thing that I really wanted and the reason I started skating in the first place. I felt awful. Talking right now was going to be difficult, but I didn't realize just how difficult.

"What happened today?" another said.

"I missed the bus to come here, which got me off on the wrong foot. I felt rushed at the arena because I was late," I said.

As soon as the words came out of my mouth, I realized I had made one of the biggest media flubs of my career.

"You're blaming a botched triple toe loop on the bus?" a reporter asked.

"No, I was just saying that I spent the day doing my makeup and then I missed the bus, so—"

"So you missed the bus because you were doing your makeup?"

I was getting twisted in my own words. The clever Johnny who also skated well had left the building. I knew I had skated poorly and was the first person to say so, but they thought I was making excuses, and nobody likes excuses. The American press that had loved me so much the day before, and the day before that, and the month before that, started to turn.

"There's a poll on the Internet asking whether people care whether you are gay or not. What's your response?"

What a perfect time to bring up my sexuality. I had to get the fuck out of there; this was starting to get ugly (I didn't realize it then but something a lot uglier awaited me back in my room. I received hate mail from many of the same people who had earlier sent me fan mail. "You failed the country. You failed us." And that was a nice letter. "You wear animals; you should die." "You lost our medal; you should die." One letter even hoped that I'd get "raped to death.")

Priscilla extricated me from the press conference from hell. As we walked back to the dressing room, I stopped to check the drug-testing list. The skaters who placed first, second, and third had mandatory drug testing. And then there was one random test—and of course it was me. What did I do to deserve this? I threw my water bottle against the wall and it burst everywhere. Walking into the locker room to change out of my costume, I practically ripped the gorgeous velvet and net creation off my emaciated shoulders, growling at no one in particular. I was a livid, crestfallen failure. This was not the Olympic moment I had wanted.

I was the first one in the antidoping room since I was the only one who didn't have to participate in the awards ceremony. Wearing their medals, Evgeni, Stéphane, and Jeffrey were excitedly talking with their coaches as they walked in about forty-five minutes later. On the American team, skaters aren't allowed to have their coach with them during drug tests, so I was all alone staring at the three Olympic medalists I had lost to. I took a seat by the window and let the tears I had been holding back since my performance fall. Nobody cared; I cried without making a sound, plus they were all too engrossed to pay any attention to me.

The event had been over for a good hour and a half before I was able to leave. I had had trouble urinating because of my wrecked nerves, so everyone else, the fans, the skaters, and the officials, were already gone when I finally exited the building.

I walked outside into the complete darkness. It was pushing one o'clock and the big paved courtyard was completely deserted. The idling engine of the waiting bus lent a feeling of drudgery to the desolate scene.

"Johnny!"

I looked over, and I saw my mom. Standing behind the bars that fenced in the courtyard, she put her arms through them and out toward me.

It would have been a security breach for me to leave the official premises, so I ran over to her and we hugged with the bars between us. When I stood back I saw her glasses were all fogged up.

"I'm so sorry," I said. "I'm so sorry for all of this—what I've done to the family, and with money, and all this stuff."

"Honey, you made it to the Olympics," she said. "I've never been more proud of you in my life."

10

After the Storm

I had been to Las Vegas before, but never like this. When I was shown into the suite at Caesars Palace that Kathy Griffin's people had put me up in, it took my breath away—and I'm the biggest snob ever when it comes to hotel rooms. Four lavish rooms, bedecked with chandeliers and gobs of marble, were capped off with a giant seashell bathtub in the middle of one of the bathrooms. I was definitely going to get some much-needed rest and relaxation in these stunning surroundings.

Kathy had asked me to appear on her Bravo reality show, *My Life on the D-List,* after she saw a reference I had made to her show in a post-Olympics interview. After I'd appeared on the cover of the *New York Times* I had told a reporter at Russia House—the country's official debauched party palace in Torino—that my new widespread notoriety put me "on the same level as Kathy Griffin and her D-List." I was joking, but someone from her team called to see if I would do an episode, and Kathy herself followed up by sending flowers.

The bouquet was unnecessary (but appreciated). A huge fan of the comedian and her show, I said yes right away. While I don't get starstruck easily, Kathy Griffin was pretty A-List to me.

With a couple of hours to go before our meeting, I took a quick shower and ordered chicken fingers with ranch dressing up to the room as my first post-season treat. Nothing could soothe me after what I had been through at the Olympics—not a truckload of chicken fingers or a twenty-room suite at Caesars—but the trip offered a welcome distraction.

Of course, making my entertainment TV debut came with its own worries. I had to watch what I said and did on air. Because Kathy was a gay icon, I didn't want to give her anything too gay or over the top. In private I had no issues with my sexuality, but I still wasn't comfortable with it as a topic of public discourse. I didn't need it put all over a TV show.

And there was the issue of what to wear. The episode's setup was that I would teach Kathy how to skate. During the Olympics I'd established myself as really into fashion, so I had to look good. At the same time, I was going to be on the ice and I'd already been away from home for two weeks, so I was on the last legs of what was still clean in my luggage. I freaked out for a good hour, trying on different ensembles and running through my suite to look at myself in various gold-framed mirrors until I settled on my skater-with-an-edge look: track pants and a giant black John Galliano hoodie that zipped off to the side. It was a little aggressive for ice skating, but with my flat-ironed hair ending in a long unruly mullet, so was I.

Greeting me at the tiny rink in the middle of Las Vegas with big, loving, open arms, Kathy immediately put me at ease. She had gathered all the kids who trained at the rink to watch from above, which was a really thoughtful move. Their clapping and screaming upon my arrival made me feel like a super A-List celebrity worthy of a TV appearance.

I held Kathy's hand for what she called a "couples skate" and tried to be professional while giving her pointers for looking beautiful on the ice. "Don't use your butt," I shouted, describing her during the session as a "liver sausage" and a "monkey." Okay, maybe I was going for funny more than professional. Whatever I did, it worked. Everyone was pleased with my performance, including Kathy, who paid me the highest compliment off-air by calling me "one of her gays."

Although I still fretted over the past season, which had ended in a monumentally disappointing Olympics and my transformation into the laughingstock of the skating world, my appearance on the *D-List* was just one example of the new and massive stage that I had entered.

Love me or hate me, everyone seemed to have an opinion about me.

By no stretch of the imagination did I kid myself then (or now) that I was famous. I'm no Britney Spears with paparazzi camped outside my house or trailing me as I pick up my dry cleaning. Still, as a top athlete with the rare ability to be myself, I became an object of curiosity and entered the pop culture radar as a tiny celebrity blip.

I knew whatever fame I found would be very fleeting, so I wanted to do as many things to get my face out there as possible, particularly because my skating was shaky enough to make me worried for my future in the sport. I loved the invitations to exclusive events, such as the opening of a club in Manhattan's meatpacking district or a party to showcase Louis Vuitton's new collection, which had started arriving at the house in Delaware. But between skating, touring, having a relationship, and getting ready for a new season, there was no room for parties (plus, I'm not really a party person; I am terrible at meeting new people). Anything that resembled a work opportunity, however, I tried to make happen.

So when two different production companies approached me right after the Olympics about making a documentary of my life, I was into the idea—although I had absolutely no clue what it meant. Totally oblivious to how most of the entertainment world worked, I figured they would shoot for a couple months, make a movie, play it somewhere, and that would be it. But the first people that approached me (they had produced the popular documentary *Murderball* about quadriplegic athletes who play wheelchair rugby) quickly disabused me of that notion. They had a plan to buy the house next to the one where I lived with my parents in order to shoot everything I did from morning until night. That was a little too aggressive for my taste.

I probably would have nixed the whole idea if it weren't for Butch and Grämz—aka David Barba and James Pellerito. When they came to my rink to propose a movie about my life and career, they were upfront: they had no sponsor and no money. Their company, Retribution Media, was basically them working catering jobs on the side to fund their shoots. A couple as well as work partners, they wanted to do the doc in a very low-key way, shooting me during scheduled times when it worked for all of us. Priscilla was fine with it, as long as it didn't detract from my training. My family was also on board, and Paris "loved it."

They dove right in, coming down from New York to Delaware about once a week to film my training in hopes they could turn my antics into a movie. Because I tend to nickname people when they come into my life, even if they come with their own nicknames, I had to rename James and David before we could get down to business. David became "Butch" because he's the smaller of the two with a little faux-hawk, which gives him a bit of a tough puppy look. And what better name for a puppy than Butch? But Butch wasn't allowed to drive because he was in this country from Mexico on a green card. So James had to do all the driving, and being from New York City, he was a terrible driver, crouching up near the steering wheel of their small rental and holding on for dear life while inching along at fifty miles an hour. I crowned him "Grams" because of his grandmotherly style of driving. But he didn't appreciate his new nickname, so I had to cool it out with *z* at the end and an umlaut over the *a*—a modern Grämz that we both could live with.

While the idea of a documentary about my life took a little bit of convincing at the outset (since there were a number of things at that time, like my love life, which I didn't want aired in public), I needed no pitch—or money—when *BlackBook* asked me to do a fashion spread. The editors of the hip fashion magazine had reached out to me because they liked my kind of elfin quality to which they wanted to add the magic of designer clothes.

I was over the moon about doing my first big photo shoot, although it represented yet another break with the skating world. Most male skaters, if they get any mainstream press, it's usually a page in *Men's Health* where they talk about their awesome abs and pose in a Team USA T-shirt. Occasionally the girls will do something a little more outrageous, like when Katarina Witt posed nude for *Playboy*. For some reason, everyone's okay when the women shed their clothes for a nudie mag. However, I knew the federation would *not* be okay with my appearing in a high-fashion spread where they planned God-knows-what kind of outfits. It would embarrass and shock them. So I went ahead and booked the shoot immediately.

I had been to New York many times, but when I arrived on the train the night before the shoot it was my first trip to the big city alone. And I get nervous my first time doing anything. It didn't help that the magazine had booked me into a hotel in one of the Villages. East or West, I'm not a big Village fan. And this hotel was vintage Village—dark and dirty and small. A homeboy in big, baggy jeans that I guess was supposed to be the desk clerk showed me and my mega Rimowa suitcase (I don't pack light, even for overnight trips) to my room where I could just feel the cockroaches staring at me. When I stay at a hotel, I like there to be room service, not a woman moaning in the room next to mine.

There was no way I was staying there. Sitting on a plastic laundry bag on the bed, I started calling every famous, expensive hotel that I could think of in New York City: the Ritz-Carlton, the Four Seasons, the Plaza. Nothing. Fully booked. Finally I found a generic business hotel in midtown with a room—three stars as opposed to the negative six-star hotel I was in—and I hightailed it out of there in time to get a few hours of sleep before my 7 a.m. start time.

All was forgiven and forgotten the minute I arrived at the studio. There were hair and makeup people, a stylist, the photographer, and his assistants running around the large white loft, which was drenched with sun pouring in through enormous windows. And there were tons and tons of beautiful clothes everywhere. The glamour! It was a big-deal fashion shoot . . . for me. (Of course, I had to say something about the "hotel." "Just for your information, it was terrible," I told the editor. But in that way New York trendy people pretend nothing is a mistake, she passed it off as though they thought it would be a cool, cultural experience.)

The photographer, David Armstrong, only used natural light, which made me nervous that I wouldn't look great. But, I mean, twenty-one years old, skinny as a rail, and in love—how bad could I look?

Plus, the clothes were the real stars. I had never seen such treasures. There were Henri Duarte jeans and Wunderkind shorts, amazing rings by Etro, a Dior jacket worth $30,000 that had flown in from a fashion show in Hong Kong the night before the shoot, plus many designers I had never even heard of despite my extensive studies.

In the spread that they called "Johnny: I'm Only Dancing," it was drama, drama, drama. I flipped over one setup (which they didn't end up using in the magazine) where I portrayed the late, legendary dancer Rudolf Nureyev with the whole pancake-on-the-face ballet makeup and hair extensions in a pulled-back ponytail.

Like the Nureyev photos, the majority of the shots we did were topless. I was all for nudity. I loved having my picture taken and wanted so much to do a good job that I would have done anything. And I pretty much did. I danced across the studio and slithered on the floor. When they brought out a pair of six-inch Gucci stilettos to go with the leggings I wore, I didn't flinch, even though I knew a photo of me in ladies' heels would cause major waves in the skating world. Hey, they make any-body's legs look better. I pranced around like a high-end call girl, which emboldened the editors to put a Gucci dress on me. I tried my hardest to cram myself into the size 00 dress, but I wasn't a miracle worker. They had to settle on letting it sit like a skirt around my waist with my arms wrapped around my, of course, naked torso while I didn't breathe. What we do for beauty.

———————

While I loved every minute of my pop culture moments, they didn't pay the bills. For that I again joined the cast of Champions on Ice in what would be my longest tour to date. From the beginning of April through August, I crisscrossed the country in a bus with the best skaters in the world, including Evan Lysacek and Stéphane Lambiel, both of whom I had lost to in the Olympics and would be once more competing against the next season.

For my number, I chose to skate to Frank Sinatra's "My Way" for its obvious symbolism. The Olympic season had nearly killed me, but at least I could hold my head up high because I had done it my way.

The actual skating is such a small part of any tour. There's a lot more traveling, waiting around, and—at least in the case of that year's Champions show—drinking. To make it through the slog of this endless tour, I drank nearly every night during dinner and lots of times while traveling on the bus. No sooner had we loaded into the bus after a performance when the Russians would whip out their bottles of vodka (or someone feeling fancy might have picked up a bottle of champagne), which we happily let them pour into our paper cups as small cities receded into the distance. I'm not a big drinker in general, but at that time, when I was superskinny from the Olympic season, I was an especially cheap date. For that spring and summer, I grew my tolerance and joined the rest of the merry band of skaters. Having a buzz made being far from home and Alex after such a rocky couple of months a little easier to swallow.

Alcohol wasn't my only solace during the tour. Marina Anissina, the 2002 Olympic Champion in ice dancing and one of my best friends, became my greatest confidante and constant dinner companion. Over absurdly glamorous meals of filet mignon or sushi (and, of course, lots of wine), I moaned to her about the clear downfall of my condition. Four months was a long time to be on the road and away from training for a competitive figure skater, but there was no other way; I needed the money if I wanted to keep skating.

So I had to strategize a way to create new programs for next year in between shows on tour. I couldn't wait until the tour finished in August because that would be too late for a season that officially begins in September. Tatiana Tarasova, who had created my programs for the last few years, was out of the question since there was no way I'd have enough time with her after she'd moved back to Moscow.

One night, while sharing quesadillas and margaritas the size of my head with Marina, I realized the solution sat right across the table from me. Marina should choreograph my new programs! I wanted a person to pull something creative and new out of me. Marina, whose powerful reputation in the skating world could only help me politically, fit the bill artistically as well. I asked her to work with me before the ice in my margarita had time to melt.

As Russians tend to do, she mulled it over for a few days, keeping me on edge before accepting the challenge. And a challenge it would be. Marina had a very different aesthetic from mine: hers was modern dance to my old-school ballet. Beyond that, Marina decided that for the upcoming season she intended to get me to skate like a man. I told her, "Good luck." But she didn't find that very funny.

For the short program, we chose a remix of "Palladio" for me to skate like a chess piece, moving deliberately backward, forward, and sideways. Very strong and assertive. Very manly. But for the long program, I wanted to do something with a hot and sultry Middle Eastern vibe. Marina didn't like that idea at all. It smacked of my old fluffy ways. So she came up with a compromise: I would portray the story of Jesus, a strong male figure who also happened to be Middle Eastern. I wasn't exactly looking for geographical accuracy in my program, but I didn't argue after I heard the mysterious, exotic music she composed with Maxime Rodriguez. Plus, after what I had been through at the Olympics, martyrdom did have a certain resonance.

I quickly realized that working with Marina would be a lot tougher than dining or shopping with her. We found some private ice time on our tour stop in Kansas City for our first day of working on the long Jesus program. By now it had been a few months since I had really pushed myself on the ice (not to mention drinking and eating like a civilian). On the ice, I felt like a waddling penguin. Marina only exacerbated my frustration level. Every single time I started a movement—any movement, from lifting my chin to doing a triple axel—she almost immediately yelled at me to stop. Whether it was in French, Russian, or English, she made herself clear.

"No more swan, Johnny. No more swan!"

"You have to be masculine."

"Be a power player!"

"No pretty fingers!"

In that moment I wished I really was Jesus and could send a lightning bolt to torch Marina. No matter what I did, I couldn't skate in a way that she liked. In fact, I could hardly skate at all since she spent most of the time screaming at me to stop. I knew she was trying to get the best out of me, but doing a complete aesthetic overhaul of an established athlete is no easy feat. Marina wanted me to be raw, but for me pretty is my comfort zone. I hated practicing a style that I didn't do well.

Marina's quest for me to man up didn't end at my skating style. She also insisted that my costumes be masculine as well— black and white for the chess piece and brown for Jesus. *Brown? Yuck.* I wasn't allowed to wear even one rhinestone. God was definitely testing me.

By August, it had been a very, very long tour, one that proved hard on everyone's moods and livers. It was also hard on my relationship with Alex, which had been deteriorating for a while. Because we hardly got the chance to see each other in person, we weren't able to solve problems or light that essential spark. Ours had become a phone relationship, and that's never good. When we talked, we were either in a deep depression or angry, the classic poles of the long-distance love affair.

I wanted so badly to make it work that right after the Olympics I talked with Alex about moving to New England. As naive as it might seem now, I wanted our relationship to be one that would last forever and ever, like many do with their first loves. I thought perhaps a change of scenery might just be the necessary ingredient, not only for Alex and me, but also for my skating career. Hoping to marry my professional and personal life, I looked for apartments and had a meeting with Alex's coach right before the tour began.

Alex was really into the idea of me moving. My never being around because of competitions, publicity events, and now the endless tour certainly had put a huge strain on our relationship. But there were issues other than our happiness to factor into the equation. Living in Alex's area would have been expensive and meant I couldn't help out my family financially at a time when my father was dealing with work-related disability issues. In addition, Alex's coach just wasn't good enough for my level of competition.

When the tour hit Colorado I knew I needed to tell Alex the truth: I wasn't moving to be with him. It wasn't a commitment thing. I knew that if I moved up there, we would have become stronger and better—and I wanted that just as much, if not more, than he did. But I couldn't put my family or career in jeopardy. As much as I loved Alex, the Weirs and skating came first and always would.

"I'm sorry, Alex," I said on the cell phone. "You know my family's situation. I can't move. I just can't financially do it."

He was pretty short with me about it.

"Okay," he said, and then moved on to other things.

Alex folded his WASP wings around himself in avoidance, and while I usually agitated for a confrontation, I wasn't going to make an issue out of a disappointment on my part.

Rolling into San Francisco, about a week before the blessed end of this road trip, my castmates and I sat glumly in the silent bus, looking out the windows like inmates about to be dropped off at prison. I was homesick as well as upset from my overwrought work with Marina on the Jesus program. Plus I hated California. It was all bad. Even drinking and eating had lost their allure.

The only thing good about San Francisco, as far as I was concerned, was the shopping. Marina and I put aside our skating differences and made big plans to get matching Chanel bags and be very cute. That was a goal I could get behind. If the tour had been hell, the money was heaven. My car was paid off and I didn't really have any bills, aside from my parents' to pay for, so I felt a little luxury was in order.

Around five o'clock the day of our big shopping spree, we sat down for a bite at a little sushi place, happy with our many purchases and ready for silky fish and soothing sake. Pouring some of the fiery liquid into my little cup, Marina started to talk about the plan for after the tour. We had the skeletons of my programs and now just needed to polish them before the season began in less than a month. The thought of it made my stomach turn.

The waiter placed a couple pieces of yellowtail sushi in front of me when my phone began to vibrate. It was Alex. Immediately, I knew something was wrong. We had a nighttime calls schedule and he was calling two hours early. I left my fish and Marina at the table to answer his call outside the restaurant.

"Hi."

"Hi."

We started to have a normal conversation but not in a normal way. It was like we were talking in slow motion. Then he said it: the worst sentence in the English language.

"I think we should take a break."

I'm not a believer in breaks. They are a pit stop on the way to breaking up. So I didn't accept it.

"Well, I don't do breaks, and you know that about me. So you either break up with me now, or we're still together."

Alex never gave into any of my bullshit, and he wasn't about to now while on the verge of a break from me.

"No," he said. "We're taking a break."

"Okay. Well, then, just know that I consider us broken up," I said.

"Okay. We're taking a break," he said.

I hung up on him, furious that he had one-upped me. After waiting a few moments to see if he'd call or text back, which he didn't, I returned to the restaurant, Marina, and my forgotten raw fish. I sat down at the table and started to sob quietly, tears running down my face from behind my sunglasses.

"What's wrong?" Marina asked with motherly concern.

I told her that Alex had broken up with me and her maternal instinct, turned into Russian wrath.

"Alex is not good enough for you anyway," she said, echoing a sentiment shared by all the Russian ladies in my life who think they know the best person for me to marry.

The love of my life was cutting me loose, but I wouldn't get any sympathy from Marina. So I suggested an alternative, that we go to a bar to get very, very drunk. We ended the night in our beautiful hotel, the Clift, sitting in the stark lobby and flirting with everyone that passed through.

"Oh, you're really going to enjoy your stay," I said as I winked at a couple checking in. "The desserts on the room service menu are amazing."

Drunk hospitality was fun while it, and my buzz, lasted. But the next morning, when I didn't get the usual wake-up text from Alex, the realization of the break hit me hard. His absence festered throughout the day, and there were many times I wanted to pick up the phone to scream, yell, beg, or anything else to make a connection. But I held back, thinking if he was going to come back, it would have to be on his terms.

That day of not speaking turned into several more until I found myself in Bakersfield on one of the very last tour dates. By then I was a shell of my former self, and the song "My Way" had become a dirge. Right before my performance, in my full costume and makeup, I stood in the alley behind the building that housed the rink and indulged in my depression. I put "Ghost" by the Indigo Girls on my iPod and let myself feel the full ache of loneliness while men carted in lights and other stage equipment. Bawling like a maimed cow, I lay down on the ground in a tragic tableau of smeared mascara and rhinestones against concrete.

Having been alerted to my predicament by some other skaters, Marina came running out of the building to find me lying in the alley. She picked me up, dusted me off, and brought me back inside. "You need vitamin C," she pronounced, and, stealing several oranges from catering, made me on-the-spot freshly squeezed juice. "Drink it," she said. I downed the juice, cleaned myself up, and did my performance, crying the whole way through the show.

A week later, after the tour was officially over, I was driving to pick Marina up for a practice at my rink with Priscilla when my phone rang. I picked up the phone. *Alex!* I thought. *Let's see what this bastard has to say.*

"How was your week?" I asked.

"Fine. How was your week?"

"It's been busy."

"Well," Alex said, "did you learn anything this week?"

"No. What do you want me to learn?"

I was getting really agitated.

"I'm really sad to hear that you didn't learn anything," he continued. "I learned something . . . I want to break up with you."

That's not at all what I had been expecting him to say. *I'm young. I'm beautiful. I'm successful. I love him. He's never going to find anyone else that loves him the way I do. He'll come to his senses*—the typical thought patterns of the desperate.

"I want to break up with you," he repeated. "You're not the same person you were when we started dating. You don't treat me like you used to."

It was nothing he hadn't said to me before but the finality of his tone left me breathless. We had been together for two and a half years, always faithful and in love, and now it was simply over? His mom loved me, and I loved her. I loved his whole family—Alex's dad had even invited me to his second wedding. Having wanted happily-ever-after, I was at a complete loss for words. "I'm really sorry that it came to this," I said, crying. "I hope I didn't waste your time. Good luck in your life."

Having made Marina and Priscilla wait for an hour and a half while I talked to Alex, I finally found the courage to peel myself off Priscilla's tarmac driveway and gather my girls for practice. Aware of what the last couple of hours had meant to my life and my happiness, Priscilla looked at me with the pity only a mother could have. Meanwhile, Marina had a far different reaction. "I thought this already happened!" she yelled in Russian.

After two hours on the ice, I drove myself home in a cried-out coma, eyes glazed over, lashes sopping wet, a broken heart.

He was the first love of my life, and there's never one like that again. It makes you crazier than any other love you'll ever have. I didn't know what my life would be like after Alex, or if I could ever love someone again. It had been a depressing summer of too much touring, drinking, and burying my head in the sand. Already August, I had to contemplate getting back into the competitive season after my crushing defeat at the Olympics and my wrecked relationship. I had always thought if I wanted something, I could make it happen. But at twenty-one, I was no longer sure what I wanted or was capable of achieving.

11

Growing Pains

Spokane, Washington, was burning with hatred when I arrived for the National Championships in January of 2007. Pastor Fred Phelps and his insane followers from the Westboro Baptist Church had decided to use the skating competition as a peg for an antihomosexual rally. The group—the same one that threatened to protest the funerals of Amish schoolchildren killed in a shooting rampage because they weren't the *right kind* of Christians—brandished signs outside the official hotel that read "Fags Burn in Hell" and screamed even more offensive epithets. For once, the rage wasn't directed at me personally. Even someone as out of touch with reality as Phelps knew competitive skating was filled with gays, no matter what the U.S. Figure Skating Association tried to promote. Still, my mom worried about my safety. "Stay inside," she said. "Make sure you don't go anywhere."

Phelps and his band of traveling haters were the least of my worries. In the event, where I was shooting for my fourth national title in a row, all the press focused on how Evan was finally going to knock me off my throne. It was true that I hadn't been skating well. My disastrous Grand Prix season leading up to the Nationals had been capped off with my withdrawal from the final after injuring myself during the short program (and after embarrassingly trash-talking Evan for withdrawing earlier because of his own injury).

The federation, understandably pissed that both Americans had taken themselves out of the Grand Prix final, had already started their campaign to make Evan the favorite a year before. The big difference going into the Nationals was that the press had finally gotten onboard. It was almost like the peasants were plotting the fall of the queen. I had been the star. And now I wasn't. In the quest for me to go down hard in punishment for my disappointment at the Olympics, the skating press held up my pop culture moments as proof of how unfocused and undeserving I had become. I was no longer portrayed as an athlete but rather a diva who needed to be put in his place—last place.

The nadir of this new trend came right before the Nationals on *Nancy Kerrigan's World of Skating,* a weekly cable television program hosted by the skating star. She had a few analysts discuss the senior men at the National Championships (basically Evan and me) and they ran me into the ground. Mark Lund, the openly gay founder of *International Figure Skating* magazine, led the charge, calling my swan program tantamount to a big flag shouting "I'm Gay!" "I can't wrap my head around how overly out he is without saying he's out," Lund said. "I'm sorry, but I don't think he's a representative of the community I want to be a part of. . . . And who designs these outfits?" Then he went on to praise Evan as having "a classical elegance and masculinity on the ice I think we need to see in male figure skating. I'm saying I don't need to see a prima ballerina on the ice." He had a right to his skating opinion, but for him to go off on my sexuality was unacceptable. By letting him run his mouth like that, Nancy, a huge force in skating, lent his opinions an air of outrageous legitimacy.

I couldn't outskate the negativity following me into the competition. Although I performed a perfect short program, which three years before would have put me ahead of the pack by a mile, Evan beat me by three tenths of a point. We were basically tied going into the long program, but I knew I didn't have a chance in hell of winning, especially since my long program had been my weak point all season. It seemed nobody liked Jesus. First of all, brown looks terrible on the ice. I tried to change the costume a few times, from brown to gray and then with a pseudocorset-rope belt, but nothing could change the fact that people just didn't want to see the Jesus story portrayed on ice. I couldn't really blame them.

Evan added to my inevitable defeat by giving the performance of his life when he landed a quad toe. I had my own quad toe planned, which I two-footed during my long program—just one in a series of jumps that disappointingly popped. Disconnected from the music and my drive to compete, I imploded in humiliating fashion, living up to the predictions by the press.

Not only did I lose to Evan but I placed third behind Ryan Bradley, a skater who should have never beaten me. Third place meant that I would still make it on the World Championship team going to Tokyo that spring, but all I could think about was one more competition to get through before I could finally say good-bye to this hateful season.

Athletes often talk about post-Olympic depression. You have this giant foe that you're trying to go up against for so long, and once it's over, once it's defeated (or it's defeated you), there doesn't seem to be any reason to go on. After that National Championship, I was just so over it. I had faced uncertainty about whether I should continue my skating career in the past. But this time was different. I felt an incredible ennui. Simply put, I had stopped caring. It was the ultimate defeat.

This depression turned everything in and around skating black, spurring me to look for diversions, albeit brief, from the outside. Right after the Nationals, I was asked to walk in a fashion show for Heatherette, a rock 'n' roll line designed by Richie Rich and Traver Rains. This would be my second time walking in one of their shows for Fashion Week (the designers had invited me to walk the previous year after I met them at an event).

The trip to New York would have to be quick since I needed to keep to my training schedule, no matter how lackluster. But I said yes, desperate to get away from home, the rink, and everyone.

Backstage at the Bryant Park tent where the show was held, I was a bundle of nerves. Walking in a fashion show, when there are tons of celebrities in the first row, is one of the most petrifying experiences, especially when you're surrounded by professional, and gorgeous, models. This year, I had been told, I was kicking off the show. I had better look *good*.

When an assistant shoved my outfit at me (everyone's always in a hideous rush at these things), at first I thought it was a joke. In my hands was a white bodysuit with glow sticks hanging off every inch of it. After finally catching and stopping another one of the assistants, she explained that I was walking in a special section of the show, without lights, wearing glow-in-the-dark clothes and leading a glow-in-the-dark dance troupe.

As the renowned makeup artist Kabuki applied neon products to my face that only showed up under black lights, I felt belittled. I thought I was going to strut my stuff in a hot outfit and makeup. Instead, I was Cirque du Soleil.

While not exactly *Men's Vogue* material, it turned out to be very funny. With people flipping behind me, I walked down the runway, shaking my glow sticks and doing my best style poses in complete blackness.

The fashion show was fun but nothing compared to being invited to Elton John's Oscar party a couple of weeks later. Now *this* was a real diversion that started the minute Paris, my date, and I stepped into the first-class section of the plane and started drinking champagne. The A-List treatment continued when we arrived at the Peninsula Beverly Hills Hotel, where we were treated to a gorgeous room, which was also gigantic. Thank God. Butch and Grämz, who had flown themselves out there coach to continue capturing my life, were also staying in it with us. The Johnny Weir documentary was so low budget that Paris and I shared one bed while Butch and Grämz had the other. It was like fancy camp.

My fashion situation didn't go down as smoothly as my accommodations. Dior had agreed to dress me but by the day of the party, no clothes had showed up. I waited as long as I could before making an emergency shopping trip to Barneys, where I picked up a pair of pants to go with my own black velvet Costume National jacket with beaded lapels that I had brought in case of an emergency. With the Weir luck there were often emergencies.

No outfit could have prepared me for the moment I stepped out of the car and into my first real Hollywood event. I hadn't expected that anyone would want me to walk the red carpet or take my picture. It had been a year since the Olympics, my biggest claim to fame, and the carpet was populated with huge stars—basically everyone who wasn't at the Oscars. But all of a sudden I found myself on this mega red carpet facing a wall of about 150 photographers and cameramen.

"Johnny! Johnny! Johnny!" they shouted.

I loved the sensation: the throng calling my name and snapping my picture. As the flashes went off, I tried to channel Tyra Banks and heed her tips on *America's Next Top Model*. I smiled with my eyes and looked up at the camera while keeping my chin down. I think Mama would have been proud.

Once Paris and I walked into the party, we became nobodies enjoying the craziness unfold. We met our host Elton John, who had no idea who I was, and the cast of *Queer as Folk*, who of course did. I had a particularly good time watching Sharon Stone auction off some car for Elton's charity. Cursing and telling dirty jokes, this famous lady was totally uninhibited in front of people, as if she didn't have a care in the world. I liked her style and envied her power.

———————

Running away to L.A. for the weekend was fun, but I still needed to get my act together in terms of my sport. Skating was who I was and I couldn't run away from it, even if it wasn't going well. Being invited to a few parties was no Plan B.

At this point, hard work wasn't enough. If I continued to skate, I needed to work in a different way. And that meant a new coach. If I stayed with Priscilla, just going through the motions, I probably wouldn't make it through another season, let alone another Olympics.

Over the season, my training situation with Priscilla had become stressed. Both of us were locked in a passive-aggressive war of silent wills. During one session, where I was training for my long program, I missed a triple salchow. I used the mistake on such a simple jump to show Priscilla how much I didn't want to be there by throwing myself down on the ice like an over-grown toddler. Instead of getting in my face about it, she stopped talking, slowly gathered her things, and got off the ice. In that moment, and many that followed, she didn't want to train with me, either.

I escalated the war by habitually calling up my rink and asking them to prep the ice forty-five minutes earlier than my scheduled morning session. After the Zamboni cleared and the ice was still soaked, I skated before Priscilla had even showed up. As she arrived for our session, I would be finishing and, to her astonishment, I would just say "bye" and walk out to the sound of her uncomfortable laughter. By the end of the season we were both avoiding each other, a ludicrous relationship for a coach and skater.

I knew how lucky I had been to start out with someone as nurturing and gentle as Priscilla. Most kids with any hope of be-coming competitive skaters begin with hard-asses who have coached Olympic champions. A lot of children drop out because these coaches are too tough too fast. I had a great skating child-hood that included the babying and pampering all kids should have. But now I needed a business partner—someone to scare me in the rink—not a babysitter.

My mom could see what was happening and, as my greatest confidante and supporter, forced me to face the situation. After some hard talks, she and I decided that by the time the World Championships finished, I should put an offer out to a new coach.

First I had to find that person. I definitely wanted a Russian coach because I liked the way many of them trained their students. The most radical idea that my mom and I discussed was my moving to Moscow in order train with Tatiana Tarasova. I loved and respected what she was able to do with her skaters. Working with her in the summers, I felt alive—and afraid. Other Russians on the list were Tarasova's ex-assistant coach Nikolai Morozov, who now taught in Connecticut, and Oleg Vassiliev, who had Olympic pair champions in Chicago.

What gave me pause with all those coaches was the fact that all of them worked in the Russian style with a stable of great skaters in a team situation, on the ice together. Growing up with one coach to myself, I worried it would be too much of a culture shock to train in a group full-time.

By the time I boarded the plane for Tokyo, I still hadn't made a decision. Tarasova was the clear front-runner. She expressed interest, but we needed to hear how much money it would be and how we might work out the complicated logistics. I had never lived away from home full-time, so for my first experience to be halfway around the world seemed a bit daunting. There were also skating politics to consider. The federation was not going to like me living and training in Russia—something no American had ever done before.

Meanwhile, Priscilla had no idea that I was planning on

switching coaches because we had kept everything very discreet—no small feat in the incestuous world of skating. I felt bad about going behind her back because Priscilla had given me so much and had been a part of the family for so long, but I couldn't tell her until I had secured a new coach.

As if purposefully trying to give me a massive guilt trip, Priscilla spent the entire time at the World Championships talking to everyone and anyone about my situation and ways to improve me next season. With the zeal of a crusading physician hell-bent on finding a cure for her patient, she grilled judges, fellow coaches, and officials to amass their best advice. My mom, who always roomed with Priscilla to keep costs down, had to do the lion's share of acting. "Priscilla kept me up until two, making a plan of your summer," my mom said to me wearily over Starbucks.

When we left Japan after the World Championships, I was no closer to finding a new coach. Nothing felt right. Having next season hang like a big question mark over my head was extremely stressful. The only thing I knew for sure was that whoever took me on had his work cut out. At the Worlds I placed eighth—a total disaster, just like the current state of my skating career.

———————

On the plane back from Japan, I got to talking with two other American team members, Melissa Gregory and Denis Petukhov, husband and wife ice dancers who also trained in Delaware. I normally hate conversing on planes, preferring to shut my eyes to the fact that I'm trapped in such close proximity to other people. But on this trip, I needed to escape from my thoughts and though Melissa and Denis weren't great friends, we bonded over our underdog status in the skating world.

Although an American citizen, Denis was born in Russia, which made him and Melissa less desirable than other pairs in the eyes of the U.S. Figure Skating Association. The married skating partners were always top ten in the World Championships but could never seem to rise to the very top of American skating. Thirty thousand feet in the air, we moaned about the role of politics in our sport and marveled at one another's inherent abilities on the ice. Just like when you're a kid making a new friend and you want to instantly start a craft project or open up a business together, so the three of us mused that we should skate together. But as we discussed it, we became more and more excited about making the concept a reality. And we had a perfect venue—an upcoming made-for-TV exhibition near my hometown in Reading, Pennsylvania, in which we were all invited to perform.

It was a shocking idea, the sort concocted on transatlantic flights, and something big-name skaters just didn't do. In general, well-known skaters don't skate in groups because of the worry that someone else might steal their thunder. And nobody ever mixed ice dancing with singles skating, or pairs skating with ice dancing. It was like dogs mating with cats, complete Armageddon. I had already freaked out the skating community with gender bending and was now fully prepared to do it with genre bending.

Before landing, we came up with the story for our program: we would play fallen angels because that's what we felt like. It would be beautiful and light, but tragic and dramatic—like us. "I'm going to skate with my two wives," Denis joked. Why not? I was already in love.

Getting approval to skate this number from the federation turned out to be like pulling teeth without Novocain. The pain was not surprising but incredibly irritating nonetheless. They absolutely didn't want us to skate together. Anything that veers from the traditional path sends them into a huge tizzy.

Their excuse was that they didn't know how to pay us because there was no scale if we skated together. But the truth is they were terrified. Here you had me, deemed publicly unreliable, and a pair of dark-horse ice dancers? Put those three scary things together and I'm sure they conjured up images of an erotic sex number that would make all the elderly folks tuning into the exhibition at home lose their dentures. We had to explain every single detail of the program, which we only had a week and a half to choreograph, and the whole story behind it. We told them how much we would be skating together and how much apart. The whole process took about a million phone calls and came right down to the deadline before we finally received approval, but the three of us were convinced it was worth the effort because the program would be a revelation.

The Marshalls Showcase was to be held twenty minutes from where I grew up. Kids from my elementary school had entered a writing contest to win tickets for the event and so the rink was stacked with fans from my hometown.

Still Melissa, Denis, and I were nervous about what was going to happen on the ice. All the elements were in place. Denis had procured us ethereal music from Globus, a band that does music for many movie and TV trailers, and we all had matching blue and white costumes as light as a cotton candy confection. The choreography expressed the essence of three angels, alone and connecting in loving, chaste, and barely there touches. I added the final drama with crazy blue makeup à la Hamburglar on our faces. But because of the fast turnaround time of the program and the effort that went into getting its approval, we had only one run-through together. It didn't help that backstage, officials and other skaters were staring at us like freaks. Three of us skating together. The horror!

On the ice, while clasping hands before beginning, I could feel Melissa and Denis's sweaty palms. We had more riding on this than just a TV performance. The three of us had become great friends, and as with all my friends I wanted to help them out. In this particular moment that meant getting them a spot on the Champions on Ice tour, which was about to begin. They needed the money and I needed the friends on tour. The only problem was Champions already had a pair of ice dancers. It would be a hard sell to bring on Melissa and Denis, but if this program made the right kind of waves, we had a shot. If it didn't go off perfectly, we would never be allowed to do it again.

I was so used to skating alone—either pissed or ecstatic with myself—but with two other people on the ice I got to be part of a team. Having been so isolated in my sport for so long, I relished the feeling of moving in sync with Melissa and Denis. The audience, even if they didn't understand the groundbreaking aspect of the moment, sensed our excitement and came along with us for the tender ride.

When we finished, the crowd rose to its feet, having received the program in the way we had hoped. The TV commentators, who had expressed wariness when we took our starting positions, offered unadulterated praise. Even the bewildered skating folks backstage slapped us on the back. The number had been an unmitigated success.

But the best attention was the mainstream interest our number garnered the next day on PerezHilton.com. The gossip blogger, who has been a big supporter for a long time because he loves my kind of crazy, found a YouTube video of the program and posted it on his site. The video ended up with upward of one hundred thousand hits over a couple of days, way more than figure skating usually gets, because Perez had exposed our work far beyond the usual scope of those tuning in to the Marshalls Showcase.

Melissa, Denis, and I had bypassed the pettiness of the federation and brought a stunning, personal moment of skating directly to the people. With hard page-view numbers behind us, we made our pitch to perform the program on the Champions on Ice tour. It took some negotiating and a trial period of a couple of show dates (where the directors realized that people bought tickets *just* to see this act), but Melissa and Denis landed the gig. That summer these three fallen angels were loved and accepted everywhere.

While on tour, I spent a lot of time talking to people about ideas for a new coach. It was Viktor Petrenko, a gold medalist in the 1992 Olympics, who first brought up someone nobody had mentioned before: Galina Yakovlevna Zmievskaya, his former coach and current mother-in-law. The idea intrigued me. A lot of the pieces seemed to be in place for a good partnership. Tough and Russian, she didn't have any major men skaters so could offer me personal attention. Galina's rink was only a two-hour ride from Newark, so I would have to move, but not as far as Moscow, which would make my mom happy. Plus, Galina had a great history, having taught my idol Oksana Baiul.

At the first opportunity, my mom and I set out to have a meeting with the great Galina. Of course the Weir family luck struck and we had a disaster getting there. Flooding in Bergen County meant we couldn't cross a certain bridge and had to weave our way through the back roads, getting very lost and arriving really late. Even though I was an Olympic athlete, who garnered a lot of attention in my sport and beyond, I still felt it was incumbent upon me to impress her. That's just the way it is when you work with coaches. Like Marina, who kept me waiting before agreeing to choreograph for me, the power dynamic always seems to spin in their direction. I worried that when we didn't show up on time, she wouldn't honor the meeting.

My fears proved unfounded. In the middle of training her daily crop of kids, she got right off the ice to greet me. A classic Ukrainian babushka with pinkish-blond hair in a red down comforter coat approached us with a formal nod. She didn't say hello or speak any English, preferring instead to have Viktor translate. The hour-long meeting was quite a family affair, with Nina, Viktor's wife and Galina's daughter, also present.

"I don't need a best friend," I said. "I need a jump start in my career."

Still pretty cocky despite my floundering career, I felt I was at a level where any new coach wouldn't really have to teach me, just kick my ass.

But Galina, exuding the air of a businesslike grandma, had devised a plan—and I hadn't even said yes to her.

"Galina already told me that she wants to work with you," Viktor said, "if it's the right fit. It's going to be hard work. There are a lot of things we want to fix. We aren't here to babysit you."

Fix? Priscilla had taught me great technique. I needed discipline but I wasn't sure about fixing.

"I've studied your skating. You're very fun and unique," she said through Viktor. "You have all this raw talent, but you're not using it. And I want you to be able to use it. I want you to have stronger technique on your jumps."

As this little Russian ballbuster rattled off my flaws, at first she made me feel mildly uncomfortable, like a film or TV actress caught outside her home with no makeup on. Then she gained my respect. I didn't think my jumps needed work, but I realized that if she's not afraid to say all these things to my face and offend me, she can probably do great things for me.

"We need to change your image to the skating world," continued Galina, wise words from a woman with years in the sport. "You need people to think you're a serious athlete."

That's what I was changing coaches for, or at least what I thought at the time. I was ready to sign up.

On the drive home, my mother and I hashed out all the details and made our decision: I'd move to New Jersey and be on the ice training with Galina by the first week in August.

The only other person I had to convince was Paris. I had never lived alone before and going through all these changes careerwise, I didn't know if I could go handle it all by myself. Paris would provide a great support system and much-needed comic relief. He also needed a change. There wasn't a lot going on in Delaware for him. He had quit skating and many of our original group of friends had moved away. Having lost his way a bit, he, too, needed to grow up. Paris was onboard, not so much for any of those reasons. He loved the idea of living close to the madness and adventure of New York City.

We headed to New Jersey with my mom for the weekend to look at apartments. When we arrived at one immaculate complex filled with perfectly appointed orchids and pictures of smiling families of all ethnicities enjoying the place's amenities, the man who showed us around turned out to be a fan of mine.

"Hi, Mr. Weir," said the agent, who was obviously a gay man. "Welcome. I've been waiting for you all day. I love your skating."

Paris and my ears perked up right away, sensing we could get something out of this guy. I didn't know what Paris was thinking—probably keys to a secret roof deck. But I was thinking about a job for my new roommate. We couldn't move up here together without him finding a job, or his parents would make him move back to Atlanta. I remembered that in one of the many career paths Paris had pranced down, he had earned a real estate license from Delaware.

After finding a great apartment that Paris and I agreed to take, I batted my lashes at the agent.

"You know, Paris has his real estate license. And he really needs a job," I said while Paris was in the other room, checking to see if the tub had a Jacuzzi feature.

"Have him send in a résumé and I'll see what I can do. He has to be legitimately able to do this job," the agent said with stars in his eyes. "But I don't see a problem with my helping him."

Paris and I practically skipped out of the complex. This crazy scheme for our lives was going to work out after all. Paris turned to me before getting in the car and made a serious face.

"Nicky, you know you're going to have to sleep with him for me to get the job," he teased.

"For you, Paris," I said. "Anything."

Telling Priscilla was going to be even harder than finding Paris gainful employment. But time was running out. I had already been selected for the Grand Prix events in China and Russia, two powerhouse places to compete, and it was getting close to the point in the season where a skater has to decide choreographers, music, costumes, and the rest.

On every break from the tour, she tracked me down.

"Johnny, I need you to come over to the house for a little bit tonight. We have to discuss the plan."

I kept dodging her, finding any and every excuse to get out of a meeting. As the weeks rolled by, her stress level and messages on my voice mail increased.

"I have a very good plan for us."

"Johnny, we need to talk about what we're going to do. Call me back!"

Finally I couldn't procrastinate any longer. I was on the cusp of moving to New Jersey and had to cut ties with Priscilla once and for all. I called her on a random Wednesday morning in the middle of touring with Champions on Ice and said my mom and I would be over that afternoon to talk. I knew that she thought it would be about the upcoming season and didn't disabuse her of the notion. My mother and I had agreed that she would be the one to break the news. "I hired her," my mom said. "It's my job to fire her." I didn't say no. I wasn't sure I would be able to walk through the door without crying, let alone let go of

Priscilla. Although we had an unworkable relationship on the ice by this point, I loved Priscilla like a second mother. She had been with me almost every day since the age of thirteen. This was going to be incredibly sad.

When we arrived at her door, we could see in her clear, open expression that she didn't suspect a thing. No sooner had my mother and I sat down awkwardly on the couch than Priscilla, perched on an adjacent love seat, began going a mile a minute about the upcoming season.

"I read this book . . ."

"I have a list . . ."

"You'll watch this video . . ."

All the ideas she had been so eager to tell me about spilled out of her in a frantic jumble. Perhaps on some level she knew what was coming and wanted to push through it with plans for progress. She seemed as manic as we were uncomfortable. Finally my mom interjected with her typical blunt force.

"Priscilla, it's come to a point where we really need a change. And it's not personal; it's not you; it's not us. It's just, for Johnny to achieve everything he wants to in skating, we have to make a change. He's not improving anymore, and we need somebody that can light a fire under him and make him improve."

"Okay," Priscilla responded, almost like she didn't believe it. "I want you to watch this video before you go."

Completely stone-faced, she stood up and took out a DVD based on the book *The Secret* that she had wanted me to watch in order to wish a medal into reality. As she pressed play, my mother and I shot each other a quick look, like, *What's happening?*

What happened is that Mom, Priscilla, and I spent the next hour watching a video about making our greatest desires happen using ancient mystical secrets by way of various inspirational-speaking palm readers with a dash of psychology and self-help thrown in for good measure. My mom and I didn't know where to go with this. We didn't need to see *The Secret;* we needed to get the hell out of there.

After the movie ended, my mom tried to get us back on the track of firing Priscilla. "We found someplace to go. Johnny is going to leave at the end of the month. And Priscilla, really, this isn't about you. We support you in anything you want to do. Johnny will never have a bad word for you because you guys have had an amazing relationship."

I nodded like a fool because I wasn't going to be able to talk and not cry. Still on her love seat, Priscilla began to slowly comprehend the reality unfolding from my mother's words. "Okay," she said. "Okay."

My mom and I got up from the couch and started to leave. While walking us to the door, Priscilla began crying.

"Priscilla, I would never be what I am, or who I am, without you," I said. "You've been everything to me. You've given me my life. I mean, I can't ever repay you. And I'm so sorry that this had to happen."

My heart was breaking. I knew Priscilla well enough to know that this was the end of our relationship as coach and student, as well as friends. It was like getting a divorce from your parents or having someone die, awful and ugly and sad. I kept telling myself that I had an objective, no matter how much it hurt her or me. I didn't have a lot of time to achieve what I wanted to achieve. *This is the right decision* I said over and over in my head.

"Thank you," I said.

"Just promise me," she said before closing the door. "No matter what, you'll do everything you can to win."

12

From Russia with Love
(and an Iron Fist)

"I'm here to see Galina," I said to the teenage boys working the front desk at my new rink in New Jersey.

"Who are you?" one asked.

Oh, lord.

"I'm Johnny Weir. I just moved here to take from Galina."

They looked at me blankly, like they would any other student at the rink. This was not helping my nerves. While driving there I had become more and more anxious. I knew with a judgmental woman like Galina, I would never be able to overcome a bad first impression (I had even practiced the drive over the weekend to make sure I wouldn't get lost and be late). For so long I had been training at the same place with the same people that my routine had become as fixed as stone. Now it crumbled in front of these lanky, pimply boys.

"Well, where do I go?" I asked.

"For what?"

"To change."

"Just go anywhere. Everyone usually sits up in the snack bar."

To change?

"Is there a locker room? I have to get undressed to change."

"You can use the bathroom, I guess."

I was starting to get irritated. Then the woman who owned the rink came around the corner to say she had a key to a locker room for me but added, "Don't tell anyone that you're sitting in a locker room." In Delaware, I could have said, "Will you set off an atomic bomb in my locker room, please?" And they would have done it. But I decided not to freak out, not on my first day at least. "I just need a place to sit that's not a toilet or a snack bar," I said.

I saw Galina on the ice teaching, but I didn't want to interrupt her so I went directly to the locker room to change and stretch. In the musty, cinder-block box, I took solace in the familiar warm-ups and rituals that I had done back in Delaware, tying my skates extra tight and lingering over my hamstring stretches. I got so comfortable that by the time I looked up at the clock, it alarmingly read three minutes past the hour—three minutes late.

With my skates already on, I dashed out of the locker room

and onto the ice. Galina looked at me with a completely straight face—no smile, no hug, no nothing—and I bowed to her as a sign of respect.

"You're late," she said in heavily accented English.

I didn't know where to go with that. With Priscilla, if I had been late three minutes, she would have said nothing and stayed an extra hour.

"Okay, get to work," she said.

I was dying. Three minutes in, I had screwed myself.

Viktor Petrenko and his wife, Nina, were in Russia shooting a TV show, which meant that it was just Galina and I on the ice alone. I started skating around on very stiff legs, doing edges and different footwork passes when she cut me off.

"That's all bullshit; you don't need any of that. We are going to jump right away."

I expected her to be hard on me, but in the first minute? Galina was there to push me, so I did what she said and started jumping. But I had years of experience with warming up for thirty minutes to get my body moving, and *then* jumping. Completely off-kilter, both mentally and physically, I fell all over the place while trying to dodge a group of kids in hockey camp. Galina just stood silently watching me.

"Viktor showed me videos," she said after what seemed like my hundredth tumble. "Your triple axel, everything you do wrong."

Um, maybe something had been lost in translation. People had always revered my triple axel as one of the best in the world because of how fast I rotated, how high I went, and how smooth the ride out and landings were. And she was telling me that I was doing it wrong? I was under the impression that she was here to push me, not change everything about me.

That wasn't even the worst part. Galina speaking in English was kind of like a teakettle about to explode with steam. Whenever she tried to talk, she was bursting at the seams to get the words out. I knew there was so much she wanted to tell me, and she couldn't do it quickly enough. I understood Russian, even if I didn't speak it fluently, but I was too overwhelmed and intimidated to stop the lesson and tell her that.

"Zees jumps vizout contrrrrol," she said, getting more and more frustrated. "Zees teknik. It doesn't vork."

Galina started waving her arms, stopped speaking in midsentence, picked up again, stopped—meanwhile I was doing my jumps the only way I knew how as she became angrier. Finally, thank God, she switched into Russian and the details started flowing. She picked apart my jump from the entrance to the landing, breaking it down with a technocrat's precision. She didn't realize at first that she was speaking Russian, but after I followed a few of her uncomfortable commands (falling even harder now) she said, "You can understand me?"

I nodded, already feeling the soreness creep up the mess that would later be my muscles.

"Well, why didn't you tell me that earlier?" she barked.

From the very first day with Galina, I had to change not only my training routine and completely overhaul my technique, but I also had to switch my official language from English to Russian (or at the very least, Englissian). It was a lot to get used to right away—especially considering I was also adjusting to living on my own for the first time.

Saying good-bye to my mother had been a particularly painful part of the transition. While helping me move in a few weeks earlier, she worried about my being alone in a strange place, especially since Paris wouldn't be arriving for several days. When it was time to go, my dad and I walked her out to the jeep while she sobbed. It took everything inside of me not to cry, but I wanted her to have that moment.

That first night, alone in my big bedroom, my courage went right out the window. Even though I was in the most secure building on the safest street, I convinced myself someone was going to come in and kill me and nobody would be around to care or find my body. Terrified, I slept with three knives next to the bed.

But the next day the sun was shining and I quickly found my touchstones—Whole Foods and the Container Store (there are no words for me and the Container Store). I set about stocking the fridge with healthy food and organizing every inch of the apartment.

When Paris arrived not long after, he immediately reversed all my hard work. It was like a tornado descended on the apartment—within minutes he had lost his keys and a $100 bill in the rental truck, put a bag of his clothes in the wrong closet and left a water mark on my new coffee table. He brought all-out madness into my serene new arrangement.

I hadn't been to New York City since I'd arrived, but Paris insisted we leave all his stuff in the car and go right away. So we hopped on a train and in twenty minutes arrived in Penn Station. It was a strange feeling of accomplishment. I mean, anyone can move to northern New Jersey. But there I was on my own, an adult, in the big city. We went directly to Pastis, a French brasserie in the meatpacking district, and had a great meal. It was no accident that the restaurant was right around the corner from one of my favorite stores—Balenciaga. That first day in the city, I bought two of my signature Work Bags in red and green as a welcome gift to myself.

After a few skirmishes with Paris over his housekeeping habits, I acclimated to my new life (the bags helped). But the biggest culture shock by far was working with Galina.

The first few weeks of training together were the most frustrating of my entire skating career. Following Galina's instructions, I no longer could land a single jump consistently. All I did was fall without understanding why. "It's because I'm changing everything," Galina said. "Just be with me. Deal with it. And do what I tell you. You're going to fall for a little bit." She didn't give me the opportunity not to trust her.

Before meeting Galina, I had a very free entrance to my triple axel. Relying on my natural talent, I would kind of wing it and fly into it, which was what made it exciting. But she wanted a very strict pattern for success on the jumps. She wouldn't let me skip a step. First position, second position, third position . . . fall. First position, second position, third position . . . fall.

My body started to scream. With Priscilla, I hadn't jumped that much because I worried about stressing my body. Galina pounded, pounded, pounded the jumps and the footwork and the on-ice running. My ankles swelled up and my body ached in places I didn't even know existed.

As I started to fall apart, the flip side to Galina's harsh taskmaster emerged in the form of a caring grandmother, who drove me in her white Mercedes to her massage therapist and cooked me chicken cutlets. She brought in weird Russian machines to stimulate my stiff hip and creams that smelled like tires. Galina dove right into the role that she wanted for herself: to control every aspect of my life. If my jumps were wrong, she'd fix them; if I was injured, she had the cure; if I were hungry, she would feed me; if I wanted to go shopping, she would take me.

When Viktor and Nina returned from Russia a few weeks after my first lesson, they were amazed by the bond that had quickly developed between Galina and me. Even more than that, they were startled by the difference they noticed in Galina. I had been so busy falling that I hadn't picked up on it, but Nina and Viktor pointed out that Galina had traded her trademark upscale sweatsuits for proper pants and jackets. She had also lost a little weight and wore her diamonds and best designer bags to the rink every day. I love a dolled-up lady, but, more important, those observations helped me realize Galina was excited about working with me. "She whistles while she's doing her makeup," Nina laughed.

Viktor, who had convinced Galina to take me on, was

thrilled things were working out. I didn't know it at the time, but she had hesitated because of preconceived notions about my personality based on rumors she had heard. Like many others, she expected me to be a diva bitch, crazy and full of myself.

She was also uncomfortable with my being gay. Galina didn't know if she would have to work with me like she would with a woman or a man. Could she yell at me, or would I be really emotional and cry? Her fears were allayed when she understood that not all of us are drama queens like on TV and that I took my falls like a man.

What took Galina longer to adjust to was my celebrity. Not only did I still have a camera crew following me around to shoot my documentary, which she did not approve of at first, but people arrived at the rink wanting interviews and details of how life with Galina was going. In an article published early into our relationship, a reporter described her as a "Bolshevik," which enraged her. How dare they call her that, Galina ranted, she had an American passport. She started to feel the sting of being associated with me.

"Galina, I'm sorry. But with me, people are going to pick you apart," I said. "That's just what we have to deal with. It makes us stronger."

Among the members of Team USA, Galina and I stood out like black sheep—or perhaps more accurately, black Russian bears.

For our first competition, less than a month and a half after we began working together, Galina had told me I needed to wear my American jacket. The event in Shin-Yokohama, Japan, called International Counter Match Figure Skating Competition USA. vs. Japan, was very team oriented. Every team official, such as our president, chairman, and the rest of the U.S. Figure Skating Association's muckety-mucks, were present. She wanted me to make a good impression.

"I don't have one," I told her.

"How come?" she asked, surprised since she had seen me wearing the Russian team uniform to practice many times.

"I shrunk it in the wash."

She shook her head and laughed.

"Please don't wear your Russian uniform, at least."

I listened to her and wore black for the official practice, but the two of us still made quite an impression in the sea of red, white, and blue tracksuits. For the occasion, Galina had decked herself out with a new dye job, diamonds, and big fur coat, despite the fact that it's still warm in Japan in September.

Galina—whose most recent competitive pupils represented countries like Israel, Japan, Ukraine, and Georgia—hadn't been exposed to the U.S. Figure Skating Association for a long time. She had worked with Scott Davis, a high-level U.S. skater, in the late '90s when I'd just started skating, but this was a whole new federation and I was a completely different story than Scott.

From the moment we arrived she didn't speak anything other

than Russian to me because she didn't want the officials and other skaters to understand what we were talking about.

"Put on your Amerikanski smile," she said, the big grin with full teeth that she called the "American smile," part of her campaign to get me to be pleasant and nice around people. Then, in Russian, she asked me to tell her who everyone was and everything about them while they sat directly in front of us. I pointed out the various officials and men and women practicing on the ice.

"That girl looks like a cow. A beautiful American cow," she said.

Galina was so ornery and wonderful. With Priscilla, I could never talk like that because she would get offended. Finally I had found a partner in crime. While everyone watched us, we traded barbs in Russian, treating the whole practice like a performance. The other team members felt uncomfortable with our foreign language and bursts of laughter. "Why are you speaking Russian?" one of the other team members asked. "It's easier for Galina," I lied in my new effort to be a politician.

We had such a great time on that trip, Galina called it our "honeymoon." She immediately snapped onto the fact that I didn't like eating or hanging out with everyone else and loved me for it. "Johnny, I hate going to team parties and eating with the kids," she said. "Let's go have some foie gras." We dined alone on the top floor of the hotel for every meal, feasting on filet mignon and skating gossip.

At the competition, everyone was waiting to see what Galina

had been able to do with me over the summer, and I didn't let her down. The program wasn't perfect—it was still extremely early in the season—but my score was way higher than the other American men. USA won the team competition because of my score.

Afterward a few of the top officials approached Galina with their big Amerikanski smiles. Pleased with the work she had done, they began complimenting her.

"Congratulations," one official said in an unusually loud voice. "He looks like a completely new person."

"A . . . new . . . skater," another said, equally loudly but also very slowly, moving his lips a lot like he was talking to a deaf five-year-old.

Even though Galina had lived in the States for eleven years, they didn't think she spoke English. But they were pleased—we had won because of my placement, after all. They commented that I was prepared (which hadn't always been the case) and skating "much more masculine." I thought it was silly how they assigned a gender category to the orderly way Galina had taught me to jump.

The only thing the federation officials wanted to see were some changes in the footwork sequence to make the program more difficult.

"That's a great idea," she said while smiling and nodding.

Once the federation officials had moved on, she turned to me and said, "Johnnychik, we're not changing anything. They won't know the difference." Galina was not only forming me as an athlete, but also helping with my PR—something I desperately needed. She told them whatever they wanted to hear (something I'm incapable of). Galina, a master at twisting situations to make it seem like she'd do anything to please, turned out to be right. We never altered the footwork sequence that season, but the officials clearly had no idea since they remarked that the program was "so much better."

Sitting in business class on the way home from Japan, we were riding high; it was the Galina and Johnny show. We both had our sunglasses on, and Galina looked particularly fancy in a gorgeous St. John suit ("I only travel in St. John. It's so comfortable," she said). She sipped champagne while I had orange juice since Galina had a strict no-alcohol policy during the competitive season.

The fourteen-hour flight home gave us ample time to talk about our plans for the season. In a month I'd be competing in the Cup of China, as my first Grand Prix event, and then, right after, the Cup of Russia—my red tour. It would be mega competing in Russia because all of Galina's Russian friends, coaches, and skaters would be watching to see what she'd done with this American.

But at that moment there was no pressure, just big hopes and dreams. I felt so good to be part of this great, great love story between the two of us. Galina had brought out the inner gentleman in me. Unfortunately no honeymoon lasts forever.

Going into the Grand Prix season, it was war. First up: China, where I would compete against Evan, who had just defeated me at the U.S. National Championships, and Stéphane Lambiel, a two-time world champion; then directly to Russia, where I faced Stéphane again. Big names right out of the gate was big pressure on both me and Galina. But we held it together as it turned cold in New Jersey. The furs came out and so did our fighting spirit. By the time we boarded the plane to China, we were both prepared—me with hard training, Galina with glowing skin from a facial and all her best things packed.

In China, after skating a clean long program, something I hadn't done in years, I significantly beat my personal best scores. Galina beamed with pride, and I saw my mother up in the stands, waving and crying. Evan skated after me, and it was close. But I won. I'd beat Evan, who placed second, and Stéphane came in third.

Landing in Moscow at the start of November when it gets snowy, cold, and very Russian, I was so excited to be back— proud of what I had just accomplished in China and content to be with a coach whom I adored. Galina, waiting at the airport, had planned a week of fun before we resumed our hard-core training for the competition. We were totally on the same wavelength, amazing for any new relationship.

The fantasy continued when I arrived at my hotel, the Metropol. Located right next to Red Square, it's one of the oldest hotels in Moscow and just a fantastic place to be. Galina hadn't believed me when I told her that I had gotten a great deal on the Internet until she saw my room: a large one boasting antique furniture, a huge chandelier, and a view of the Bolshoi Theatre. Very five-star, but old five-star, so my style.

I woke the next morning feeling like royalty. After training and a massage in the morning, I had lunch with one of my best friends, Russian skater Alexander Uspenski. Then that evening I was set to accompany Galina and her best friend Elena Tchaikovskaya, someone with a lot of history and influence in Russia, to see *Swan Lake* at the Bolshoi. (Elena Tchaikovskaya, Tatiana Tarasova, and Galina Yakovlevna were long considered a troika of the Russian skating world. The grand dames were the best of friends, but Galina and Elena had a particularly close bond and took vacations every May together in the resort city, Sochi.)

At lunch near my hotel, Sasha (as Alexander was known) and I toasted my success in China with a couple of glasses of wine. I knew Galina would have a fit if she found out, but it was only a couple of glasses. Unfortunately that was enough to get me tipsy and make me lose track of time. Our marathon lunch seemed to pass by in minutes.

I raced back to my hotel to shower and change, but Galina, standing outside the Bolshoi in the freezing cold waiting for me, was already calling every two minutes. Just as I was about to exit my hotel and make a beeline for the Bolshoi, I ran into one of my most ardent fan girls. She was hard to miss, with her meticulously applied false eyelashes and giant bust packed into a satin dress. "I want you to escort me to the ballet," she said.

She had somehow found out where I was staying and that I was going to the theater. I wasn't too surprised. In Russia, you can find out anything you want.

"Oh, you're going to the theater, too?" I asked in my wine haze. "Okay, I'll walk you."

I don't know what I was thinking, showing up to meet Galina late, tipsy, and with a girl who looked like a prostitute. Clearly the alcohol had affected me more than I realized because it was the stupidest move ever.

"Get away from him!" Galina shouted at my fan, who instantly scattered in fear. Galina could get really scary.

Then she got up very close to me, peered in my eyes, and sniffed my breath.

"Johnny, you're drunk!"

I wasn't drunk, just a cheap date. Galina let loose with a stream of insults, screaming at the top of her lungs about how disrespectful and shameful I was.

"How Russian can you get?" she said before pushing me inside. "Showing up at the ballet drunk, with a whore."

Luckily all was soon forgiven (even though I slept through half of the performance) and the three of us enjoyed a lavish mini vacation mostly organized by Elena. That week we went to see a stage version of *Yunona I Avos,* which I wasn't drunk for, and watched international skating competitions from the comfort of Elena's grand apartment.

The highlight was dining at a restaurant in Moscow where only famous people are allowed (Tchaikovsky and Pushkin both worked in the dark, quiet place while in town) called Klub Pisateliy. Elena ordered a full Russian feast of *chebureki*, chicken Kiev, piroshki, blini, and, my absolute favorite, black caviar. Although there was a ten-year ban on farming black caviar because of depleted supplies, in Russia certain people can get whatever they want.

When Elena asked for the illegal caviar, the waiter politely said, "Madam, you know we can't give you black caviar."

"I know better," she replied.

The waiter nodded and returned with a huge platter heaped high with black caviar that must have cost a small fortune. I slathered the black gold on one after another lacy blini. God, I love Russia.

That was just the start of the celebration. At the Grand Prix a week later, I skated better than I had in China and won the competition by many points. I made Galina proud . . . for a short while.

After the exhibition skate, I returned to my room to get ready for the skaters' closing banquet, where I was asked to give a thank-you speech on behalf of the athletes in English and Russian. Once I had finished dolling myself up, I went down the hall to Galina's room to pick her up. When she opened the door, I was astonished to find her in a kimono and face mask.

"Aren't you coming?" I asked.

"No. I wasn't invited."

And then she slammed the door in my face.

I was late, of course, and didn't have time to deal with whatever hot flash had caused her to go insane. When I got to the banquet, I asked one of our team leaders why Galina didn't have a ticket. "You didn't pay for one," he said. Uh-oh. I had messed up bad. Because Priscilla had never attended the banquets, I had no idea I was supposed to buy my coach a ticket. I had just assumed the event would provide her with one. I quickly got a ticket and ran back up to Galina's room.

She was still in her kimono when I begged her to come to the banquet: "I'm so sorry for the mix-up. Please throw some clothes on and come with me."

"No, no, no. I'm fine," she said with raised eyebrows, an expression that I would get to know all too well, and closed the door.

I turned back and headed for my celebration, dejected after experiencing my first real taste of Galina's coldness. After three weeks on the road, we were starting to grate on each other. That amount of togetherness would strain any new romance.

———————

I awoke to a searing pain in my neck. My head, neck, and shoulders felt like a single block that didn't belong to the rest of my body. I tried to move my head but couldn't, an alarming discovery less than a week before the National Championships. As I got out of bed, my entire back spasmed, sending wince-inducing shocks through my hips and down to my toes. If this mysterious injury didn't kill me, Galina was certain to.

Although I had a great beginning to the season with my wins in China and Russia, I had failed at the Grand Prix Final in Torino: Evan had beaten me. That made winning at the Nationals my only shot at regaining my supremacy over him. Since returning from defeat in Italy, Galina had been way more taskmaster than grandmother. She was intolerant of any mistake and not too impressed with any success.

I arrived at the rink hoping that my back would miraculously loosen up or that I could fake it through practice. But in order to jump you have to turn your head to see where you're going. From the minute I hobbled on the ice, it was clear to me, and Galina, that I couldn't possibly skate. I had to fess up about my pain.

She started kicking the walls, spitting and screaming.

"What did you do? Are you partying? Are you . . . ? What's going on . . . ?"

"I don't know why. Maybe I did it lifting groceries, or vacuuming."

"Go home," Galina said.

No matter what my chiropractor or masseur tried, neither could work out the spasms or my stiff neck. I took anti-inflammatories and used an electric stimulation machine but my back remained in pain even as I boarded the plane to Saint Paul, Minnesota, where the competition was held.

Nobody knew about my back injury let alone how severe it was. Galina used the electric stimulator on my back right before I went out on the ice, where I fought against the pain and skated perfectly clean. In first place, I beat Evan, who had made a mistake. But our scores were very close, so I knew if the judges could have found any excuse to put him in first they would have.

In the long program, I faced the judges' bias, back pain, and the first quad toe I had attempted since last year's Nationals. Because of my bad back, I hadn't skated a full long program for almost two weeks, which left me worried that I wouldn't make it from beginning to end. To add to the pressure, I was the very last skater in the championships—not only of all the men, but also of the pairs and women. I had to be a showstopper.

I moved past the pain and landed my quad toe. Other than one small mistake on the last one, I landed all my jumps: the triple axel, a triple toe, and another triple axel. Every element fell into place. The crowd jumped to its feet, and I started crying. Galina, who knew how hard I had fought to keep it together, teared up while I bowed to her and Viktor. Comparing the crowd's reaction to Evan to what they were giving me, I sat in the kiss and cry expecting national title number four. Galina gave my hand a little excited squeeze.

My score popped up in the little TV set at our feet—244.77. The number put me in an *exact* tie with Evan.

It was ludicrous, with the new and intricate judging system, to have two people with the exact same score. Getting hit by a meteor in the middle of the rink seemed more likely.

Our scores were tied, but Evan officially won the title because he had beaten me in the long program by a tenth of a point. Even though I was better, and the audience wanted me to win, I still lost.

Afterward there was a shit storm in the media and people protested the results, accusing the judges of fixing it. Gay websites cried gay bashing. *USA Today* did a huge analysis comparing my performance to Evan's and the score breakdown. Johnny's Angels started a petition and flooded the federation with letters. Whatever the conspiracy, people were behind me because I had proven I was serious again and deserved everything I achieved. The fans wanted a fairy-tale ending, but they would never get one. In the days after the Nationals, the federation did nothing. They never made even one comment on the matter.

I was more tired than angry. Immediately after the competition, I had to stick around the rink for the medal ceremony and exhibition skate, so I lay down on a couch backstage and fell dead asleep. I was exhausted from what had been a long year. It wasn't just the typical rigors of training and competing that had worn me down but also my new relationship with Galina. She wasn't exactly low maintenance. I found it hard to always be up and play the quiet, sweet, lovely skater, although that's what I wanted for her—a student upon whom she could rely.

Viktor woke me up, and Galina slapped some makeup on me before ushering me onto the podium where I stood, very unhappily, accepting the silver medal.

While I waited to do my exhibition skate, Viktor, Galina, and I sat around drinking: beers for them, a Coke for me. Not usually an optimist, Galina found the bright side of the situation.

"Johnny, you know, this sucks. But it's good PR. People are

saying that you were clearly better. They think you were wronged," she said. "You're the angel in this situation. And people love an angel."

For the exhibition, I skated to Josh Groban singing "Ave Maria"—it doesn't get more angelic than that. But when I got off the ice, I learned of the latest drama in my battle with Evan to wear the halo. It turned out he had coincidentally planned to skate to "Ave Maria" as well. When he heard my music come over the loudspeaker, he ran directly out of the rink and back to the hotel to get a different costume and piece of music. I guess he was worried he wouldn't measure up.

———

Oh, this would not do. It wouldn't do at all. My hotel room in Gothenburg, Sweden, home to the 2008 World Championships, was impossibly tiny, and even worse, right next to Galina's.

While I had long ago accepted her controlling everything from my eating to massages, I didn't need her sleeping in the room next to mine, listening to me take showers and watch movies through the wall. When I'm competing, I need some space from everyone, including my coach.

The front desk found me a bigger room, away from both Galina and, as a bonus, the rest of the U.S. skating team on that floor. I was in the process of pulling all my luggage together to move when Galina stormed into my room and demanded to know what I was up to.

"My luggage can't even fit in this room. So I'm moving."

"Johnny, this is a perfect situation. I need you here. I don't need you running around with all of your friends and partying before the competition and losing your energy."

Partying? What friends? Did she even know me?

"You need to be here. You're moving just because I'm next to you."

She wasn't completely wrong, but I didn't feel like getting into it with her.

"I'm moving to a different floor."

Galina slammed the door. "Oh, no, you're not," she said, taking the luggage out of my hands. I had experienced enough of her guilt trips to know I was never going to win a fight with her.

"Fine. Fine. I don't need another room, Galina. I'll stay here," I said, annoyed that going into my first Worlds competition where I really had a chance at a title someone inside my circle was giving me grief.

The next day, after practicing and going to the grocery store, I was relaxing in my room listening to music when Galina pounded on my door.

Storming in with Viktor in tow, she started looking around my tiny room, under the bed, in the wardrobe, in the bathroom, out the window, and on the roof.

"Galina, *what* are you doing?"

"I'm looking for that girl."

"What girl?"

"You know exactly which girl."

"I have no idea what you are talking about."

"The girl from the ballet."

"One of my fans?"

Galina had seen the same Russian fan I had appeared with at the Bolshoi walking through the lobby while I was having my wild moment buying bottled water and Ricola at the store.

"Yes, your prostitute."

I was going to have to explain to Galina that gay didn't just mean a love of fashion.

Viktor sat down on the bed and told me to sit beside him.

"Johnny, what are you doing?" he said. "You're completely ruining your chances at doing well in this competition. You're aggravating Galina. She doesn't need this. She's an old woman. She doesn't need this on her heart."

Meanwhile, Galina was repeating from the other side of the room, "Who's here? Who's here? I know somebody's in this room with you."

The insane scene was like something out of a bad Russian soap opera. Finally I looked at both of them and said, "Get the fuck out of my room.

"There's been no one in my room aside from you right now," I said. "And you're doing more to me right now than anyone could ever do. I will see you at the practice. Now get out."

Galina left with fire in her eyes and Viktor walking slowly and methodically behind her.

I tried to listen to music and do my makeup, but I couldn't

relax. The two of them were literally making me crazy. I thought they knew me and that the rumors about my wild reputation were completely unfounded. My problems with competing had to do with psychology, not parties.

By the time I got to practice that night, I was livid. Galina, Viktor, and Nina acted jovial because all the media had showed up, but I don't play games. I'm not about to fake it for anyone. So I didn't speak to any of them. While putting on my skates, I became more and more furious, slamming my laces into the holes. For the first time since I had started with Galina, I didn't bow to her before I began.

Back at the hotel after the practice, Galina and I had the unfortunate luck of winding up in the elevator together. She was so angry that she stood close to the doors, with her back to me, jamming the button for our floor over and over as if it would get us there faster.

I really didn't need this. If she wasn't going to stand behind me for this competition, I would have my mother by the boards. Galina had done her job training me, and I was ready. If we parted now, it would be okay.

I knocked on her door.

"Galina, we need to talk."

"Johnny, this all started because you wanted to switch rooms. All the drama is because of you. I don't trust you right now. I don't trust that you have your best interest at heart."

Then she rattled off all these skaters, through the years, who had hung out with their friends through competitions, partying and drinking and losing. Galina listed all the people I had hugged and said hello to, accusing me of inviting them to my room to play and have fun.

"You're going to ruin yourself."

"Galina, I wanted to move rooms to get away from this whole team . . . and you."

"You can do what you want," she said. "But I want you to know that I'm watching, no matter where you are."

The drama was done, but she didn't accept me and I didn't accept her. The tension didn't abate until after I had skated my short program better than I had skated all season and earned a new personal best score. I was in second place, the highest I had ever been in the World Championships. The slate had been wiped clean. Galina, Viktor, and I all hugged as if nothing had happened. Winning will do that to you.

Going into the long program, it was very important I do well, not just for me but also the entire U.S. skating team. The men were closing the Worlds this year, and so far no Americans had won any medals—no women, no pairs, nothing. Our country had done terribly, which was pretty embarrassing since it was a year the federation had spent a lot of extra money creating a program with the specific purpose of winning more medals.

Pride wasn't the only issue. It was important for the following year's World Championships in Los Angeles that the Americans place high enough to secure three starting positions. It would be humiliating if we had bad placement in the Worlds hosted on our home turf. Not only that, but the World Championship in L.A. also decided how many spots the United States would get for the next Olympics.

With Evan having withdrawn from the World Championships a week before because of an injury, I was the top American in Sweden and the last chance for a medal.

In addition to all this drama with Galina and Viktor, there was also this crushing burden to win a medal for my federation, which didn't appreciate me, and, of course, win my first medal for myself.

It's no wonder then that when I got on the ice for the long program, stiff and cottonmouthed, that it went by in a flash. While it wasn't unusual for me to finish a performance and not remember exactly what happened, this time it was literally like a big blank; I had no idea what I had done in the past four minutes.

"Did I do the quad toe?" I asked Galina in the kiss and cry.

"Yes. Two feet on the landing."

"The triple axel?"

"Yes, you did."

My score brought me out of the surreal moment and back to reality: I was in first place with a few more skaters remaining to skate. Before long I learned that I had earned a bronze, not the medal I had hoped for, but still a huge victory. I had earned my first Worlds medal and the only one for the United States. I came through for my country and helped secure three spots for next year's World Championships in Los Angeles. I was ecstatic.

This finally seemed like the fairy-tale ending everyone had been hoping for.

After the euphoria had mellowed, the press conference finished, the drug tests taken, and I made my way back to the hotel, I found myself again knocking on Galina's door. She answered, wearing her kimono. All's well that ends well, but I still needed closure on why she had created so much chaos.

"If we're going to continue to work together, I really need to understand what this was," I said.

"Well, Johnny, when you go to competitions, you always need some kind of drama. Before China, it was trouble with your skate sharpening. Before Russia, you know, we had the fight about you showing up drunk to the ballet. Before the National Championships, you had your back problem." She's like, "Everything was moving along too smoothly on this trip, so I wanted you to be upset. I wanted you to be angry so that you would skate well. I did this for you."

I didn't believe a word of it. She was pissed that I had wanted to change rooms and tried to play it off like she was inspiring my fighting spirit. I found myself aggravated yet again, because I couldn't call her on it. If I had called her a liar, she would have thrown me out the window.

"Congratulations," I said wearing my Amerikanski smile. "We did this together. I'll see you when we get home."

Boarding the plane back to New York, I was extremely grateful the season's end had finally come and that I was traveling alone. Galina had certainly done a lot for me—bringing me back from the brink of disaster to a World medal—but we needed a little break from each other.

Just as I had settled into my seat, closed my eyes, and prepared for a relaxing, silent trip, one of the flight's crew got on the PA system. "Ladies and gentleman," he said. "We would like to announce that our new World Championships bronze medalist Johnny Weir is on the flight with us." Everyone onboard started clapping. Fairy-tale endings might be something I could get used to.

13

Weircapades

Waking up alone in a Korean hotel on Christmas Day was just sad. Even though I'm not one to really celebrate holidays (not only does my tightly structured life not allow me time to enjoy them, but I'm also not a big believer in enforced fun), this was a little too *Lost in Translation* even for me.

But I couldn't say no to the amazing, charity gig where I'd be performing in a Christmas show with the country's top champion Kim Yu-Na. So four days after I competed in the 2008 Grand Prix finals in Seoul, I was back at JFK to return in what would be my twelfth flight to Asia that year.

Another Grand Prix season had flown by in a whirlwind of

travel, training, and, alas, unlike the previous one, defeat. The year started out on the wrong foot when I discovered that my blades weren't aligned properly on the new skates I had received at the end of the summer. It felt like I was walking on a stiletto with one foot and a ballet flat with the other. Not comfortable. On the ice, I couldn't stand straight and had a lot of problems with my jumps. But it was too late to get new boots because the process of breaking them in to a point where a skater can jump safely takes time. I just had to make the best of my stiletto-ballet combo.

At my first event, Skate America, a competition I had avoided until this point in my career because of the early date and the bias against me in my own country, Evan and I lost to an unknown Japanese skater. Evan placed third, and I second, which was humiliating for both of us in our own country. The only highlight was seeing Evan, who had gone to Tarasova for help with his programs that year, come out in a crazy costume that made him look like a waiter. The sparkly penguin suit signaled to me that Tarasova, who had always promoted my skating over Evan's in her TV commentary, was messing with him.

Then I came down with bronchitis for my second event in Japan. With an army of my Japanese fans in tow to help her translate, Galina mined the pharmacy for every remedy allowed under the international skating regulations. With death warming me over, I competed and miraculously placed second. But there were no more miracles left by the Grand Prix final in Seoul. After two solid weeks of fighting with Galina, feeling sick, and skating on my wonky blades, I had no more fight left. I fell in the short program and placed third.

It was a tribute to my Asian fans, whose love didn't waver with my uneven scores, that I was the only non-Korean invited to perform in this huge Christmas spectacular. So although I was wrung dry by the last couple of months, I still felt proud to be there (plus, I loved the star treatment they lavished on me from the minute I stepped off the plane).

On Christmas, the day of the show, I didn't have too long to experience the holiday blues because my new manager, Tara Modlin, landed in my hotel room like a hurricane. I had changed from my previous manager at Michael Collins Enterprises—one of two big skating agencies—after Tara wooed my mom and me over a cozy meal at Elmo. A former skater, she understood my world but was young and new to the business. I wasn't worried. By that point a homeless person could have done a better job than my manager, who would literally take two months to return my call. My previous manager even went as far as to go on Nancy Kerrigan's TV show (only a year after I had been publicly humiliated on it when Mark Lund made rude comments about my skating and sexuality) to say, "Johnny will do better this year because he hasn't been partying as much." With the Olympics looming, I wanted a go-getter and Tara fit the bill. She's a very forceful girl who loves cowboy boots, rhinestones, ruffles, sparkles, and polka dots. She's also very clever and gets what she wants.

Although Tara had been my agent for only a few months,

this was our first real experience together, because at competitions Galina didn't like her talking business anywhere near me.

After quickly washing her blond bangs in the sink, Tara escorted me to the rink for the show. On the way there, I started to feel a little queasy but I made a joke of it, teasing Tara that her perfume was making me sick. But after the rehearsal, where I learned the opening number, I was no longer joking around; something was terribly wrong with me. I felt like a narcoleptic because I couldn't keep my eyes open. When the shaking began, I lay down in front of a heater. Then the puking started. I couldn't stand up straight without puking. I couldn't lie down without puking.

With only three hours before showtime and me puking nonstop into a box that Tara held like a champ, a team of doctors ran in to cure me, or at least get me through the next three hours. Their medicine was as foreign to me as their country. One doctor tried to bleed the illness out of me by pricking all my fingers, while an acupuncturist put needles in my stomach and head.

Everyone needed me to get on that ice, most of all me. It was big, big money, and if I didn't perform I would have traveled to Korea, missed Christmas with my family, pissed off my mom, and become sick for nothing. I told myself that I would skate, even if I had to puke into a sparkly glove during the show.

While lying on a massage table in a parka and under fourteen blankets, I asked Tara to pull the mirror over to me. With only one eye open at a time, I started putting my makeup on my stone-white face. Then Tara took my pants and top off like she

was changing a baby and helped me into my costume. Five minutes before my number, three Korean doctors carried me to the
ice with Tara holding a giant box in which for me to get sick.
With no warm-up, no nothing, I threw up in the box, got on
the ice and skated to the center.

Somehow, I skated both my numbers without throwing up
or fainting, although I could sense fear in Yu-Na's eyes as she
took my hand in our pairs performance.

As soon as I finished, I skated right for the back door, where
I puked three times into my box before an ambulance picked me
up. The paparazzi waiting outside took photos of me swaddled
in coats and blankets like a big baby. People in the hospital also
took pictures of me as they wheeled me to a private room.

After weighing me and discovering that I had lost eight
pounds in one day, they wanted to hook me up to an IV immediately. Suffering from dehydration and exhaustion, I was sicker
than I had ever been in my life. I wanted to feel better, but it's
terrifying for an athlete to be in a situation like this where you
have no idea what they are putting into you. We had to find a
doctor who could translate from Korean into English, and then
call an American doctor before they put any needles in me. It
was the middle of the night on Christmas Eve back in the States,
so it would have to be a Jewish doctor—Tara found one in five
minutes flat.

A much harder task was calling my mother. "Patti, everything is okay," Tara said in her sweetest voice. "Don't freak out.
We're in the hospital but it's under control."

Of course my mother freaked out and burst into tears.

"He just has exhaustion," Tara explained. "He threw up his entire life today, but he'll be fine."

———————————

By now Galina was used to me crying since I had done it just about every day at practice since returning from Korea. The National Championships were only two weeks away, and I still hadn't been able to regain the strength I had lost from my illness over the holidays. Galina yelled at me out of frustration, reminding me over and over that she had warned me not to go to Korea. Still, I would sleep through morning practices out of sheer exhaustion. The weight I had lost during my illness had taken my already thin frame into concentration camp territory. I had no energy and now no jumps.

It was a terrifying moment when my jumps left me. Stuff that I could do since I was thirteen vanished. It's not uncommon for skaters to wake up one day and find they've lost technique, but it had never happened to me. Going into my triple axel, all of a sudden I didn't know what to do and landed flat on my back where I stayed, crying, of course.

This year's Nationals was an even bigger deal than usual because it decided the U.S. skaters that would go to the upcoming World Championships, held in our backyard. No matter how international I felt or how many of my fans came from abroad, I wanted to compete against the world on American soil.

All I wanted to do was make the World Championship team whatever way I had to do it. But it was going to be tricky. Going into the Nationals, I knew there was no way I would do well. I was a total mess. And the U.S. Figure Skating Association, unlike most other countries, based their world team almost strictly on placement at the Nationals. Even if I was third, I'd be fine with it. I just wanted to be on that team.

Once we arrived for the event in Cleveland, Ohio (where I'd had my disaster in the National Championships as a junior-level skater), Galina forbade me from telling anyone—media, fellow skaters, and, God forbid, officials—about my sickness. This wasn't a new policy. She had always been very strict about not discussing illnesses or injuries. "Nobody's going to care. It doesn't matter if you're sick, if your mom just died, if your leg is falling off," she said. "If you show up and you're planning to compete, you compete. Nobody cares about the backstory."

So I went in for my short program looking inexplicably shaky, white, and as emaciated as a heroin addict. I wish I *had* been on drugs after the performance I gave. Although Galina and I had worked back from the basics to rebuild the jumps I had lost, instead of a planned triple axel, I only did a single axel, among many other minor mistakes, all of which landed me in seventh place. I had never been lower than sixth place in a senior National Championship, and that was at my very first.

People were bewildered. Conspiracy theories for my terrible condition abounded: I had a drinking problem; I was on drugs; I was having orgies.

I screwed up the network programming—television had to air the event for the long program earlier because I was no longer in the last group of the top six competitors. When I took to the ice for my long program, many of the audience hadn't yet filed into the building. I was skating to crickets.

With my thin frame barely holding up my costume, I began by popping another triple axel into a single. Then all ninety pounds of me started to fight back. I did the second triple axel followed by a difficult combination. I poured every last bit of strength that I had onto the ice and felt a small seed of hope bloom from my exhaustion. I went up for the last jump and then, *bam,* I fell on my face.

Even though my condition was beyond terrible, I was in total disbelief that I hadn't pulled it together. My scores went up, pronouncing a very bad fate: I got fifth. "I can't believe you let this happen to yourself," Galina said under her breath while smiling for the cameras and crowd.

Immediately after the event, Galina ran into the hallway to start campaigning on my behalf, finding out who was in charge and what we had to say to get a spot on the World team. I was close enough to the top three that the committee could conceivably do something to get me to the World Championships.

In first place was Jeremy Abbott, who was legitimately the best and deserved to go. Evan, a clear champion, was third and should also go. But the second place spot had gone to a skater fresh off the junior level who'd had that wow moment. He had won the silver medal in the Nationals fair and square but most likely wasn't ready for a huge international event, especially one that determined the number of skaters that the United States would be able to send on its men's roster to the 2010 Olympic Games. The problem was the committee couldn't justify replacing a boy in second with me and keeping Evan, who was in third.

The selection committee went behind closed doors right after the event to hash out the possibilities. A few people wanted to see the junior boy go to the Junior World Championships and learn to compete internationally before heading to the big leagues. But it would be especially painful if he got trounced the year the competition was held in the United States. I still had a chance.

Finally, after a torturously long time, a little old woman shuffled out of the meeting room and taped a small piece of paper to the wall, right under our event results. I was named the second alternate for the World Championships, not even the first alternate. That was the end of my season.

I was the only American skater in any discipline to win a world medal the previous season, and the reason that the United States could send three men to the World Championships in the first place, but none of it counted. I had no money in the bank as far as the federation was concerned. I had lost fair and square, by their count, and didn't deserve a spot on the team.

All I wanted to do now that my fate had been sealed was return to my hotel room and kill myself. But I still couldn't leave. In a cruelly ironic twist, I had won the *USFSA's Skating* magazine's Reader's Choice for favorite skater of the year and had to stick around to accept the award. The timing couldn't have been worse. It seemed the federation thought so, too, because minutes before I took the podium with my prepared speech they had asked me earlier that month to give, someone let me know there would be no speech.

I was glad that they didn't give me the opportunity to speak, because nothing pretty would have come out of my mouth. Wearing a USA jacket that I borrowed from somebody else (another stipulation for getting onstage), I accepted the award, waved at the audience, got off the stage, then threw the jacket onto the floor and walked across it.

Back at the hotel, everyone was gathered in the lobby bar celebrating the end of the event and the season. Skaters, coaches, parents of skaters, they were all drinking and having a merry time. That is, until I walked through the door. Every single person's head turning to look at me made a collective whooshing sound. Then the place went silent in wait for my reaction.

I made a beeline for my mom, who was sitting with Tara, my grandmother, and my aunt Diane. Everyone was crestfallen and drinking, even my grandma. I went to my mother, puffy-eyed and drinking Southern Comfort, and hugged her. Sometimes, as an athlete in a solitary sport like skating, it's hard to realize there are all these people who want you to succeed as much, if not more than, you do.

"I'm so sorry," my mother said.

It was too much for me to take. I could barely contain my

disappointment, let alone that of my family and friends. I rushed out of that scene, past the gossiping skating mothers and my fans from Japan crying in the lobby.

In my room, I called down to room service and ordered three orders of chicken fingers and french fries with a soup bowl full of ranch dressing. After it arrived, I locked the door and ate every last chicken finger and left only a random scattering of fries, crying the whole way through my meal.

Then I called room service again and ordered some cake. I was having a major depressed-girl eating situation. A Russian woman, who worked in the kitchen and knew what had happened to me, sent an assortment: a giant piece of chocolate cake, apple cake, pie, and tiramisu. My spies are everywhere.

I vowed right then and there that I would never do a thing to please anyone in that federation ever again. While I had never conformed to their ideal image, I had also never gone against them in any major way. Through all the years of gossip and judgments about me, I always felt the federation supported me in the most important way—by sending me to competitions. But after the debacle of last year's tie at the Nationals, their decision to keep me off the World team felt like an unbearable stab in the back. I would never again wear the American jacket. Not because I don't love and support my country, but I refused to wear anything that had to do with the United States Figure Skating Association.

The grudge between me and my federation was permanent, and mutual. By the next Nationals in 2010, we were in a full-on war.

I was really angry going into the Grand Prix season. After Evan, my chief rival, had won the World Championships, I couldn't help but wonder what would have happened if I had been able to compete. As a gold world medalist, Evan was now the definitive reigning angel.

Russia and Japan, my countries, had picked me for their Grand Prix events. When I got to my first event in Russia, it had been more than nine months since I had set foot in a competitive environment. The time away showed and I placed fourth. In Japan I redeemed myself, placing second before going on to the final, also held in Japan, where I placed third. Although Evan was in first, my place on the podium at least proved I was an Olympic contender.

The whole season was sped up for the Olympics, so the Nationals came on the heels of the Grand Prix final, just after the new year. Back in good old Spokane, Washington, for the event, I knew that I would have to do well here to go to the Olympics. The big question was whether the federation would *let* me do well enough.

At least this time I wasn't at death's door. As with most of the Grand Prix season, my short program went off without a hitch at the Nationals. Evan was ahead of me, and then Jeremy Abbott, who skated shortly after, also jumped ahead of me by a few points. Because he had skated the exact same elements as I had, it seemed like there was some clever judging going on. It had been a consistent theme in my season that my best was never good enough.

Galina and I studied the score sheets as soon as an official posted them. The technical scores were unarguable, but the artistic ones were subjective. That's where the "judging" came in. Among the numbers that were typical for a top-level athlete like myself (the range is normally between 7.0 and 9.0), I saw a few 6's and then one number that made my eyes pop: a 3.75.

"Galina, what is that?" I said.

"Maybe it's a misprint. It should be eight seven five. Eight and three can look like alike," she said.

"I don't think so."

Galina marched up to one of the officials, demanding to know what had happened. A score that low wasn't just bad for me, it was bad for the entire U.S. skating team. It sends a message to the rest of the skating world that one of America's Olympic team is no better than a 3.75—unless they weren't planning on sending me to the games.

Although the identities of the judges are supposed to be kept from their scores for obvious reasons, the official assured us, "We know which judge it is. And we're going to talk to him."

After what had happened at Nationals the year before, I had tried to stop caring about what anyone thought of me. I just wanted to show off what I slaved over every day of my life to the best of my abilities. But it was hard not to care. This sport was all about judgment. Those numbers determined my future.

After the bitterness of receiving a 3.75, I didn't exactly soar into my long program. I skated and did okay, nothing spectacular. Knowing I had no chance of winning, I skated to get the job of going to the Olympics done. It wasn't a conscious decision, but an inevitable one.

By the end of the competition, I was in third place, exactly where the federation wanted me. As I accepted my bronze medal, I became more and more incensed. While waiting for the ceremony, I heard that they were never going to leave me off the team because of my popularity and ability to get a mass audience to watch skating.

After finally finishing the documentary about my life, Butch and Grämz premiered *Pop Star on Ice* that summer at festivals around the country. It was such a success that the Sundance Channel bought it and launched a multi-episode series, *Be Good Johnny Weir,* using the documentary as the first episode. A skater with a reality show on cable, I was a complete anomaly. As if to highlight that truth, Sundance aired the series' promo during the Nationals that showed me in heels jumping out of a giant Fabergé egg. As I said, an anomaly.

Apparently that helped me get an Olympic spot—otherwise they would have sent Ryan Bradley, who placed fourth, ahead of me. I was going to my second Olympics, not as a world-class competitor, but as a trained monkey to sell tickets. I was a token, and there's no worse feeling.

If the federation wanted attention for skating leading up to the Olympics—well, I got it for them. But perhaps not in exactly the fashion they had hoped.

It started immediately after the Nationals with my exhibition skate to Lady Gaga's "Poker Face." The genesis of the program—as far as I could go from the typical Disneyesque fare offered by my sport without getting censored on network TV—was a Fashion Week event the year before. *V Man* magazine had asked me to skate to Beyoncé's "Single Ladies (Put a Ring on It)" at a party celebrating the end of Fashion Week. Beyoncé was so not my style, so I suggested something by Lady Gaga.

Ever since she hit the scene, I have been a fan of La Gaga. Although she's obviously got an obscure vision, she's a real artist. I love her music but am most inspired by the fact she clearly doesn't give a shit about what anyone thinks. Gaga will wear a big old lobster on her head or a dress made out of Coke cans if that's what she wants. Anyone that conforms bores me, and anyone who doesn't has my complete admiration.

The fashionistas at the party held at Manhattan's Chelsea Piers loved the "Poker Face" number, and Perez Hilton put it up on his website where it came to the attention of the Lady herself. She invited me to her concert at Radio City Music Hall, where I sat next to her mother. Mama Gaga, a fan of figure skating, and I got along very well (in general, mothers love me). Dressed in a cashmere twin set and pearl necklace, she stood making the sign of the horns with her hand, sticking out her tongue, and screaming like crazy while her daughter humped a piano bench onstage.

It was a wonderful family portrait. That's how I'd like to think of my mom watching me skate.

True to the spirit of Lady Gaga and her very sexual song, my exhibition number was also very suggestive. Wearing makeup that resembled disco-style war paint and a black, slightly sado-masochistic, corseted costume, I was really excessive for a figure skating show on NBC during a Sunday afternoon. No surprise, a big hoopla followed immediately because even though the program itself was a year old, for the majority of Americans it was their first taste of Johnny Weir since the last Olympics four years ago. Of course it was everywhere in the skating press, but all the entertainment shows featured it as well. People went crazy over watching this silly faggot in makeup, shaking his ass on the ice for TV.

"Poker Face" amplified everything. I mean, it drove people insane. Those who loved me loved it, and those who hated me hated even more. My dirty, sexy dance also made my sexuality a hot topic of conversation. Again.

All the gay websites brought up the question of whether or not I was gay—or, rather, they knew I was gay but couldn't figure out why I was such a jerk that I wouldn't talk about it. This was nothing new. I had been dealing with questions surrounding my sexuality since I was sixteen, when skating fanatics began bringing up the issue on message boards. But now, like my persona, the desire to know who I liked to do it with had grown a hell of a lot bigger. A lot of the gays got downright angry about my silence.

In my career, the gays from an older generation had always been some of my biggest detractors because I refused to perform in the dog and pony show of the traditional coming-out story. When *The Advocate,* a national gay magazine, offered me a cover story after the 2006 Olympics if I came out in the article, I declined. There was no way I would seek publicity with an article focusing on my being gay when that is the smallest part of what makes me me.

Many of those who had to fight for their rights to a gay life think I'm disrespectful because I haven't been out and proud. I'm the first to say it takes enormous cojones to fight to change the world, but not everyone can be an activist. I could never be one; I'm way too passive-aggressive.

Pressure is the last thing that would make me want to "join" a community. I don't appreciate when others push anything on me. I had to fight my entire career in skating to be an individual and not play a role that I was told to, so I wasn't about to step into the chorus line just because the gay community told me to. Yes, I have some very stereotypical gay traits (I love flowers, smelling good, fashion, and I'm an ice skater, for Christ's sake). But I also have traits stereotypical of a Jewish mother (I'll feed anyone I can get my hands on and have a wicked way with guilt) and a regular ol' rural male (I'm not afraid to get my hands dirty and chicken fingers are my favorite food). Being gay is not a choice. I was born gay just as I was born white and male. I don't hold pride parades for the color of my skin or the fact that I have a penis, so why would I do it because I was born a gay man?

Putting people in boxes—whether the label is lesbian, gay, nerd, or freak—is just phony. In our society, too many people box up their personalities, stowing away aspects of themselves that don't fit in the confining shape. In that sense, I wish people would come out, to live freely and openly. I wear my heart on my sleeve. Whether it's with my mother, best friend, or lover, I give everything that I am. To me, gay and straight is only sex. Love is completely without boundaries. The pressure on me to come out was silly because I don't ever remember being in.

So the massive backlash against me in the gay media and community before the Olympics didn't hurt me; it only made me dig my "closeted" heels in further. There were so many articles about my glaring flamboyance that Paris and I talked about how it would be the least shocking thing in the world if I did come out. Apparently everyone in the universe already knew I was a huge flamer. And as someone who's gone far by being controversial in a beige world, the last thing I ever want is to be obvious.

"I should come out as a Pacific Islander," I said. "That would be really shocking."

"No, you should come out as a black woman," Paris said.

"A sumo wrestler."

"Lupus sufferer!"

"French maid."

My true coming-out tale became a running joke between Paris and me, but our fantasies turned out to be far less absurd than the reality of my biggest pre-Olympics scandal. The one that eclipsed my un–family friendly performance after the Nationals and my mysterious sex life, sprung from the tiniest, most mundane detail imaginable.

It all began when I added a patch of real fox fur to one shoulder of my costume because I thought it looked stunning. Anyone who knows me knows I love fur. I think it's glamorous and love the way it feels. I make no apologies for it.

Like me, fur is one of those hot-button issues that stirs up love or hate in people. And the haters are particularly vicious, which I discovered immediately after giving an interview where I talked about the fur detail on my costume. Almost the instant the item posted on the Internet, Tara and Stephanie, my costume designer, were inundated with angry calls. I received hundreds of emails on Facebook about how much I sucked.

Then it started to get really out of control. There were people threatening to obstruct my Olympic performance by showing up in Vancouver to throw blood on the ice while I skated. Someone faxed Tara a death threat and said my head was worth a few million dollars (I was more upset about the paltry bounty than the threat), so she called the FBI. Police were stationed at my rink and circled my apartment complex: a few followed me everywhere in the lead-up to the Olympics.

Although the fur fiasco story had been reported everywhere from CNN to Perez Hilton, Galina hadn't heard about it because she pretty much only consumed Russian media. And I didn't involve her in these kinds of problems because it wasn't part of her job description. She's my coach; she teaches me ice skating and drives me crazy and that's it.

A couple of weeks before the Olympics, she called me on a Saturday afternoon.

"Johnnychik, what's happening?"

"Galina, what do you mean?"

"I just heard on Russian radio that you are in trouble because of the fox."

"Yes, Galina. But I didn't want to bother you with that."

"But why? It's fun!"

"Well, I got death threats."

"Oksana Baiul once got a letter that had actual shit smeared on it because somebody from Ukraine didn't like Oksana, or her mother, rest her soul."

"That's disgusting."

"Don't worry, Johnny. No one's going to kill you. But I still think you should take the fur off."

"Why?"

"Stephanie picked the fur out of some trash bin at a fabric store," she said. "Johnny, that fox is very bad quality. It's a fox that's been dead thirty, forty years."

14

The Last Stand

When I walked into the church late at night, the air felt as thick as honey. The interior's only light source stemmed from dozens of yellow wax candles, which added mystery and emotion in their reflections off the walls' stunningly intricate gold details. There was a weight to this place where so many supplicants had come before, just like me, asking for divine intervention.

I had arrived in the beautiful Russian Orthodox church four days before leaving for the Olympics to receive a blessing after Galina had gotten the idea into her head while watching the Russian Olympic team on TV get similarly blessed by the

Russian Orthodox patriarch in Red Square. In our own corner of New Jersey, she had heckled the local priest (and probably greased a few palms) into giving me a special ceremony reserved for more typically members of the armed forces than athletes.

With the majority of our training team behind me, I stood motionless at the front of the church. In the dark, hushed place, the priest intoned a long series of prayers on our behalf in an esoteric language similar to Russian. Clad in a long ominous black robe, he placed a solid twenty-four-karat gold-covered Bible on my forehead. The coolness of the precious metal sent shivers down my spine as if to jolt me into the rarity of the moment. Then he shook holy water over me, and I felt the emotional magic, a brilliant cleanse of spirit.

I'm not religious, nor am I an atheist. I wouldn't even call myself agnostic. I think there is wisdom to be had in organized efforts toward holiness, but I know there is also wickedness. So I believe in all the *good* in every religion. Around my neck I wear a chain adorned with a Star of David, a *hamsa,* a Russian Orthodox protection ring, and more that symbolize good and also hold my "powers." I'll take whatever blessings I can get.

Despite my far-reaching dabbling in the ways of God, I had never experienced anything like I did during this ceremony. I could feel everyone standing behind me, trying to push me up. It was a stunning array of love. The priest sweated with emotion as he made me strong for competition and confrontation.

In the last and most glorious preparation for the Olympics, I relieved my soul of all the trials I had gone through in the last four years. I was now ready to head into battle.

———————

Galina popped out of the overloaded van at the Olympic Village in Vancouver wearing a pair of heels and a long mink dyed the color of merlot. I followed her in knee-high, pointy-toed boots and a big, black, furry jacket that screamed *ta-da!* One of the helpers deposited our luggage (we each had something like six pieces) and then sped off to another area.

Passing us on all sides were Russians in their Bosco Sport uniforms, Americans decked head to toe in red, white, and blue, and Italians in sleek Lycra courtesy of Mr. Armani. Literally every single person ran around, all day, every day, wearing a patriotically inspired athletic ensemble. Even their underwear had flags on it.

With everyone in sneakers and sweats, they stared at us in our fanciest (and perhaps most ridiculous) getups and most likely thought, *Whose team are* they *on?*

Answer: we weren't part of any team. Not really.

Despite all the usual stress and strain of an Olympic season, Galina and I managed to maintain a great relationship and spent the entire games on the same wavelength, which was completely independent. We didn't feel a part of the Americans because of all the bad blood, and yet we couldn't get too cozy with the Russians for political reasons. So it was always just the two of us—decked in our finest amid a sea of sportsmen.

During team processing, Galina, in Russian, mocked the American team uniforms, saying that they looked like an exact replica of the jackets worn by construction workers in Moscow. Adding to the improbability that any of those clothes would touch my body, there were no uniforms available in my size. Instead, one of the officials handed me a jacket and pants with Day-Glo detailing in size extra-large, which sent Galina off on a stream of untranslatable and unprintable insults. She didn't like the uniforms but wanted to be the one to reject them.

After the team processing meetings, we went to find our accommodations. Newly built, million-dollar condos right on the water that had yet to hit Vancouver's real estate market housed members of the Olympic teams during our stay. In the building reserved for the American team, Galina and I headed up to the sixth floor, and as soon as we stepped off the elevator almost had a heart attack. The walls looked like they were bleeding.

One American team leader from Kansas had decorated the entire hallway with hundreds of small plastic American flags and red-white-and-blue streamers. It was very festive and rah-rah in a blinding sort of way.

Galina and I split up as one of the coordinators showed me down the dizzying hall and around the corner to my room. The door opened to a gigantic apartment with magnificent floor-to-ceiling windows that boasted a view of the harbor as well as the planetarium, which had been taken over and decorated for

Russia House. Huge signs saying "Sochi," the Russian city hosting the next winter Olympics, covered the domed building. I
found the sight incredibly cheerful.

I grabbed the bigger bedroom because my roommate, Tanith
Belbin, wasn't going to be arriving for a few days, and flopped
down on the bed, letting my pointy boots hang off the end.
Soaking in my palatial surroundings (way better than the five-
women-to-two-bedroom ratio Galina faced down the hall), I felt
empty.

My slightly depressed state was so different from that of my
first Olympics, when I'd found myself bouncing off the walls
with excitement. In the back of my mind a sobering thought
loomed: my innocence was almost over. I would soon have to
grow up and become a real person whose life isn't planned out
from morning to night. It was as foreboding as the harbor's
black, choppy water that I stared at from my bed. This Olympics
almost certainly marked the end of my competitive career. My
entire identity, the thing that I had breathed almost every
moment of my life since the age of thirteen, would suddenly
change. And yet I had no idea what lay ahead. What would I do
without skating?

That heaviness remained with me for the opening ceremonies. As I've said, when it comes to parties and anything where
there's an enforced protocol, I'm not a big fan. And there's nothing more enforced than the Olympics' opening ceremony. The
American team members had a very specific costume we had to
wear (explained in detail on a printed handout), and if you didn't

follow it, you couldn't walk. While wearing the sweater, hat, pin, and other mandatory garb, I tried my best to make myself look like I wasn't part of the masses as I gave my cheekbones extra definition and let my hair peek out from under the hat.

Even though Vancouver hosted the first indoor opening ceremonies for the Winter Olympics, all the athletes still wore sweaters, parkas, hats, and boots. It was the winter games, after all, and we had to look the part. But with balmy outdoor temperatures in the forties and fifties, it became excruciatingly hot with thousands of bundled-up bodies waiting in a concrete sweat lodge beneath the stadium. It got pretty disgusting.

When they released us from burning up in the pen into a winter wonderland with fake snow raining down inside the stadium, I walked the whole lap, trying to soak up the spirit from the crowd screaming with enthusiasm. Once I finished the lap, I told a helper from the organizing committee: "Okay, I'm ready."

Back in my room, I took a bubble bath to clean myself up from my sweaty mess. Relaxed after a nice long soak, I walked out onto the balcony, which afforded a bird's-eye view of the stadium and the opening ceremonies still going on. Sitting for a while alone, I could hear the roar of the crowd and see the ending display of fireworks that looked from a distance like nothing more than a child's sparkler. When the cold began to penetrate my clothes, I went back inside and spent the rest of the night doing laundry.

The day of the short program, I felt so confident and so good it was bizarre. I had slept well and even taken a nap comfortably—shocking for a bad sleeper like me. But Canada is good for sleeping. I didn't get sweaty palms doing my hair and makeup. I was so prepared for battle that nothing could affect me, not even the debacle of my practice the day before.

I was the only one of the three American men who chose to do the late-night practice, which was published in the official schedule for everyone to see. The practices, like everything else at the Olympics, are an extremely formal affair because it's required for at least one official and one doctor to attend whenever an athlete is on the ice.

But when Galina and I got to the rink that night, we were the only ones there. After a few minutes I turned to Galina and said, "Nobody's here."

It was a shocking oversight in a place where, for random drug-testing purposes, athletes can't even leave a building without alerting an official.

"Well, Johnny, you knew coming into this we'd be alone," she said.

I did know that, but it had never been so in my face. The night before one of the biggest performances of my life, my country couldn't even show me the respect of coming to my last practice. I had done my part, giving great practices, interviews, and the publicity they wanted for the team. Still, they couldn't even do the basics of their job when it came to me.

As a sign of respect, I had worn to practice one of the jackets from the team processing—although, in keeping with my vow after the Nationals, this one didn't say "USA." But I immediately took it off and threw it on the other side of the boards. I was my own team, representing my fans and my country but not the federation.

Galina told me to get on the ice. "Our doctor's here," she said, pointing to the Russian doctor standing right behind her. Two Russian officials, who had come for Evgeni Plushenko's practice before mine, kindly stayed to monitor me.

The next day at the competition I thanked them again for their help, choosing not to engage in any way with my own team officials who made no excuses for their absence at my practice. Yes, the Olympics could be a little like high school.

Alas, the ridiculousness wasn't over. As we warmed up, the organizing committee had decided to air mini bios of each skater, flashing portraits of us on a jumbo screen and broadcasting thumbnail sketches of our lives through the stadium. As part of the second to last group, I skated with five other big contenders. Everyone's string of credits—like Brian Joubert's titles that included world champion and two-time European champion—sounded formidable over the booming loudspeaker.

And then came mine. I got on the ice and as my picture popped up, the announcer read: "Johnny Weir from the United States of America. Johnny speaks French and Russian. He has a TV show and enjoys fashion." I couldn't believe my ears. *Why do I have that?*

While everyone else had their hometown and skating credentials, my description sounded like a fucked-up singles ad. Johnny loves Bordeaux and long walks on the beach. No mention that I was the three-time United States national champion, world bronze medalist, or Grand Prix final bronze medalist. Nope, my whole life of dedicating myself to this sport boiled down to this fact: "Oh, he likes fashion."

Galina was laughing when I got off the ice, and I'm pretty sure a lot of other people were, too. But nothing could shake me. I was ready to literally show my life's work to the world.

I took my starting position for my program, which I had titled *I Love You, I Hate You,* a fairly accurate description of my relationship to the skating world. The music by Raul Di Blasio started out slowly in a reflection of my classical side, and feeling the beauty of the melody, I nailed my first three jumps. After I went into a spin, the music flipped into a dirty rumba, where I could showcase a spicier side. I wiggled my butt and started giving major face, flying through the steps and actually having fun. I flirted with the audience and the judges, and before I knew it, the whole thing was over.

After months and months of single-minded determination in the lead-up to the Olympics, my first moment on the ice was over, and it had been perfect. My astonishment gave way to excitement and a tremendous sense of accomplishment. Even Galina was happy. "Poker Face" came on the loudspeakers as I moved to the kiss and cry, and I danced in my seat to my celebratory anthem.

Then my scores came up and they were anything but a celebration. I had placed a shocking fifth, and there were still six more skaters after me. That meant I could wind up in a stomach-churning eleventh place. What had I done? What was wrong? I thought my skating had been podium worthy, and there were only a few times in my career where my perceptions and scores had not matched up. Galina, sensing my quickly surfacing outrage, said between smiling teeth for the camera: "Of course they did this to you. Don't be shocked. Just deal with it. The people love you and respect you."

The audience started booing and whistling. It was an incredibly harsh moment on the heels of such a feeling of triumph. While the fans may have loved and supported me, those in charge of the medals, and pretty much my value as an athlete, weren't buying it.

I ended up in sixth place after everyone competed in the short program. But it could have been a lot worse. Despite my poor placement, I still had a fighting chance for a medal. The pressure was on. In the long program, I would be the second to last skater in the entire competition, the opening act to Plushenko's finale.

But my scores were so low, I was barely ahead of people that had made mistakes and nearly fallen. It was a depressing hole to dig out of from a competitor's perspective.

I wasn't happy. What Olympic athlete, even one as weird as me, doesn't want to win a medal? Going into the long program, however, my main objective was no longer winning. How could it be? Instead, I wanted to take everyone watching me—in the building, on the judges' panel, on TV at home—on a journey. I wanted to make them all cry, or at least feel something. Making people cry was the goal of my free program from the beginning and the first way I described what I wanted to do to Galina.

The journey was my own. I had conceived of my long program, entitled *Fallen Angel,* as my life story on the ice. Throughout my career, there were high moments when everyone loved me, but the minute I fell, I plummeted to the lowest depths of hell. Soaring or broken, spinning or still, this was me for everyone to see.

Right before I took the ice for my final Olympic competition, I certainly had enough emotion in me to share with every member of the crowd. In quite possibly my last moment in the spotlight, the stress and passion of the last thirteen years turned into pure energy; my life flashing before me faster than a boy on skates.

"You can do this," Galina said. "You're the prettiest, the smartest, the strongest. Just let yourself do this."

Then there was just ice and the lights, and nothing else mattered.

Every arena is very bright and has its own special aura. But in Vancouver it was as if I were skating in a bubble of light. Like a moth to a flame, the light, which I normally shunned, drew me in and made me feel gorgeous.

Angelic voices sent me off on my final journey. The movements that I had honed in countless hours on the ice, and in countless more of deprivation off of it, carried me through the steps. Artistry took me to the end. Every person in that arena held his breath until the music and I stopped in a big flourish. As I lay upside down in a backbend, the ice became the sky, my trapped version of heaven.

I remained on my knees for a few moments, forever the supplicant, but when I stood up, I saw people were also standing, as well as crying. I got exactly what I wanted. At that point it didn't matter what result came up. It didn't matter what place I got. It didn't matter who was ahead of me. In that moment I felt like I was the Champion, the only one.

The rest is history. I placed sixth overall to boos and cries of outrage, and Evan took home the gold, the first American to win the Olympic title since 1988.

In sports, you have to come up with your own concept of victory, because you won't always win. Yes, I wanted recognition in my sport through medals. It hurt when all the years I had spent falling, hurting, bleeding, and crying got chalked up to my liking fashion. In the last four years of my career, the problem of my appearing like a flake worsened. People never talked about my skating. Instead, they talked about the crazy things that I enjoyed or said. I'm colorful and entertaining, but that's not all I am. As an athlete, I'm extremely competitive.

But I was able to leave any bitterness behind for my last Olympic performance. For whatever reason—and I'm not a big believer in a personal god—I felt that God was with me and all I had done up to then was leading me to that very moment. Having been beaten down so many times, I proved one more time that I always rose back up.

So this was no longer a competition. At least not for me. Obviously, realizing you aren't going to win is a hard thing for an athlete to accept. But as a person you have to take the victories where you get them. And my victory was showing my face. The Olympic champion got to where he was because he worked very hard, as I did, and played by the rules, as I did not. People that win may not always win on their own terms. Looking out at the Olympic ice, I had the honor of having arrived there on my own terms.

After the public and private outcries, shock, and ultimately acceptance, I left the stadium, and a chapter of my life, returning to my room in the quiet of late night. Tanith was already sleeping, so I tiptoed through the apartment and went into the bathroom.

As I began wiping the makeup off my face, I had my first chance to really look at myself. The eyes looking back at me almost seemed like they belonged to a different person. When they started watering, I thought the makeup remover was the culprit. I tried wiping them with a tissue, but soon enough I realized these were tears of emotion.

All I wanted to do was scream to release whatever was growing inside me. But I couldn't because Tanith was sleeping. So I got into the big stone shower, and, sitting underneath the stream of very hot water, let myself yell and cry as loud as I wanted. I was in there for more than an hour because I couldn't stop the flow of aggression, frustration, and happiness that I had pent up as a warrior.

When I got out of the shower, I had seventy or eighty voice mails and hundreds of text messages, but I only answered one. "Thank you, Mom," I texted. "I love you. I'm going to bed."

Although I was still crying softly, I had to get on with it. So I moisturized, watched half an episode of *The Rachel Zoe Project,* took an Ambien, and passed out.

First thing the next morning, I went to the condo where my family was staying. Walking into the house, it felt like a funeral had just taken place. I hadn't seen my mother since before my Olympic moment, and she was the first one to grab me. She had dark circles under her eyes from exhaustion and immediately upon seeing me, her lip started to quiver. Neither of us could speak because of those familiar tears that began to well up. Finally my mom choked out a small, tight "I'm so proud of you."

I moved on to the rest of my family, all of whom were crestfallen. My dad, brother, aunts, grandmother, and cousins, none of them knew what to say to me. It was just like when somebody's died. They all wanted things to be different, for me to have walked away with any color of medal as a material symbol that the last thirteen years of my life, and all of our lives, had been a success.

We just sat there and talked about everything, except what had happened the night before. "Oh, we have this cake from

Whole Foods," one of my cousins offered. "It's really good if you heat it up in the microwave."

In the middle of this strained attempt at normal conversation, my mother blurted out, "Johnny, I am so fucking pissed."

Everyone else went silent.

"Mom, you don't even have to talk to me. I know. I'm with you."

To be honest, I wasn't pissed at that point. It did break my heart to see my family so devastated, but perhaps the hardest part was that we didn't have a "next thing" to talk about. I didn't have anything planned or to plan. Galina and I had talked about my going to the World Championships a month after the Olympics, and we had practice time booked a few days later to begin training. But inwardly I had pretty much decided that I wouldn't go. It would crush me to have two events in one month where I did my best and didn't get rewarded for it. I didn't want to risk that kind of defeat.

For the duration of my time in Vancouver, I found it far easier to deal with the media than my family—a good thing since Tara had me booked for days from morning until night. The constant whirlwind of going from gigs to interviews, giving everyone my best Johnny flair, kept any kind of existential crisis at bay.

In the middle of the madness, Dorothy Hamill was set to interview me for *Access Hollywood,* but before filming started she said, "I have something delicate I want to talk to you about. Tell me if it's okay."

Two broadcasters from Quebec had said on air that I needed a gender test, because they didn't know if I was a man or a woman. They also complained that I set a "bad example" for boys who want to skate because parents feared they'd end up like me. Apparently they felt that my costume and body language made me a degenerate.

"Yeah, of course, it's fine," I told Dorothy. I didn't really think anything of it because it was just two assholes speaking in French on a small network in Quebec.

Boy, was I wrong. A whole new round of interview requests came in. Everyone wanted me to respond to these random guys calling me a woman—not exactly an insult in my book. I could have talked about it for hours; what did I care? But Tara didn't like my freewheeling style and had me hold a press conference to address the randoms in a more dignified and official manner.

Ten days after I had placed sixth, when I should have been a total irrelevance at the Olympic games, I walked into a room crowded with reporters looking for me to talk about two Quebecois frat boys. Okay, if that's what the people wanted, I was more than happy to oblige.

The funny thing is that I wasn't offended. I made it clear in the press conference that I hoped these guys didn't get fired, because I believe in freedom of speech and freedom of opinion. But I refuted the notion that I set anything but a great example for kids.

I'm not ashamed to be me. On the contrary, I think I turned

out pretty great and am proud of my individuality. I mostly had my parents and the caring and free way they raised me to thank. More than anyone else I know, I love my life and accept myself. What's wrong with being unique?

My speaking out was not just for the gay world, not at all. At the Olympics, I had received bucketloads of hand-drawn cards from kids, and I thought if there is one out there like me, but who doesn't have a supportive family or friends, then I owe it to him. So it was for gay kids, but also the kids who like science even if it's not cool, or kids who like to stand like a flamingo with one leg tucked up underneath for hours, as I did as a child. My message was for all the "weirdos" of the world.

I'm not sure I would have held a press conference like that before my experience at the Olympics where I fully realized the beauty and power in making a connection with others. Despite my heartbreaking loss, I was made whole again by having people say to me in letters or on the streets of the Olympic Village, "We went on this journey with you. We felt you." As clichéd as it sounds, their sentiment was worth its weight in gold.

My entire life came down to those ten minutes that I spent in front of the world in February of 2010. Whether alone, in front of a single person, or, like me, millions, everyone experiences an instant when one's essence is brought forth in a single act of bravery. To the universe, you say: this is who I am. In my performance I revealed my guts, my gusto, my heart, everything that I am. I showed my soul. Because of that, it was and will always be the moment of my life.

Epilogue

The ice is frozen, like always. The rink is cold and familiar. I am bundled in one too many sweatshirts, the outermost one with "Russia" embroidered across the back. Staring at a dozen children, all under ten years old, flying around the ice with a look that's a mixture of bliss, concentration, and a little bit of terror, I can't help but wonder what will become of them. What kind of people will they grow into? Will they have happy lives? Will any of them become an Olympic star? One of the children soars into the air to practice her single axel, crashing to the ice with an indignant thud.

Watching the girl brings me back to the first time I did an

axel. Only fourteen years have passed since my first foray onto the ice in the group of Orange Circles. Only fourteen years since I'd shed tears from the blistering cold of flying around on ice outdoors in the dead of winter. Only fourteen years since I'd turned my entire family's life upside down financially and emotionally for a dream. Only fourteen years to go from a nothing in a nothing town to a two-time Olympian and artist.

Even though it has been months since my greatest artistic breakthrough at the Olympics in Vancouver, I am still as regimented and tight-assed about my life as always. Old habits die hard. Because my public life is such a constant peacock display of insanity, my life behind the scenes needs to be as strict as a communist regime. I wake up early once a week and do everything I can possibly do to make my home a spotless oasis of serenity and glamour, including vacuuming my carpet and freshly mopping and Swiffering my wood floors. All the dishes are washed (the Fabergé crystal goblets by hand). The cupboards are fully stocked with only the best things Whole Foods has to offer. I do laundry and catch up on dry cleaning. The Louboutins are freshly polished. The photos and tchotchkes are shining with a new coat of Windex.

Everything is absolutely precise, a trait I learned from my father. Dinner happens before five p.m. Bedtime is promptly at ten p.m. And skating still takes precedence over all other activities.

My life at home is so concrete because a job pushed aside never gets done—and the only person who knows how to do the job correctly is me. So despite jet lag, preparing for a skating show, personal appearances, recording a song, or raising my family of Dingles (aka my closest group of friends), I never stray from a level of compulsion that most would find terrifying.

That side of me seems so opposite to my public persona—overly flamboyant, wildly optimistic, incredibly sparkly, and Liza with a *z*—that one could accuse me of being bipolar. But isn't every true artist a little crazy?

I only let colorful Johnny out on special occasions, like my recent twenty-sixth birthday.

To prepare for the big bash, my makeup professional, Joey from MAC, met me at Tara's Manhattan apartment to unleash my inner lady with a lot of product. Tara—who started using a cleaning lady because I can't prepare for anything in chaos and I'm in her apartment almost daily for one reason or another—applied her own fake lashes in her spotless bathroom.

As bottles of champagne chilled in the fridge, a hundred balloons wrapped in a giant plastic condom were delivered to me and released in the apartment. Joey fluttered his wrist in a final application of bronzer.

"Girl, you're gorgeous," he said, admiring his work.

"Thank you, Josephina!"

Tara trotted into the living room on five-inch stilettos, which made me proud.

"Are you ready?" she asked.

"I was born ready."

Twenty minutes later all the Dingles and other friends

started pouring into the apartment. Tara's boyfriend Marshmallow arrived followed by a slew of Russians. Paris came fashionably late with NicoFierce, just before my costume designer swooped in for a birthday eve hug. After lots of champagne toasts, the billion people, crowded into Tara's small place, crowded into a Hummer limo and headed to da club.

When I got out of the giant luxury car, I was greeted by a swarm of paparazzi and a club manager, who warned me "*Page Six* is here" and undoubtedly tipped them off. They were in good company. Inside, so many people had gathered to wish me well: famous fashion designers Chris Benz and Richie Rich, New York socialites, The Beauty Bears Eric and Joey. It seemed everyone had a "+7" next to their names on the list. *Come one, come all.* I don't party often, but when I'm in charge of the party, everyone is invited.

I fluttered around pouring champagne and chatting with everyone just like any mother would do. Out of the corner of my eye, I saw boys kissing boys, ladies grinding with drag queens, men having heart to hearts (I prefer soul to soul). Among the inexplicable fashions and inspired dancing, I stood alone next to a banquette, and in a quiet, shocking moment realized the fogged-up atrium was filled with people I loved. Each, in some way, represented a small piece of my soul, who I am deep down. The colorful, the demure, the bold, the clever. I looked closely at my family and friends for an image of myself, as they are my mirror.

Back in the rink, watching the child fall on her axel attempt, I'm faced with another kind of mirror. *Life is gonna knock you down a lot, honey.* I think to myself of all the times I've been knocked down. The betrayals of childhood friends, the numerous dips in my career, falling on quad attempt after quad attempt, being judged for things I had no control over, starving myself for the sake of art, and the list goes on and on. The common denominator of all those moments was the ferocity with which I forced myself to claw my way back up and move ahead. Fail on your first try at the Olympics? Go again and prove you aren't a quitter and you are tough as nails. Give the people in your life someone to be proud of but, most important, make yourself proud. Love yourself.

Love myself I do. Not everything, but I love the good as well as the bad. I love my crazy lifestyle, and I love my hard discipline. I love my freedom of speech and the way my eyes get dark when I'm tired. I love that I have learned to trust people with my heart, even if it will get broken. I am proud of everything that I am and will become. I am proud to have the honor of being born with the last name Weir (no matter our bad luck, it is my father's name). I love that I am my mother's son, and that she is my confidante and main inspiration in life. I love that I am a big brother to the gentlest soul yet the toughest exterior that is Boz. Yes, I love myself, and every time I fall down, especially when I fall down, I find that love again.

"JOHNNYCHIK! JOHNIK! CHEBURASHKA U NAS (OUR CHEBURASHKA)! GET BACK TO WORK! DAVAI!"

Like a voice from across Siberia, the sound snaps me out of my reverie. Distinct and knowing, rich and cultured, terrifying and loving, it's Galina Yakovlevna Zmievskaya cajoling me to continue skating. I glide away from the small girl who's now skating into another axel jump with that familiar look of anticipation that says, *Will I succeed or fail?*

A small smile breaks my porcelain exterior as I remember a young boy running across his backyard in a pair of hand-me-down ice skates, arms flailing wildly as he slides onto a frozen cornfield in the middle of nowhere, wrapped in snowsuits lovingly applied by his mother and, in his mind, imagining himself on the world's biggest stage, full of pride, honor, and love.

Acknowledgments

The list of people who I need to thank seems impossibly long and thanking them is simply not enough. I have undying gratitude and love for all of you, and I hope we can all continue to make each other proud and strong simply by being.

First and foremost I need to thank my legions of fans around the world. I would never be who I am without you. Johnny's Angels were the first real group to take shape, and I have been so honored to go on my journey through life with you and with your full support. Your group begat so many others: weir.ru in Russia, Johnny's Japanese Angels in Japan, and many others from China to Ukraine, France to South America. You all really are angels, in every sense of that word, and I am forever in your debt.

My family has been my greatest inspiration and support system since I came into this world, and they have never wavered in their love for me despite how difficult I can make it for them. My grandparents, Marcella and Robert "Puff" Moore and Faye and John Weir; my aunts Diane, Cindy, Terry, and Deborah; my uncles Joel and Bobby; my cousins Joel, Audra, Timothy, Stacey, and Shannon; and most of all my parents, John and Patti Weir, and my little brother, Boz. We have a giant extended family—and I wish they would give me extra pages to thank all of you by name—but you all know I love you and am thinking of you. You are all the light of my life.

My coaches and choreographers have given me the gift of sport and taught me about the world outside my small town upbringing and given me the freedom I so desperately crave: Priscilla Hill, Galina Zmievskaya, Nina Petrenko, Viktor Petrenko, Tatiana Tarasova, Marina Anissina, David Wilson, Elena Tchaikovskaya, Yuri Sergeev, Denis Petukhov, Melissa Gregory and Faye Kitariev. Thank you for helping me show the world what I am made of.

I would go absolutely nowhere without my amazing agent and resident Jewish sister, Tara Modlin. I often say that I am a rhino, and Tara is the little bird sitting on my shoulder and telling me about danger and triumph, and that analogy couldn't be truer. I want to also thank Tara's family and especially Grandma Connie, who is the original reason we got together. I love you, Taryuha!

I am possibly one of the most difficult friends to have, but my friends make up my inner circle, my confidants, the true loves of my life: Paris Childers, Christa Goulakos, Nicole Haddad, Michael Dudas, Christopher Gale, Jodi Rudden, Kelly Bailey, Dirke Baker, Bradford Griffies, Drew Meekins, Kendra Goodwin, Tanith Belbin, Irina Slutskaya, Evgeni Plushenko, Marina Anissina, Alexander Uspenski, Rudy Galindo, Sasha and Roman Zaretsky, Ksenia Makarova, Michela Malingambi, and many, many more of you who I love to no end.

Thank you to figure skating, and those who created a platform for me to perform, and inspire myself. Thank you to David Raith and Patricia St. Peter for being two angels among many devils. Thank you to the skaters, past, present, and future for giving us beauty and showing us what a real sport is.

I absolutely need to thank everyone who helped me on this project, otherwise it never would have gotten to the point where people could actually read it! Everyone at Gallery Books and Simon & Schuster; Patrick Price, my amazing editor; Jen Bergstrom for getting this project off the ground; Mitchell Ivers and Jessica Webb for shepherding the work in house. Thank you to Dan Strone, CEO of Trident Media Group, my amazing literary agent, who believed in me so much, and his assistant Lyuba DiFalco; and Rebecca "Lucky" Paley, my muse for this entire project, never wavering in her support or love for me, and, although neither of us "play well with others," became such a close friend and confidante. Thank you for believing in me.

It doesn't seem fitting to "thank" the people who have made

my life difficult or who have given me a fight every step of the way, but I salute everyone who has ever criticized me, not believed in me, or belittled me, for you are the ones who have given me a thick skin and made it possible for me to fight for everything I believe in and fight for those I love. You also have given me the will to succeed in every facet of my life.

I need to thank the visionaries and divas of the world for dancing to your own tunes and making it possible for the younger generations to have hope and strength to be unique. I gained strength from people like Elton John, Christina Aguilera, Lady Gaga, Ricky Martin, Alexander Pushkin, Rudolf Nureyev, Mikhail Baryshnikov, Edith Piaf, Karl Lagerfeld, and many more; and for your unknown contributions to my life I thank you.

A mother's love is what sustains us as humans, and I have the best possible image of what a mother would, should, and could be. Patti Ann Moore Weir is my mother, my best friend, and my constant cheerleader. She has been the greatest inspiration in my life, and will be that for me until my last breath. There are no words grand enough to thank her with. I love you, Mama.

Who Owns America?

Who Owns America?

Social Conflict
Over Property Rights

Edited by
Harvey M. Jacobs

THE UNIVERSITY OF WISCONSIN PRESS

The University of Wisconsin Press
2537 Daniels Street
Madison, Wisconsin 53718

3 Henrietta Street
London WC2E 8LU, England

1   3   5   4   2

Printed in the United States of America

Library of Congress Cataloging-in-Publication Data
Who owns America?: social conflict over property rights /edited by
Harvey M. Jacobs.
286 p.   cm.
Includes selected papers from a conference held in 1995.
Includes bibliographical references and index.
ISBN 0-299-15990-6 (cloth: alk. paper).
ISBN 0-299-15994-9 (paper) : alk. paper)
1. Land tenure—United States.   2. Land tenure—Government policy—
United States.   3. Right of property—United States.   4. Eminent
domain—United States.   5. Public lands—United States—Management.
6. Land use—Environmental aspects—United States.
I. Jacobs, Harvey Martin, 1952–
HD205.W53   1998
323.4'6—dc21   98-3321

CONTENTS

MAPS AND TABLES

Maps

Tables

PREFACE

This volume emerges most ostensibly out of a conference, but more generally out of the North American Program initiative of the Land Tenure Center (LTC) of the University of Wisconsin–Madison.

LTC has existed at the University of Wisconsin–Madison for over thirty-five years. Born in the turbulent and exciting 1960s, it has worked in developing countries on resource tenure and institutional aspects of rural development. Initially focusing the expertise of faculty and staff on Latin America, LTC has, over the decades, worked in every developing region of the world, including most recently in the newly democratic countries of Eastern Europe and the former Soviet Union. In all these places, LTC staff have undertaken research, policy analysis, and teaching from the point of view that decentralized and secure land tenure–individual, well-protected ownership and control of land, natural and environmental resources–has a direct relationship to issues such as community well-being, resource sustainability, and well-functioning markets.

In the early 1990s the governing board of LTC wondered if it wasn't time to bring the lessons of three decades home. That is, since the 1960s the idea has been that developed countries understood the "answers" to the questions of land tenure and policy, and the role of LTC was to bring these answers to developing countries. But by the 1990s, the board began to wonder if the issues facing North America were really that different than those LTC had encountered abroad.

The loss of agricultural land by African-American farmers in the South, conflicts over land- and natural-resource tenure rights between Native Americans and their neighbors and state governments (so-called treaty rights conflicts), the management of heavily polluted lands in America's cities for which no one wants to take responsibility (brownfields), the rise of the private property rights movement to challenge the environmental movement's call for increased regulation of privately owned land, and the increasing social and cultural conflicts over forests, urban-fringe agricultural land, and unique ecological lands, all mirror the types of issues that prompted LTC involvement in other countries.

During 1993 and 1994 LTC, with the aid of a planning grant from the

Ford Foundation, explored initiating a North American Program. At a planning conference held in Madison, Professor Frank Popper of Rutgers University congratulated "the Land Tenure Center of the University of Wisconsin with discovering a new country–the United States of America." Popper went on to relate how he became interested and involved in domestic land-tenure research in the 1970s, how he heard about LTC, and how, when he contacted the center for information, it had little of substance to share with him. His story was similar to the experiences of many at that initial conference, including some contributors to this volume; Popper's enthusiasm for LTC's new venture was widely shared.

That planning conference was followed by a national conference in the early summer of 1995, titled "Who Owns America?" Nearly three hundred scholars, researchers, government officials, and community activists from across North America (the United States, Canada, and northern Mexico) came together to share information and to advise the new North American Program about its possible shape and direction. As a prelude to the national conference, the North American Program's governing group commissioned a set of papers on key topics from recognized scholars and researchers. These papers form the core of this volume, supplemented by selected papers delivered at the conference.

Understanding who owns America is facilitated by familiarity with the concepts that underlie many of the chapters in this book. Among these are the "bundle of rights" theory of property and the role of federal law (specifically the so-called takings provision of the Fifth Amendment to the U.S. Constitution) in shaping private landownership and use.

In most Western countries, including the United States, land is conceptualized, fictionalized, as a bundle of rights or, as it is commonly discussed in the legal literature, a bundle of sticks. Ownership of land does not mean only the possession of the physical soil within a defined set of boundaries. For the purposes of the law and the economy, ownership means the possession of a recognizable, fungible bundle of rights, which the owner may use, sell, trade, lease, and/or bequeath. It is this bundle of rights that society recognizes as ownership. In theory, this bundle comprises rights such as the air right (the ownership of the air space above the legally defined parcel), the water right (the ownership of the water flowing over and under the legally defined parcel), the right to control access to the property (more commonly known as the right of trespass), the right to harvest natural resources (such as trees and minerals), and the rights to develop, sell, and lease the land in its entirety or to develop, sell, and lease selected rights.

In theory, when an owner owns all the rights in the bundle, he or she is said to have fee-simple ownership or freehold property. In practice, how-ever, no private owner ever has all of the rights in the bundle. Society, as expressed in the form of government, always reserves some of these rights, or some portion of these rights. For example, few owners expect to own the wildlife (fish, deer, bear, etc.) on their property and, thus, the right to har-vest them at any time and in any amount they please. Wildlife ownership and harvesting seasons long have been a right reserved to and regulated by the state (government). Government also reserves the right to enter onto prop-erty (to violate the right to control access) to carry out necessary social func-tions. Even given these reservations, private property ownership has long been thought of as consisting of a robust bundle of rights, relatively free of obligations to the state or others. In fact, the classic Latin phrase describing this state of fee-simple/freehold property is "cuius est solum eius est usque ad coelum et usque ad inferos"—whoever owns the soil owns all the way to heaven and all the way to the depths.

But, the composition of these rights is not static. Prior to the invention of air travel an individual private property owner's air right really was de-fined as extending "est usque ad coelum" (all the way to heaven). Thus, applying a late-nineteenth century definition of private property, newly in-vented airplanes were guilty of trespass when they passed through the air space of a landowner. Clearly, as air travel went from a novelty to a commer-cial enterprise, this definition of private property was no longer socially functional. To the extent landowners could claim trespass of their property by airplanes, air travel would become either too cumbersome or too expen-sive. So, in the early twentieth century, U.S. courts took from private land-owners their air rights above a certain elevation and reappropriated to the public bundle of rights air space above that elevation. In effect, the courts created a new commons where one had not existed. The creation of this new commons responded to changing social needs and was pushed, in part, by changing technology.

In the 1960s, changing social values about racial relations also led to a redefinition of rights in the private bundle. Ownership of a business is just like ownership of a house, and, in theory, the owner should be allowed to decide who comes onto the property by exercising his or her right of access. Therefore, a restaurant owner could decide whom to serve based on race, gender, religion, etc. After a change in social values, society removed from the individual property rights bundle the right to make that decision. Own-ership of a business no longer carries with it the right to exclude based on the owner's values.

What is important about this legal and economic conception of owner-ship is how it allows land to respond to changing social circumstances. If land is conceived of as a bundle of rights, then rights can be taken from or added to the bundle, and the very shape and content of those rights can change.

The second foundational concept is the role of federal law in shaping private landownership and use. Unlike most Western countries, the United States does not have a national land law. Instead, we have a provision of the Bill of Rights to the U.S. Constitution, adopted in 1791, which speaks to the relationship of government to private ownership.

The closing clause of the Fifth Amendment to the U.S. Constitution, known as the takings clause, is phrased as follows: *nor shall private property be taken for public use, without just compensation.* As legal scholars have noted, this phrase establishes four distinct concepts for U.S. law and policy–that private property exists, that it may be taken from private owners, that there shall be a class of uses known as public use, and that owners shall be reimbursed for any taking by means of just compensation. What is as important about this phrase as the concepts it establishes is the relationships between the concepts. As interpreted by the U.S. courts, the phrase means that private property may only be "taken" from a landowner when the use to which it will be put is a public use and the owner is given just compensation.

What *exactly* does this phrase mean? In the eighteenth century, it was clear. A takings was a physical claim on land for public purposes–land for a school, a road, or other public facility–and the owner was compensated. In early America, the taking of private land was not much of an issue. The new country had land in abundance, and it was the disposition of public land, not the acquisition of private land, that dominated the public agenda. Largely, this is how it remained until the twentieth century.

Beginning in the early part of this century, and gaining force throughout the century, U.S. society has moved to regulate private property with greater breadth and specificity. Local zoning may be the most well-known of such regulations, but a vast array of regulations exist, from the federal level to the local, which impact the free choices available to individual landowners as to how they may choose to use their land, their bundle of rights.

When the regulatory state first came into being, there was no question about what it was doing and what this meant under the takings clause of the Constitution. A regulation was not a physical taking of property for another, public use. In fact, zoning was validated by the U.S. Supreme Court in 1926, in part under the theory that it prevented public and private harms; that is, regulation was not an imposition on the private landowner but rather a reasonable restraint under modern interpretation of ancient nuisance rules.

But in this same period, the U.S. Supreme Court decided another case which laid the seeds for the dissenting view on this matter and showed how the courts, the legislatures, and the polity could be of two minds on the same subject. In 1922, the famous U.S. Supreme Court jurist Oliver Wendell Holmes noted that a public regulation can be so severe in the demands made on an individual as to constitute, in effect, a taking. What he did not say then, and what the Court has never said, is exactly when that occurs.

But the social debate about takings is clear. Many Americans firmly believe that ownership of private property means ownership of a full bundle of rights. "It's my land and I can do what I want with it" is a sentiment often expressed at public hearings around the country. For this set of owners, regulation of land as it affects individual property rights must either be compensated, as they believe is required under the Fifth Amendment, or not undertaken. For others, private property is socially defined and socially reshaped, neither sacrosanct nor immutable. For this second group, ownership is not just a matter of rights but also of responsibilities. One gets to exercise private use and control of land to the extent one acknowledges one's responsibilities to neighbors and others. For these owners, regulation of land is a reasonable way to balance the private and public rights in the ownership bundle.

Who Owns America? is divided into five sections. In the introduction, Professor Louise Fortmann's provocative essay, using the 1960s television show *Bonanza!* and several other elements of popular culture, frames a set of key issues in the area of domestic land tenure. As someone long involved in both international and domestic land tenure research and activism, she very directly takes up the question of what domestic land tenure research and activism can learn from the international experience.

In part one, "Private Property Rights and the Public Interest," four authors examine issues related to public regulation of private land, focusing on the recent emergence of the so-called anti-environmental/private property rights/wise use movement and its calls for greater individual freedom in private land use decision-making. Professor Dan Bromley surveys, in broad historical terms, the emergence of private property as a social institution in Western society. He argues that the complete individual freedom called for by the private property rights movement has never been the point of private property; instead, private property always has been about the relationship between the owner and other members of society, with government as the mediator between the two. Bromley speculates on the future of private property and predicts that the insertion of public rights into the private property bundle through environmental regulation is likely to continue. In the second chapter, I examine the structure and impact of the private property movement. I argue that their "wisdom" is partly attributable to their ability to understand (and exploit) strongly felt cultural symbols about the relationship of land tenure to other fundamental American values, such as liberty and freedom. Professor Don Last ponders what Thomas Jefferson might say about the private property rights movement, since members of that movement seem to invoke his words in its defense so frequently. Last is skeptical about whether Jefferson would have been one of the movement's defenders. Richard Castelnuovo ends part one with a detailed discussion of the efforts by the private property rights movement to use and expand upon provisions of the National Environmental Policy Act (NEPA) to achieve its goals. He argues that the structure and intent of NEPA are very different from seemingly similar legislation proposed by the movement, and he further suggests that the private property rights movement's claims for legitimacy under that act could be, in fact, as forcefully used against them. All four authors write from the perspective that the private property bundle of rights is neither static nor unchanging and is, as Bromley argues, created by society to fulfill its goals for land and natural resource management.

In part two, "Private Interests in Public Lands," the authors examine a set of issues related to public land management in the United States. Keith Wiebe, Abebayehu Tegene, and Betsey Kuhn from the U.S. Department of Agriculture look at claims about private property rights in the context of the evolution of federal land policy. They show the varied ways the federal government has been and continues to be involved in the creation, distribution, and management of private land tenure, and thus the complex intertwining of public goals and private ownership. Professor Arthur McEvoy highlights the conflict in the legal system, especially the courts, over the ethic that should prevail in the management of public lands. For most of this nation's history, public land policy has reflected a market ethos of land in active use. Only recently has an alternative ethic emerged, and the legal system is having a difficult time accommodating to new ideas. Professors Jess Gilbert and Alice O'Connor examine two public experiments in land reform in the United States to provide secure land tenure to poor rural residents. These experiments, in the 1930s and the 1960s, are used by Gilbert and O'Connor to show how difficult it is to do in the United States what we so often preach in less-developed countries. Entrenched interests that are well served by existing tenure relationships and a market ethos make explicit, redistributive efforts at land tenure reform extremely difficult. Finally, Professor Charles Geisler and Barbara Bedford look at one of the new "hot" concepts in federal public land management, the idea of ecosystem management. They want to answer the question of who becomes entitled; that is, who has land tenure? For Geisler and Bedford, as for most of the authors in this section, the public and private spheres are not separate. They coexist, actively creating one another, reflective of larger cultural values.

The issue of culture is the explicit focus of part three, "Land, Culture, and Place." Here the authors utilize the often underappreciated concept of culture to demonstrate its impact on land use, land management, and thus land tenure. Professor Sonya Salamon, who has written extensively on this subject, introduces the section by demonstrating the role culture plays in the land-use and land-transfer decisions of farm families. Salamon, drawing from her research on family farmers in the Midwest, discusses how issues such as land as a commodity or a resource, the rights of children to family land, and the social statement made by landownership reflect different ethnic and cultural values. Lynne Heasley and Professor Ray Guries look at the same issue but focus on forest land-use decisions in southwestern Wisconsin. Drawing from the perspective of the new environmental history, they look at tenure changes in the Kickapoo Valley to see what these say about larger cultural values and preferences. Professor Ron Trosper takes up the same matter as it impacts the land-use decisions in what he refers to as "Indian country." He discusses the different concepts of land tenure between Native Americans and European settlers and how certain traditional Native American institutions may provide a basis for more sustainable environmental management. The section ends with a chapter by Professor John Gaventa, a pioneer in contemporary domestic land-tenure research. Professor Gaventa was a leader in the pathbreaking study, *Who Owns Appalachia?* (published in 1983). Here he revisits and updates this study. Like Professor Fortmann, Professor Gaventa emphasizes a set of issues that are taken for granted in international development (for example, the relationship between decentralized ownership and a vibrant economy) and asks why these issues are so hard to bring to the fore in the United States. All of these authors stress the complexity of land and how its noneconomic characteristics are so often the source of social conflict.

In the final chapter, I ask "Who owns America?" That is, what sense do we make of what has been presented? It is the question most often posed to the North American Program. People—researchers and activists—want to know. Unfortunately, it is not an easy question to answer. Most often we do not have the right kind of data to answer the question in a meaningful and specific way. What we do know is that land use and land tenure is the source of social, cultural, and political conflicts. Just because the United States is a developed country does not mean that land-use conflicts here are less significant than in less-developed countries. Land is both a basic physical resource and a unique social and economic commodity. Land use and nonuse are pivotal to the economic and social health of rural areas, cities, regions, and the nation, and to the ability of individuals to acquire and maintain homes in stable yet vibrant rural and urban places.

In 1996, the North American Program of LTC received funding support from the Ford Foundation, the W. K. Kellogg Foundation, and the

Otto Bremer Foundation to fully engage the issues raised by the authors writing here and by the participants at our conferences. This volume is the first of what we envision to be many related products—books, reports, papers, conferences and courses—through which we further our understanding about land tenure in North America and, ultimately, who owns America, and how and why it matters.

July 1997   HARVEY M. JACOBS

ACKNOWLEDGMENTS

This book owes a debt to many people. I would like to thank a few of them.

Most immediate are several of my colleagues at the University of Wisconsin–Madison. William Thiesenhusen, director of the Land Tenure Center, deserves thanks for welcoming and facilitating the initiative for a North American Program. Gene Summers, director of the North American Program, breathed life into the program, blowing on fading coals when it looked as if the fire would go out. In the process, he taught me an invaluable lesson about the practice of program development. It is his "fault" that I took on the task of editing this collection, and to his credit he never got angry when inquiring how the various pieces of the project were moving along.

Kurt Brown, at the Land Tenure Center, served as the technical editor for this volume. I could not have asked for a more competent and collegial colleague. In fact, without his participation it is unlikely that this volume would have been born. With consistent good humor he gently kept prodding this project along, all the while bringing to bear his formidable skills as a writer and editor. *ANNAGRAPHICS* (Anna Storkson) creatively assisted in preparing all the maps that appear in this volume.

My now-retired intellectual mentors at Cornell University helped germinate the seeds I had about issues in domestic land tenure and policy. John Reps, Professor Emeritus of City and Regional Planning, saw more in my questions about land policy than I myself understood, and Howard Conklin, Professor Emeritus of Agricultural Economics, was forever tolerant, even curious, about the city planner so interested in the rural perspective. Together they introduced me to the intellectual issues, the scholars, and the history of land tenure research and activism in the United States. While we didn't agree on all that we studied together, we fully enjoyed arguing about it.

Finally, it is essential that I acknowledge the very deep and full debt of gratitude I owe my spouse, Susan. She knew me before I even knew about land policy, and continues to remind me that there is more to life than land policy. For over a quarter century we have traveled together, and she has tolerated, mostly with good humor, the roads we have found ourselves on. I savor the idea of our continuing travels.

Who Owns America?

Bonanza! The Unasked Questions: Domestic Land Tenure through International Lenses

Louise Fortmann

Property as a Cultural Touchstone

Readers over 40 will remember that no one on *Bonanza!* ever asked, let alone answered, questions such as: "So, how much land did the Cartwrights have anyhow?" "Just how did they get this land?" "Who used to own it and use it?" Property just never entered into it. "Forty acres and a mule" and a "man's home is his castle" have long been American[1] watchwords, reflecting property's role as a cultural touchstone; yet, American culture involves a tangle of contradictory views of property. On the one hand, property is viewed as flat and unproblematic lines on a map: tidy, two-dimensional property encountered in the offices of tax assessors and title companies. A moment's flipping of the radio dial, however, will get you

> I'm goin' through the Big D and don't mean Dallas,
> I can't believe what the judge had to tell us
> I got the Jeep and she got the palace
> I'm going through the Big D and don't mean Dallas.
> "Goin' Through the Big D"—Mark Chesnutt (1994)[2]

and

> That's my house and that's my car,
> That's my dog in my backyard,
> . . . .

This chapter first appeared, in a slightly different form, in the journal *Society and Natural Resources*. It is used with permission from Taylor and Francis 1996.

1. When I say American, I mean United States, the inhabitants of which unfortunately have appropriated the more inclusive word, American, as the adjectival form of their name.
2. "Going Through the Big D." Words and music by Mark Wright, Ronnie Rodgers, and Jon Wright. Copyright © 1994 Maypop Music, a division of Wildcountry, Inc. (BMI), EMI Blackwood Music, Inc. (BMI), Living Wright Music (BMI), and Songs of Jasper, Inc. Used by permission. All rights reserved. International copyright secured.

There's my kids and that's my wife—
But who's that man runnin' my life?
"Who's That Man?"—Toby Keith (1994)[3]

In these lyrics, property of many sorts plays prominently in individual identity and social drama.[4]

Property dramas are played out at the collective level as well. John Nichols' (1974) book, *The Milagro Beanfield War,* paints vivid pictures of community struggles over access to, control of, and meanings of water, land, and forest. These struggles are pictured in more literally sharp-edged terms in Clover's (1992) exploration of land seizure as a major theme in horror films. At a symbolic level, she points out, "A remarkable number of horror films turn on 'title disputes' between present living owners and past dead ones," representing perhaps the original "land seizure of fantastic dimensions" from the Native Americans (ibid., p. 134). More concretely, she makes the perceptive point that city-revenge films such as *Deliverance, Hunter's Blood, The Hills Have Eyes,* and *Prophecy* (in which urban/suburban characters on forays into the country have truly nasty experiences and respond in equally nasty ways) readily admit "urban crimes against the country (dammed rivers, stripped forests, dirt-biked and snowmobiled wilderness, mercury-filled lakes, irradiated rangeland) and by extension against those who have been economically dispossessed in the process" (ibid., p. 134).

The unasked questions of *Bonanza!* thus are asked in other far less comfortable genres. The struggles set off by the destruction of property, livelihoods, and culture that they describe have no place in the tidy settings of the tax assessor's office and the title company. Indeed, that is the whole point of these films (ibid.).

These examples from a television show, country-and-western lyrics, and horror films show that, although official discourse about property may seem clear-cut, a simple matter of contract, popular discourse gives a far more fluid, up-for-grabs picture. Popular culture expresses the "common" knowledge that property is mutable: stealable, destructible, and convertible.[5] Popular discourse poses the questions, "Who lost America?" and "What are they doing about it?" If we turn to the international literature, we see that it has much to offer in illuminating property relationships in the United States and the questions raised by popular culture.

To begin, Shipton and Goheen (1992, p. 307) note in their survey of

3. "Who's That Man?" Written by Toby Keith. Copyright © 1994 Songs of Polygram International, Inc. and Tokeco Tunes. Used by permission. All rights reserved.

4. Thanks to Mark DeWitt, Department of Music, University of California at Berkeley, who dragged these refrains out of his memory and provided the discography.

5. My thanks to Carol Clover, who articulated the role of property in popular culture particularly clearly for me.

landholding in Africa, that people use land "for many purposes: not just to produce the material conditions of survival and enrichment, but also to gain control over others and to define personal and social identities."

Some of the more general scholarship on property in the United States has been cognizant of these issues. For example, Morris Cohen (1978) enunciated the principle of property as sovereignty in a speech at Cornell University in 1927, and Post (1991) explores issues of privacy, personality, and property. But domestic land tenure scholarship has not always been as successful as the popular culture or even journalism (see, for example, Trillin 1976) in getting to the guts of the social relationships of property. In contrast, the international experience in studying land tenure has brought home to us the diversity of property arrangements, the diversity of ways in which struggles over property are conducted, and the diversity of ways we can look at property.

Six particularly important lenses emerge from international scholarship: property as social process, customary tenures, common property and community management of resources, gender, the complexity of tenancy relationships, and land concentration. While some of these have been addressed in domestic work, they often appear more consistently and in clearer relief in international work.

Property as Social Process

Property is process; therefore, to understand it, one must focus on the social processes through which people define and struggle over access to and control of property. Through this lens we can view three interrelated images of property: social networks, definitions, and narratives.

Social Networks

Not all land and resources can be purchased with cash. Access sometimes depends on social relationships. Perhaps the scholar best known for focusing on investment in social networks as a means through which both groups and individuals jockey for rights to resources, including land, water, and trees, is the economic historian of Africa, Sara Berry (1988), who points out that instead of investing in direct increases in productive capacity, individuals may invest in social relationships in the form of ceremonies, the careers of their children, or cattle for bridewealth in order to establish or reaffirm advantageous identities for themselves—identities that strengthen their claims to land and other natural resources. In some recent work on Ghana (Berry 1995), she has explored "political economy of indecision," in which she has argued that some land disputes are not meant to be resolved, there will always be a way to open another round of contestation. These are concepts that might be applied profitably to a number of ongoing land disputes in the United States prominently covered by media.

Definitions

Understanding the social process of property involves recognizing the importance of definitions: the definition of resources, the definition of control, and the definition of a claimant group itself (Shipton and Goheen 1992).[6] Peters (1987, p. 193) has highlighted the importance of the "power to define, to attribute meaning, and to assign labels" in the context of struggles over water points and grazing land in Botswana.

Orlove (1991) extends Peters' point into the visual sphere in his study of maps of reed beds in Lake Titicaca, which were the object of a struggle for control between peasant communities and the Peruvian state. Maps drawn by the peasants detail communities and their territories, communities that are presented as jointly controlling the whole region and its reed beds. Urban centers are omitted from the maps altogether. The state is visible only in the form of flags in certain community centers. In contrast, the state maps depict only communities that are inside the Titicaca National Reserve or which are incorporated into a state administrative structure. The area that resisted establishment of the reserve and state control of reed harvesting most fiercely is not even identified on the government map. These maps represent the state as controlling the reed beds. As Orlove (ibid., p. 31) points out in the terms of Anderson's (1983) concepts of imagined communities, these are two "very different imagined countrysides" coexisting on two different sets of maps and in the minds of two different sets of people— resident peasants and urban government officials. From the Buffalo Commons to the Oregon rainforest, it is clear that we have many contested places and resources that might benefit from Orlove's understandings of definition and the presentation of place and control.

The international literature also tells us that *who* is making the claim to control property is crucial and that a group can make itself into a more

---

6. Justice (1994) provides a wonderful example of the definition of both the human population of a community and its geographic boundaries through performance in medieval England. The three days before Ascension were the days when villagers paraded around the village boundaries with the village priest holding aloft the host at the back of the procession. As Justice notes, "The festivities were a communal mnemonic, preserving the precise definition of locality from year to year against insensible encroachments. The process made visible the community as a *population*—displayed the village to itself—while recalling and making visible the community as a *locality*, a place and a unit of production."

influential *who*. Moore (1994) demonstrates how the Tangwena people consciously nurtured their group identity as a strategy to regain control over ancestral land in post-independence Zimbabwe. In doing so, they played heavily on the enormous service their chief did for the now-President of Zimbabwe during the War of Liberation. The relevance of the importance of the creation and utilization of identity to Native American struggles for tribal recognition and control over land, to the nurturing of "cowboy" identity and culture in the struggle over federal grazing lands, and to the endless struggle over "who is local," is obvious.

Property and Narrative

A third part of the social process lens is narrative. Narrative is not altogether missing from the domestic literature. In her exquisite essay, "Property as Storytelling," Carol Rose (1990) points out the reliance of the Grand Old Men of Property Theory on stories to hold the awkward bits of their theories together. Then she describes how a storyteller, by structuring the audience's experience and imagination, helps to turn her audience into a moral community. Moreover, by structuring our experience of events, the storyteller in effect constructs our memories and consciousness so that we can draw on this new stock to act in the future. She concludes that in such stories we might find the roots of common property.

Whereas Rose is concerned with the role of narrative in an alternative theory of how property regimes arise, the scholarship from Asia, Africa, and Latin America opens a window onto the role of property in the nitty-gritty of everyday struggles over land, water, and forest. This scholarship illuminates the critical importance of the power to interpret or reinterpret historical events in order to legitimate claims to land (see Shipton and Goheen 1992). (Or, in Rose's [1994] terms, to persuade others that a property right is there.) It portrays everybody—the state, the elites, and the local residents—as constructing, reconstructing, and selectively using history and custom in struggles over property.

For example, Berry (1992, p. 335) details how local residents in West Africa used British colonial officers' interest in "tradition" to further their own interests and quotes an exasperated official's comment, "knowledge of ancient traditions is, in fact, small, but the manufacture of new ones has been raised . . . to the status of a rural industry." In Zimbabwe, Cheater (1990) traces the construction and reconstruction of varying myths of communal landholding by the government to buttress changing government policy and objectives over time. Peel (1984, pp. 113, 115, 128) describes the role of stories of the past in Ijesha land disputes, noting the tendency to "rework the past so as to make it appear that past practice has governed present practice." Fortmann (1995) shows the stories told by villagers and neighboring white commercial farmers varied in their telling of the same events and in the moral principles those stories presented to buttress claims to the same land.

International scholarship has taught us to look not just at statute and common law, but at the stories that are told about property—by governments, lawyers, ordinary people, novelists, filmmakers, and songwriters. It tells us to look at stories about more general "property themes"—what does property mean?—and at different versions of specific events told by different people. It tells us to look at the stories told by the poor and dispossessed and also at the stories told by the powerful to preempt the discourse of the powerless (Scott 1990, pp. 18, 45–47).

To date, such stories have often been the purview of the folklorist or the historian. A classic example is Ives' (1988) renditions of stories about the poacher George Magoon, stories that retain their emotive power to enunciate outraged property claims many decades after the event. The clear message of international property scholarship is to borrow the folklorist's lens and take a good hard look at property and land tenure.

Customary Tenures

A major concept we have brought home from overseas is that of customary tenures. International scholars have long known that the state is not the author of all law and that long-standing local practice can establish a customary law. And customary law, Bruce (1988) has pointed out, is dynamic and rapidly changing, especially in regard to land.

Although it is common to think that all U.S. property law is state-based, in fact customary tenures are common: the law of the open range (see Ellickson 1986; Hahn 1982), poaching (which can be understood as the exercise of customary usufructuary rights to wildlife), the allocation of lobster fishing grounds by lobster fishers (Acheson 1987), and so on. If we want to know how resources are managed and what the likely outcomes of that management are, then we need to learn to identify customary claims to rights.

The events in a California mountain community in the mid-1980s provide an excellent example. The town, normally a placid, conservative sort of place, was the site of three public protests in three years. One was a straightforward protest over the imposition of fees for cutting fuelwood on national forest land. The second was a straightforward environmental protest. The third was a straightforward anti-environmental protest. Most of the town was involved in all three protests. Obviously there's a puzzle here (or else the town had a real mental health problem). The solution to the puzzle was not psychiatrists, it was in understanding the protests not as struggles over environment but, using the lens from African land tenure scholarship, as struggles over customary claims to property rights—the right to use forest resources for the good of community residents. Once that was understood, it was clear that in each protest the community was defending customary claims to forest resources against outsiders (see Fortmann 1990).

This is hardly an isolated example. It is clear that customary claims and other "nonstandard" forms of property should become a more prominent part of our land scholarship.

Common Property

In his introduction to readings on property theory, C. B. Macpherson (1978, p. 3) identifies a major difficulty with the concept of property: that is, the treatment of property as being identical with private property. Indeed, if we return to the unproblematic, two-dimensional property in the tax assessors' office posited earlier, we will find that it is usually private property or state property. The notions of a commons (although it was a fine old New England custom) did not appear in U.S. property literature for years.

But numerous international empirical studies such as Cordell's (1989) study of the intricate and sophisticated fishing commons in Bahia, Brazil, Gilles and Jamtgaard's (1981) descriptions of real pastoralists' management of real commons (stunningly different from Hardin's [1968] imaginary ones), Leach's (1994) detailing of the use of forest and bushland resources in Sierra Leone, and Wade's (1986) research on grazing and irrigation commons in India have shown the variety of successful institutional arrangements for the management of common-pool resources.

This has opened the door to a wider recognition of existing and possible commons in the United States. In its wake have come the international examples of new community-based resource management regimes. Perhaps the best known of these are the Zimbabwean CAMPFIRE program, in which villages have been given proprietary rights to wildlife, with the result that poaching has dropped dramatically and local livelihoods have benefited from a new source of cash (Murphree 1991), and forest co-management in West Bengal (Arnold and Stewart 1991). Much could be learned from the international experience by those involved in emerging efforts in the United States to manage natural resources in "meta-tenures" that cross property boundaries, such as community management of watersheds, community co-management of natural resources with federal agencies, and cross-resource industry endeavors such as salmon fishers and timber operators cooperating to restore and preserve salmon habitat.

Gender

Work overseas has demonstrated that both space and tenure are often gendered and that women are often the losers in these systems, particularly when their status changes, as in the case of divorce or widowhood. Although specific circumstances vary widely, in general women have repeatedly been shown to be less likely to own or control land, to own smaller amounts of land, to have less security of tenure, and to feel less secure in their tenure (Hardy 1989; Davison 1988). Women often have to rely on the good graces of a male relative—a husband, father, or brother—to get access to land and other resources. They often use specialized spaces, including what Dianne Rocheleau calls the "spaces in between" for their production (Rocheleau and Fortmann 1988; Moore 1994). Poor women in particular frequently have been shown to have to rely on the commons for their livelihoods. "Household" has been shown to be a problematic concept (Guyer and Peters 1987) and the intra-household distribution of property rights to be a major arena of struggle (Carney and Watts 1990; Schroeder 1993).

If we return to our country-and-western lyrics for a moment, both the similarities and the questions we should be asking should be striking. Just how often does she actually get "the palace"? How often does she inherit it or the farm? And the equation of property in cars, backyards, dogs, women, and kids in the second song is almost too obvious for comment.

There is domestic work on gender and property. Francis Hill's (1981) work in the United States found that women were being excluded from rights in family farming corporations. Recent work has revealed that an increasing percentage of people who rent *out* farm land are now women, often widows (Rogers and Vandeman 1993). We must continue to look at such questions as, Do women and men manage their rental property with different economic or ecological outcomes as their goals? Do women and men get comparable rents from their tenants? And we need to look at the role of women in creating and managing the meta-tenures noted above.

The Complexity of Landlord/Tenant Relations

Most of us probably associate tenancy with poor sharecroppers falling farther and farther into debt to the landowner, yet international scholarship provides a more complex view. Krisnawati Suryanata's (1994) study of Indonesia's apple industry has shown that ownership of working capital can be more important than landownership. Her research has shown that, over time, the institutional arrangements involved in tree sharecropping have come to favor the tenant capital owners. She points out that "many fields have effectively turned into monoculture apple orchards and deprive the landowners of access to their land. Tree leasing contracts effectively become land leasing contracts as contract amendments buy out the residual rights of landowners" (ibid., p. 1574).

This has already been shown to be relevant in California's agricultural Salinas Valley, where, as Margaret FitzSimmons (1983, p. 320) tartly puts it, large agricultural tenant farmers have freed themselves of "the costs and impediments of landownership." Up to the end of World War II, landowners were able to require their tenants (who had long leases) to practice crop rotation and green-manuring, but as leases began to shift from shares of the crop to cash rents, the balance of power shifted, and, with it, environmentally friendly agricultural practices disappeared (ibid., pp. 259–261).

Clearly, we need to look carefully at the meaning and practice of tenancy.

Land Concentration

Table 1 shows three international and one domestic example of concentrated farmland distribution.

Why should we care about these sorts of land distribution? Again, the international literature is illuminating. In a case study of six countries, Griffin (1976) found that when the distribution of agricultural land is highly skewed, even if overall incomes (including agricultural incomes) are rising, the incomes of the majority of farmers either stagnate or fall, driving them into agricultural wage labor or sharecropping arrangements, which in turn drives down wage rates. Similarly, in a fourteen-country study using 1973–

Table I.1. Concentration of farmland ownership in four areas

Place	Date	Percentage of farmland owned	
Morocco	early 1960s	33% of farmland owned by 4% of households	16% of farmland owned by 48% of households
Guatemala	1950	72.2% of farmland owned by 2.1% of farms	14.3% of farmland owned by 88.4% of farms
Ecuador	1968	61% of farmland owned by 4% of farms	10.2% of farmland owned by 74.3% of farms
California	1970	58% of farmland owned by 25 owners	61% of farmland owned by 0.01% of commercial farmers

Sources: Griffin (1976, pp. 85, 162, 189); Fellmeth (1971, p. 6).

83 data, El-Ghonemy (1990) found, first, that the lower the concentration of landownership/holdings, the lower the level of absolute poverty in rural areas (irrespective of the level of a country's average income per head) and, second, that realizing high rates of agricultural growth is not conditional upon greater concentration of land and the dominance of large estates. Dorner and Thiesenhusen (1992) relate the quality and quantity of land held as well as security of tenure to out-migration.

These findings are clearly relevant to local economies and the dynamics of out-migration from rural U.S. counties. There are numerous examples. Some scholars argue that the Sagebrush Rebellion was as much a protest over the fact that *private* owners have locked up most western land as over the extent of federal landholding (Geisler 1993). Another example: the people of Plumas County, California, refer to their area as Plumas Colony. The natural resources are controlled by outsiders: big timber companies, the utility company, the U.S. Forest Service, and urban vacation-home owners. The people voice frustration over their inability to protect the natural resources around them or earn a sustainable living from them (Kusel and Fortmann 1991). Brown (1995) describes a steady out-migration of blue- and pink-collar residents from Josephine County, Oregon, at the very time that wealthier in-migrants were streaming in; they eventually put in place zoning that affected the ability of the poor to stay in the area. One of her respondents sums it up, "[My] one feeling is that our town got bought without us selling it" (ibid., p. 58).

In other words, here in the United States just as overseas, concentrated and/or absentee landownership, and land-use controls, affect the local quality of life and the ability of local residents to earn a livelihood and find a place to live. There have been a few studies done, often by political activists such as Fellmeth (1971) or the Appalachian Land Ownership Task Force (1981). We clearly need more. We also need to look at the social, economic, and ecological consequences of national and international patterns of land and resource control by transglobal corporations.

Conclusion

At the end of the long intellectual journey home, California and Oregon and Tennessee and Pennsylvania look a lot like Zimbabwe and India and Guatemala and Indonesia. In a globalized political economy, the need to use international property scholarship to illuminate our own issues and problems should be obvious. The similarities should tell us that we may need to join hands across international borders to solve some of the problems we have created with our own set of property arrangements.

References

Acheson, James M. 1987. "The Lobster Fiefs Revisited: Economic and Ecological Effects of Territoriality in Maine Lobster Fishing." In *The Question of the Commons: The Culture and Ecology of Communal Resources,* edited by Bonnie J. McCay and James M. Acheson, pp. 37–65. Tucson, AZ: University of Arizona Press.

Anderson, Benedict. 1983. *Imagined Communities: Reflections on the Origin and Spread of Nationalism.* London: Verso.

Appalachian Land Ownership Task Force. 1981. "Land Ownership Patterns and Their Impacts on Appalachian Communities: A Survey of 80 Counties." Washington, D.C.: Appalachian Regional Commission.

Arnold, J. E. M., and W. C. Stewart. 1991. *Common Property Resource Management in India.* Tropical Forestry Papers no. 24. Oxford: Oxford Forestry Institute, Department of Plant Sciences, University of Oxford.

Berry, Sara. 1988. "Concentration without Privatization? Some Consequences of Changing Patterns of Rural Land Control in Africa." In *Land and Society in Contemporary Africa,* edited by R. E. Downs and S. P. Reyna, pp. 53–75. Hanover, NH: University Press of New England.

Berry, Sara. 1992. "Hegemony on a Shoestring: Indirect Rule and Access to Agricultural Land." *Africa* 62 (3): 327–356.

Berry, Sara. 1995. "California and Africa—Conversations about Commonalities: Macrolevel and Global Factors." California and Africa: Conversations about Commonalities Lecture Series. February, Department of Environmental Science, Policy, and Management and African Studies Center, University of California at Berkeley.

Brown, Beverly. 1995. *In Timber Country: Working People's Stories of Environmental Conflict and Urban Flight.* Philadelphia: Temple University Press.

Bruce, John. 1988. "A Perspective on Indigenous Land Tenure Systems and Land Concentration." In *Land and Society in Contemporary Africa,* edited by R. E. Downs and S. P. Reyna, pp. 23–52. Hanover, NH: University Press of New England.

Carney, Judith, and Michael Watts. 1990. "Manufacturing Dissent: Work, Gender and the Politics of Meaning in a Peasant Society." *Africa* 60 (2): 207–237.

Cheater, Angela. 1990. "The Ideology of 'Communal' Land Tenure in Zimbabwe: Mythogenesis Enacted?" *Africa* 60 (2) : 188–206.

Chesnutt, Mark (performer). 1994. "Goin' Through the Big D" by Mark Wright, Ronnie Rogers, and Jon Wright on *What a Way to Live.* Decca DRNC-11094.

Clover, Carol. 1992. *Men, Women, and Chain Saws: Gender in the Modern Horror Film.* Princeton, NJ: Princeton University Press.

Cohen, Morris. 1978. "Property and Sovereignty." In *Property: Mainstream and Critical Positions,* edited by C. B. Macpherson, pp. 153–175. Toronto: University of Toronto Press.

Cordell, John. 1989. "Social Marginality and Sea Tenure in Bahia." In *A Sea of Small Boats,* Cultural Survival Report 26, edited by John Cordell, pp. 125–151. Cambridge, MA: Cultural Survival.

Davison, Jean, ed. 1988. *Agriculture, Women, and Land: The African Experience.* Boulder, CO: Westview Press.

Dorner, P., and W. Thiesenhusen. 1992. *Land Tenure and Deforestation: Interactions and Environmental Implications*. Geneva: UNRISD.

El-Ghonemy, M. Riad. 1990. *The Political Economy of Rural Poverty: The Case for Land Reform*. London: Routledge.

Ellickson, Robert C. 1986. "Of Coase and Cattle: Dispute Resolution among Neighbors in Shasta County." *Stanford Law Review* 38: 623–687.

Fellmeth, Robert C., ed. 1971. *Power and Land in California: The Ralph Nader Task Force Report on Land Use in the State of California*. Washington, D.C.: Center for Study of Responsive Law.

FitzSimmons, Margaret Irene. 1983. "Consequences of Agricultural Industrialization: Environmental and Social Change in the Salinas Valley, California, 1945–1978." Ph.D. diss., University of California at Los Angeles.

Fortmann, Louise. 1990. "Locality and Custom: Non-aboriginal Claims to Customary Usufructuary Rights as a Source of Rural Protest." *Journal of Rural Studies* 6 (2): 195–208.

Fortmann, Louise. 1995. "Talking Claims: Discursive Strategies in Contesting Property." *World Development* 23 (6):1053–1063.

Geisler, Charles. 1993. "Ownership: An Overview." *Rural Sociology* 58 (4): 532–546.

Gilles, Jere, and Keith Jamtgaard. 1981. "Overgrazing in Pastoral Areas: The Commons Reconsidered." *Sociologia Ruralis* 21(2): 129–140.

Griffin, Keith. 1976. *Land Concentration and Rural Poverty*. New York, NY: Holmes and Meier.

Guyer, Jane, and Pauline Peters. 1987. "Conceptualizing the Household." *Development and Change* 18 (2): 197–213.

Hahn, Steven. 1982. "Hunting, Fishing and Foraging: Common Rights and Class Relations in the Postbellum South." *Radical History Review* 26:37–64.

Hardin, Garrett. 1968. "The Tragedy of the Commons." *Science* 162 (December): 1243–1248.

Hardy, Mary Elise. 1989. "An Economic Analysis of Tenure Security in West Africa: The Case of the Senegalese Peanut Basin." Ph.D. diss., University of California at Berkeley.

Hill, Francis. 1981. "Farm Women: Challenge to Scholarship." *The Rural Sociologist* 1 (6): 370–380.

Ives, Edward. 1988. *George Magoon and the Downeast Game War: History, Folklore and the Law*. Urbana, IL: University of Illinois Press.

Justice, Steven, 1994. *Writing and Rebellion: England in 1381*. Berkeley, CA: University of California Press.

Keith, Toby. 1994. "Who's That Man?" on *Boomtown*. Polydor 314–523 407–4.

Kusel, Jonathan, and Louise Fortmann. 1991. *Well-Being in Forest Communities*. Vol. 1. Sacramento: Forest and Rangelands Assessment Program, California Department of Forestry and Fire Protection.

Leach, Melissa. 1994. *Rainforest Relations: Gender and Resource Use among the Mende of Gola, Sierra Leone*. Washington, D.C.: Smithsonian Institution Press.

Macpherson, C. B., ed. 1978. *Property: Mainstream and Critical Positions*. Toronto: University of Toronto Press.

Moore, Donald. 1994. "Contesting Terrain in Zimbabwe's Eastern Highlands: Political Ecology and Peasant Resource Struggles." *Economic Geography* 69 (4): 380–401.

Murphree, Marshall W. 1991. "Communities as Institutions for Resource Management." CASS Occasional Paper Series. Centre for Applied Social Sciences, University of Zimbabwe, Harare.

Nichols, John. 1974. *The Milagro Beanfield War.* New York, NY: Holt, Rinehart and Winston.

Orlove, Benjamin S. 1991. "Mapping Reeds and Reading Maps: The Politics of Representation in Lake Titicaca." *American Ethnologist* 18 (1): 3–38.

Peel, J. D. Y. 1984. "Making History: The Past in the Ijesha Present." *Man* 91 (1): 111–132.

Peters, Pauline. 1987. "Embedded Systems and Rooted Models: The Grazing Lands of Botswana and the Commons Debate." In *The Question of the Commons: The Culture and Ecology of Communal Resources,* edited by Bonnie J. McCay and James M. Acheson, pp. 171–194. Tucson, AZ: University of Arizona Press.

Post, Robert C. 1991. "Rereading Warren and Brandeis: Privacy, Property and Appropriation." *Case Western Reserve Law Review* 41 (3): 647–680.

Rocheleau, D., and L. Fortmann. 1988. "Women's Spaces and Women's Place in Rural Food Production Systems: The Spatial Distribution of Women's Rights, Responsibilities and Activities." Paper presented at the Seventh World Congress of Rural Sociology, Bologna, Italy, June 25–July 1.

Rogers, D. M., and A. M. Vandeman. 1993. "Women as Farm Landlords: Does Gender Affect Environmental Decision-Making on Leased Land?" *Rural Sociology* 58 (4): 560–568.

Rose, Carol M. 1990. "Property as Storytelling: Perspectives from Game Theory, Narrative Theory, Feminist Theory." *Yale Journal of Law and the Humanities* 2 (1): 37–57.

Rose, Carol M. 1994. *Property and Persuasion: Essays on the History, Theory, and Rhetoric of Ownership.* Boulder, CO: Westview Press.

Schroeder, Richard. 1993. "Shady Practice: Gender and the Political Ecology of Resource Stabilization in Gambian Garden Orchards." *Economic Geography* 69 (4): 349–365.

Scott, James C. 1990. *Domination and the Arts of Resistance: Hidden Transcripts.* New Haven, CT: Yale University Press.

Shipton, Parker, and Mitzi Goheen. 1992. "Understanding African Land-Holding, Power, Wealth and Meaning." *Africa* 62 (3): 307–325.

Suryanata, Krisnawati. 1994. "Fruit Trees under Contract: Tenure and Land Use Change in the Upland Java, Indonesia." *World Development* 22 (10): 1567–1578.

Trillin, Calvin. 1976. "U.S. Journal: Costillo County, Colorado." *New Yorker* (26 April): 22–132.

Wade, Robert. 1986. "Common Property Resource Management in South Indian Villages." In *Proceedings of the Conference on Common Property Resource Management, April 21–25,* edited by the Panel on Common Property Resource Management, Board on Science and Technology for International Development, National Research Council, pp. 231–257. Washington, D.C.: National Academy Press.

PART I

Private Property Rights and the Public Interest

Rousseau's Revenge: The Demise of the Freehold Estate

Daniel W. Bromley

In 1754, a Geneva-born gentleman residing in Paris entered an essay competition sponsored by the Dijon Academy. The academy had asked its respondents to address "the source of inequality . . . and whether it is authorized by natural law." Our main character was not unknown in scientific circles, having published, four years earlier, *Discourse on the Sciences and the Arts.* While he did not win the competition, the biting indignation he managed to muster in the face of the French Enlightenment drew attention to his efforts. One year later his essay was published as an assault on many of the precepts of early modernism.

One can well imagine the shock when, upon turning to part 2 of *Discourse on Inequality,* the reader encountered the following:

> The true founder of civil society was the first man who, having enclosed a piece of land, thought of saying, "This is mine," and came across people simple enough to believe him. How many crimes, wars, murders and how much misery and horror the human race might have been spared if someone had pulled up the stakes or filled in the ditch, and cried out to his fellows: "Beware of listening to this charlatan. You are lost if you forget that the fruits of the earth belong to all and that the earth itself belongs to no one!" (Rousseau 1994 [1755], p. 54)

I reveal no great secret if I suggest that the freehold estate is in a rather bad state. Just how serious is the threat can be assessed by the aggression of the many new organizations whose sole purpose is to celebrate and protect private property. Were the freehold estate secure, there would be no need for this type of reaction.[1] When power is secure and unnoticed, overt coercion

---

1. I have in mind here some of the more extreme actions in response to environmental regulations such as the Endangered Species Act. Landowners have been known to threaten to destroy certain species found on their land as a means to foil regulations aimed at habitat conservation. The Contract with America emanating from Congressional Republicans in 1994 contained a "property rights" clause that demanded compensation for reduced land values arising from regulations. Most of these new legislative initiatives have not been enacted. (See chapter 2 of this volume.)

is unnecessary. On the contrary, power is most tenuous when those well served by the status quo must undertake activities to shore up their current situation by threatening others (Dugger 1980). For much of U.S. history, the power inherent in the control of private land was secure and unnoticed.

We are now entering an era in which the subtle power that emanates from the control of private property is both obvious and tenuous. It is obvious because of the recent prominence of property rights groups in many political discussions, and it is tenuous precisely because these groups have—in their desperation—raised their voices. This apparent need to be shrill in defense of the freehold estate is rather stark evidence that the general public's commitment to thoroughgoing private property is in need of serious bolstering. As we teach students in law school, when the facts are not with you, raise your voice.

I want to explore some of the broad themes in the history of the freehold estate. One theme concerns the changing social role and significance of land over time. A second concerns the purposeful conflation of landownership with possessive individualism and freedom. John Locke enters here. I will then turn to the expropriation, indeed the distortion, of Locke during the age of exploration, conquest, colonialism, and full imperialism. This leads to the arrogance of individualism that is the underpinning—the moral "justification"—of the freehold estate. I will close with the observation that it is only now, practically a millennium since the Norman invasion of a rather small Anglo-Saxon island, that the nexus between land and governance is about to be broken. We are, you see, almost beyond feudalism. We are on the verge of becoming post-feudal, and the influence of those who own land is in its final stages of decline. And that is Rousseau's Revenge.

In essence we are discussing the social purpose of land. In the developed world, the future struggle over the ultimate social meaning of land will be carried out in an age of material abundance and situational scarcity. We will, in other words, be pondering the social purpose of land in an age of private wealth and public squalor.

To explore the changing social role of land I identify five broad eras in Western history. In the beginning—up to approximately ten thousand years ago—land is distinguished by its irrelevance. Hunting and gathering peoples regarded land as mere place and space. Not much social significance there. My second era saw a growing sense of group cohesion and the rise of what I shall call the social ownership of land. This was the period of the great city-states. Agriculture was an urban, not rural, activity. This second era came to a close when the Roman Empire began to crumble about fifteen hundred years ago. Out of its ruin arose a new institutional innovation of unforeseen complexity and sophistication. Although the word was not used at the time, historians have labeled this institutional complex feudalism. This is my third era in the history of land. I will spend some time on it because it is the precursor of the freehold estate.[2]

Whatever one might want to say about feudalism, the core idea was simple: governance through the intermediation of land. While history books tend to stress the military-agricultural dimensions of feudalism, the essence of the feudal complex was to solve what economists refer to as the agency problem down through a nested hierarchy. It helps to think of feudalism much as you might think of the governance problems facing, say, IBM. In feudalism, land was the instrument—along with local authority in dispute settlements—whereby the nascent centralizing state (in the name of the king) acquired coherence down through an articulated system. What we think of as classic feudalism arose around fifteen hundred years ago west of the Rhine and north of the Loire; we know the bulk of this area as Normandy. Within two hundred years, Charlemagne became the most prominent beneficiary of this system of governance, and the Carolingian Empire took feudalism to its most refined form. Finally, on Christmas Day, in the year 800, Pope Leo III affirmed the obvious and crowned Charlemagne as Emperor of the West.

Feudalism operated by picking out promising allies at the local level and elevating them above their neighbors. Ordinary vassals became super vassals and thereby acquired local authority and privilege. In Normandy, they were called counts, and they became the king's ministers and judges in the "counties." Ironically, this ultimate grant of authority and autonomy, along with the gift of land, created the very conditions for the demise of feudalism in France. Devolution diluted the unique claim to authority of the Carolingian kings. Less than one hundred years after Charlemagne became emperor, his second son, Charles the Bald, formally acknowledged a practice that had been underway for some time. When Charles left for Italy in 877, he issued the Decree of Quercey that formalized the loss of the most essential ingredient of feudalism: the right of automatic reversion to the king of the landed estate upon the death of a vassal (Keen 1985).

With the loss of reversion, Norman kings set the essential conditions for the rise of the freehold estate. While dues were still payable upon succession of the eldest son, and pledges of homage and fealty were still required, land began to pass from father to son without reverting to the king for his disposition. The more important aspect of this for our purposes is that governance through the instrument *of* land began to evolve into governance by those *with* land. By 987, just over a century after Charles the Bald's declara-

---

2. Excellent references for this period include Brooke (1961); Chadwick (1905); Denman (1958); Harvey (1984); Keen (1991); MacFarlane (1978); Postan (1973); Powelson (1988); Sayles (1950); and Tabuteau (1988).

tion, the first French king, Hugh Capet, came to the throne with feudalism so weakened as to be unrecognizable. These circumstances explain much of the regional autonomy and provincialism in contemporary France—quite in contrast to the much more centralized rule in England.

Within a short while, one branch of the Carolingians found fertile soil across the English Channel. With William's conquest in 1066, the structure of land control in England changed profoundly. In William's time, most land in England was held by the king, by ecclesiastical landlords, and by about 180 great barons. When, in 1086, William convened the suspicious barons at Salisbury and compelled them to swear fealty to him, he was addressing the agency problem in one quick step. Within two decades the grip of the great barons had been loosened significantly. Within a century of the conquest, alodial land had disappeared, and the doctrine of universal derivative tenure was accepted everywhere.[3] In other words, William understood that effective governance could not occur as long as barons held land while, at the same time, denying the ultimate primacy of his grant of those lands. He established in England the feudalism that his ancestors had lost in France.

The next several centuries saw two opposing forces in England. The centralization of political authority had important implications for the evolving individual control of land. While the barons and major lords were stripped of much of their prior autonomy over land, at the bottom of the social hierarchy individual autonomy over land was elaborated in important ways. At the upper reaches of the social ladder, land was not an economic asset but was, rather, a claim and an affirmation of both situation and location in the political back-and-forth that always characterized medieval times. The lords certainly did not wish to enter into land transactions for the obvious reason that no currency could compete with the benefits of land control. Money was not yet the stuff it was to become, and what possible transaction could tempt a lord?

Not so for the despised classes. Here the aggressive tenant, or even a mere subtenant, could hoard a few pennies now and then from the clever marketing of a surplus and acquire a strip here and there. Widows might sell, brothers might die and leave their tiny plot vacant, and, in due consideration, one could surely acquire the parcels of others. Markets in land were beneath the lord, but for the great unwashed every day brought opportunity for minor advance. When you are at the bottom, nothing is beneath you. And so the land market bubbled up from the very depths of post-Norman England (Denman 1958; MacFarlane 1978).

The second important event in the history of the freehold estate oc-

---

3. Alodial land is held without obligation of vassalage or fealty; it is the opposite of feudal land.

curred on June 15, 1215. While historians tend to regard the Magna Carta as a profound victory for the common man, there is another dimension of relevance to land and landownership. Specifically, the Magna Carta suggests just how far England had moved from classical feudalism toward a centralized state by the time William's great-great-grandson John Sans Terre (notice his absence of land) occupied the English throne. In particular, a contract such as the Magna Carta would not have been necessary under classical feudalism because feudal kings lacked the authority that was to reside with post-conquest English monarchs. The feudal structure was much too devolved and decentralized to require the sort of protest embodied in the Magna Carta. Governance collateralized *by* land in Norman times had evolved, once again, as it had earlier in France, to governance by those *with* land. The burst of English feudal revitalization under William and his sons soon gave way to the rise of a landed class intent on governance. The Magna Carta is testimony to this.

The various English kings succeeded more quickly than their French counterparts to assert centralized control over justice, while ceding greater economic autonomy to the peasantry. The full development of individual property rights in land occurred more quickly in England than elsewhere in Europe. Perhaps that is because even the lowest serf of pre-Norman times had always been a landowner. The Norman Conquest may have slowed the evolution to a freehold estate, but all of William's many castles could not prevent that process from moving forward.

What was the nature of this evolved ownership? Who owned the land? It would be easy to assume that it was the family group; yet, if we look more closely at both the de jure and de facto situation, as reflected in both legal textbooks and in the proceedings in the court rolls, it appears that this is a misrepresentation. Land did not belong to the family group, but to the individual. This was the case with both freehold and customary tenures from the thirteenth century onwards. There were no inalienable birth rights, either for the eldest child or any other (MacFarlane 1978).

By the middle of the fifteenth century, feudalism was gone from the English countryside. The great landlords had begun to take an interest in land as an economic asset, but this required some justification that went beyond mere meddling in the affairs of state. Two hundred years would pass before John Locke managed to legitimize possessive individualism over land. Whereas prior interests in land among the comfortable classes had been for the purpose of influence in the matters of state, Locke managed to link land to a more modern idea: liberty. To Locke, land became the essential instrument whereby liberty was to be attained.

The relieved acceptance of Lockean ideas among the landed gentry coincided with the age of exploration and conquest in the new world—to the everlasting detriment of native peoples who happened to get in the way of European ideas about manifest destiny. Locke believed that humans, especially Europeans, were endowed with an obligation to take possession of God's commons. By being endowed with natural rights in their person, the act of conquest and "improvement" converted the commons into the individual property of the conqueror. And while the natives might well have been roaming about on God's commons, they were not serious landowners. After all, they had not built any fences.

The followers of Locke found much comfort in this line of argument. Indeed, latter-day Lockeans find his idea absolutely mesmerizing. Proudhon was only half right: private property is not necessarily theft, but a lot of theft has ended up as private property. And that theft had a Lockean sanction in the name of natural rights. Even Thomas Jefferson gave this notion of institutionalized theft of the common lands of others a facade of respectability. After all, the Indians were not mixing much labor with the land. The various Homestead Acts were institutionalized versions of Lockean doctrine. Not only did the European immigrants to the United States mix a lot of labor with someone else's land, but when the original occupants protested, the settlers had a rationale for systematic annihilation. The Lockean myth served them very well indeed. But that does not make Locke right on logical, philosophical, or moral grounds (Christman 1994).

The period of great philosophical debates about individualism—what we now call the Enlightenment—happened to coincide with the formative years in the New World. Small wonder that we in America find full-blown acquisitiveness and possessive individualism so agreeable. It was during the Enlightenment that Rousseau, at the urging of his friend Diderot, had the audacity to attack individualism in general, and private property in particular. Meanwhile, in the new America, a form of feudalism, call it cryptofeudalism, was the order of the day. Once again governance proceeded intermediated by land. Today, we see the full extent of this in the declamations of various property rights groups that claim that any redefinition of the legality of their land-based actions requires that they be compensated from the tax receipts of the public purse. And so we find ourselves approaching the last of my five eras.

My argument—as suggested at the outset—is that this posturing by various groups is the best evidence of the imminent redefinition of property rights in land across America. The Lockean legacy had it very wrong indeed. Locke envisioned a helpless and overburdened individual cowering before the predations of a scavenger state. Everywhere he turned, monolithic power and greed posed a serious threat to the freedom and peace of mind of the yeoman or the struggling shopkeeper. This view, so prominent in the public discourse about property rights, starts from a flawed conception of the problems we face.

There are not two parties—the individual and a predatory government—in this plot. Rather, there are three participants. Let us call these me, the rest of you, and that third party who alone can mediate disputes between us. Property rights issues are not dyadic, the individual versus government; rather, they are triadic: my dreams for a piece of land I claim to control, your disgust at the thought that I may actually be able to realize my dreams on that land to your detriment, and this third party called "government." The dispute is between the two of us, with government as the arbiter of our conflicting and mutually incompatible interests (Bromley 1991).

This era in which we find ourselves is one in which society, once again, is trying to confront those who imagine that by owning land they have some special claim on the nature and direction of public policy. More than five hundred years after feudalism disappeared in Europe, those who own land still play an inordinate role in the machinery of governance; yet, just as happened in Normandy and later in England, this land-governance nexus is destined to be broken. This is Rousseau's Revenge.

In some respects, these current land-based struggles illustrate just how feudal we still seem to be. Landownership continues to forge a powerful and unique bond between the owner of land and the coercive power of the state. How else can we understand a Supreme Court decision affirming the payment of almost $1 million to a South Carolina landowner for being denied the opportunity to build homes on barrier islands that had actually been underwater for six years in the early 1960s?[4] How else can we understand the continual declaration of the economically comfortable that the primary purpose of government is to protect private property? How else can we understand the frequent claim that landownership bestows the compensable right to visit various social costs on the rest of us?

In feudalism, Alpha gave land to Beta so that Beta could be enlisted to control Gamma. That is the feudal dyad. Today, the Betas and Gammas are fighting between themselves about the social purpose of land and Alpha gets called in to mediate. Alpha (now the government) must protect the interests of one or the other.

It is essential to understand that things and circumstances are not protected because they are property. Rather, those things and circumstances that are protected become, by virtue of that protection, property. What I own depends on what you agree that I own, not what I assert that I own. Therein lies the social dimension of property. Forbearance is the essential

---

4. *Lucas v. South Carolina Coastal Council,* 112 S.Ct. 2886, 2904 (1992).

idea. It is what Kant (1991 [1797]) called *intelligible possession,* and it requires the application of pure reason. Intelligible possession exists in a civil society. In the absence of reason, one has mere empirical possession—a dog with a bone.

Some will no doubt imagine that the often extreme claims of the "property rights" groups signal an ascendancy of possessive individualism with respect to the landed estate. I suggest that these claims must be seen as signaling precisely the opposite. We are some decades into the full realization of Rousseau's Revenge and the indignation of property rights groups is clear evidence that they know something is afoot. We are well on our way to seeing land as it once was seen. That will constitute what I call the "social ownership of the landed estate."

Of course, coming so close on the heels of the horrors in the former Soviet Union, this may frighten us; yet, there is a profound difference between the social ownership of land, as we are coming to know it, and the Stalinist tyranny that the victorious West has labeled "socialism." Stalinism was not socialism any more than the coming social ownership of land is socialism. Labels are often used to scare politicians and the general public, but let us be clear: by social ownership of land I have something very simple in mind. We can grasp it with a few examples. At the moment, farmers must be bribed with cost-sharing arrangements and other subsidies to induce them not to cause serious soil erosion. Industry is helped along with various tax concessions to induce other desired behaviors. Other landowners are able to resist new institutional arrangements with a clear and beneficial public purpose. Social ownership of land would simply shift the liability structure in the other direction. We would not need to bribe farmers with tax dollars to take better care of the land. Rather, they would pay into the treasury if they wished to produce soil erosion as a by-product of their crop. And, in one of the most controversial aspects of contemporary land-use policy, landowners with unique habitats—or with endangered species— would not be able to extort us to pay them to preserve those environmental resources (Bromley and Hodge 1990).

The current fad among some landowners is to eliminate certain endangered animals or plants to preclude their land from being noticed as a unique habitat. There exists a monetary fine or a prison term of sufficient seriousness that this emerging trend of environmental terrorism could be snuffed out rather quickly. The larger question is where, precisely, did those who own land acquire the idea that they have the right to tyrannize society at large?

The current struggles over land arise from the fact that land in America has been asked to take on too much work in the service of civil liberties. In addition, land has become a substitute for other forms of personal savings. Land is, and long has been, a speculative commodity. Little wonder that individuals take extreme positions in their defense of the freehold estate. They apparently have come to believe that the word "free" in freehold pertains to the acceptable range of actions on the land rather than referring to the absence of feudal dues and fines for the king. Or, perhaps, they have come to believe that the word "absolute" in "fee simple absolute" refers, once again, to the extent of their ownership.

Social ownership of land will not drive farmers out of business, bankrupt small businesses, or destroy beachfront lots in South Carolina, but it would certainly redefine the cost-benefit calculation of many landowners. And it would get local units of government out of the extortion trap being set by the extreme property rights groups. These changes arise because of the evolving social context of land. The material abundance that now characterizes modern life in the developed world diminishes land as a productive asset and puts it instead in the center of situational concerns. Interestingly, this means that land in America is almost back where land was some ten thousand years ago—as space and place. Land in America is not territory, it is not dominion, and it is certainly not a bulwark against the coercive power of a king or predatory state.

Land—whether urban or rural, whether gorgeous mountains or rolling prairie—is simply social space. It figures, therefore, that social space should have the benefit of social ownership. This is not as radical as it may seem. We have already moved in this direction. Urban zoning has changed the presumptive rights bundle of land in very profound ways, and few people seem to notice or to care. It has been too long since there has been a serious look at who owns America, but the answer has been obvious for some time now: we all own America. Rousseau would be pleased.

References

Bromley, Daniel W. 1991. *Environment and Economy: Property Rights and Public Policy.* Oxford: Blackwell.

Bromley, Daniel W., and Ian Hodge. 1990. "Private Property Rights and Presumptive Policy Entitlements: Reconsidering the Premises of Rural Policy." *European Review of Agricultural Economics* 17: 197–214.

Brooke, Christopher. 1961. *From Alfred to Henry III: 871–1272.* New York, NY: Norton.

Chadwick, H. M. 1905. *Studies on Anglo-Saxon Institutions.* Cambridge: Cambridge University Press.

Christman, Jack. 1994. *The Myth of Property.* Oxford: Oxford University Press.

Denman, D. R. 1958. *Origins of Ownership.* London: George Allen and Unwin.

Dugger, William. 1980. "Power: An Institutional Framework of Analysis." *Journal of Economic Issues* 14: 897–907.

Harvey, P. D. A., ed. 1984. *The Peasant Land Market in Medieval England.* Oxford: Clarendon Press.

Kant, Immanuel. 1991 [1797]. *The Metaphysics of Morals,* translated by Mary Gregor. Cambridge: Cambridge University Press.

Keen, Maurice. *The Penguin History of Medieval Europe.* New York: Penguin.

MacFarlane, Alan. 1978. *The Origins of English Individualism.* Oxford: Blackwell.

Postan, M. M. 1973. *The Medieval Economy and Society.* Berkeley: University of California Press.

Powelson, John P. 1988. *The Story of Land.* Cambridge, MA: Lincoln Institute of Land Policy.

Rousseau, Jean-Jacques. 1994 [1755]. *Discourse on the Origin of Inequality,* translated by Franklin Phillip. Oxford: Oxford University Press.

Sayles, G. O. 1950. *The Medieval Foundations of England.* Philadelphia, PA: University of Pennsylvania Press.

Tabuteau, E. Z. 1988. *Transfers of Property in Eleventh-Century Norman Law.* Chapel Hill, NC: University of North Carolina Press.

The "Wisdom," but Uncertain Future, of the Wise Use Movement

Harvey M. Jacobs

Introduction

Nearly fifty years ago Aldo Leopold, a University of Wisconsin ecologist, penned what has become a modern classic of land and environmental literature: *A Sand County Almanac* (Leopold 1968 [1949]). In "The Land Ethic," the most well-known and often-cited essay in that book, Leopold bemoaned the state of people-land relations: "There is as yet no ethic dealing with man's relation to land and the animals and plants which grow upon it. Land, like Odysseus' slave-girls, is still property. The land relation is still strictly economic, entailing privileges but not obligations" (ibid., p. 203). He then laid out the need for an alternative relationship, an ethical relationship:

> The land ethic . . . enlarges the boundaries of the community to include soils, waters, plants, and animals, or collectively: the land. . . . A land ethic . . . affirms . . . [the] right [of resources] to continued existence, and, at least in spots, their continued existence in a natural state. . . . [A] land ethic changes the role of *Homo Sapiens* from conqueror of the land-community to plain member and citizen of it. (ibid., p. 204)[1]

When Leopold wrote this in the late 1940s, his ideas of an ethical relationship between land (environmental) resources and people seemed nothing but a philosopher's dream. Here he was contemplating an alternative relationship as America stood at the edge of its postwar expansion. The baby boom, the building of the interstate highway system, and suburbanization, not an ethical relationship to environmental resources, characterized the

---

1. For a contemporary, comprehensive examination of the ethical bases of and for land use, see Beatley (1994).

    These ideas of an extension of the ethical community to natural objects, and people seeing themselves as embedded within the natural community and but one part of it, are similar those espoused by a group of modern ecophilosophers known as "deep ecologists"; see, for example, Borelli (1988) and Jacobs (1995b).

country in the 1950s and 1960s. If anything, the American relationship to land in this period was even more exploitative than it had been in the decades before the war. Economic and spatial growth equaled a social sense of progress, and the needs of America's urban areas took precedent over its rural and ecological zones (see Jacobs 1989). A cultural predilection toward land exploitation combined with technological means (widespread ownership of automobiles and an inexpensive way to build single-family housing) and fiscal tools (widespread access to housing credit and steadily growing household income) to realize this phenomenon.

If in the late 1940s Leopold's ideas seemed to stand in opposition to the mainstream of American thought and action, within a generation it appeared that his dream was about to become reality. In 1969, twenty years after the publication of *A Sand County Almanac*, Wisconsin's former governor and then U.S. senator helped design a watershed event: Earth Day 1970. Earth Day is broadly recognized as having launched the contemporary environmental movement (Shabecoff 1993). Here seemed evidence that people cared deeply about environmental resources and were willing to demand individual and social action that reflected a new land ethic.

A few years after the first Earth Day, again in Wisconsin, the state supreme court issued a landmark ruling in the case of *Just v. Marinette County* (201 N.W.2d 761 [Wis. 1972]). This ruling turned upside down traditional American notions of private property. The court held that a landowner has no reason to presume use rights to land other than to keep it in its natural state (Large 1973). This ruling embodied a Leopoldian land ethic and became a holy grail to the emerging environmental movement (Stone 1974). Combined with an avalanche of environmentally oriented legislation of the same period, it seemed as if Leopold's land ethic was coming to be.

Now, a generation-plus after the first Earth Day, one of the social values which most characterizes the American people is widespread support for the environment. Public opinion polls consistently show that a significant proportion of the U.S. public identify with environmental values and back public policy action to protect the environment (Dunlap 1991). In fact, almost all politicians, regardless of political party, find it necessary to identify themselves as "environmentalists" of some stripe in order to have the necessary public credibility to run for and remain in office.[2]

This does not mean that the modern environmental movement has been

2. The Republican Party, which won national power in 1994 in part on a strong anti-environmental platform, used the occasion of the 1996 Earth Day to emphasize its sympathies for environmental values and its commitment to expunge anti-environmental action in its 1996, election-year legislative agenda.

without critics or backlash. On the political right, during the early years of the Reagan presidency, a movement emerged to attack environmentalism and environmentalists as elitist and out of touch with the values of the common person (Dunlap and Mertig 1991). Leopold seemed to have provided warning of this phenomenon. In the closing section of "The Land Ethic," he noted that "conservation is paved with good intentions which prove to be futile, or even dangerous, because they are devoid of critical understanding either of the land, or of economic land use" (1968, p. 225). To Leopold's list needs to be added the cultural meaning of land and its political power in the U.S. context.

At least initially, the response to the Reagan-inspired backlash was a surge of support for environmental organizations, with increases in membership, activism, and influence (Dunlap and Mertig 1991). As the 1980s ended, however, and the runaway economy of the period gave way to global economic recession, environmental values, policies, and programs were once again under attack. This time the attackers belonged to self-proclaimed, self-described "wise use/property rights movement" (Gottlieb 1989; Yandle 1995). According to the environmental community, the wise use movement is really an anti-environmental movement (Deal 1993; Echeverria and Eby 1995; Brick and Cawley 1996).[3]

The wise use movement is an umbrella for a broad range of groups disaffected with the current power of mainstream environmental activism. The movement's focus is promotion of a wise use alternative to what they characterize as the radical, restrictive focus of mainstream environmental policy. From a wise use perspective, current environmental activism and policy illegitimately fosters an anti-private property and anti-people focus (Miniter 1994).

With regard to private property, the movement characterizes environmentalism as seeking to create a form of late twentieth-century feudalism— a set of institutional relations where the individual will hold little freehold property and will instead be dependent on a central authority (government) to dispense use rights as it sees fit (McClaughry 1975; 1976).[4] Wise use advocates argue that freehold property is inextricably linked to the existence of a modern democratic state and that actions that increase the power of the state over the individual decrease the institution of democracy.

---

3. I use the phrases "wise use movement," "property rights movement," and "anti-environmental movement" interchangeably throughout this chapter. It should be noted that one component of the movement describes itself as "free market environmentalism" (see, for example, Anderson and Leal 1991).

4. This is precisely the line of argument in the *Just* case that the environmental community found so laudable.

The Beliefs, Structure, and Impact of the Wise Use Movement

The wise use movement emerged from a 1988 conference convened by the Center for the Defense of Free Enterprise. The center is the vehicle for the work of its two key employees: Ron Arnold and Alan Gottlieb. Arnold is the intellectual leader of the wise use movement.[5] He comes to it as a former Sierra Club member, knowledgeable about the values and strategies of mainstream environmentalism. In the 1970s, a decade before the anti-environmental movement took formal shape, Arnold wrote a series of articles in corporate forestry magazines in which he pointed out the need for an alternative activist movement to counter the political power of environmentalism (O'Callaghan 1992).

The tangible result of the 1988 conference was production of *The Wise Use Agenda* (Gottlieb 1989). The notion of "wise use" came into being as a conscious attempt to echo the early, turn-of-the-century debates within the environmental movement between John Muir, founder of the Sierra Club, and Gifford Pinchot, founder of the national forest service. Muir championed the sanctity of nature and the necessity for preserving natural areas; Pinchot pioneered utilitarian, multiple/wise use resource management (Fox 1985). Through this century their conflict has defined a major axis within the U.S. environmental movement. Reverberating with Pinchot's rhetoric, the preface to the *Agenda* states that humans "must find ways to use the earth wisely and find ways to understand that *the earth can be used wisely*" (Gottlieb 1989, p. xvii; emphasis in original).

The *Agenda* delineates a series of goals, which are tied together by the perspective that public lands are to be used actively for economic development and in economic production, and public actions that impact private property rights must be compensated. Among the top goals of the *Agenda* are opening all public lands to commercial mineral and energy production, allowing commercial clear-cutting of old growth forests on national forest lands, rewriting the Endangered Species Act so as to substantially weaken it as a tool for environmental protection, allowing oil drilling in the Arctic National Wildlife Refuge, promoting commercial development within the national parks, and establishing private property rights in lease-based grazing arrangements on public lands (ibid.).

The wise use movement itself is a coalition of local and regional groups

5. There are other prominent and significant activists and organizations in the wise use/property rights movement. I focus on Ron Arnold and the wise use movement because they serve as a useful lens with which to focus the discussion of the larger movement's intent and structure.

pursuing political action on the individual goals. At one point, wise use leaders claimed an array of five hundred constituent groups (Poole 1992). The influence of large corporate capital within the movement is significant, reflecting the support of mineral extraction, energy, agribusiness, and forestry corporations (Nixon 1992). One example is the funding and leadership of People for the West, a prominent member of the wise use campaign. According to one investigation, 96 percent of its funding came from corporate sources, and twelve of the thirteen members of its board were associated with the mining industry (O'Callaghan 1992). Other examples of this sort abound (Lewis 1992; Deal 1993). The annual meetings of the wise use movement are co-sponsored by groups such as the American Mining Congress, National Cattlemen's Association, Independent Petroleum Association of America, and the American Forest Council (Stapleton 1992).

The actual membership of the movement is hard to quantify. Wise use promoters claim an active membership of 5 million, with a pool of up to 120 million sympathizers; critics suggest these are self-serving, wildly inflated estimates (O'Keefe and Daley 1993). The movement's most sympathetic members come from the western states where the vast majority of public land exists and where some states are dominated by the land-use decisions of federal land agencies. The movement is not restricted to the West, though; significant wise use activities are documented in the northeastern and midwestern parts of the country (Burke 1992; Classen 1996).

Ron Arnold's rhetoric leaves no doubt as to the wise use movement's own sense of the importance of its mission. He has been known to say, for example, "Environmentalism is the new paganism, trees are worshipped and humans are sacrificed at its altar. It is evil. And we intend to destroy it" (Nixon 1992, p. 34). Evil, war, and destruction are consistent themes in his rhetoric about environmentalism and the environmental movement. Why? Because, according to Arnold, mainstream environmentalism has run amuck; it is wrecking America, in part by "trashing the economy" (Arnold and Gottlieb 1993). In fact, "If things continued like the way they were going, the environmentalists were going to destroy all industry and private property within twenty years" (quoted in Lewis 1992, p. 6).

Since its formation, the wise use movement has had formidable success. For example, professional land resource managers in the West have argued for decades about the need to coordinate management of public holdings in the greater Yellowstone ecosystem. Here the federal government owns lands used for parks, forest management, and as wildlife refuges. Even though these lands adjoin each other, planning and management efforts are not undertaken together. What would have been one of the most innovative efforts at integrated ecosystem management was derailed by the successful lobbying of private property advocates who argued that federal efforts were really intended to "take" private land (Stapleton 1993).[6]

Wise use/private property advocates also were the intellectual leaders behind President Reagan's Executive Order 12,630 in 1988 (Pollot 1989; Folsom 1993). This order, titled "Government Actions and Interferences with Constitutionally Protected Property Rights," required, in essence, preparation of a private property rights impact statement on all federal regulatory action. Bills put forth in the U.S. Senate and sponsored by the Bush administration sought to codify this order (Jacobs 1995a). These legislative proposals have continued unabated (Freilich and Doyle 1994; Jacobs and Ohm 1995).

Even under the Democratic Clinton administration, and before the Republican congressional victory in November 1994, the wise use movement had significant influence. Efforts to float grazing fees on federal lands to market levels have been hampered by its lobbying, as have efforts to close more federal lands to off-road vehicle use. Most dramatically, efforts to elevate the Environmental Protection Agency to a cabinet department, a key promise of the 1992 Clinton campaign to the environmental community, were aborted by private property advocates (Cushman 1994).

During 1993, the wise use movement targeted its national efforts upon the legislation to create a National Biological Survey and amendments to the Endangered Species Act. In each case, they attempted to insert a takings amendment that would ensure financial reimbursement to affected landowners for any federal regulatory action that substantially decreased property value (Adler 1994). In 1994, the 103rd Congress took up 22 separate pieces of legislation that were introduced to offer some level of protection to private property rights (Meltz 1994). Perhaps more significantly, the movement has been associated with efforts to get similar pieces of legislation passed by the states (Lund 1994; Marzulla 1995). In 1995, 101 takings bills were offered in thirty-nine states; in thirteen states these bills became law. Since 1991, 25 states have enacted laws for the protection of private property rights (Emerson and Wise 1997; Jacobs 1995a; Jacobs and Ohm 1995; Thomas 1996).[7]

But the wise use movement is not just focused on federal and state-level policy issues. This is a broad-based anti-environmental movement. One

6. See the preface of this volume for a discussion of takings. The specific social debate around takings has to do with the extent of regulatory action that may occur absent compensation. The more general social debate centers around the necessary integrity of landownership to the existence of a democratic society (Ely 1992).

7. The number of bills and the number of states in which they are being put forth has increased each year.

component, for example, is known as the county movement. Drawing upon a local experiment in New Mexico, members of the county movement are promulgating land-use plans for adoption in rural counties throughout the United States. These plans assert the private property rights of individual landowners as part of the normal culture and custom of the area and then direct local officials (such as the county sheriff) to undertake official action against any party (including federal officials) that seeks to commence action in violation of these county plans. In part, these plans are promoted based on provisions of federal environmental laws that direct federal agencies to take local plans into account in their own planning (Arrandale 1994; Jacobs and Ohm 1995). At least forty counties have adopted these plans, and upwards of three hundred (10 percent of U.S. counties) have shown interest in doing so. This is in spite of an explicit, well-publicized legal decision against the legitimacy of these plans.[8]

A common presumption is that the wise use movement is a 1990s version of the Sagebrush Rebellion—the antifederal public lands movement of the early Reagan years (Popper 1984). However, observers suggest that, while many of the underlying corporate-capital interests are the same, there is a qualitative difference (Stapleton 1992; Lewis 1992). The Sagebrush Rebellion was a blatant and disorganized effort by corporate interests and state legislatures to seek privatization of western public lands. The wise use movement is highly organized. Having learned strategy from environmental activism, the wise use movement's interests are now clothed in the guise of grassroots, populist citizen action, and its agenda is broader, speaking to a larger segment of the American people (Yandle 1995; Miniter 1994; Stapleton 1992; Lewis 1992; Baum 1991).

The grassroots authenticity of the wise use movement is challenged, however, by the actions of Alan Gottlieb, the other half of the Arnold-Gottlieb team. He is in the direct mail business and has long been associated with fund-raising for conservative causes. In a *New York Times* interview in 1991 he spoke about the need, from a business point of view, to create a new "evil empire" to replace communism (Egan 1991). His publishing firm, which distributes wise use books, also sells volumes on gun rights and the illegitimacy of the federal income tax system. Gottlieb acknowledges the movement's congruence with the broader agenda of the radical and racist right (O'Keefe and Daley 1993). Because of this, some citizen activists from groups that the wise use movement believe should be under its umbrella have refused recognition by or connection with the wise use coalition (O'Callaghan 1992).

---

8. *Boundary Backpackers et al. v. Boundary County, et al.* 913 P. 2d 1141.

Social Conflict over Private Property Rights

The wise use movement raises a set of genuine and important issues, both activist and theoretical. Wise users have an impact upon policy formation, an impact drawn from their theoretical presentation. Wise users are not wholly wrong when they suggest that contemporary environmentalism is premised on an evolution of private property rights.

One way to understand the contemporary (post-1970) environmental movement is to see it as a movement that has argued the social dysfunctionality of private property rights. From the point of view of environmentalists, land-use and environmental problems arise precisely because property rights are privately held and managed. As a result, individuals make land-use management decisions that do not take into account the broader public interest and a more expansive economic calculus. A litany of common land-use and environmental issues—farmland depletion at the urban fringe, wetland loss, suburban sprawl, downtown deterioration, etc.—have all been depicted as issues that arise from a version of "the tragedy of the commons" (Hardin 1968). In these instances, the tragedy is that individual landowners make decisions that are economically and socially sensible to them but are not judged to be as sensible to the broader public. From the environmentalist's perspective, the traditional solution to this situation is to take property rights from the private bundle and shift them to the public bundle—to "public-ize" previously held private property rights. The rationale is that by doing this, better land use and environmental decisions will result.

Yet the individualist social myth represented by private property rights resonates strongly with many Americans. The United States was settled by Europeans searching for religious and political freedom and the access to freehold land unavailable in Europe (Ely 1992). The cultural myth of freehold private property—the open spaces of the American West, the attitude of "it's my land and I can do what I want with it!"—define the American character as much as any characteristic. To be an American is to own and control private property. So, while public opinion polls show that environmental protection is supported by most Americans, many of these same citizens can be deeply disturbed by the public regulatory programs developed to achieve this goal.

That there should be social conflict over property rights is not surprising. Given the historical role of private property in U.S. social history and cultural myths, actions to establish a strong public regulatory presence are bound to meet resistance (ibid.). What is significant is the apparent strength and organization of the wise use movement as a counterforce to the environmental community. From a legal-historical perspective, though, there is a strong basis for suggesting that the wise use movement is on shaky ground. Much of its public policy thrust attempts to enshrine a particular concept of private property. It is a concept that sees private property as foundational to American democracy, where the individual's bundle of sticks should be kept as intact as is feasible, absent a compelling public need. This perspective is not without historical and theoretical support (McClaughry 1975; 1976).

There were intensive debates among the country's founders about the relationship of private property to citizenship and democratic structure (Ely 1992). Drawing from the writings of John Locke, the founders saw that one of the principle functions of forming a government was protection of property. As James Madison wrote in the *Federalist* no. 54, "Government is instituted no less for the protection of property than of the persons of individuals." Others, including Alexander Hamilton and John Adams, concurred. Adams (1851 [1790], p. 280) noted, "Property must be secured or liberty cannot exist. The moment the idea is admitted into society that property is not as sacred as the laws of God, and that there is not a force of law and public justice to protect it, anarchy and tyranny commence."

But this view of the relationship of property to democracy, and the assertion of property's primacy, was not monolithical. Also drawing from Locke, others saw the need for private property ownership to bow to social needs. Locke (1952 [1690], pp. 68–69) wrote:

> For it would be a direct contradiction for any one to enter into society with others for the securing and regulating of property, and yet to suppose his land, whose property is to be regulated by the laws of the society, should be exempt from the jurisdiction of that government to which he himself, the proprietor of the land, is a subject.

Echoing these sentiments were Thomas Jefferson, Benjamin Franklin, and others. As Franklin (1967 [1789], p. 59) noted with force, "Private property . . . is a creature of society, and is subject to the calls of that society whenever its necessities shall require it, even to its last farthing."

The history of public imposition on private property rights seems, ultimately, to come down in favor of the position taken by those who see private property as necessarily secondary to social needs. In multiple instances, society has re-formed the concept of private property reflective of new social relations and new technology. So, for example, southern slave owners were not compensated when their "property" (the slaves) was taken through emancipation, even though some sued for such compensation after the Civil War. During the 1960s, owners of commercial establishments lost their private property right to choose whom they would serve, once more reflecting changing social attitudes on race and human relations; again they were not compensated (Hecht 1964). And early in the twentieth century, when the airplane was invented, landowners lost their airspace for the greater public good of creating a navigable airway (Jacobs 1995a).

Bromley (1993) seeks to demonstrate how it is that the very nature of property originates with society and how society is never illegitimate in its action toward private property. Drawing from Kant, Bromley (ibid., p. 653) argues that the reality of private property is that "What I own is a function of what the members of the polity say I own—not what I say I own." When society's actions appear to represent a departure from a prior set of rules governing individual-social interaction, society is just articulating new rules, reflective of new social circumstances and necessities. Society is never obligated to any a priori rule structure. As Bromley presents it, property is a completely moldable social construct, established by society to fulfill social needs, and thus changeable as social circumstances require it.

As one example of this, Bromley notes the widespread acceptance of public actions that prevent a landowner from cultivating marijuana or running a house of prostitution. He ponders why this is socially acceptable but regulatory action to protect wetlands or farmlands is not. More precisely, he wonders why one action is not considered a violation of private property rights under the provisions of the Fifth Amendment to the U.S. Constitution while the other is (ibid.). Other scholars have noted that restrictions on private property are broad and long-standing, reaching back to the country's founding (Ely 1992).

Anticipating the sentiments that underlie the wise use movement, Bromley summarizes his position by acknowledging that "land use and environmental policy is contentious precisely because it joins claims of individual freedom and private property rights." He then reflects the environmentalist response by talking about the "myth of the overarching sanctity of private property" and by arguing that "the public cannot continue to be held hostage to the extortion that emanates from this view." He concludes that this myth and this view have "no basis . . . in economics, in philosophy, or in the law" (1993, p. 682).

Ultimately, the anti-environmental wise use movement presents a paradox. It is decidedly out of step with legislative and judicial trends throughout this century (Bosselman, Callies, and Banta 1973). In general, these trends have allowed for increasingly broad governmental reshaping of private property rights so as to achieve an ever-evolving and expanding definition of the public interest—a Leopoldian land ethic (Jacobs and Ohm 1995; Freilich and Doyle 1994). Legal and philosophical analyses supporting these trends emphasize the social basis and construction of private property.

But the "truth" of a legal/philosophical/political-economic analysis doesn't take away from the emotional power of private property in the

United States as a cultural symbol. It is this cultural symbol that is the driving force behind the wise use movement at all levels.

An Uncertain Future

What is the likely future of the wise use movement? Informed speculation on this matter can be drawn from several sources. One is the experience of a social movement with seemingly opposite goals—the European green parties, especially the one in Germany. The German Greens came together in 1979 from disparate, pre-existing social movements—the peace, feminist, and environmental being the most prominent (Boggs 1986). These movements set aside their differences for the advantage that a coalition offered them.[9] Much to their own surprise, they achieved rapid and significant success in the early 1980s and sustained this success throughout the decade (Hulsberg 1988). With success, however, came serious internal tensions about priorities. As Greens moved from the position of being critics outside the system to players inside the system who had to propose solutions and be part of governance, the party's coalition structure began to fracture. By the late 1980s, the party began to come apart and reform itself as several smaller parties (Doherty 1992). Like the Greens, the wise use/property rights movement is a coalition movement. It appears that what draws members of the coalition together is stronger than that which might drive them apart; yet, as with the Greens, the umbrella the movement has opened is so wide that tensions are bound to develop. Some already have.

Another basis for speculating about the future of the wise use movement arises out of the object of its activism. At the federal level, the movement has targeted the national laws that protect endangered species and wetlands. Often, the basis for these attacks are stories showing the burden these laws can cause to ordinary citizens. This effort, however, has proved less successful than anticipated. While the American public does not like unfair burden, polling data suggest that in considerable numbers they continue to support environmental policies and programs.

Thus, the thrust of the movement seems to have shifted to state legislatures. Here the movement has a different problem. To assail the legitimacy of government regulation is to assault the very fabric of state and local governmental activity. The object of the movement's ire often becomes zoning

9. In Germany, groups that organize as political parties and then receive more than 5 percent of the vote in elections become a formal part of the legislative body. Party status also provides access to federal funds, given in proportion to vote totals, and the credibility of presenting a public position under the auspices of a national political party (Schmid 1987).

regulations—that simplest but most widespread and long-standing of tools used by state and local governments to manage conflicting land-use relationships. The problem with attacking zoning is that property rights proponents forget that zoning was an invention of conservative private property rights forces in the early part of the century (Babcock 1966; Haar and Kayden 1989). Zoning was developed to protect threats to private property rights and property values from competing, nonregulated market forces, and it was defended before the U.S. Supreme Court as a reasonable exercise of governmental authority because it served the private property rights interests of landowners.[10]

Environmental proponents dub property rights bills "the pornography shop owner's Bill of Rights." Their point being that, without government regulation of property, land-use relationships would be subject only to market forces, and those forces would select land uses based on their highest and best use from a solely economic point of view. In the two instances where property rights bills have been put to public referendum, in Arizona in 1994 and in Washington in 1995, voters soundly defeated them by 60 percent to 40 percent margins in both states (Kriz 1996).

Finally, the movement's efforts to build support for its core issues suffered from the militia-linked terrorist bombing of the federal building in Oklahoma City in 1995. This tragic event brought the citizen-militia phenomenon to the eyes of the public. Stories appeared in national news weeklies about the network of radical antigovernmental forces in the United States. The wise use/property rights movement was listed as one of the affiliated activities. Clearly, this is painting the movement with too broad a brush. There are many dedicated activists within the movement with very legitimate concerns, grounded in sound theory, history, and abusive administrative practices. Yet, it is also true that there are elements of the movement that ally themselves with the agenda of the radical and racist right in the United States (Helvarg 1994; Dees and Corcoran 1996).

There can be no foregone conclusions about the future of the wise use/ property rights movement in the United States. The Greens in Germany have not been destroyed by their internal debates and difficulties; in fact, throughout Europe and the world, green politics is growing. Likewise with the wise use movement. Regardless of its affiliations, the corporate influence on its agenda, and even the forthright cynicism of one of its co-founders, the movement exists and has influence precisely because its message strikes a chord with the American citizenry.

Wise use is not a question of law or philosophy, it is a question of cul-

10. Zoning was found constitutional by the U.S. Supreme Court in 1926. In the prior decade, it had already spread throughout the country, and the decision only reinforced this trend (Haar and Kayden 1989).

tural myth and politics. The wise use movement taps into and exploits a cultural myth about private property that runs deep with the American people. With the birth of the wise use movement, the politics of environmental policy in the United States have become more sharp, more contentious, and more dimensional. The wise use movement offers a serious challenge to the realization of Leopold's land ethic. At least for the near future, this movement's influence is likely to grow, not weaken.

The prognosis for the long-term future is different, however. Long-term trend analysis suggests that while the movement is giving voice to an important component of Americans' myth about themselves as freehold property owners, ultimately the element of American culture that requires private property to be subjugated to social needs will prevail. While it is not clear when and if Americans will ever fully embrace Leopold's land ethic, in its fragmented, incremental way, the U.S. public sphere, at the local, state, and national levels, with the support of the American people, is likely to keep asserting socially based environmental concerns over those of private property.

References

Adams, John. 1851 [1790]. "Discourses on Davilia, A Series of Papers on Political History." In Volume 6 of *The Works of John Adams,* edited by Charles Francis Adams. Boston, MA: Little, Brown.

Adler, Jonathan. 1994. "Takings Cause." *National Review* 46 (24): 32–36.

Anderson, Terry L., and Donald R. Leal. 1991. *Free Market Environmentalism.* San Francisco: Pacific Research Institute for Public Policy and Boulder, CO: Westview Press.

Arnold, Ron, and Alan Gottlieb. 1993. *Trashing the Environment: How Runaway Environmentalism Is Wrecking America.* Bellevue, WA: Merril Press.

Arrandale, Tom. 1994. "The Sagebrush Gang Rides Again." *Governing* (March): 38–42.

Babcock, Richard F. 1966. *The Zoning Game: Municipal Practices and Policies.* Madison, WI: University of Wisconsin Press.

Baum, Dan. 1991. "Wise Guise." *Sierra* 76 (May/June): 70–73.

Beatley, Timothy. 1994. *Ethical Land Use: Principles of Policy and Planning.* Baltimore, MD: Johns Hopkins University Press.

Boggs, Carl. 1986. "The Green Alternative in West Germany." In *Social Movements and Political Power: Emerging Forms of Radicalism in the West,* pp. 170–221. Philadelphia, PA: Temple University Press.

Borelli, Peter. 1988. "The Ecophilosophers." *Amicus Journal* 10 (2): 30–39.

Bosselman, Fred, David Callies, and John Banta. 1973. *The Taking Issue: A Study of the Constitutional Limits of Land Use Control.* Washington, D.C.: U.S. Government Printing Office.

Brick, Philip D., and R. McGreggor Cawley, eds. 1996. *A Wolf in the Garden: The*

Land Rights Movement and the New Environmental Debate. Lantham, MD: Rowman and Littlefield.

Bromley, Daniel W. 1993. "Regulatory Takings: Coherent Concept or Logical Contradiction?" *Vermont Law Review* 17 (3): 647–682.

Burke, William Kevin. 1992. "The Scent of Opportunity: A Survey of the Wise Use/Property Rights Movement in New England." Cambridge, MA: Political Research Associates.

Classen, Larry. 1996. *Fool's Wisdom: An Analysis of the Anti-Conservation Movement in the Midwest*. Madison, WI: Wisconsin's Environmental Decade Institute.

Cushman, John H., Jr. 1994. "E.P.A. Critics Get Boost in Congress." *New York Times* (February 7): A1, A15.

Deal, Carl. 1993. *The Greenpeace Guide to Anti-Environmental Organizations*. Berkeley, CA: Odonian Press.

Dees, Morris, with James Corcoran. 1996. *Gathering Storm: America's Militia Threat*. New York, NY: HarperCollins.

Doherty, Brian. 1992. "The Fundi-Realo Controversy: An Analysis of Four European Green Parties." *Environmental Politics* 1 (1): 95–120.

Dunlap, Riley E. 1991. "Trends in Public Opinion Toward Environmental Issues: 1965–1990." *Society and Natural Resources* 4 (3): 285–312.

Dunlap, Riley E., and Angela G. Mertig. 1991. "The Evolution of the U.S. Environmental Movement from 1970 to 1990: An Overview." *Society and Natural Resources* 4 (3): 209–218.

Echeverria, John, and Raymond Booth Eby, eds. 1995. *Let the People Judge: A Reader on the Wise Use Movement*. Washington, D.C.: Island Press.

Egan, Timothy. 1991. "Fund-Raisers Tap Anti-Environmental Sentiment." *New York Times* (December 19): A12.

Ely, James W., Jr. 1992. *The Guardian of Every Other Right: A Constitutional History of Property Rights*. New York, NY: Oxford University Press.

Emerson, Kirk and Charles R. Wise. 1997. "Statutory Approaches to Regulatory Takings: State Property Rights, Legislation Issues, and Implications for Public Administration." *Public Administration Review* 57 (5): 411–422.

Folsom, Robin E. 1993. "Executive Order 12,630: A President's Manipulation of the Fifth Amendment's Just Compensation Clause to Achieve Control over Executive Agency Regulatory Decisionmaking." *Boston College Environmental Affairs Law Review* 20 (4): 639–697.

Fox, Stephen R. 1985. *The American Conservation Movement: John Muir and His Legacy*. Madison, WI: University of Wisconsin Press.

Franklin, Benjamin. 1967 [1789]. "Queries and Remarks Respecting Alterations in the Constitution of Pennsylvania." In Volume 10 of *The Writings of Benjamin Franklin*, edited by Albert H. Smith. London: Macmillan.

Freilich, Robert H., and RoxAnne Doyle. 1994. "Takings Legislation: Misguided and Dangerous." *Land Use Law and Zoning Digest* 46 (11): 3–6.

Gottlieb, Alan M., ed. 1989. *The Wise Use Agenda*. Bellevue, WA: Free Enterprise Press.

Haar, Charles M., and Jerold S. Kayden, eds. 1989. *Zoning and the American Dream: Promises Still to Keep*. Chicago, IL: Planners Press.

Hardin, Garrett. 1968. "The Tragedy of the Commons." *Science* 162 (December): 1243–1248.

Hecht, Neil. 1964. "From Seisin to Sit-In: Evolving Property Concepts." *Boston University Law Review 44* (4): 435–466.

Helvarg, David. 1994. *The War against the Greens: The "Wise Use" Movement, The New Right and Anti-Environmental Violence.* San Francisco, CA: Sierra Club Books.

Hulsberg, Werner. 1988. *The German Greens: A Social and Political Analysis.* New York, NY: Verso.

Jacobs, Harvey M. 1989. "Debates in Rural Land Planning Policy: A Twentieth-Century History from New York State." *Journal of Rural Studies* 5 (2): 137–148.

Jacobs, Harvey M. 1995a. "The Anti-Environmental, 'Wise Use' Movement in America." *Land Use Law and Zoning Digest* 47 (2): 3–8.

Jacobs, Harvey M. 1995b. "Contemporary Environmental Philosophy and Its Challenge to Planning Theory." In *Planning Ethics: A Reader in Planning Theory, Practice and Education,* edited by S. Hendler, pp. 83–103. New Brunswick, NJ: Center for Urban Policy Research.

Jacobs, Harvey M., and Brian W. Ohm. 1995. "Statutory Takings Legislation: The National Context, the Wisconsin and Minnesota Proposals." *Wisconsin Environmental Law Journal* 2 (2): 173–223.

Kriz, Margaret. 1996. "Taking Issue." *National Journal* 28 (22): 1200–1204.

Large, Donald W. 1973. "This Land Is Whose Land? Changing Concepts of Land as Property." *Wisconsin Law Review* 4: 1041–1083.

Leopold, Aldo. 1968 [1949]. *A Sand County Almanac.* New York: Oxford University Press.

Lewis, Thomas A. 1992. "Cloaked in a Wise Disguise." *National Wildlife* 30 (October/November): 4–9.

Locke, John. 1952 [1690]. *The Second Treatise of Government,* edited by Thomas P. Peardon. Indianapolis, IN: Bobbs-Merrill Educational Publishers.

Lund, Hertha L. 1994. *Property Rights Legislation in the States: A Review.* Bozeman, MT: Political Economy Research Center.

Marzulla, Nancie G. 1995. "State Private Property Rights Initiatives as a Response to 'Environmental Takings.' " *South Carolina Law Review* 46 (4): 613–640.

McClaughry, John. 1975. "The New Feudalism." *Environmental Law* 5 (3): 675–702.

McClaughry, John. 1976. "Farmers, Freedom, and Feudalism: How to Avoid the Coming Serfdom." *South Dakota Law Review* 21 (3): 486–541.

Meltz, Robert. 1994. "Property Rights Legislation in the 103 Congress." Washington, D.C.: Congressional Research Service Report for Congress no. 94–588A. July 22.

Miniter, Richard. 1994. "You Just Can't Take It Anymore: America's Property Rights Revolt." *Policy Review* no. 70: 40–46.

Nixon, Will. 1992. "Wising Up to Wise Use." *E: The Environmental Magazine* 3 (September/October): 34.

O'Callaghan, Kate. 1992. "Whose Agenda for America?" *Audubon* 94 (September/October): 80–91.

O'Keefe, Michael, and Kevin Daley. 1993. "Checking the Right: (Conservative Backlash Against the Environmental Movement)." *Buzzworm* 5 (3): 38–44.

Pollot, Mark L. 1989. "The Effect of the Federal Takings Executive Order." *Land Use Law and Zoning Digest* 41 (5): 3–7.

Poole, William. 1992. "Neither Wise nor Well." *Sierra* 77 (6): 58–61.

Popper, Frank J. 1984. "The Timely End of the Sagebrush Rebellion." *Public Interest* no. 76: 61–73.

Schmid, Carol. 1987. "The Green Movement in West Germany: Resource Mobilization and Institutionalization." *Journal of Political and Military Sociology* 15 (1): 33–46.

Shabecoff, Philip. 1993. *A Fierce Green Fire: The American Environmental Movement.* New York, NY: Hill and Wang.

Stapleton, Richard M. 1992. "Greed vs. Green." *National Parks* 66 (November/December): 32–37.

Stapleton, Richard M. 1993. "On the Western Front." *National Parks* 67 (January/February): 32–36.

Stone, Christopher D. 1974. *Should Trees Have Standing? Toward Legal Rights for Natural Objects.* Los Altos, CA: William Kaufman.

Thomas, David A. 1996. "The Illusionary Restraints and Empty Promises of New Property Protection Laws." *Urban Lawyer* 28 (2): 223–261.

Yandle, Bruce, ed. 1995. *Land Rights: The 1990s' Property Rights Rebellion.* Lanham, MD: Rowman and Littlefield.

Private Property Rights with Responsibilities: What Would Thomas Jefferson Say about the "Wise Use" Movement?

Donald Last

Introduction

Environmentalists support restrictions on uses of land that might adversely affect people or natural resources. Leaders of the "wise use" movement, however, contend that government land use controls are destroying America (Jacobs 1995). Accordingly, these leaders have urged a return to the views on private property that they say guided the actions of the founding fathers. Wise use advocates maintain that the nation's leaders of two centuries ago, including Thomas Jefferson, believed that social progress was dependent on "free enterprise" and that democracy could not prosper if economic freedom was restrained by government. They assert that the function of government, then and now, is to ensure citizens' rights to property as well as to life and liberty.

Jefferson, more than any other eighteenth-century American, has been identified as the father of democracy. He certainly was a champion of human rights and an advocate of government by the people. If he were alive today, what would he say about the wise use movement? It could be argued that he would be sympathetic to some of the views expressed by the movement's leaders, but it is debatable whether he would have agreed with all their dogma.

The Meaning of the Land Rights Advocacy Movement

Rarely do proponents of the wise use movement and federal resource managers find common ground regarding the common lands of the western United States (e.g., northern spotted owl v. old growth forests). East of the Mississippi, the debate between the protectors of private property rights and government regulators focuses on the issue of landowner compensation when economic value of property allegedly is "taken" by the government in its application of land use restrictions (e.g., *Lucas v. South Carolina Coastal Council*[1]) .

The wise use movement is characterized by its critics as a malevolent effort to gut congressional acts on endangered species, clean water, wild and scenic rivers, wilderness, and national forest management. It is said to be an ill-conceived attempt to perpetuate "give-away" public grazing and mining policies of the federal government. Some analysts view the private property rights movement as a misguided crusade (built upon the Fifth Amendment of the U.S. Constitution), the objective of which is to recapture private property owner rights "lost" through the enforcement of environmental rules designed to protect public health and safety. Opponents believe the landowning members of these "grassroots" groups, in some instances, are duped by resource extractive industrialists who would benefit from relaxations of public land management rules or from the weakening of private land use regulations (Rouse 1995, pp. 3–4).

In this chapter, I have combined the wise use movement with the private property rights movement and labeled the combination the "land rights advocacy movement." The gospel of the land rights advocacy movement includes a narrow view on the absolute rights of landowners and users. This message is preached by charismatic "patriots" who skillfully flame the fears of farmers, ranchers, and loggers by making dire predictions about loss of income or jobs brought on by excessive government control over land uses. Adherents of this movement not only criticize government regulators, they also blame the environmental community for its role in advancing rules that hinder resource-based economic activity.

Land rights advocacy groups have become a powerful force in shaping today's laws and administrative rules on public and private land management and likely will gain strength in this era of growing hostility toward perceived excessive government control over individual freedom. Therefore, the movement could be a potent shaper of resource management policy well into the next century; accordingly, it is important to become familiar with its goals and strategies.

An important step in this awareness process is a critical evaluation of the "patriotic American" principles upon which the movement is based. This chapter explores the beliefs of an acknowledged American patriot, Thomas Jefferson, and evaluates the degree to which his views are parallel with the views of persons who identify with the land rights advocacy movement.

1. *Lucas v. South Carolina Coastal Council,* 112 S. Ct. 2886, 2904 (1992). (See the preface of this volume, for a discussion of the takings issue; see chapter 6 for a discussion of *Lucas.*)

A Genuine American Patriot

Few will argue with the statement that Jefferson was among the most influential of the American revolutionaries. He contributed to writing the declarations on independence and human rights that continue to affect the lives of Americans today. Jeffersonian scholars have described him as "one of the greatest champions of human liberty in the history of any country" (Moscow 1960, p. 8), as the "guardian of democratic rights for the individual . . . and the states" (Koch and Peden 1944, p. xxxvi), and as a leader "fundamentally committed to the idea of a limited government through a written constitution" (Ellis 1986, p. 132).

Evidence of whether Jefferson would support or oppose the leaders of today's land rights advocacy movement is present in the records of his writing, speeches, and actions as they relate to landownership. Let us consider samples of these words and deeds from both his private life and public service.

Jefferson's Private Landownership Words and Deeds

Jefferson had a deep understanding of land tenure. This knowledge was grounded in theoretical and practical elements of landownership, use, and management. Most of his theoretical views about land and property reflected his readings of John Locke (*Second Treatise of Government* [1690]) and Sir William Blackstone (*Commentaries on the Law of England* [1768]). Jefferson subscribed to their view that humankind possessed certain natural rights endowed by the creator. Jefferson listed life, liberty, and the pursuit of happiness as the primary rights of humankind when he penned the Declaration of Independence. Notably, he used the phrase "pursuit of happiness" rather than the word "property" to characterize the third important right although he was aware that other documents of the time (e.g., the Continental Congress Statement on Rights and Virginia's Constitution and Bill of Rights) linked the rights of life and liberty with the right of property. By Jefferson's reasoning, "property was certainly embraced in the pursuit of happiness" (Donovan 1968, p. 141). Furthermore, Jefferson's use of the word "happiness put the matter on a moral plane; [while the word] property did not" (ibid., p. 142). Jefferson "did not and could not logically regard [property] as inherent and inalienable" (Beitzinger 1986, p. 89).

Much of Jefferson's law practice concerned disputes over boundaries, ownership, or transfer of land. He was intimately familiar with the land laws of England and France. To expand his understanding, he read about Roman laws on land tenure. As a practicing lawyer, he recognized that law and government served to enhance the liberty of some persons while limiting the freedoms of other persons. He certainly was not voicing an absolutist view when he wrote that property ownership involves a "right to what we acquire . . . without violating the similar rights of other sensible beings" (quoted in ibid., p. 89). He held the view that persons surrender some of their rights when they collectively establish a government that thereby becomes a greater force to protect the people's remaining rights.

Jefferson lovingly cared for the 16,000 acres of inherited land he owned.[2] He also was keenly aware of the land tenure practices of his countrymen, the Native American population, and the occupants of European nations where he traveled and lived. He equated landownership with economic and political independence (Scott 1977, p. 57). In his view, farmers were best equipped to maintain such independence. He envisioned a nation of many farmers, each owning at least 50 acres. Writing to John Jay in 1785 he said that, "cultivators of the earth are the most valuable citizens" (quoted in Koch and Peden 1944, p. 377), and that farmers, because of their self-reliance, vigor, and virtuousness, were wedded to the country's liberties. Such persons, he believed, would be motivated to guard their land as the tangible symbol of the freedom they enjoyed. Landownership also was important to Jefferson because, in his time, such ownership was a condition for persons wishing to vote.

Jefferson believed "property should be distributed widely and more or less equally among independent individuals" (quoted in McCoy 1986, p. 105) so everyone would benefit from using nature as a production resource. He once remarked, "The earth is a common stock for man to live and labor on. It is not too soon to provide by every possible means that as few as possible shall be without a little portion of land" (quoted in Koch and Peden 1944, p. 390). Jefferson encouraged landownership by the many and feared landownership by the few. Although he never advocated a forced redistribution of private property from the wealthy to the landless, he believed that

2. At a young age, he inherited 5,000 acres of land from his father. When his wife's father died, approximately 11,000 acres were added to his landholdings. Most of this land remained in a natural condition. The balance of his land was cultivated primarily to support his family and the more than one hundred slaves that lived and worked on his estate. He was a lifelong observer of the landscape and its natural forms, including the soil and plants (recording many of these observations in journals and in his garden book). Eventually, he gave up his law practice to concentrate on the management of his considerable landholdings. Despite his knowledge of land and nature, he was not skillful in the financial aspects of property management. Consequently, near the end of his life, he asked the government of Virginia to allow him to conduct a lottery to sell some of his land to satisfy outstanding debts. To raise additional funds, he also sold his personal library to the federal government and these volumes became the nucleus for the Library of Congress. Nonetheless, when Jefferson died, his debts exceeded his assets.

"legislators cannot invent too many devices for subdividing property" (ibid., p. 389). During his careers as lawyer and politician, he fought to change the laws basing inheritance on primogeniture, which tended to concentrate landownership, because he believed the abolition of that practice was vital to a republican society. He disliked the possibility that a land-rich aristocracy could evolve in America as it had in Europe.

Jefferson's Public Landownership Words and Deeds

Jefferson first came to appreciate government ownership and management of land as governor of Virginia. Later, he became involved with public land in a greater way while serving as president of the United States. This man, who envisioned a nation of many private landowners, orchestrated what arguably could be called the most important public land purchase in the entire history of the nation. It was President Jefferson who negotiated with Napoleon for the United States' purchase of the Louisiana Territory. After that purchase, he attempted to restrict the ability of speculators and fortune-seekers to obtain this public land.[3]

Jefferson's interest in the ownership and use of lands west of the Appalachians surfaced long before he led the effort by the federal government to acquire the Louisiana Territory. While a member of the Congress of the Confederation, he authored a plan for mapping, administering, and reserving some mineral rights for lands of the western territory to be ceded to the new federal government by the states. This plan became the foundation of the Land Survey Ordinance of 1785, which was superseded by the Northwest Ordinance of 1787. His ideas for the management, use, and privatization of public land largely "determined the development not only of the Old Northwest but of all the territories in American history" (Ellis 1986, p. 123).

Jefferson understood that, in response to changing conditions, it was sometimes necessary for government to intervene in the affairs of citizens and in the use of their property (Caldwell 1973, pp. 211–213). In times of warfare, he believed, the private rights of people could be sacrificed for the common good (Cunningham 1987, p. 38). For instance, during the Revolutionary War, Governor Jefferson authorized the confiscation of goods and property of private persons for the benefit of the American army. Many

---

3. Jefferson was eager to know how suitable these lands would be for settlement by farmers. Therefore, he commissioned Lewis and Clark to explore them—foreshadowing the time to come when the federal government would have large agencies charged with inventorying and managing public lands. During Jefferson's presidency, in fact, a federal land office was established in the Treasury Department.

years later he wrote that, when General Washington had besieged York-town, "he leveled the suburbs, feeling that the laws of property must be postponed to the safety of the nation" (quoted in Koch and Peden 1944, p. 607).

Jefferson on Private Property Owner Rights and Responsibilities

In a letter to Thomas Paine in 1789, Jefferson said the chief function of government was to protect and preserve property (Koch and Peden 1944, p. 479). While he thought of government as instituted primarily to protect the right of property, he also felt the people had a right to alter or abolish any government that destroyed this right (Donovan 1968, pp. 80–81) because the government derived its power solely from the consent of those governed (Cunningham 1987, p. 50). He had an interest in protecting the rights of persons from potential abuses of government authority and urged his coun-trymen to supplement the U.S. Constitution with a bill of rights as further protection against an intrusive government (Meltzer 1987, p. 197). How-ever, because he was representing the U.S. government in France when the Bill of Rights was written, he was not involved with its drafting (which included the drafting of the Fifth Amendment, limiting the "taking" of pri-vate property by the federal government).

Jefferson had a strict constructionist view of the U.S. Constitution and the Bill of Rights. Based on his interpretation of this central guideline for government action, he advocated actions by the states to check the power of the national government. Furthermore, he feared a national government that would become meddlesome. This view of limited government was a central theme in his first presidential inaugural address. Jefferson said, "A wise government . . . shall leave [people] free to regulate their own pursuits of industry and improvement and shall not take from the mouth of labor the bread it has earned. This is the sum of good government" (quoted in Koch and Peden 1944, p. 323).

Conclusion

Landowners in Jefferson's time (and ours) were entitled to certain use rights; however, these rights were never absolute (Bromley 1993). Owners were responsible not only to themselves for land-use decisions they made but also to neighboring owners and to those who would own and would be dependent on the land for many generations (Callies 1985). "The framers' efforts to directly and indirectly protect the interests of property owners did not, and were not meant to, preclude considerable public regulation of property" (Glendon 1995, pp. 184–185).

Today, environmental advocates hold the view that natural resource regulations *benefit* society. In contrast, wise use and private property rights proponents believe such regulations burden society. In fact, resource protection and management rules are both a benefit and a burden. Furthermore, individual rights regarding land use cannot be uncoupled from land-use responsibilities.

Based on my acquaintance with the beliefs of Thomas Jefferson and my understanding of the pronouncements of land rights advocacy groups, I have formed an opinion regarding the central question raised in this chapter. In understanding my answer to this question, readers must recognize that the nation in Jefferson's time was significantly different from the nation today. Jefferson and other national leaders were dealing with the problem of too much land and not enough people to make use of it. Today this situation is reversed. Jefferson would have found it hard to imagine a future time when ownership would be claimed for every acre of the New World. Nor could he have imagined the multitude of competing uses now possible on these lands. Jefferson did not foresee the establishment of today's pseudo-aristocrats, whose influence is based not on their lineage but rather on their controlling interest in multinational corporations. It is improbable that he would have anticipated the technological advances that have so greatly increased humankind's capacity to foul its own nest. In short, today there are more landowners in more places with more ideas about use of the land and who have greater ability to abuse the land, resulting in significantly more opportunity for landowners to threaten the health, safety, or welfare of their neighbors.[4]

Would Jefferson have been bothered by the large role that government today plays in controlling the uses of private property? He probably would be astounded—especially with the pervasiveness of the federal government in the lives of Americans. Nonetheless, he likely would support government measures to protect the lives, liberties, *and* properties of those citizens— including greater restraints on land practices that could prove potentially harmful to other landowners or to the land that serves as a basis for their livelihood.

Jefferson probably would not have considered himself to be a natural-

---

4. Temporal, spatial, and technological differences have brought on changes in attitudes toward private property ownership in America among most of its citizens (Large 1973). These contemporary beliefs have been translated into greater restrictions by government of individual rights to keep people from harming each other or each other's property (Jacobs and Ohm 1995).

resource preservationist (in the tradition of John Muir), but neither would he have thought of himself as a natural-resource exploiter. Jefferson favored responsible use of land as a means of economic production (in the tradition of Gifford Pinchot); thus, he was of the opinion that the rights of landowners can only be exercised to their fullest when coupled with landowner responsibilities—to the life-sustaining earth and to fellow citizens of the land.

Jefferson most assuredly would have objected to attempts by both environmental and land rights advocacy groups to gain popular support for their agendas with campaigns based on distortion or misinformation. He was committed to the use of reason and decisions based on verifiable facts. He would not have tolerated the exhortations of "sky is falling" environmental extremists. Neither would he have stomached the rhetoric of free enterprise fanatics who claim that the government, through regulating private property, is taking the bread from our children's mouths.

References

Beitzinger, A. J. 1986. "Political Theorist." In *Thomas Jefferson: A Reference Biography,* edited by Merrill D. Peterson, pp. 81–99. New York, NY: Charles Scribner's Sons.

Bromley, Daniel W. 1993. "Regulatory Takings: Coherent Concept or Logical Contradiction?" *Vermont Law Review* 17 (3): 647–682.

Caldwell, Lynton K. 1973. "The Jurisprudence of Thomas Jefferson." *Indiana Law Journal* 18: 193–213.

Callies, David L. 1985. "Regulating Paradise: Is Land Use a Right or a Privilege?" *University of Hawaii Law Review* 7: 13–28.

Cunningham, Nobel E., Jr. 1987. *In Pursuit of Reason: The Life of Thomas Jefferson.* Baton Rouge, LA: Louisiana State University Press.

Donovan, Frank. 1968. *Mr. Jefferson's Declaration: The Story Behind the Declaration of Independence.* New York, NY: Dodd, Mead.

Ellis, Richard E. 1986. "Constitutionalism." In *Thomas Jefferson: A Reference Biography,* edited by Merrill D. Peterson, pp. 119–133. New York, NY: Charles Scribner's Sons.

Glendon, Mary Ann. 1995. " 'Absolute' Rights: Property and Privacy." In *Let the People Judge: Wise Use and the Private Property Rights Movement,* edited by John D. Echeverria and Raymond Booth Eby, pp. 182–190. Washington, D.C.: Island Press.

Jacobs, Harvey M. 1995. "The Anti-Environmental 'Wise Use' Movement in America." *Land Use Law and Zoning Digest* 47 (2): 3–8.

Jacobs, Harvey M., and Brian W. Ohm. 1995. "Statutory Takings Legislation: The National Context, the Wisconsin and Minnesota Proposals." *Wisconsin Environmental Law Journal* 2 (2): 173–223.

Koch, Adrienne, and William Peden, eds. 1944. *The Life and Selected Writings of Thomas Jefferson.* New York, NY: Random House.

Large, Donald. 1973. "This Land Is Whose Land? Changing Concepts of Land as Property." *Wisconsin Law Review:* 1039–1083.

McCoy, Drew. R. 1986. "Political Economy." In *Thomas Jefferson: A Reference Biography,* edited by Merrill D. Peterson, pp. 101–118. New York, NY: Charles Scribner's Sons.

Meltzer, Milton, ed. 1987. *The American Revolutionaries: A History in Their Own Words,* 1750–1800. New York, NY: Thomas Y. Crowell.

Moscow, Henry. 1960. *Thomas Jefferson and His World.* New York, NY: American Heritage.

Rouse, Jon. 1995. "Freedom and Responsibility: What We Can Learn from the Wise Use Movement." In *Let the People Judge: Wise Use and the Private Property Rights Movement,* edited by John D. Echeverria and Raymond Booth Eby, pp. 1–10. Washington, D.C.: Island Press.

Scott, William B. 1977. *In Pursuit of Happiness: American Concepts of Property from the Seventeenth to the Twentieth Century.* Bloomington, IN: Indiana University Press.

Turning NEPA on Its Head: Assessments That Advance Property Rights at the Expense of the Environment

Richard Castelnuovo

Introduction

Opposition to environmental protection is not new, but the "wise use" movement has tapped mainstream support by attacking government regulations and their restrictions on private property use (Yandle 1995). Ironically, the movement has achieved success by imitating strategies pioneered by the environmental movement (Jacobs 1995). In particular, different factions have used the National Environmental Policy Act (NEPA) of 1969. Those seeking to enhance government control at the county level claim that NEPA requires federal authorities to "coordinate" their actions with local officials to maintain local customs and culture (White 1993; Miller 1993). Those seeking to strengthen protection of property rights have pursued assessment procedures that mimic those of NEPA's environmental impact statement (EIS) to restrain government actions that result in a taking of private property without compensation.[1]

Although it originated as an executive order in the Reagan administration, the takings impact assessment has realized its greatest success at the state level. State legislatures have considered bills with titles such as the Private Property Protection Act, which reflect the movement's populist theme of pitting the embattled citizen against overreaching government (Levinson 1994). Those crusading for takings assessment legislation see themselves as creating a charter for property rights in the same way environmentalists fashioned a charter with NEPA (U.S. House 1993). Groups such as the Defenders of Property Rights have worked to exploit positive associations with NEPA. As Nancie Marzulla of the Defenders observes, "I have a hard time seeing why anyone would object to this type of statute—it's really a 'look-before-you-leap' law" (quoted in Lavelle 1993, p. 1). With NEPA as

---

1. See preface, this volume, for a discussion of takings.

a point of comparison, the average citizen can fairly ask why the public should not hold government accountable for protection of property using the procedures that worked for protecting the environment. It is claimed that these measures, like NEPA, force accountability. The American Farm Bureau Federation, a leading advocate of property rights legislation, argues that such laws enact a form of procedural accounting that would produce truth in the cost of government regulation, similar to the protection society receives through truth-in-lending and truth-in-advertising laws (U.S. House 1993).

Yet the difference between the two far outweighs a superficial resemblance, as the Audubon Society's John Echeverria has emphatically pointed out (U.S. House 1993). Takings assessments turn NEPA on its head by converting procedures originally designed to protect the environment into a weapon to dismantle environmental protections.

A critical examination shows that takings assessment laws are disingenuously trading on NEPA's good name. It is vital to clarify the distinctions between the two types of assessments. It is particularly important to understand assessment laws because they are more appealing, but potentially more costly, than property protection legislation that proposes to enhance compensation for diminished land value (Elder 1995).

Assessing the Assessment Schemes

In the 1960s, the government was ill-equipped to respond to the rising tide of environmental concerns (Sax 1970). NEPA filled this void, introducing a disciplined structure for evaluating environmental impacts, opening new channels of communication, infusing new values and perspectives into agency decision-making, and erecting new standards of accountability. Since passage of NEPA, federal and state governments have used impact analyses to tackle a series of problems related to energy, inflation, economics, employment, and discrimination. In particular, President Reagan used this technique to re-direct agency behavior. Takings impact analysis first took form in President Reagan's 1988 Executive Order 12,630, "Governmental Actions and Interference with Constitutionally Protected Property Rights." The order was issued ostensibly to avoid unplanned takings of private property, thereby protecting the public fisc. The directions provided federal agencies the opportunity to go beyond a statement of takings law and attempt to advance concepts of regulatory takings not endorsed by courts. The order invented the term "takings implications" to cover actions that do not fit what courts have said amounts to a taking. Agencies are required to document their assessment of takings risks in internal written records known as takings impact analyses (TIAs). TIAs must "estimate, to the extent possible, the potential cost to the government in the event that a court later determines that an action constitutes a taking" (*Attorney General's Guidelines* 1988, p. 35; see also Folsom 1993). National organizations such as the Defenders of Property Rights and the American Legislative Exchange Council have trumpeted the order as a model for state legislation (Pollot 1989). State takings assessment laws, however, have not been equipped with the mechanisms found in NEPA that improve agency decision-making (Herz 1993).

Filling a Void or Adding Red Tape?

NEPA filled a void that courts and administrative agencies pursuing traditional approaches were unable to address. Administrative agencies narrowly defined public interests based on a single-minded view of their mission, regulatory approaches could not accommodate the complicated variables presented by environmental impacts, and courts lacked the institutional capacity to effectively intervene to protect the environment because they were required to settle disputes immediately before them and, therefore, could not generate the searching inquiry needed to assemble the broad spectrum of scientific and technical information essential to understanding the environmental consequences of a planned action.

NEPA's process of open-ended inquiry offers an alternative that is well suited to tackling impact problems. According to the ecological model, human interaction with natural systems must be understood from a holistic perspective, recognizing that everything is related. The causal chain is not linear; initial impacts ripple with long-term consequences. Freed from the demands of crisis management, NEPA permits decision-makers to go beyond present impacts and look into the future, enabling them to draw a picture of possible cumulative impacts.

Responding to property claims is basically a matter of routine judicial adjudication. A typical regulatory takings case involves an ad hoc balance of interests related to a specific place at a specific time. Takings cases do not benefit from abstract thinking. An unfocused inquiry greatly complicates legal analysis because court decisions over the course of seventy years have avoided establishing any set formula for determining when a regulation is a taking.[2] Courts specialize in resolving fact-intensive disputes. Judges are accustomed to settling economic issues involving real property, including impacts on property values. Even staunch property rights advocates ac-

---

2. *Lucas v. South Carolina Coastal Council*, 505 U.S. 1003,1015 (1992).

knowledge the value of painstaking factual inquiry by judges, including visits to the places in dispute, "which enhances their ability to speak authoritatively about the effects of the government's regulatory schemes upon private property" (Marzulla and Marzulla 1990, p. 550).

Those pushing takings legislation have invented a phantom problem. According to its originators, Executive Order 12,630 was prompted by ominous signs in the Supreme Court and outstanding takings claims against the government in the neighborhood of $1 billion (Marzulla 1988). In the three years before Reagan issued Executive Order 12,630, no court found a regulatory taking against a federal agency subject to the order (Jackson and Albaugh 1988). Since the order, the predicted deluge of takings claims has not materialized. Federal agencies that enforce environmental laws are primary targets of those who argue for this property rights protection, but court records demonstrate that these agencies are not violating property rights. Takings awards from 1985 to 1987 rarely involved regulatory takings—the focus of the order—but were mostly confined to nonregulatory takings, including claims against the government by lessors and contractors (ibid.).

At the state level, where property rights legislation is moving forward with greater speed, there seems even less reason for action. States have not been subject to the few large takings judgments imposed on the federal government. Maryland Deputy Attorney General Ralph Tyler testified before Congress that these laws are "a solution looking for a problem"; from 1985 to 1993 no one had successfully prosecuted a regulatory takings case against his state (U.S. House 1993, p. 169).

Clarity or Confusion?

NEPA defies the skeptics who insist that process is irrelevant without substantive commands. Evidence indicates that the NEPA process has changed agency thinking and enhanced sensitivity to environmental issues. A 1976 evaluation by the Council on Environmental Quality (CEQ) concluded that "assessments and impact statements have substantially improved government decisions" (Herz 1993, p. 1705). In a leading study of the U.S. Army Corps of Engineers and U.S. Forest Service, Taylor (1984, p. 130) found that "all districts and forests do better in terms of avoiding environmental damage than they did before NEPA." As a result of NEPA, the Corps of Engineers abandoned 41 projects, delayed 102, and significantly modified 347 from 1970 to 1978 (Herz 1993). The Forest Service, after legal battles between 1977 and 1984, committed itself to using the NEPA process in the Northwest—performing broad-ranging analysis of herbicide risks in vegetative management, considering alternatives, making use of public input, and changing policy to indicate a preference for nonchemical means of controlling unwanted vegetation whenever possible (O'Brien 1990).

On the other hand, takings assessments can result in paperwork without producing clarity. Impact statements do not sharpen decision-makers' sensitivity to potential takings. They ask agencies to do what the Supreme Court and all lower courts routinely refuse to do in handling takings claims: anticipate facts in advance of government action. Even when confined to a specific setting, the ad hoc factual inquiry challenges courts, which must apply broad and ill-defined criteria, while the methodology baffles government actors trying to anticipate specific takings claims and private parties trying to decide the merits of a particular claim.[3] Property rights advocates complain that the takings standards are impossible to apply and desperately need revision, yet insist that agencies are up to the task of a takings analysis (U.S. House 1993).

Agencies must do more than predict whether a regulation may affect some landowner somewhere. They must anticipate and calculate the impacts of a regulation or policy on every landowner in their jurisdiction. It is an immense task that cannot be realistically accomplished (U.S. House 1993). An exacting analysis requires both insight into existing law and anticipation of the law's future developments. Legal scholars do not agree on the meaning and future of takings decisions such as *Lucas* (Berger 1992). Less experienced lawyers working for government agencies surely can do no better. On top of unrealistic legal analysis, some states require an estimation of the anticipated cost of compensation for takings—what many believe to be an impossible task.

The experience in Delaware, a state with one of the first assessment laws, testifies to the lack of precision in an analysis performed out of context. Officials applying the law have thrown up their hands, concluding that the impact of regulation "depends on the facts of each case" (U.S. House 1993, p. 215). What was supposed to be a useful assessment turned out to be a

---

3. In *Bowles v. United States,* 31 Fed.Cl. 37 (1994), Chief Judge Lorin Smith, a strong supporter of property rights, made this point in a plea to find a better method of balancing legitimate public goals with fundamental individual rights:

> This case presents in sharp relief the difficulty that current takings law forces upon both the federal government and the private citizen. The government here had little guidance from the law as to whether its action was a taking in advance of a long and expensive course of litigation. The citizen likewise had little more presidential guidance than faith in the justice of his cause to sustain a long and costly suit in several courts . . . Courts, however, cannot produce comprehensive solutions. They can only interpret the rather precise language of the fifth amendment to our constitution in very specific factual circumstances.

meaningless observation that regulation may or may not result in a taking depending on the circumstances (U.S. House 1993). Even a staunch advocate of property rights such as Nancie Marzulla concedes that assessment laws "have serious weaknesses" in this regard (Marzulla 1995). The Delaware attorney general has confessed to providing "canned" analyses of takings impacts (Sugameli 1993).

Empty analysis is only half the problem. These laws encourage state officials to overstate the risks of takings and discourage them from protecting the public. A Congressional Research Service review of scholarly literature found that legal experts were "largely critical" of the order for these reasons (U.S. House 1993, p. 172). The order also imposes special and unnecessary restrictions on health and safety regulations that are not justified by case law (U.S. House 1993). Leading legal scholars, in a 1993 letter to President Clinton, identified several of these unnecessary hurdles to regulation. They cited directives stating that regulations must "substantially" and not just "rationally" advance a government purpose, be "no more restrictive than necessary," and be designed to prevent harms that are "direct, immediate and demonstrable" (U.S. House 1993, pp. 139–41). Since many health and safety regulations operate in a world of imperfect knowledge, where preventive action precedes scientific certainty, these hurdles could shut down rules that protect people from unsafe drugs, dangerous workplaces, and carcinogenic chemicals. Yet states such as Utah, North Dakota, and Arizona included similar language in their laws to inhibit public protection.

States have borrowed and will continue to borrow from the executive order to write their laws and will no doubt use the order and its interpretative guidelines as sources for developing their own guidelines. Inaccurate and faulty interpretations may find their way into state guidelines or agency practices even if they are excluded from authorizing statutes. The Wyoming law encourages state officials to supplement the guidelines with "any other relevant information as may be determined by the agency." Also, takings assessment laws provide states opportunities to invent their own rules for takings. Louisiana, North Dakota, and Texas laws seek to redefine takings in terms of actions that reduce the market value of property by a certain percentage. While these laws carve out exceptions for certain measures, they impose an unprecedented standard for a taking, running counter to the long-established principle that "mere diminution in value of property, however serious, is insufficient to constitute a taking."[4]

States such as Washington have attempted to steer clear of the biases

---

4. *Concrete Pipe Products v. Construction Laborers Pension Trust for Southern California,* 113 S.Ct. 2264, 2270 (1993).

in the executive order. Making one of the stronger cases for these laws, John Martinez (1994) claims that checklists like the one enacted in Washington by and large perform a useful function, alerting agencies to "warning signals" indicating that their actions may result in an unintended taking of private property. Certainly schemes confined to procedure are better analytical tools than those advancing a substantive agenda. Nonetheless, laws such as Washington's share many troublesome features with other takings assessment laws and, on balance, are not an improvement in decision-making. While the Washington law may focus attention on property rights, there is no evidence that any analytical structure can reduce the burdens of litigation. State officials simply cannot predict what might happen in court. The Washington attorney general's advisory memorandum offers guidelines that are as likely to trigger false alarms as to provide valuable signals. For example, the memorandum calls for caution if the regulation has a severe impact on a landowner's economic interest (ibid., pp. 343–344). The U.S. Supreme Court has greatly minimized the significance of a severe impact.[5] Using this test, an agency could easily overestimate its liability.

Making Constructive Use of Assessments

A process designed to educate and enlighten should place information in the hands of decision-makers in a timely manner, preserving maximum opportunities for them to act. The earlier concerns are raised, the more likely agencies are to investigate alternatives or modify project designs to meet environmental concerns without sacrificing project goals. Once an agency is well along in the planning process, it has an investment it is not likely to abandon. NEPA places a premium on assessments that provide timely information, allowing staff to pursue alternatives and adjust government actions to accommodate assessment findings.

CEQ regulations require that preparation start "early enough so that it can serve practically as an important contribution to the decision-making process and will not be used to rationalize or justify decisions already made."[6] The "scoping" requirement means that an agency cannot set study objectives and research design without input from outsiders. This early foothold enables outsiders to have their concerns addressed before an agency commits its resources and reputation to a particular position.

In contrast to NEPA, takings assessment laws do not contain provisions

5. In *Penn Central*, 438 U.S. at 133, the court said "It is, of course, true that the Landmarks Law has a more severe impact on some landowners than on others, but that in itself does not mean that the law effects a 'taking.' "
6. 40 C.F.R. s. 1502.5.

designed to ensure constructive use of assessment findings. Unless the assessment procedures provide for these opportunities, agency process naturally tends to foreclose options and prevent accommodation of interests outside their primary mission.

Takings assessments do nothing to reverse these tendencies. Generally they fail to situate assessments in the decision-making process in a way that provides meaningful feedback in planning agency action. Washington and Idaho instruct officials simply to apply the guidelines without reference to timing. In Missouri, where the assessment is public, filed along with the proposed rule, regulators are faced with the same temptation to complete the assessment at the last moment. In those states, such as Tennessee and Indiana, where the attorney general conducts an end-of-the-line analysis, the law consigns takings assessments to the limited role of a stoplight. They either allow the rule to proceed or they stop it.

One of the most significant advantages of analysis is lost if it cannot be constructively used by decision-makers. Few decisions present black-and-white alternatives; they involve compromise. Assessment findings can facilitate compromise and adjustment in policy decisions but only if they are made available to decision-makers in a way that permits their meaningful use. NEPA operates on this premise, while takings assessments do not.

Accountability or Secrecy in Decision-Making?

Asking an agency to conduct impact analyses is an exercise in trust since these assessments complicate an agency's work. NEPA preserves an agency's discretion to use its expertise while encouraging thoughtful and conscientious action concerning matters outside an agency's ordinary realm of business. Unless agencies are prodded into action, however, they may not take their responsibilities seriously.

The NEPA process is open and public. This commits agencies to reduce information and evaluations for public review, and there is a mechanism for agencies to respond to public comment. The documentary trail moves from a draft of the EIS to the preparation of a record of decision, in which an agency states its final decision, explains its reasons for the decision, identifies alternatives to the proposed action, and explains why the alternatives were rejected. These records assure the public that an agency is fulfilling its obligations and provide an opportunity for public participation and comment.

The law introduces authoritative and multiple voices into the decision-making process, exposing agency staff to interpretations and perspectives not driven by agency politics. At different stages of EIS preparation, the lead agency is required to afford opportunities for input concerning its proposal.

Probably the most significant opportunity for comment occurs when the agency circulates its draft EIS to the public and other agencies for comment and then responds to outside concerns. This requirement of public exchange is "unique among environmental and, perhaps, all government obligations" (Herz 1993, p. 1709). Contributions by outsiders can improve the quality of decision-making by disclosing alternatives and mitigation strategies that an agency may not have uncovered, while responses from a lead agency force critical issues to the surface and require the agency to formally stake out its position.

Agencies cannot passively wait to receive information but must help generate a dialogue. Among other things, NEPA directs lead agencies to obtain comments from outsiders, and "study, develop and describe appropriate alternatives." It requires them to "consult with and obtain the comments of any Federal agency which has jurisdiction by law or special expertise with respect to any environmental impact involved." The opinions of experts from other government agencies carry considerable weight. Lead agencies are sensitive to what colleagues say and have incentives to anticipate and accommodate objections to avoid trouble (Taylor 1984, p. 183). Also, lead agencies face a serious challenge to their position if they cannot reconcile conflicting viewpoints from these reliable sources (Blumm and Brown 1990).

Judicial supervision dramatically shifts the incentives to respond to environmental values. O'Brien (1990), the author of the study of herbicide use by the Forest Service, concludes that, "the only effective incentive for an agency to produce an excellent . . . EIS is the specter of litigation and the likelihood of committed judicial review." Nothing in NEPA provides for enforcement, judicial review, or citizens' suits. Courts took it upon themselves to interpret the law to create legally enforceable duties, starting early by halting the Trans-Alaska Pipeline for failure to develop an environmental impact statement (Rabin 1986). Early judicial interventions reflected an active interest in administrative actions and these decisions opened many possibilities for enforcement of NEPA. This early activism was a product of its time. During the 1970s, courts were influenced by legal developments that encouraged judicial oversight. The Supreme Court had expanded the concept of standing to sue and endorsed the "hard look" doctrine of review for administrative action (McGarity 1990).

Faced with the prospects of close judicial scrutiny, agencies approached their obligations under NEPA very seriously. As courts retreated from their activism, agencies confronted fewer NEPA violations and injunctions and had less incentive to scrupulously follow NEPA's mandated analysis.[7]

7. In 1977, when 938 lawsuits were filed, 22 percent of cases (202) resulted in injunctions; in 1987, 80 NEPA cases were filed, and courts issued only three injunctions (4 percent) (Blumm 1990).

In a major departure from NEPA, the executive order established as a baseline an internal process without any mechanism for open deliberation, public participation, and judicial oversight. States tended to follow the precedent set by the order. Washington and Idaho created a wholly internal process, relying on the attorney-client privilege to erect a wall around the analyses performed by agencies. Under Indiana law, the attorney general's review of regulations for their takings potential is shielded by the same privilege. The Utah law requires specific deliberation before an agency can take action restricting private property use for the protection of public health or safety and treats the documents related to this deliberation as internal.

Involvement of outsiders can provide specific facts and the legal insights needed by agencies to perform takings assessments. Surely lawmakers in Virginia believed this to be the case when they expanded the economic impact analysis performed by the Department of Planning and Budget to include an assessment of "the impact of the regulation on the use and value of private property." The economic impact analysis is embedded in a process that is noteworthy because it resembles NEPA process. The regulatory review provides for public disclosure of the assessments, creates opportunities for outside participation, and promotes interagency consultation. Virginia's law recognizes that exposure to outside thinking counters the tendency of agency personnel to develop tunnel vision and opens an agency to alternatives that are less intrusive on individual rights. It also recognizes the valuable function of public input apart from its power to change outcomes. By providing channels of communication and dialogue, the NEPA process satisfies the public's desire to receive an explanation for a government decision, to participate in decision-making, to have views taken seriously, and to receive responses to input (Herz 1993). As it stands, takings assessments typically allow decisions without public debate about important policy questions involving property rights and the environment, thus secretly deciding who will bear the costs of protecting the public and the environment.

By and large, takings laws do not provide for accountability through the courts. Probably the most important lesson from NEPA involves the critical role of the courts in pushing agencies into compliance. Again, Washington and Idaho take a strong position similar to the one in the executive order, which insulates government from accountability. They explicitly deny private parties "a right to seek judicial relief requiring compliance." Here is where Martinez's (1994) arguments for the Washington model are put to their greatest test. He claims these laws will protect expectations related to private property. Without a mechanism for accountability, how can anyone have confidence in an analytic process that, in many ways, runs contrary to the best interests of the agencies that perform the analyses?

Delaware reduces the scope of judicial review to a formality, focusing on trivial issues, such as whether the attorney general reviewed the action and informed the issuing agency in writing. States such as Utah, Tennessee, and Wyoming have laws that are silent about remedies in court. It is argued that courts will respond to challenges under takings assessment laws in the same way they responded to NEPA lawsuits ("Recent Legislation" 1994). Today, private parties are less likely to convince courts to review takings assessments than they were in the 1970s, in the early NEPA cases. More conservative than the judiciary of the 1970s, today's judges are unlikely to take a hard look at agency action. Moreover, the executive order, as the model for these laws, offers judges a precedent to avoid review.

The lack of accountability in the case of the executive order has produced expected results. Roger Marzulla, the assistant U.S. attorney general who drafted the executive order, laments that "executive agencies have utterly ignored the Executive Order" (U.S. House 1995, p. 60).[8] Supervision by another executive agency has not proved to be an adequate substitute for the courts. Unlike courts, the executive branch is immersed in politics. In passing on an agency decision, executive agencies are not confined to a review simply for adherence to analytic standards or to exercise the independent judgment of courts.

There are exceptions to this lack of accountability, most prominently in Texas, which requires publication of assessments before proposed actions go into effect and which sanctions citizen lawsuits to invalidate government actions implemented without a takings assessment. But these few strands of accountability do not duplicate NEPA's comprehensive structure, which was designed to inform and improve decision-making. Instead they appear to function as checks on government's authority to regulate.

Degree of Burden

NEPA distinguishes significant from insignificant actions. Without such a screening process, agencies must divert organizational resources needed to maintain the quality of their work and risk demoralizing staff who are assigned to analyze trivial matters (Taylor 1984). The law requires agencies to engage in this process only for "major Federal actions significantly affecting the quality of the human environment." Agencies are given considerable leeway to decide which proposed actions have a "significant" effect on the environment,[9] although Congress has stepped in from time to time to exempt certain actions as "insignificant" (Rodgers 1990).

Agencies have faced very manageable costs related to implementing

---

8. A more objective source, the *Congressional Daily*, also reported that Executive Order 12,630 "has gone mostly unused" (Marzulla 1995, p. 630).
9. *Sierra Club v. United States Army Corps of Engineers,* 701 F.2d 1011, 1029 (2d Cir. 1983).

NEPA. In the mid-1970s, when more EISs were prepared than today, the Corps of Engineers estimated its 1974 costs at 1.2 percent of its annual budget, while the Nuclear Regulatory Commission's 1975 expenditure on EISs was $14.9 million, or about 2.2 percent of the cost of one nuclear power plant (Council 1976). Nonetheless, courts in the 1980s responded to concerns about agency burdens and loosened the requirements for preparation of EISs by shrinking the boundaries of a "major action."[10]

In theory, almost every takings assessment law demands costly and time-consuming assessments of nearly every action proposed by agencies. Often, there is no ceiling on the resources dedicated to this process because these laws apply across the board to regulatory and legislative action. No funds are ever allocated to support takings assessments, so what is consumed by assessments is unavailable for other uses.

Turning to Martinez's (1994) arguments in favor of the Washington model, it is clear that the law fails on this score. It requires "state and local governments to evaluate proposed regulatory or administrative actions" without limitation. Although Martinez (ibid.) claims that the use of the Washington model would avoid most public costs, he never confronts the law's failure to discriminate between different types of government action. Surely the milk inspector who issues a warning or citation to a producer cannot be expected to perform a takings assessment each time she acts in her administrative capacity; yet, that is what many of these takings assessment laws seem to require.

Takings assessments reach unimaginable proportions. The North Dakota law adopts a standard that requires analysis of nearly every conceivable action, stating that an assessment is required for a rule "that may limit the use of private real property." Several states do not limit the assessment to real estate. For example, Utah defines "private property" to include "any real or personal property" protected by state or federal constitutional provisions. The Texas law, according to one commentator, applies so broadly that it is best described by what it excludes (Grimes 1996). This categorization fairly describes the scope of many of the state takings assessment laws.

For these and other reasons, takings assessments are extremely vulnerable to cost-related arguments. Attacks on the cost of takings legislation have been persuasive, contributing to the repeal of the Arizona legislation. Cost studies produced in state after state present overwhelming evidence that makes legislatures stop and think before heeding the demands of property rights lobbyists. In response to a 1993 proposal in New Mexico, the Fish and Game Department estimated that its costs of review would range from

---

10. *River Rd. Alliance Inc. v. Army Corps of Engineers,* 764 F.2d 445, 450–51 (7th Cir. 1985), *cert. denied,* 475 US 1055 (1986). (Courts have loosened standards to avoid the costs of an EIS, recognizing that pre-EIS assessments are more thorough.)

15 to 87 percent of its $17 million budget (Freilich and Doyle 1994). The Colorado Department of Health pegged annual costs for reviewing regulations at $8 million, while the State's Department of Transportation estimate was $3 million (U.S. House 1993, p. 131). One of the more extensive fiscal estimates prepared by the Wisconsin Department of Agriculture, Trade and Consumer Protection predicted that takings assessments would add $10 million in costs. Assessments would apply to over one hundred administrative rules administered by the agency, including programs related to food safety, pesticide labeling and control, groundwater protection, product safety, unfair and deceptive business practices, and land and water regulation. In addition, takings assessments would disrupt routine activities such as meat inspections and even reach actions that few proponents of these laws ever intended, such as disciplinary actions that put at risk an employee's property rights.[11]

Confronting astronomical cost, agencies likely would look for loopholes and shortcuts. They may end up with filing cabinets filled with meaningless paperwork purchased at a high price. Or they may decide to regulate less and avoid the issue entirely.

Neutral Process or Biased Analysis?

For better or worse, NEPA has been held within its procedural channel. This is not to say that environmentalists have not attempted to infuse substantive elements into the law. Beginning with the original legislative initiative to include a right to a clean environment in NEPA (Platt 1970), however, these efforts have been turned aside. In particular, a string of hostile Supreme Court decisions thwarted attempts to arm the law with substantive clout.[12] As a result, NEPA process takes a neutral approach toward its subject of analysis—namely, environmental impacts. Even though NEPA is "action-forcing," it does not force certain outcomes, allowing agencies room to decide these issues. This discretion may lead to anomalous consequences: agency decisions that scrupulously follow NEPA procedures but result in environmentally unwise choices.[13] But this is a tradeoff for NEPA's

---

11. Department of Agriculture, Trade and Consumer Protection, Fiscal Estimate for 1993 Wis. A.B. 1185, 1993–94 sess. (Jan. 1, 1994). The estimate was also attached to an identical bill introduced into the Senate, 1993 Wis. S.B. 757.

12. The hostile decisions began in 1975 with *Aberdeen & Rockfish R.R. v. Students Challenging Regulatory Agency Procedures* (SCRAP II), 422 U.S. 289 (1975) and continued in 1989 with *Robertson v. Methow Valley Citizens Council*, 490 U.S. 332 (1989).

13. *Robertson*, 490 U.S. at 350–351 emphasizes that NEPA imposes no substantive environmental obligations on federal agencies and merely prohibits uninformed—rather than unwise—agency action.

open architecture, which seeks to inspire thoughtful consideration and informed action to protect the environment. This design has made a difference. Joseph Sax's (1986, p. 804) insights into NEPA are particularly noteworthy, because he converted from being an early detractor of NEPA to a proponent:

> My own recent study of the behavior of federal land management agencies persuades me that legitimating public participation, and demanding openness in planning and decision-making, has been indispensable to a permanent and powerful increase in environmental protection, and that the presence of citizen-initiated litigation is a major factor that keeps public agencies from slackening in their resolve to see that environmental laws are enforced.

NEPA is more than impact statements. It is a unique combination of features that improve decision-making by providing a public forum to seriously consider environmental concerns of government actions. Because it is flexible and ideologically neutral, NEPA has staying power, as reflected in its over twenty-five years of service without amendment. Special interests have placed certain projects beyond its reach but have not dismantled the law.

Takings assessment laws are steeped in the Reagan agenda to limit government and to cut regulation. Reagan officials seized on controversial ideas about property rights to design what former U.S. Solicitor General Charles Fried (1991, p. 183) has termed an "aggressive" and "quite radical project." Their aim, Fried says, was

> to use the Takings Clause of the Fifth Amendment as a severe brake upon federal and state regulation of business and property. The grand plan was to make government pay compensation for a taking of property every time its regulations impinged too severely on a property right—limiting the possible uses for a parcel of land or restricting or tying up a business in regulatory red tape. If the government labored under so severe an obligation, there would be, to say the least, much less regulation.

The order and its interpretative guidelines are not a neutral summary of law but a wish list of interpretations designed to enlarge the sphere of protected property interests and thereby restrict the reach of regulations (U.S. House 1993). It is no wonder that the originators of this radical project wanted to exclude public participation, keep documents secret, and cut off meaningful judicial review.

State variations of Executive Order 12,630 incorporate and even expand on these antiregulatory themes. In the words of James C. Miller III, head of the Office of Management and Budget under President Reagan, the state initiatives carry on "the unfinished business of the Reagan Revolution" (quoted in Miniter 1994, p. 40). By targeting natural-resource protection, farming, and forestry, Louisiana, Oregon, and West Virginia took on rules that were especially disliked by regulatory reformers. Tennessee requires that the attorney general withhold approval of "rules that would effect an unconstitutional taking." There appears to be no latitude to approve regulations. The potential cost to the public: a regulation with well-documented benefits can be derailed by the most incidental violation of the takings law. Texas law imposes a high price for failure to perform a takings assessment. It voids government actions where an assessment is required but not prepared.

State laws can indirectly dampen interest in regulating. Texas permits citizens to sue to invalidate regulations implemented without a required takings assessment. North Dakota adopted a mechanism to chill regulation by linking payments for takings claims with agency budgets. State agencies must prepare a written assessment that estimates the cost of any takings judgments and then "identify the source of payment within the agency's budget for any compensation that may be ordered." This extra step of identifying payment sources is the brainchild of Mark Pollot (1993), who realized that this tactic would force agencies to choose property rights over public protection. To avoid the disruption that payment might engender, an agency contemplating action may set aside funds in reserve to be used for compensation. These funds become unavailable for programming and other primary obligations of the agency. Of course, agencies always have an alternative to encumbering their budgets: they can abandon regulatory efforts and avoid the takings problem.

Takings assessment legislation is a convenient and indirect way to enhance public acceptance of property rights, insinuate property protections into government policy, and attack government regulation that restricts property use. It capitalizes on the good image of impact assessments fostered by NEPA and, by infusing substance into impact analyses, it allows property rights proponents to make alterations without direct confrontation. As so many of these advocates say, this legislation is only a first step.[14] Environmentalists and others with a stake in regulation must confront the property rights movement on its own ground. They must aggressively challenge takings assessment laws because these laws make a mockery of the impact analysis designed to produce thoughtful action.

Turning Takings Laws on Their Head

A formidable weapon in the arsenal of the property rights movement, takings assessment laws are intended to eviscerate agency resolve to regulate

---

14. For example, Senator Phil Gramm testified that "we are not going to fix the problem of regulatory takings with one bill" (U.S. House 1993, p. 21).

for the protection of public health, safety, and welfare. But takings assessment legislation has the potential to be a double-edged sword. Environmental regulations are not the only means of injuring property rights. Agencies can adversely affect property by inaction as well as by action that degrades the quality of the environment in which property is located. So much of property's value depends on the quality of the environment. State takings assessment laws may impose obligations on government agencies to consider injuries to property resulting from government actions that degrade the environment.

Environmental legislation does not protect property owners' expectations related to the investment in their homes. For example, those who buy property on a lake or riverfront anticipate that the setting will not only enhance their pleasure but their investment. NEPA will not help them if pollution permitted under state law lowers the value of their property. Of course, sewage disposal and other government activities benefit everyone. Even polluting industries provide benefits by providing jobs and paying taxes. Nonetheless, why should individual property owners be forced to surrender part of what they purchased to achieve these public benefits? Why should the state recognize regulations as takings without addressing these deprivations? Few environmental injuries may rise to the level of a taking, but more claims may qualify for assessment under state laws that seek to expand the definition of a taking.

Environmental quality directly correlates with property values. Water and air pollution can decrease the value of property in the surrounding area (Epp and Al-Ani 1979; Mark 1980). Likewise, other studies have shown that airport noise significantly contributes to a decrease in property values (Gautrin 1975; Mieszkowski and Saper 1978). Other disamenities—hazardous waste sites (Michaels and Smith 1990), electricity utility plants (Bloomquist 1974), and nuclear plants (Folland and Hough 1991)—can also reduce value. What is significant for this discussion is the evolution of takings law toward "an increasing acceptance of the possibility of takings without any physical invasion" (Stoebuck 1977, p. 17). Courts have awarded damages under the Fifth Amendment and state constitutional counterparts for government activities resulting in a nuisance that diminishes the value of property.

State courts steadily applied the theory of "taking by nuisance" to different cases, creating what Stoebuck describes as "parts of one developing body of law" (ibid., p. 17). The most articulate of these decisions dates from the early 1960s. *Thornburg v. Port of Portland* involved a claim for compensation based on noise from an airport.[15] The plaintiff did not fit within the

15. 233 Ore. 178, 376 P. 2d 100 (1962).

precedent permitting a recovery for those living directly underneath a flight path and who were thus subject to an aerial easement. In this case, the property right with which the state had interfered was the right to be free from interferences with the use and enjoyment of land. The Oregon court decision established a principle that has been "almost universally" followed by the other state courts deciding similar claims (Kahn 1995):

> [A] taking occurs whenever government acts in such a way as substantially to deprive an owner of the useful possession of that which he owns, either by repeated trespass or by repeated nontrespassory invasions called "nuisance." If reparations are to be denied, they should be denied for reasons of policy that are themselves strong enough to counterbalance the constitutional demand that reparations be paid. None has been pointed out to us in this case.[16]

The law of takings by nuisance is sufficiently well-developed that states cannot assess impacts on property without considering nuisance implications of their actions (Stoebuck 1977). Clearly, if the action involves a government construction project such as an airport, highway, or other public improvement, case law raises the possibility of takings by nuisance. Utilities and other entities with the power to condemn are subject to takings claims based on the loss of a landowner's use and enjoyment of property. For example, courts have ordered power companies to pay compensation for the loss of property values resulting from fear of power lines (Brown 1992). There are other instances when government operates less directly to sanction activities that pollute or damage the environment. A typical example involves environmental regulators who issue permits allowing industries to discharge pollutants into the air and water. Certainly these discharges can create a nuisance. For the purpose of a takings assessment, however, a private nuisance is not sufficient. Government must be sufficiently connected with these discharges to transform a nuisance into a taking. By analogy to the airport cases, a well-developed body of law supporting takings by nuisance, one can build the case for holding government accountable for these private activities authorized by discharge permit. In the airport cases, a taking was found even though government facilities—the buildings and runways—did not create the nuisance. Noise and other disturbances resulted from private parties using the airport with permission from the government.

Ultimately, the duties of state officials depend on the language in their takings assessment laws. Broadly worded statutes and policies can bolster the case for assessment of environmental impacts on property. In certain cases, they will mandate an assessment for proposed actions that injure property rights without rising to the level of "takings by nuisance." In most other situations, the decision to assess will be a matter of complicated interpreta-

16. 233 Ore. at 192, 376 P. 2d at 106.

tion. Under a requirement to analyze takings implications, state officials may act at their peril by ignoring the negative environmental impacts of proposed actions. Since assessments are designed to reveal the potential for takings, officials cannot avoid analysis based on doubts that a taking will actually occur. Interpretative guidelines can strengthen the case for assessment of environmental impacts. Under Washington's guidelines, for example, analysis is triggered by a severe economic impact. Without question, the decision to site a nuclear reactor or landfill is likely to reduce severely surrounding property values. If state environmental regulators follow the Reagan guidelines, which encourage review of proposed actions that interfere with informally recognized expectations related to property investment, they may assume obligations they never anticipated. In the case of a permit to discharge pollution into a lake, the agency would be required to consider more than technical information about effluent limits. It would have to examine the effects on property rights. Operators of recreational facilities and developers certainly would have a claim on the state's attention. Pollution can destroy their ability to make a living. Since a home is typically a family's biggest investment, residential homeowners should be permitted to make a case that pollution denies their reasonable, investment-backed expectations.

Arguing for expanded use of assessments may not seem so far-fetched when one remembers that takings assessment laws operate in a different world than court-developed takings law. States have set standards for performing assessments independent of the potential of government action to result in a takings under traditional law. North Dakota, for example, requires an analysis of any rule "that may limit the use of private real property." A proposed rule that relaxes water pollution standards could create environmental impacts that limit the use of property by riparian landowners and thus merit analysis by North Dakota officials. By expanding the definition of takings to embrace government actions that reduce the market value of property, North Dakota, Louisiana, and Texas have opened the door to claims based on environmental injuries.

Texas business interests anticipated the demand for takings assessments in these situations and fought to limit application of the law to "real property that is the subject of the governmental action" (Elder 1995, p. 4). This limitation purportedly cuts off claims of property owners who border objectionable land uses sanctioned by the government such as feedlots and landfills. Even if their property is reduced in value by 25 percent or more, these landowners have no claim to protection because their property is not the subject of government action. Environmentalists argue for equal consideration, urging that assessments ought to cover landowners adversely impacted by proposed actions such as the repeal or modification of landfill regulations by the Texas Natural Resource Conservation Commission (TNRCC) (Grimes 1996). In a case in Travis County district court, opponents of a proposed 11,000-head swine farm are challenging the TNRCC's interpretation that the law applies only to parties seeking a permit to operate a regulated business and not to adjacent landowners whose property values are reduced by the permitted activity (Elliott 1996). Environmental advocates in Texas have a fallback position to frustrate government moves to repeal or soften regulations. Relying on a provision that confers standing on property owners affected by a government action, they contend that a property owner who has not suffered a taking can still sue to invalidate an action performed without a required takings assessment (Grimes 1996).

Because takings assessments were not tailored to protect environmental interests, they must be stretched to reach the claims discussed in this section, and the fit will not always be as tight as in cases where property owners are claiming a taking based on the burdens of environmental regulation. But these laws have gaps that limit property rights advocates as well as environmentalists. By and large, these laws avoid the problems of municipal zoning, which has a greater impact on the average landowner than state action. They also do not reach federal regulation, such as the protection of endangered species, that generates much of the demand for property rights reform (ibid.).

Nonetheless, environmentalists could take advantage of the opportunities to appropriate takings assessments as a vehicle for protecting the environment. Framing questions of environmental degradation in terms of property values can expand the realm of claims available to those seeking redress for environmental injuries. In cases such as claims based on the harmful effects of electromagnetic fields, landowners living near power lines may not be able to prove the elements of traditional tort cases. Science cannot establish that harm results from exposure to this hazard. With this type of exposure, the extent of personal injuries cannot be readily anticipated. Potential plaintiffs, however, can press their claims by showing the link between power lines and reduced property values (Brown 1992).

Of course, the strategy of tying environmental protection to property rights has its limits. These laws do not address important environmental values, such as biodiversity, that are not reflected in property values. This approach also denies people without property the standing to raise claims that they and their homes suffer from environmental degradation. Yet confronting the property rights movement on this level is unavoidable, particularly if more states pass legislation that authorizes judicial review or if courts on their own initiate review. As was true with NEPA, the supervisory power of the courts may add a powerful dimension to these impact assessments.

Property rights advocates cannot be permitted uncontested access to the courts to peddle their vision of property rights, a vision that disregards the role of government regulation and environmental quality. What better way to turn the tables on the property rights movement than to use its own law to protect the environment?

References

Attorney General's Guidelines for the Evaluation of Risk and Avoidance and Unantici-pated Takings (53 Federal Regulation 8859). 1988. Environmental Law Reporter (Admin. Materials) 18: 35, 168–180.

Berger, Michael M. 1992. "Recent Takings and Eminent Domain Cases." *American Law Institute-American Bar Association Land Use Institute: Planning, Regulation, Litigation, Eminent Domain, and Compensation, ALI-ABA C750:* 75–95.

Bloomquist, G. 1974. "The Effect of Electric Utility Power Plant Location on Area Property Value." *Land Economics* 50 (1): 97–100.

Blumm, Michael. 1990. "Symposium on NEPA at Twenty: The Past, Present and Future of the National Environmental Policy Act: Introduction: The National Environmental Policy Act at Twenty: A Preface." *Environmental Law* 20 (3): 447–483.

Blumm, Michael, and Stephen Brown. 1990. "Pluralism and the Environment: The Role of Comment Agencies in NEPA Litigation." *Harvard Environmental Law Review* 14 (2): 277–309.

Brown, Todd. 1992. "The Power Line Plaintiff and the Inverse Condemnation Alternative." *Boston College Environmental Affairs Law Review* 19 (3): 655–694.

Council on Environmental Quality. 1976. *Environmental Impact Statements: An Analysis of Six Years' Experience by Seventy Federal Agencies.* Washington, D.C.: Executive Office of the President, Council on Environmental Quality.

Elder, Robert, Jr. 1995. "Taking the Property Rights Plunge: Now That Texas Has the Most Powerful Takings Law in the Nation, It Will Take a Tangle of Adminis-trative Hearings and Litigation to Determine Its Value—and Its Potentially Stag-gering Costs." *Texas Lawyer* (July 31): Section 3: 4.

Elliott, Janet. 1996. "AG's 'Takings' Guidelines Don't Offer Much Guidance." *Texas Lawyer* January 29: 4.

Epp, Donald, and K. S. Al-Ani. 1979. "The Effect of Water Quality on Rural Non-farm Residential Property Values." *American Journal of Agricultural Economics* 61 (3): 529–534.

Folland, S., and R. Hough. 1991. "Nuclear Power Plants and the Value of Agricul-tural Land." *Land Economics* 67 (1): 30–36.

Folsom, Robin E. 1993. "Executive Order 12,630: A President's Manipulation of the Fifth Amendment's Just Compensation Clause to Achieve Control over Ex-ecutive Agency Regulatory Decisionmaking." *Boston College Environmental Re-view* 20 (4): 639–697.

Freilich, Robert, and RoxAnne Doyle. 1994. "Taking Legislation: Misguided and Dangerous." *Land Use Law and Zoning Digest* 46 (10): 3–6.

Fried, Charles. 1991. *Order and Law: Arguing the Reagan Revolution, a First-Hand Account.* New York, NY: Simon and Schuster.

Gautrin, Jean-François. 1975. "An Evaluation of the Impact of Aircraft Noise on Property Values with a Simple Model of Urban Land Rent." *Land Economics* 51 (1): 80–86.

Grimes, George, Jr. 1996. "Texas Private Real Property Rights Preservation Act: A Political Solution to the Regulatory Takings Problem." *St. Mary's University (San Antonio) Law Journal* 27 (3): 557–612.

Herz, Michael. 1993. "Parallel Universes: NEPA Lessons for the New Property." *Columbia Law Review* 93 (7): 1668–1737.

Jackson, Jerry, and Lyle Albaugh. 1988. "A Critique of the Takings Executive Order in the Context of Environmental Regulation." *Environmental Law Reporter* 18: 10,463–10,478.

Jacobs, Harvey M. 1995. "The Anti-Environmental 'Wise Use' Movement in America." *Land Use Law and Zoning Digest* 47 (2): 3–8.

Kahn, Robert. 1995. "Inverse Condemnation and the Highway Cases: Compensation for Abutting Landowners." *Boston College Environmental Affairs Law Review* 22 (3): 563–591.

Lavelle, Marianne. 1993. "The 'Property Rights' Revolt." *National Law Journal* (May 10): 1.

Levinson, Nancy. 1994. "Give and Takings: When Do Land-Use Rules Trample Property Rights?" *Architectural Record* 182 (10): 50–53.

Mark, Jonathan H. 1980. "A Preference Approach to Measuring the Impact of Environmental Externalities." *Land Economics* 56 (1): 103–116.

Martinez, John. 1994. "Statutes Enacting Takings Law: Flying in the Face of Uncertainty." *Urban Lawyer* 26 (2): 327–345.

Marzulla, Nancie G. 1995 "State Private Property Rights Initiatives as a Response to 'Environmental Takings.' " *South Carolina Law Review* 46 (4): 613–640.

Marzulla, Nancie, and Roger Marzulla. 1990. "Regulatory Takings in the United States Claims Court: Adjusting the Burdens that in Fairness and Equity Ought to Be Borne by Society as a Whole." *Catholic University Law Review* 40 (3): 549–569.

Marzulla, Roger. 1988 "The New 'Takings' Executive Order and Environmental Regulation—Collision or Cooperation?" *Environmental Law Reporter* 18 (7): 10,254–10,260.

McGarity, Thomas O. 1990. "Judicial Enforcement of NEPA-Inspired Promises." *Environmental Law* 20 (3): 569–609.

Mears, Jennifer. 1995. "Road to Property Rights Is Often Full of Bumps." *Los Angeles Times* (January 15): B3, quoting Larry Morandi of the National Conference of State Legislatures.

Michaels, R., and V. Smith. 1990. "Market Segmentation and Valuing Amenities with Hedonic Models: The Case of Hazardous Waste Sites." *Journal of Urban Economics* 28: 223–242.

Mieszkowski, Peter, and Arthur M. Saper. 1978. "An Estimate of the Effects of Airport Noise on Property Values." *Journal of Urban Economics* 5: 425–440.

Miller, Anita. 1993. "All Is Not Quiet on the Western Front." *Urban Lawyer* 25 (4): 827–840.

Miniter, Richard. 1994. "You Just Can't Take It Anymore." *Policy Review* no. 70: 40–46.

O'Brien, Mary. 1990. "NEPA as It Was Meant to Be: NCAP v. Block, Herbicides, and Region 6 Forest Service." *Environmental Law* 20 (3): 735–745.

Platt, Rutherford H. 1970. "Toward Constitutional Recognition of the Environment." *American Bar Association Journal* 56: 1061–1064.

Pollot, Mark. 1989. "The Effect of the Federal Takings Executive Order." *Land Use Law and Zoning Digest* 41 (5): 3–7.

Pollot, Mark. 1993. *Grand Theft and Petit Larceny: Property Rights in America.* San Francisco, CA: Pacific Research Institute for Public Policy.

Rabin, Robert. 1986. "Federal Regulation in Historical Perspective." *Stanford Law Review* 38 (5): 1189–1326.

Rauber, Paul. 1994. "Bill the Public to Save Nature." *Sacramento Bee* April 3: F1.

"Recent Legislation: Property—Constitutional Law—Takings—Utah Requires Agencies and Localities to Conduct Takings Impact Analyses—Utah Code Ann. Secs. 63–90–1 to -4; Secs. 63–90a-1 to -4 (Supp. 1994)." 1994. *Harvard Law Review* 108 (2): 519–524.

Rodgers, William H., Jr. 1990. "Symposium on NEPA at Twenty: The Past, Present and Future of the National Environmental Policy Act: Keynote: NEPA at Twenty: Mimicry and Recruitment in Environmental Law." *Environmental Law* 20 (3): 485–504.

Sax, Joseph. 1970. "The Public Trust Doctrine in Natural Resource Law: Effective Judicial Intervention." *Michigan Law Review* 68: 471–566.

Sax, Joseph. 1986. "Symposium: Environmental Law: More Than Just a Passing Fad: Introduction." *University of Michigan Journal of Law Reform* 19 (4): 797–804.

Settle, Richard L. 1983. *Washington Land Use and Environmental Law and Practices.* Seattle, WA: Butterworth Legal Publishers.

Smith, James. 1995. "Private Property Protection Legislation and Original Understandings of the Takings Clause: Can They Co-Exist?" *Journal of Legislation* 21: 93–110.

Stoebuck, William. 1977. *Nontrespassory Takings in Eminent Domain.* Charlottesville, VA: Michie.

Sugameli, Glenn. 1993. "Takings Issues in Light of *Lucas v. South Carolina Coastal Council:* A Decision Full of Sound and Fury and Signifying Nothing." *Virginia Environmental Law Journal* 12: 439–504.

Talbot, Allan R. 1972. *Power Along the Hudson: The Storm King Case and the Birth of Environmentalism.* New York, NY: Dutton.

Taylor, Serge. 1984. *Making Bureaucracies Think: The Environmental Impact Statement Strategy of Administrative Reform.* Stanford, CA: Stanford University Press.

U.S. House. 1993. Subcommittee on Department Operations and Nutrition of the Department of Agriculture. *Private Property Protection Act of 1993: Hearings on H.R. 561.* 103rd Cong., 1st sess. Nov. 3.

U.S. House. 1995. Subcommittee on the Constitution and the Judiciary Committee. *Hearings on Protecting Private Property Rights from Regulatory Takings.* 104th Cong., 1st sess. Feb. 10.

White, Ron. 1993. "Using County Government to Protect Your Customs, Culture, and Economy, Federal Lands." *Federal Lands Update* (August): 1–4.

Woodward, Bob, and David S. Broder. 1992. "Quayle's Quest: Curb Rules, Leave No Fingerprints." *Washington Post* (January 9): A1.

Yandle, Bruce, ed. 1995. *Land Rights: The 1990s Property Rights Rebellion.* Lanham, MD: Rowman and Littlefield.

PART II

Private Interests
in Public Lands

Land Tenure, Land Policy, and the Property Rights Debate

Keith D. Wiebe, Abebayehu Tegene, and Betsey Kuhn

Land Tenure in the United States

Of the 2.3 billion acres that make up the United States, 29 percent are owned by the federal government, an additional 2 percent are held in trust by the federal government as Indian reservations, and 9 percent are owned by state and local governments (U.S. Department of the Interior 1994; U.S. General Services Administration 1995; Daugherty 1995). The remaining 60 percent are privately owned.

These numbers are deceptively simple. What does ownership mean? Care is important here, because misunderstanding about the nature of ownership fuels the current controversy over property rights. Specifically, much of the popular support for property rights reform appears to be based on the perception that landownership implies the right to use land in whatever way the landowner wishes.

Property and Ownership

Property and ownership are legal concepts rooted in social institutions. They refer not simply to material objects but to the relations between individuals and society that govern access to material objects. "The legal concept of property does not denote the tangible or intangible objects that are termed property in common speech. Rather, property as a legal concept refers to rights and interests in such objects" (Youngman 1993, p. 45).

Real property refers specifically to interests in land. There are typically many interests even in a single parcel of land, including rights to grow crops, draw water, graze livestock, extract minerals, dispose of waste materials, or build a house. The public and its representatives, including the federal government, have long played a dual role in shaping the distribution of these rights. First, through legislation, regulation, and court decisions, public agencies help establish and define the distribution of property rights within which markets function. Second, public agencies participate in the resulting markets, for example by buying and selling interests in land. Public agencies have used both of these roles throughout U.S. history to influence public and private land use in ways that balance public and private objectives.

The uses that a landowner may legally make of his or her land depend on who holds what particular rights within the bundle of rights that constitutes ownership of that land. "The universal existence of some form of public restriction on an owner's use of private property shows that a nominal owner or titleholder in fact never possesses the entire set of rights that together make up the property as a whole" (Youngman 1993, p. 51). For example, in order to protect the interests of other members of society, various levels of government generally reserve the right to prevent actions that harm others (the police power). As Coase (1960, p. 44) writes:

> What the land-owner in fact possesses is the right to carry out a circumscribed list of actions. The rights of a land-owner are not unlimited. [For example,] it may or may not be possible to erect certain types of buildings or to grow certain crops or to use particular drainage systems on the land. This does not come about simply because of Government regulation. It would be equally true under the common law. A system in which the rights of the individual were unlimited would be one in which there were no rights to acquire.

Other rights generally reserved by governments include the rights of taxation, eminent domain (the right to acquire private property for public purposes, with compensation), and escheat (the right to take possession of land left by a person who dies without heirs) (Closser 1993).

The bundle of rights and responsibilities that constitute landownership may be further allocated among multiple parties, both public and private, on a voluntary basis. For example, a farmland owner may rent her land to a farm operator. The farm operator then holds the right to use the land for agricultural production for a specified period of time, while the farmland owner retains the underlying title and the right to use the land as she chooses in subsequent periods. The same farmland owner may sell drilling rights on the same parcel of land to an energy company, which then holds perpetual rights to extract oil and natural gas. These are fairly straightforward examples. Other interests in land are less well understood but are becoming increasingly important. For example, if a parcel of undeveloped land has potential for conversion to residential, commercial, or industrial use, the owner holds "development rights" that may be highly valued by developers, government agencies, and conservation organizations.

Much like certain interests in private land are held by public agencies, certain interests in publicly owned land may be held by private citizens or corporations, including rights of way, oil and gas leases, and mineral leases (Laitos and Westfall 1987). The distribution of interests across multiple holders thus blurs the conventional distinction between what we think of as "public" and "private" land.

Seen from an economic perspective, legally defined rights and interests in land, along with contracts between parties that influence land use, represent expectations about what uses will be permissible over time, as well as expectations about the returns that those uses will generate. Returns may be derived from farming, development, extraction of mineral resources, and recreational and other uses. Land values reflect these alternative current and potential uses and will change over time as expected returns to these uses change.

Landownership consists of multiple interests that are generally held by more than one agent. Use of the 2.3 billion acres that make up the United States depends not just on whether they are publicly or privately owned but rather on how the multiple interests in each acre are distributed among public and private individuals and agencies. Public agencies have played a dual role with regard to property rights throughout U.S. history—via market creation and market participation—to influence land use in ways that balance public and private objectives.

The Evolution of Federal Land Policy

The evolution of federal land policy can be summarized in three overlapping phases. In the first phase, from independence through the mid-1800s, the federal government acquired lands through treaty, purchase, annexation, and cessions by the original thirteen states (National Research Council 1993). In the second phase, beginning in the nineteenth century and lasting well into the twentieth, the federal government conveyed lands to states, settlers, railroad corporations, and others (U.S. Department of the Interior 1994), and provided incentives for their conversion and use. In the final phase, over the course of this century, the federal government gradually has withdrawn incentives for land-use intensification and replaced them with restrictions on land use and incentives for land conservation and restoration.

Acquisition

Between 1781, when the original thirteen states began ceding territory west of their present boundaries to the United States, and 1867, when Alaska was purchased from Russia, the federal government acquired roughly 2 billion acres of land (the land within the original thirteen states, comprising 305 million acres, never belonged to the federal government; Hawaii's 4 million acres were annexed in 1898) (National Research Council 1993). Through cessions, treaties, purchase, and annexation, the federal government's goal during this period was to establish the territorial extent of a growing nation (see Map 5.1).

Disposition and Incentives for Land Conversion

Even before the process of territorial establishment was completed, the federal government began selling, granting, and otherwise conveying newly acquired lands to states, settlers, railroad corporations, and others to encourage westward expansion, settlement, and growth. A total of 328 million acres were granted to states for the construction of schools, roads, and for other purposes (U.S. Department of the Interior 1994). Nearly 288 million acres were granted or sold on favorable terms to homesteaders, and another 61 million acres were granted to veterans as military bounties. Over 94 million acres were granted to railroad corporations. To date, a total of 1.1 billion acres have been conveyed by the federal government to states and other nonfederal entities, with much of it later sold or transferred to private ownership.

In addition to the disposition of lands, the federal government also played an influential role in the ways that state and private lands were used. In some cases, land grants were themselves conditional on subsequent land conversion and use. For example, homesteaders received land on condition that the land was settled and cultivated or otherwise developed within a specified period of time. Among the 328 million acres granted to states were 65 million acres of wetlands, transferred on condition that the proceeds from their sale to individuals be used to convert wetlands to farmland (Carey, Heimlich, and Brazee 1990).

In addition, the federal government provided incentives for private landowners to use their lands in more intensive ways. Direct incentives included agricultural commodity price support programs and federal assistance for levee construction and wetland conversion, including assistance with drainage and channelization. Indirect incentives included favorable tax treatment of capital gains from land conversion (Wiebe and Heimlich 1996). Whether via conditions on land disposition or direct or indirect incentives to private landowners, a primary goal of federal land policy during this period was to encourage land conversion and use as a basis for economic growth.

In time, it became apparent that the benefits of westward expansion, widespread land-use changes, and economic growth were not without cost.

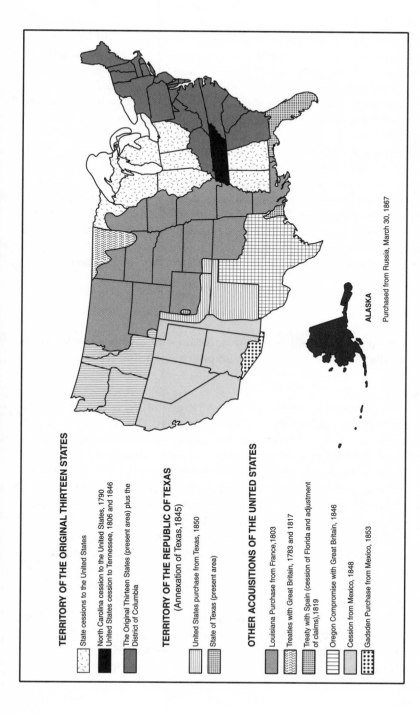

TERRITORY OF THE ORIGINAL THIRTEEN STATES

State cessions to the United States

North Carolina cession to the United States, 1790
United States cession to Tennessee, 1806 and 1846

The Original Thirteen States (present area) plus the
District of Columbia

TERRITORY OF THE REPUBLIC OF TEXAS
(Annexation of Texas, 1845)

United States purchase from Texas, 1850

State of Texas (present area)

OTHER ACQUISITIONS OF THE UNITED STATES

Louisiana Purchase from France, 1803

Treaties with Great Britain, 1783 and 1817

Treaty with Spain (cession of Florida and adjustment
of claims), 1819

Oregon Compromise with Great Britain, 1846

Cession from Mexico, 1848

Gadsden Purchase from Mexico, 1853

ALASKA

Purchased from Russia, March 30, 1867

Map 5.1. Acquisitions

83

For example, in the lower forty-eight states as a whole, about half the area under wetlands two hundred years ago has since been lost, the majority of it due to agricultural conversion. In many midwestern states, wetland losses approach 90 percent (Dahl 1990). Soil erosion became a national issue in the 1930s, when the Dust Bowl and unprecedented flooding along the lower Mississippi River were blamed on loss of vegetative cover and inappropriate cultivation practices.

While most of the land under midwestern prairie was quickly brought into private ownership and converted for cultivation, the pattern was much different in the drier and mountainous western states. There, bottomlands with fertile soil and better access to water were often homesteaded while adjacent uplands were left in federal ownership. Farmers and ranchers enjoyed virtually unrestricted access to these public lands for livestock grazing until the turn of the century, when the cumulative effects of drought and overgrazing raised concerns about the condition of federal rangeland.

Conservation

Concerns about rangeland degradation, soil erosion, and flooding led eventually to the third phase of federal land policy evolution: conservation.

Rangeland

Concerns about the condition of federal rangeland led to regulation and management by USDA's Forest Service and the Department of Interior's Bureau of Land Management (BLM) (National Research Council 1994). A grazing permit and fee system was established on Forest Service-administered land in 1906 and on BLM land in 1934. The 1960 Multiple-Use/Sustained-Yield Act and the 1976 Federal Land Policy and Management Act established that public lands would be retained in federal ownership and managed for sustained yields under multiple uses, including timber, minerals, energy, grazing, water, recreation, and wildlife (U.S. General Accounting Office 1988). The 1978 Public Rangelands Improvement Act established the formula currently used for setting fees charged to farmers and ranchers who graze livestock on federal lands. Grazing program objectives set forth in these acts and other legislation include income support for ranchers and ranching communities, prudent use of federal resources, and recovery of federal program administration costs (U.S. General Accounting Office 1991). Today the Forest Service and BLM manage more than 250 million acres of federal rangeland, most of it in sixteen western states.

Soil erosion

The combination of events that drew nationwide attention to soil erosion in the 1930s contributed to the creation of the Soil Conservation Service (SCS) in 1935. Over the next several decades, SCS provided technical assistance to farmers through a variety of programs aimed at reducing soil erosion, restoring soil productivity, and conserving water on the land (Heimlich 1991). The Soil Bank Program, established in 1956, paid farmers to establish protective cover on land taken out of crop production to reduce commodity inventories. At the peak of the program, in 1960–61, there were nearly 29 million acres under contract (Laycock 1991).

By 1969, after most contracts had expired, only 20 percent of the land enrolled in the Soil Bank Program stayed in permanent vegetative cover (Myers 1991). A perceived global food crisis, strong export demand, and rising commodity prices beginning in the early 1970s led to the conversion of over 20 million acres to cropland between 1975 and 1981 (Heimlich 1986). Annual cropland retirement programs were suspended in 1973 (Berg 1994). Rising concern over the potential environmental consequences of this increase in cultivated area combined with growing commodity surpluses in the early 1980s to motivate another shift in soil conservation policy. By 1983, cropland idled under the acreage reduction requirements of annual federal commodity programs had increased from zero to 78 million acres (Heimlich 1991; U.S. Department of Agriculture 1992a). Desire for longer-term action eventually led to the sodbuster and conservation compliance provisions of the 1985 Farm Bill, which restricted the conversion and cultivation of highly erodable land and also established the Conservation Reserve Program (CRP), through which over 36 million acres of cropland have been retired from crop production for ten-year periods and placed in protective cover of grasses or trees (Osborn 1994; see Map 5.2).

Wetlands

It is only in recent decades that the beneficial functions of wetlands—such as water-quality improvement, floodwater retention, groundwater replenishment, fish and wildlife habitat, and recreation—have come to be appreciated. The problem for policymakers is that these benefits are primarily public in nature, whereas an estimated 75 percent of remaining wetlands are privately owned (U.S. Environmental Protection Agency 1993). Thus, short of outright public acquisition of wetlands, protection of wetlands and their benefits requires land-use regulation and/or incentives to guide private decision-making.

The shift in attitudes toward wetlands preservation has resulted in the gradual reversal of federal wetlands policy in recent decades, including the

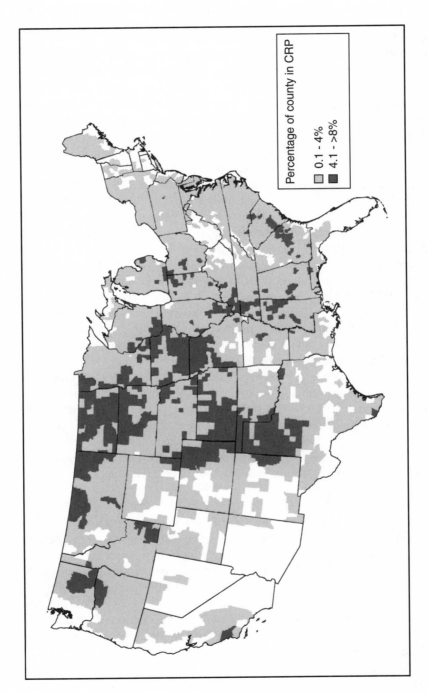

Map 5.2. Conservation Reserve Program. Redrawn from Wiebe et al. 1996.

withdrawal of publicly provided incentives for wetlands conversion and the establishment of regulations and incentives for wetlands protection and even restoration. The principal regulatory tool has been the Section 404 permit program of the Federal Water Pollution Control Amendments of 1972. Even so, normal agricultural practices are exempted, so wetlands on agricultural lands have not been greatly affected (Carey, Heimlich, and Brazee 1990). In the Prairie Pothole Region of the Upper Midwest, the Fish and Wildlife Service began acquiring permanent easements on wetlands and adjacent uplands in 1958. In the same area, USDA's Water Bank Program began negotiating renewable ten-year contracts to protect wetlands in 1972. President Carter's Executive Order 11,990 in 1977 ended all direct federal assistance for wetland conversion, including assistance with drainage and channelization. Some indirect incentives were eliminated by the "swampbuster" provisions of the 1985 and 1990 farm bills, which deny program benefits to farmers who convert wetlands or plant annual crops on wetlands converted after 1985. Other indirect incentives were eliminated by the Tax Reform Act of 1986, which eliminated favorable treatment of capital gains from land conversion and restricted landowners' ability to write off drainage costs. These initiatives have helped slow the rate of wetlands conversion, particularly for agricultural purposes. In recent decades, urban development has replaced agriculture as the major threat to remaining wetlands (U.S. Department of Agriculture 1994).

The Wetlands Reserve Program (WRP), established in the 1990 Farm Bill, goes beyond earlier efforts to slow wetland conversion by restoring converted wetlands and protecting them with permanent easements purchased from willing landowners (see Map 5.3). An Emergency Wetlands Reserve Program (EWRP), established in response to the Midwestern floods of 1993, provided special emphasis on converted wetlands damaged by the flooding. To date, about 400,000 acres have been enrolled in these two programs (Weibe, Tegene, and Kuhn 1996).

Economic Interests Inherent in Federal Land Policy

As noted above, grazing permits were introduced to rectify the de facto open access that private ranchers once held to adjacent federal rangeland. Although program rules specifically deny the conveyance of any legal interest in land to permit-holders, grazing permits allow limited private use of federal land for specified periods of time (U.S. Department of Agriculture 1992b). Permittees pay annual grazing fees, but the permits themselves are free and generally change hands with the privately owned base property to which they are attached. Some twenty-four thousand farmers and ranchers

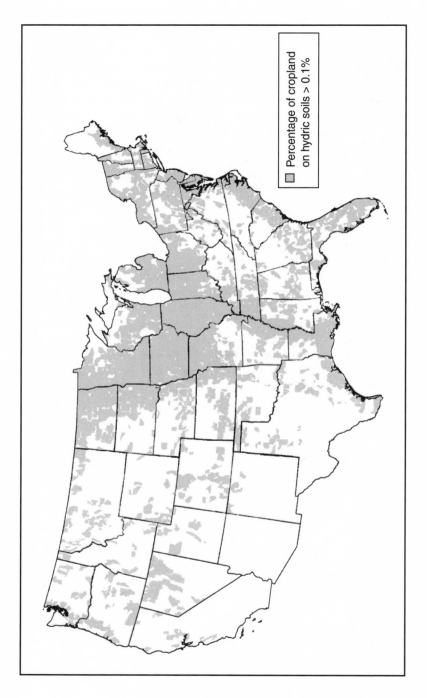

Map 5.3. Wetlands Reserve Program. Redrawn from Wiebe et al. 1996.

Percentage of cropland on hydric soils > 0.1%

currently hold federal grazing permits, generally for ten-year periods (U.S. Department of Agriculture, Forest Service, and U.S. Department of the Interior, Bureau of Land Management 1992).

CRP contracts represent more formal interests in land. Like grazing permits, they are generally written for ten-year periods. In contrast to grazing permits, however, which allow private use of public lands, CRP contracts represent interests held by the federal government in private land. About 375,000 contracts have been signed under the program, the first of which began to expire in 1995 (Osborn 1994).

WRP and EWRP easements, like CRP contracts, represent interests held by the federal government in private land. They differ from both grazing permits and CRP contracts, however, in that they are recorded in the deed, and in that they are generally binding over a longer period of time. (Until October 1996, all WRP and EWRP easements were perpetual. Since then, under the provisions of the 1996 Farm Bill, one-third of new WRP acreage has been enrolled under perpetual easements, one-third under thirty-year easements, and one-third under restoration cost-share agreements.) Over one thousand easements are at various stages in the process of enrollment and recording.

The Property Rights Debate

Debate over property rights can be traced at least as far back as 1791, to the Fifth Amendment to the Constitution, which states that private property shall not be taken for public use without just compensation. Until this century, government restrictions on land use have not been considered takings. Then, in a landmark 1922 decision, the U.S. Supreme Court ruled that "while property may be regulated to a certain extent, if regulation goes too far, it will be recognized as a taking."[1] Since that ruling, federal courts have considered the effect of a regulation on a property's value along with other criteria—such as the nature of the public purpose achieved by federal action—in determining whether a taking has occurred. Even in considering a regulation's effect on property values, the courts have generally required that the diminution in value be complete, for the parcel as a whole, before a taking is found.

The strictness of this test has meant that takings challenges are rarely successful in the courts. According to the Congressional Research Service, of 135 federal takings cases between 1990 and 1994, only 21 were found to be takings—and the ratio declined over the period (Meltz 1995). The prop-

1. *Pennsylvania Coal Co. v. Mahon*, 260 U.S. 393 (1922).

erty rights movement draws in part on frustration with this lack of success in the courts and directs its attention at legislative reforms instead.

Property Rights Reform Proposals in Congress

Property rights received unprecedented congressional attention in the 104th Congress. In 1995, the House of Representatives passed legislation that would establish a landowner's right to compensation from the federal government whenever the value of any portion of a property is diminished by 20 percent or more as a result of use restrictions imposed under various provisions of federal environmental, agricultural, or water law. Compensation would be determined as the loss in value of the portion of the property on which use had been restricted.

Such legislation would require compensation whenever the threshold diminution in value is met or exceeded, whether a legally defined right is actually taken from the landowner or not. This is a critical departure from prior takings law. This departure is significant, since it means that compensation requirements would cover not only regulatory programs but also other federal actions that affect expectations about future returns to land—including conditions placed on voluntary programs. In fact, alongside regulatory programs like the Endangered Species Act and Section 404 of the Clean Water Act, the House legislation specifically targeted the swampbuster and conservation compliance provisions of the 1985 Farm Bill—conditions placed on farmer participation in voluntary programs administered by USDA—even though such conditions are not considered takings (and thus require no compensation) under current law.

Although the 104th Congress ultimately adjourned in 1996 without enacting a takings bill, property rights concerns are likely to resurface during debate over reauthorization of other environmental laws, including the Clean Water Act and the Endangered Species Act. Due to growing public recognition of the potential fiscal and environmental costs of proposed compensation requirements, such debate almost certainly will be more moderate in substance and tone than that which took place in 1995.

Conclusion: the Property Rights Debate Reconsidered

What insights does a review of land tenure and the evolution of federal land policy provide for the property rights debate? We have seen that ownership of any parcel, "public" or "private," consists of multiple interests held by a variety of public and private agents. Far from allowing any use that a landowner wishes, landownership bears both rights and responsibilities. The public and its representatives, including the federal government, have long sought to balance these rights and responsibilities between public and private agents on both public and private land.

In the period of land acquisition, the federal government acquired, through cession, treaty, purchase, and annexation, 2 billion of the 2.3 billion acres that today make up the United States. Such acquisitions reflected the federal government's interest in establishing the territorial extent of the new nation. In the period of land disposition, the federal government granted or sold on favorable terms hundreds of millions of acres to states, individuals, and private corporations. This process certainly reflected an interest in private ownership and local authority, but it also reflected a national interest in speeding the settlement and growth of the country as a whole. In the most recent of the three phases of land policy summarized in this chapter, the federal government continues the process of property rights definition and market participation. Regulations to protect wetlands and endangered species habitat help define and protect public interests in clean water, flood prevention, and scientific and recreational opportunities. CRP contracts and WRP or EWRP easements recognize the interests of landowners in lands that have already been converted for crop production.

In each of these periods, the federal government has played a dual role with regard to balancing public and private interests. First, in the acquisition and disposition of federal lands, as well as in the introduction of grazing permits, wetland conversion permits, and conditions on participation in commodity programs, the federal government has maintained a process of establishing and defining the distribution of property rights in society. This is an essential step in the creation of a market system within which private agents can interact. It also is necessarily a political process in which the interests of society as a whole are balanced against the interests of individual landowners. Second, the federal government has participated in the resulting market for interests in land, for example by entering into CRP contracts or by purchasing WRP or EWRP easements from willing landowners.

While the specific objectives of federal land policy and the tools used to achieve them have evolved over time, what has not changed is the overall goal of balancing competing interests through a broad strategy of defining property rights definition and market participation. This strategy has demonstrated the ability to seek an appropriate balance between changing public and private needs and objectives. In the case of wetlands, for example, this has resulted in reliance on a combination of market-defining efforts (the Section 404 permit process and the swampbuster provisions) as well as market participation (through the WRP) to restrict wetland conversion and encourage wetland restoration. Better understanding of these dual roles—in a wide variety of resource policy contexts—is essential for a more informed debate on property rights.

References

Berg, Norman A. 1994. "The Genesis of the CRP." In *When Conservation Reserve Program Contracts Expire: The Policy Options,* conference proceedings, pp. 7–12. Ankeny, IA: Soil and Water Conservation Society.

Carey, Marc, Ralph Heimlich, and Richard Brazee. 1990. *A Permanent Wetland Reserve: Analysis of a New Approach to Wetland Protection.* Washington, D.C.: U.S. Department of Agriculture, Economic Research Service, Agriculture Information Bulletin no. 610.

Closser, Jay E. 1993. "Assessing Land Under Conservation Restrictions." In *Proceedings of the 59th Annual Conference of the International Association of Assessing Officers.* September 19–22, 1993. Washington, D.C.

Coase, Ronald. 1960. "The Problem of Social Cost." *Journal of Law and Economics* 3: 1–44.

Dahl, Thomas E. 1990. *Wetlands Losses in the United States, 1780's to 1980's.* Washington, D.C.: U.S. Department of the Interior, Fish and Wildlife Service.

Daugherty, Arthur B. 1995. *Major Uses of Land in the United States: 1992.* Washington, D.C.: U.S. Department of Agriculture, Economic Research Service, Agricultural Economic Report no. 723.

Heimlich, Ralph E. 1986. "Agricultural Programs and Cropland Conversion, 1975–1981." *Land Economics* 62 (2): 174–181.

Heimlich, Ralph E. 1991. "Soil Erosion and Conservation Policies in the United States." In *Farming and the Countryside: An Economic Analysis of External Costs and Benefits,* edited by Nick Hanley, pp. 59–90. London: CAB International.

Laitos, Jan G., and Richard Westfall. 1987. "Government Interference with Private Interests in Public Resources." *Harvard Environmental Law Review* 11 (1): 1–75.

Laycock, William A. 1991. "The Conservation Reserve Program—How Did We Get Where We Are and Where Do We Go From Here?" In *The Conservation Reserve—Yesterday, Today, and Tomorrow.* Symposium Proceedings, U.S. Department of Agriculture, Forest Service, Rocky Mountain Forest and Range Experiment Station. General Technical Report RM-203: 1–6.

Meltz, Robert. 1995. "Court Rulings during 1994 on Constitutional Taking Claims against the United States." Washington, D.C.: The Library of Congress, Congressional Research Service.

Myers, Peter C. 1991. "Future Costs and Benefits of Conservation Reserve Lands." In *The Conservation Reserve—Yesterday, Today, and Tomorrow.* Symposium Proceedings, U.S. Department of Agriculture, Forest Service, Rocky Mountain Forest and Range Experiment Station. General Technical Report RM-203: 43–45.

National Research Council. 1993. *Setting Priorities for Land Conservation.* National Research Council, Commission on Life Sciences, Board on Environmental Studies and Toxicology, Committee on Scientific and Technical Criteria for Federal

Acquisition of Lands for Conservation. Washington, D.C.: National Academy Press.

National Research Council. 1994. *Rangeland Health: New Methods to Classify, Inventory, and Monitor Rangelands.* National Research Council, Board on Agriculture, Committee on Rangeland Health. Washington, D.C.: National Academy Press.

Osborn, Tim. 1994. RTD *Updates: Conservation Reserve Program.* Washington, D.C.: U.S. Department of Agriculture, Economic Research Service, Resources and Technology Division.

U.S. Department of Agriculture. Economic Research Service, Resources and Technology Division. 1992a. *Agricultural Resources: Cropland, Water, and Conservation (Situation and Outlook Report).* Washington, D.C.

U.S. Department of Agriculture. Forest Service. 1992b. *Grazing Statistical Summary, FY1991.* Washington, D.C.

U.S. Department of Agriculture, Forest Service, and U.S. Department of the Interior, Bureau of Land Management. 1992. *Grazing Fee Review and Evaluation Update of the 1986 Final Report.* Washington, D.C.

U.S. Department of Agriculture. Natural Resources Conservation Service. 1994. *Summary Report: 1992 National Resources Inventory.* Washington, D.C.

U.S. Department of the Interior. Bureau of Land Management. 1994. *Public Land Statistics 1993.* Washington, D.C.: U.S. Department of the Interior, Bureau of Land Management.

U.S. Environmental Protection Agency. 1993. *Wetlands Fact Sheet no. 30: Partnerships with Landowners.* Washington, D.C.: U.S. Environmental Protection Agency, Office of Water, Office of Wetlands, Oceans, and Watersheds.

U.S. General Accounting Office. 1988. *Rangeland Management: More Emphasis Needed on Declining and Overstocked Grazing Allotments.* GAO/RCED-88–80. Washington, D.C.

U.S. General Accounting Office. 1991. *Rangeland Management: Current Formula Keeps Grazing Fees Low.* GAO/RCED-91–185BR. Washington, D.C.

U.S. General Services Administration. 1995. *Summary Report of Real Property Owned by the United States Throughout the World as of September 30, 1993.* Washington, D.C.: U.S. General Services Administration, Public Buildings Service, Office of Governmentwide Real Property Relations.

Wiebe, Keith D., and Ralph E. Heimlich. 1996. "The Evolution of Federal Wetlands Policy." In *The Best of Choices, 1986–1996,* edited by Harry W. Ayer, pp. 63–68. Ames, IA: American Agricultural Economic Association.

Wiebe, Keith D., Abebayehu Tegene, and Betsey Kuhn. 1996. *Partial Interests in Land: Policy Tools for Resource Use and Conservation.* Agricultural Economics Report no. 744. Washington, D.C.: U.S. Department of Agriculture, Economic Research Service.

Youngman, Joan. 1993. "Concepts of Property and Taxation." In *Land Ownership and Taxation,* edited by Gene Wunderlich, pp. 45–59. Boulder, CO: Westview Press.

Markets and Ethics in U.S. Property Law

Arthur McEvoy

Introduction

The law of property in the United States contains a profound bias toward developmental uses and against such nonmarket values as the health and welfare of the communities that live on the land or, indeed, the ecological well-being of the land itself. This bias is so deeply ingrained in the U.S. legal culture that it presents itself as a law of nature: the fundamental liberty of private owners to develop their property as they please is the cornerstone of American civil and economic freedom, while relatively unlimited access to the resources of the public lands is an all but inviolate principle in American politics.[1]

This pro-developmental bias is a historical artifact, built into our law over the course of the nineteenth century by courts, legislatures, and private citizens for whom economic development was the key to the nation's security and prosperity. It is not essential to the nation's law or to any of its institutions. Indeed, since the beginning of the nineteenth century it has existed in constant tension with other, contradictory values that uphold responsibility to communitarian, social, and environmental concerns as a counterweight to narrow economism and individual profit-seeking. This tension inheres in law governing both the public lands and private property and manifests itself in each in similar ways. Since Thomas Jefferson, this communitarian aspect of U.S. property law focused its concern primarily on such social values as education, economic stability, and participatory democracy. Ecological concerns have emerged as an important factor in debates over land use in the second half of the twentieth century, but these are only the latest manifestations of the long-standing, Jeffersonian concern for nonmarket values that runs through the nation's history.

---

1. On the ways in which law and legal culture "naturalize" certain aspects of social order while leaving others open to political questioning, see Gordon (1984, 1985).

The Public Lands

Today the United States owns perhaps 690 million acres of land, or about one-third of the country's total land area.[2] The public lands include such parcels as the national forests, the national parks, military bases, the White House, and the continental shelf. Federal ownership of these lands was an essential precondition to the birth of the United States: confederation between the thirteen original states would not have taken place if those states with significant claims to lands on the western frontier had not agreed with states that did not have such claims that the western lands would be ceded to the national government and administered by the Congress as a common fund for the benefit of all (Gates 1976). This agreement survives today in Article IV, Section 3 of the U.S. Constitution, which provides that "The Congress shall have Power to dispose of and make all needful Rules and Regulations respecting the Territory and other Property belonging to the United States."

From the beginning, the United States was unusual among nations in two respects. First, the national government used the public lands as a primary instrument of social policy. Second, the United States has a broad diffusion of private landownership among its citizens, who have great liberty to do with their land as they please. The early United States was an ambitious experiment with an uncertain future. It had relatively little capital available for investment and short supplies of labor and entrepreneurship. One thing the country did have, however, was land and lots of it. At the founding, the national government owned 200 million acres of land, stretching from the crest of the Appalachian Mountains to the Mississippi River. By 1860, public landholdings reached as far as the Pacific Ocean and had increased to over a billion acres with Jefferson's purchase of the Louisiana Territory from Napoleon, the acquisition of Florida from Spain and Oregon from the British, and the thinly disguised theft of the northern third of Mexico in the 1840s. In 1867, the nation purchased the Alaska Territory from Russia, adding another 200 million acres or so. This land was among the richest on the planet: it contained gold and other precious metals, vast expanses of timber, and some thirty million buffalo, among other resources (see Gates 1968; Hurst 1964).

The effort to manage this endowment as a common fund for the benefit of the whole people was crucial to the success of the republican experiment in the United States and has been perhaps the single most powerful influence on the nation's history. Law has been the medium through which this process has taken place. Americans rely on law as a kind of corporate brain

2. On the public lands generally, see Clawson (1983); Wilkinson (1987; 1989); Coggins (1990, 1994); Mansfield (1993).

for their society, using legal processes and institutions to identify problems that require public attention, to consider and choose among alternative strategies for addressing these problems, and to carry out the strategies they do choose (Hurst 1977).[3]

The people made two crucial decisions regarding public lands at the outset. The first was to carve the western lands into territories that, after a period of modified self-government under congressional supervision and a presidentially appointed territorial governor, would ultimately be admitted to the Union as equals to the original thirteen states. The United States would thus develop as a republic, not as a colonial empire on the British, Spanish, and French models. The Confederation Congress embodied this decision in the Northwest and Southwest Territorial Ordinances of 1785 and 1787, which were ratified by the new Congress under the 1787 Constitution (Gates 1976; Hurst 1956).[4] The second decision was to put the land inside these new states into the hands of private citizens. Congress took the first step toward this goal in a 1796 statute that established the Cadastral Survey: this divided the landscape into abstract rectangles—the essence of the republican form—with the goal of making the public lands easy to administer and easy to market, both before and after the initial sale to private individuals. At this point, however, there emerged a fundamental disagreement over public lands policy, which continues to this day. As a nation we have never been sure whether the public lands should be administered primarily for their productive potential or for their potential to provide social or ethical benefits to the people.

One side in this debate was market-oriented in its outlook. Its chief exponents were the Federalists, whose ideological leader was the Washington administration's treasury secretary, Alexander Hamilton. Hamilton's idea was to market the land as quickly as possible so as to generate cash to be used for government purposes. Government would not involve itself in the administration of land use per se; market forces would determine which lands would be developed, when, and to what purposes. The Federalists reasoned that government simply did not have the bureaucratic resources required to administer the public lands; market forces naturally would employ the far greater collective genius of the people in making productive use of the land. The goal, then, was to use the land to generate market benefits in the form of revenue for government purposes and economic development by and for private citizens. Political and social benefits would accrue naturally, as a by-product of market forces that were more or less inexorable in any event (Gates 1976; Friedman 1985).

3. Useful introductions to legal history include Friedman (1985) and Hall (1989).
4. On the early administration of the land laws, see Rohrbough (1968).

The other side in the debate was suspicious of market forces and hoped that government would administer the lands more deliberately to promote social and political goals. The chief exponent of this theory was Thomas Jefferson, who dreamed of creating not a commercial republic, as Hamilton envisioned, but an autarkic, agrarian republic of independent, small-scale, diversified farmers. This would entail distributing the land slowly and carefully into the hands of actual settlers, at a rate determined by the growth of the population rather than by market forces and at a price designed to promote a broad diffusion of landed property among the citizenry. The primary goal of public lands policy would be to promote social and political goals directly, to fashion a nation of orderly, "virtuous" communities of independent, self-governing citizens (Hurst 1956; 1964).[5]

Of the two visions, that of the Hamiltonians better anticipated the future course of the nation's development. Jefferson's vision was firmly rooted in eighteenth-century social thought. His view of the economy was essentially mercantilist: the wealth of a nation consisted in the land it held under cultivation and the stock of wealth it had on hand. Fundamental economic change was not part of this picture: to Jefferson, the world was essentially stable and orderly. Progress consisted of slow and steady accretion to the national wealth through population growth and the gradual addition of newly cultivated lands to the nation's stock.[6] Economic development and industrialization were to be avoided. In Europe, Jefferson thought, manufacturing was necessary to support surplus population for which no new lands were available. The United States, however, was blessed with "an immensity of land courting the industry of the husbandman." Public policy, then, should put new lands into the hands of farmers as the demand for them arose. As he wrote in *Notes on the State of Virginia,* farmers were "the chosen people of God, if ever he had a chosen people, whose breasts he has made his peculiar deposit for substantial and genuine virtue" (1955 [1787]).

Given his eighteenth-century view of a steady-state economy and the policy it suggested for the public lands, Jefferson anticipated that it would take many generations to settle the Louisiana Territory. He was wrong in this, of course: it took no more than two or three. The Hamiltonians, with their emphasis on market development and economic diversification, had a clearer view of the world that was coming into being at that very moment. They saw the world not in terms of enduring structures, as did Jefferson, but in characteristic nineteenth-century terms of dynamic change proceeding according to immutable laws.[7] Evolution was one such law that would be

---

5. On the importance of "civic virtue" to early American republicanism, see Wood (1969).
6. On eighteenth-century views of economic value and policy, see Foucault (1970).
7. On nineteenth-century economics, see Foucault (1970).

discovered later on; Marx's dialectical materialism and Durkheim's modernization were others.

In the nineteenth-century view, what drove economic change was the law of supply and demand, which inexorably pushed resources toward their most efficient uses. Industrialization was not only to be welcomed but would be essential to the nation's survival and prosperity. No government could anticipate the changes that industrialization would eventually bring to the economy and society. With the political and industrial revolutions of the late eighteenth century, as Michel Foucault (1970) put it, "history had been restored to the irruptive violence of time." Efforts to confine social and economic change, the Hamiltonians saw, would be utterly futile. It was better to liberate the capacity of the citizens to move change along by opening the public lands to them as rapidly as possible and to let the collective wisdom of the market determine how those lands would be used.

Behind the leading edge of history as it was, the Jeffersonian perspective nonetheless was built into U.S. laws and institutions and remains so to this day. U.S. public lands policy thus contains elements of both Jeffersonian and Hamiltonian motives, in schizophrenic tension. One can see the market-oriented side of the policy manifested in the rapid sale of the public lands to speculators as well as to settlers, in the outright pro-development grants of land to railroad corporations in the mid-nineteenth century, and in the consistent federal practice of selling water, timber, and minerals from the public domain to private developers at below-market rates. Above all, the Hamiltonian legacy manifests itself in the consistent and nearly wholesale government abdication to market forces of the responsibility for determining the nature of land use (Gates 1936; Hurst 1956).

The Jeffersonian, ethical side of public lands policy also has remained strong throughout the nation's history, however. Beginning in 1862, Congress passed a series of Homestead Acts that offered free land to actual settlers who would develop it. The Morrill Act of 1862 created a system of land-grant colleges to promote public education in the agricultural and mechanical arts. After 1890, there emerged an evolving system of federal reservations for forest conservation, national parks, wildlife refuges, and so on, all designed to shield the public lands from the blind rapacity of market forces and to reserve opportunities for recreation, contemplation, and natural experience for an increasingly industrial, urbanized nation (Olpin 1994).[8]

Overall, despite the apparent schizophrenia of the strange amalgam of Hamiltonian and Jeffersonian impulses it contained, U.S. public lands policy worked remarkably well to serve both market and nonmarket goals

8. On the birth of the national forest system, see Hays (1979).

through most of the nineteenth century. It settled the country with astonishing rapidity. Public lands policy was crucial to the Union victory in the Civil War, insofar as it put the lands north of the Ohio River and east of the Mississippi into the hands of a great many independent, small-scale, Jeffersonian farmers, who then supplied food, soldiers, and matériel to the Union Army in such quantities as simply to overwhelm the Confederates. By the end of the century, it had midwifed the birth of the world's largest industrial economy.

The profligate waste of land, timber, wildlife, and other resources that attended this growth did not escape notice at the time. "The thirst of a tiger for blood," wrote John Quincy Adams (quoted in Hurst 1956), "is the fittest emblem of the rapacity with which the members of all the new states fly at the public lands. The constituents upon whom they depend are all settlers, or tame and careless spectators of the pillage. They are themselves enormous speculators and land-jobbers. It were a vain attempt to resist them here."

There was not a lot that government could do to tame the process, however, given the size of the continent, the energy of the settlers, and the government's own vestigial capacity to enforce what law there was. Francis A. Walker (1890) admitted that nineteenth-century American agriculture had exploited the land "in some degree at the expense of future generations" and that traditionally wasteful land-use practices would have to change. But nineteenth-century lands policy had laid the foundation both for an industrial economy and a more careful, intensive agriculture. To this extent the policy made economic sense: Walker compared the nation's behavior to that of "the strong, courageous, hopeful young man, who puts a mortgage on his new farm, that he may stock it and equip it for a higher productiveness," in contrast to that of "the self-indulgent man of middle life who encumbers his estate for the purposes of personal consumption" (ibid.) Until the 1890s, at any rate, there seemed to be abundant reserves of timber, wildlife, and other resources on the public lands.

Private Property

Though the goal of both the mercantilist-minded, egalitarian Jeffersonians and the forward-looking, modernizing Hamiltonians was to transform the public lands into the property of private individuals, this did not mean that the government's interest in how the land was to be used was at an end. In the United States, private property has never amounted to absolute, unqualified dominion over land. The social contract meant that private landowners remained subject to the great triad of government powers: *taxation,* by which the government extracts a share of its citizens' wealth through constitutionally ordained procedures; *eminent domain,* through which the government may expropriate private property entirely, so long as the taking is for a legitimate public purpose and the owner receives fair compensation; and *police power,* with which the government may regulate the private use of land. As Chief Justice Lemuel Shaw of the Massachusetts Supreme Court put it in 1851, "All property . . . is derived directly or indirectly from the government, and held subject to those general regulations, which are necessary to the common good and general welfare."[9] Under U.S. law, then, private property amounts to a more or less limited *franchise* from government to pursue one's private ends so long as they correspond in a general way with those of the community.

Determining the scope and extent of that franchise, however, is a political process that takes place through lawmaking under constitutional restraints. Thus subject to popular sovereignty, the law of private land use also has been subject to an enduring schizophrenia that closely conforms to the conflict that has inhered in lawmaking for the public lands. Here, as a nation, the United States has never been sure whether the main purpose of private property has been to serve market goals primarily, or whether it should give equal or greater weight to social, political, or ethical considerations that are hard to formulate in market terms. Is the end of the property-based social compact to promote social stability and virtue among the citizenry, or is it merely to generate wealth? (Rose 1984). As in policymaking for the public domain, environmental concerns have emerged in the last few decades as perhaps the most important nonmarket concern in the regulation of private land use, but they are only the most recent manifestation of a tension that is built into our institutions and has endured since the founding.

On one side of this divide at the beginning were people like Jefferson and Thomas Paine, for whom private property was the key to a political ideology of civic republicanism that valued participation with other citizens in self-government as the highest good. Jefferson and Paine valued private property above all for the independence of thought and action that it guaranteed, thinking this independence to be essential for one's capacity for altruistic citizenship. Modern heirs to the Jeffersonian tradition include such scholars as Charles Reich and Frank Michelman, who value property rights as did Jefferson because they insulate political minorities both from oppression by the rich and powerful and from the whims of legislatures and government agencies that too often serve only the needs of the powerful (see Rose 1984; Reich 1964; Michelman 1981). Such legal devices as rent control and zoning laws, for example, require people to temper their market avarice with a

9. *Commonwealth v. Alger,* 7 Cush 53, 83–84 (Mass., 1851).

measure of altruistic, civic-minded concern for others perhaps less powerful than they. Theoretically, they subordinate individuals' dominion over the use of their property to the good of the community.

On the other side of the divide were philosophical liberals, such as Locke or James Madison, who thought that Jeffersonian civic virtue was a slender reed on which to build a political system. As the experiences of the ancient republics showed, government that required consistently selfless behavior on the part of its citizens was exceedingly fragile and doomed to fail. It was far more reasonable, as Madison (reprinted 1981) explained in *The Federalist Papers,* to expect people to be self-regarding most of the time but to devise a political system that would diffuse individual avarice and economize what public-regarding, civic altruism might be available (see also Ackerman 1984). Federalism and the separation of powers was the key to this process within government. A wide diffusion of independent property interests throughout society at large, Madison and other liberals thought, was the essential foundation for stable republican government (Rose 1984).

Liberalism thus predicted that an infinite number of self-regarding decisions by an infinite number of autonomous property owners would not only lead to the efficient use of resources in the economy but also to government in the best interest of the whole people. Government thus need not get into the messy business of determining that one way of living or using one's property was better for the community than another. Although Madison never would have thought this way, at its extreme this liberal view eventually collapsed voting into consumerism: both politics and markets were efficient, the one trading votes and the other dollars. The public interest therefore consisted of no more and no less than the algebraic sum of all the private interests. One of the most articulate proponents of this view today is Justice Antonin Scalia of the U.S. Supreme Court, whose vision increasingly dominates the law of land-use regulation in the federal courts.

Throughout the nineteenth century, the victory of this utilitarian, market-oriented approach to the law of private land use was nearly total. As William Cronon (1983) has shown, even from the first settlements in the New World, Europeans brought with them an economy that was based on the transformation of land to commercial use. This economy, which treated the land as no more than a bundle of potentially marketable commodities, was incompatible with and utterly displaced the Native American system of land use, which, although it was complex, law-bound, and built on rights to harvest resources, knit itself into the natural functioning of the land so as to maintain the natives' subsistence economy over the long run. The disruption of native societies was at the same time a military, economic, and, above all, ecological process.

As between Euro-Americans, traditional common-law restrictions on property ownership for centuries had limited the uses to which individual owners could put their property, likewise so as to preserve the stability of the traditional agrarian economy over the long run. Common-law rules, which frequently authorized complaining neighbors to put a stop to offensive uses themselves without waiting for formal authorities to step in, limited the harvest of wildlife, the diversion of rivers and streams from their natural courses, even the erection of structures that blocked neighbors' access to light and air (Horowitz 1977; Scheiber 1980). In the early nineteenth century, many of these traditional restrictions fell away as American courts overturned these "anti-developmental" property rules and replaced them with market-oriented, pro-development doctrines so as to encourage what the legal historian J. Willard Hurst (1956) called the "release of entrepreneurial energy." The relative "reasonableness" of competing uses for land or water, for example, came by 1850 to be measured and compared in terms of their dollar contribution to the community's net economic product: in a process that the economist Joseph Schumpeter (1950) called "creative destruction," the law permitted new and more efficient factories, mills, and mines to expropriate land, water, and even sunlight from their older and less efficient competitors. Utilitarianism thoroughly infused the law of private land use: a private nuisance came to be defined as a use that generated more costs to neighbors than it did benefits to the user, while a public nuisance was any use where the benefits to a developing property owner did not outweigh its external costs to society at large.

Between private citizens and the state, market-oriented utilitarianism entered the law of property rights when private landowners claimed that police power regulations so hindered their ability to use their property as they saw fit as to amount to an exercise of eminent domain, in which case the state owed the aggrieved property owner fair compensation for the expropriation of his or her property. When a government body needed to take possession of a citizen's land outright, it found some public purpose for the taking and paid some compensation, however minimal that compensation might become in the hands of creative judges and lawyers (Scheiber 1973).

When the claim was that the law had made it impossible for owners to use their property as they wished, even though they retained possession, the matter was more complicated. State legislatures have always had a great deal of authority to proscribe uses of land that they deemed detrimental to the public health, safety, or morals. In the famous case of *Mugler v. Kansas* in 1886, the U.S. Supreme Court held that a state prohibition law worked no taking against the owner of a brewery, even though it denied him the only possible economic use of his plant.[10] What distinguished takings from ordinary police regulations was that in the latter case the benefit to the public

---

10. *Mugler v. Kansas*, 123 U.S. 623 (1887).

health, safety, and morals outweighed the inconvenience to the regulated property owner.

Justice Oliver Wendell Holmes moved toward a more strictly monetary utilitarianism in the 1922 case of *Pennsylvania Coal Company v. Mahon:* there, a state statute prohibited the underground mining of coal where it would cause overlying residential properties to subside. Justice Holmes found that the statute imposed a greater cost on the coal company than it conveyed benefits to the homeowners and thus qualified as a taking.[11] Generally, however, governments have wide authority to weigh moral, aesthetic, or even ecological values against the monetary loss to property owners. It is extremely rare for a court to find a so-called regulatory taking such as the Supreme Court did in the *Mahon* case: typically anything short of outright expropriation of an owner's title qualified as a reasonable exercise of the police power, no different from a food-inspection law, say, or a speed limit (see Sax 1964).

As in the case of the public lands, the utilitarian, market-oriented calculus that defined nuisance law, which marked off the boundaries between private landowners, and takings law, which defined the frontier between individual landowners and public power, worked reasonably well to serve both economic expansion and the preservation of public virtue for quite some time. One reason was that legislatures, through the political process, retained lots of authority to incorporate nonmarket, nonmonetary values into a broader utilitarianism. Another reason, however, was that land itself remained cheap and plentiful until the end of the nineteenth century brought with it the end of the frontier. Petty expropriations by powerful neighbors or by the state generally hit landowners at random, diffused here and there across society so that only rarely would losers organize into a politically effective mass. The relative ease of picking up and moving on, as compared to the cost of trying to fight the law and those who called its expansionary tune, also tended to keep opposition to a minimum. Even John Locke (reprinted 1960), however, wrote that private property could serve as the medium of the social contract only so long as there remained "enough, and as good left; and more than the yet unprovided could use" (see also Rose 1987). In the twentieth century, the stakes would rise.

Late Twentieth-Century Law: Market Values v. Ecological Values

The contest between market and nonmarket values, between the "revenue" approach of the early Hamiltonians and the "settlement" approach of Jeffer-

---

11. *Pennsylvania Coal Co. v. Mahon*, 260 U.S. 393 (1922).

son and his followers, has persisted throughout the history of the U.S. legal system, both in struggles over the management and disposition of the public lands and in conflicts over the use of private property, both between private neighbors and between private owners and state authorities. In the late twentieth century, the revenue-settlement dichotomy most often presents itself to public view in the form of contests between market or developmental values and environmental ones. For Jefferson, the values that most needed legal protection from the corrosive effects of the free market in land were essentially political ones: the independence and self-sufficiency that citizens needed in order to keep the virtuous republic from unraveling. Today, people who fear the corrosive effects of the market are more likely to speak on behalf of ecology, which knits society into the natural environment that sustains it. The issues, at bottom, are the same: should landowners have complete license to develop their resources in pursuit of their private, self-defined goals, or are there more diffuse, intangible, hard-to-monetize values that require landowners to sacrifice a measure of their private gain for the good of the community as a whole? Two recent decisions from the U.S. Supreme Court, one of them dealing with the management of public lands and the other with state regulation of private land use, display the economistic, developmental bias that suffuses U.S. land law and remains its dominant theme. Both, however, also manifest the tension between the developmental main theme and its Jeffersonian antithesis, now emergent in the form of claims that affirm the interconnections between ecology, land use, and human community.

Lyng v. Northwest Indian Cemetery Protective Association came down from the U.S. Supreme Court in 1988.[12] *Lyng* is famous in the law schools and on bar-review courses as a First Amendment, freedom-of-religion case, but it had its origins in a controversy over the management of public lands. Forests and fisheries were the resources at stake; the contestants were a handful of California Indian tribes and the U.S. Forest Service.[13] Immediately at issue was a Forest Service plan to complete the middle section of a logging road through a remote part of the Six Rivers National Forest in northwestern California. Loggers and the Forest Service claimed that the road was necessary to provide access to marketable timber. Environmentalists, however, claimed that the road, which would cut through rugged and unstable terrain, would cause intolerable soil erosion and would injure water quality in the Klamath River system, which was home to a seriously depleted salmon fishery. The Klamath watershed also contained an Indian reservation: Yurok, Karok, and Tolowa Indians had lived in the region since aboriginal

---

12. *Lyng v. Northwest Indian Cemetery Protective Association*, 485 U.S. 439 (1988).
13. Commentaries on the Lyng decision include Spreng (1994), Miller (1990), Ripani (1990), and Falk (1989). On the background to *Lyng*, see McEvoy (1986).

times and used areas near the road site for traditional religious practices. Advocates of religious freedom, tribal autonomy, and environmentalism thus all came together on one side; the Forest Service and the timber industry were on the other.

The Forest Service had commissioned a study of the area as part of its obligations under the National Environmental Policy Act (NEPA); this study recommended that the road not be completed. The area was indispensable to the religious practices of these Indian communities, with specific mountaintops, rocks, and other sites being used for observances. "Successful use," the report continued, "depends upon certain qualities of the physical environment, the most important of which are privacy, silence, and an undisturbed natural setting."[14] The road would "cause serious and irreparable damage to the sacred areas which are an integral and necessary part of the belief systems and lifeway of Northwest California Indians."[15] NEPA does not require that government agencies follow the advice of such reports, however, only that they generate the information and look it over.[16] The Forest Service went ahead with its plans to build the road, and the Indians sued.

Although the *Lyng* plaintiffs had sued to enjoin the construction under a number of statutes, it was their constitutional claim under the First Amendment that made it to the Supreme Court on appeal, and on that claim they lost. It is well-settled that Congress has nearly plenary authority to manage the public lands as it sees fit, subject of course to constitutional restraints.[17] As to this particular constitutional claim, Justice O'Connor's opinion for the majority was that the First Amendment did not require the government to conduct its own internal affairs so as to comport with the religious beliefs of particular citizens.[18] "Internal affairs," in this case, meant building roads and harvesting timber on Forest Service land. The government's ownership of the land was key to the decision: like any private owners, the government was entitled to develop its property as it saw fit, and the religious beliefs of a tiny minority of citizens could not be allowed to stand in the way.

Whatever the Forest Service's calculations had been, at the Supreme Court level the *Lyng* decision did not involve even the most rudimentary consideration of costs and benefits, much less a careful balancing between market and nonmarket concerns in managing the public lands for the benefit of the common people. As the dissent pointed out,

---

14. Quoted in *Lyng*, 485 U.S. at 442.
15. Id.
16. *Strycker's Bay Neighborhood Council, Inc., v. Karlen*, 444 U.S. 223 (1980); *Robertson v. Methow Valley Citizens Council*, 490 U.S. 332 (1989).
17. *Kleppe v. New Mexico*, 426 U.S. 529 (1976). See Goble (1986), and Brodie (1981).
18. *Lyng*, 485 U.S. at 451–452.

> Today's ruling sacrifices a religion at least as old as the Nation itself, along with the spiritual well-being of its approximately 5,000 adherents, so that the Forest Service can build a six-mile segment of road that two lower courts found had only the most marginal and speculative utility, both to the government itself and to the private lumber interests that might conceivably use it.[19]

The private losses involved were huge, while the public benefit was negligible. Here, the government stood in the position of a private owner rather than a trustee, and a particularly irresponsible one at that.

Nonetheless, the Indian respondents in *Lyng* did articulate the link between the land, their spiritual life, and their social order. Indian reservations have become increasingly important to environmental politics for a number of reasons. First, developments in the law over the last few decades have strengthened the tribes' political autonomy and their authority to protect their resources from damage, both directly from activities on the reservation and indirectly from competing uses on neighboring lands. In addition, the importance of "natural" land uses to the Indians' traditional economies and societies means that the tribes tend to use their authority to protect environmental and other nonmarket values more vigorously than do non-Indians. Finally, because ecology links the health of Indian resources with economic activities far beyond the boundaries of Indian jurisdictions, Indian rights and Indian culture will increasingly place limits, backed up with the force of law, on resource-development practices in regions of the country where Indian communities survive. Like endangered species, the law commits the United States to ensuring the survival of what Indian economies remain and to restraining development so that the environment can continue to support those economies. The irrational and unjust result in *Lyng v. Northwest Indian Cemetery Protective Association* only underscores the strength of the general trend.

Lucas v. South Carolina Coastal Council was another recent U.S. Supreme Court decision that upheld an expansive view of the reach of a landowner's autonomy: here, however, the owner in question was a private party rather than the U.S. government.[20] David Lucas was a real estate entrepreneur who built a residential development on a barrier island east of Charleston, South Carolina, and, in 1986, purchased the last two lots in the development for his own account. Under the federal Coastal Zone Management Act, South Carolina had for some years placed restrictions on beachfront development, although as the law stood at the time Lucas's development was perfectly legal. In 1988, however, two years after Lucas bought his parcels, the state tightened its restrictions on development in

19. *Lyng*, 485 U.S. at 476 (Brennan, J., dissenting).
20. *Lucas v. South Carolina Coastal Council*, 112 S.Ct. 2886 (1992).

such a way as to prohibit construction on the two lots that Lucas had bought for himself.

The South Carolina legislature justified the restrictions on several grounds. It found that beaches all along the state's shoreline were eroding and that construction had exacerbated the problem, thus exposing life and property to danger from storm damage. Seawalls and other engineered protections were not as effective as natural beaches in preventing the erosion. The state's beaches were important to the local economy as tourist attractions and as habitat for wildlife. Acting within what it thought was the traditional scope of its power to protect the public health, safety, and morals, the legislature allowed existing construction seaward of the prohibition line to stand; no new construction could take place, however, including the houses that Lucas had planned to build on his two lots.

Lucas sued, claiming that this was no ordinary police-power exercise but rather a taking of his property without due process of law, in violation of the Fourteenth Amendment of the U.S. Constitution. In what looked like a decision tailor-made to raise a constitutional challenge under the cost-benefit calculus of *Pennsylvania Coal Company v. Mahon,* the trial court (sitting without a jury), found that the state regulation had deprived Lucas's property of all of its economic value. The state Supreme Court, relying on the "take-title theory" of *Mugler,* the 1886 Kansas brewery case, held that Lucas was still in possession of his lands: the restrictions on beachfront development were a legitimate use of the police power to protect the public welfare and thus did not amount to a compensable taking.[21]

In 1992, the U.S. Supreme Court reversed the state decision and remanded the case for further consideration. For the majority, Justice Scalia developed a new, two-part approach to "regulatory takings" according to which the state courts were to decide the case on remand. First, the courts were to decide whether or not the regulation in question had deprived the complaining party of 100 percent of the economic value of the lands. If some economic value remained, the regulation fell onto the police-power, as opposed to the eminent-domain, side of the constitutional takings line. If there was a so-called total taking of economic value, then the courts were to inquire whether or not the prohibited use violated "restrictions that background principles of the State's law of property and nuisance already place[d] upon ownership."[22] If the prohibited use was a traditional common-law nuisance—a slaughterhouse, say, or a gravel pit, or perhaps even a brewery—the court was to presume that Lucas had bought the parcels in the first place knowing that the state had the authority to keep him

21. *Lucas v. South Carolina Coastal Council,* 304 S.C. 376, 404 S.E.2d 895 (1991).
22. *Lucas,* 112 S.Ct. at 2900.

from proceeding. Justice Scalia noted in passing that residential construction was "the essential use of land" and would probably not fall under his "background principles" of common-law nuisance, but that was for the lower court to decide.[23]

Lucas was a case that was brought in order to "play for rules"—its managers designed the case so as to give the courts an opportunity to write doctrine into constitutional law as much as to resolve the particular dispute at hand. The decision itself as a very narrow one, applying only to the tiny handful of imaginable cases where regulations deprive owners of all economic use of their land *and* the regulating agencies are unable plausibly to describe the prohibited uses as nuisances. It likely will have a much greater impact in the law schools, then, than it will in the world at large. It has received a great deal of attention and criticism, however, both from the environmental Left and from the property-rights-oriented Right (see Bromley 1993; Epstein 1993; Sax 1993; Michelman 1993). What is of particular interest here is the role that "background principles of property and nuisance" play in Justice Scalia's takings scheme.

According to Joseph Sax (1993), a leading environmental law scholar, the *Lucas* court's underlying agenda was to prevent states from regulating land use "by requiring owners to maintain their property in its natural state as part of a functioning ecosystem." The majority drew its historical "background" from the frontier days of the nineteenth century, when the common law was straightforwardly pro-development and when nuisance findings (cases like *Mugler v. Kansas* aside) generally turned on a strictly monetary, cost-benefit calculus. Whatever nonmarket values did make up part of the nineteenth-century background, they certainly did not include ecological ones. Indeed, the Court had a hard time imagining that environmental values could be of any real concern to a state legislature: of all the legislative findings that went into the South Carolina beachfront protection statute, the one that the majority seized upon as the "real" purpose behind the statute was the enhancement of tourism. This made the statute look more like a transfer of rights from owner Lucas to beachgoing tourists—technically, the public condemnation of a "visual easement"—and thus more like a specific expropriation than a police regulation generally applicable to all.[24]

That land could have real value to the public as part of a functioning ecosystem seems not to have been within the reach of the majority's collective imagination. Quoting the seventeenth-century jurist Edward Coke, Justice Scalia asked, "For what is land but the profits thereof?"[25] The opinion

23. *Lucas,* 112 S.Ct. at 2901.
24. *Lucas,* 112 S.Ct. at 2898 n. 11.
25. *Lucas,* 112 S.Ct. at 2894.

thus took an extreme Hamiltonian view of the nature of property, beyond anything that James Madison or any nineteenth-century judge would have allowed. Land that the state wishes to dedicate to "natural" functions is to that extent public land and thus incompatible from private ownership, which consists solely in the right to turn the land to a profit. If the state wishes to promote ecological functions of land to the exclusion of developmental ones, it necessarily does so at the expense of the private owner and must compensate that owner for pressing his or her property into public service.

The several dissenting opinions in *Lucas* pointed out that the case was not ripe for review, that the Court had reached down into the system to bring it up for review in a play for doctrine, and that the decision had upset long-settled eminent domain law with its theory of "total economic takings" and substituted for it an entirely new and unprecedented alternative. The dissenters pointed out that property and nuisance law never had allowed the autonomy of property owners to trump absolutely the public, community-serving attributes of private property. In the nineteenth century, judges like Lemuel Shaw of Massachusetts had used Jeffersonian rhetoric to underscore the authority of state legislatures to promote economic growth, even if at the occasional expense of private owners who stood in the way. U.S. legislatures historically have recognized different goals for property and nuisance law and changed those laws accordingly: at one time to promote the Jeffersonian values of civic republicanism, at another to promote industrialization and economic growth, lately to promote environmental conservation. Environmentalism is simply the most recent manifestation of the structural tendency of U.S. law to keep market and nonmarket values in constant tension in the process of regulating the use of public and private lands.

Conclusion

The decisions in *Lyng v. Northwest Indian Cemetery Protective Association* and *Lucas v. South Carolina Coastal Council* take uncommonly rigorous positions on one side of the dichotomy between developmental and nonmarket values, a dichotomy that has kept the law of land use in the United Sates in tension since the founding of the Republic in the late eighteenth century. This tension first manifested itself in the conflict between settlement-oriented Jeffersonians and revenue-oriented Hamiltonians over the management of the public domain, and it appears today as a conflict between those who would manage the public lands on behalf of jobs and industry and those who would give higher priority to environmental, cultural, and spiritual values. The same tension runs through the U.S. law of private land use, which upholds both the freedom of landowners to pursue profit as they see fit and their responsibility to conform their behavior to community notions of the public good, whether the community—through politics and self-government—defines that good in terms of Jeffersonian agrarianism, of entrepreneurial dynamism, or of ecological interdependence. The *Lyng* and *Lucas* decisions are bad news for environmentalists, but they are interesting in that they bring the two sides of American land law into such sharp relief.

One of the most important roles that the U.S. Supreme Court plays in our legal system is to draw out such philosophical conflicts from time to time and to subject them to reasoned analysis in the light of contemporary concerns, just as it did in the *Lyng* and *Lucas* cases. The Supreme Court hardly has the last word on the law, however, much less in the ongoing political struggle to define the values that will control the nation's interaction with its natural environment. The genius of the Founders was to embed the Court, like all other levels and branches of government, in a tripartite, dual-level system of checks and balances that, ideally, would economize on what little communitarian, "other-regarding" civic virtue might be available in the system as a whole. If civic virtue now entails a concern for the natural environment and such concern seems to be in short supply in the federal courts, Federalist theory suggests that it should appear elsewhere in the system, so that the tension between competing values remains more or less in equilibrium.

Just as Madison would have predicted, although the federal courts are no longer the friends of environmentalism that they once were, other branches and levels of government seem more willing to balance environmental and developmental concerns in a different way. In the 1972 case of *Just v. Marinette County*, the Wisconsin Supreme Court affirmed, on facts nearly identical to those in the Lucas case, that it was "not an unreasonable exercise of power to prevent harm to public rights by limiting the use of private property to its natural uses."[26] Some states explicitly include ecological values within the scope of the regulatory power: unlike NEPA, a number of state environmental protection statutes impose substantive limits on both public and private activity (see Renz 1984). Even the federal Congress has only limited power to undo such statutes as the Clean Water Act and the Endangered Species Act, both of which have come under strenuous attack from developers because they can require private landowners in some cases to leave their land in its natural state. Many interesting and valuable experiments have taken place within administrative agencies at both state and federal levels, in which government agents cooperate with Indian tribes and other private groups in the management of land, water, wildlife, and other

26. *Just v. Marinette County*, 56 Wis. 2d 7, 17, 201 N.W.2d 761, 768 (1972).

resources. If environmentalists wish to see their modern version of Jeffersonian values given more weight in the law of public and private land use, their only recourse is to the traditional remedy of active, civic-minded participation in republican government through democratic politics.

References

Ackerman, Bruce A. 1984. "The Storrs Lectures: Discovering the Constitution." *Yale Law Journal* 93: 1013–1072.

Brodie, Albert W. 1981. "A Question of Enumerated Powers: Constitutional Issues Surrounding Federal Ownership of the Public Lands." *Pacific Law Journal* 12: 693–726.

Bromley, Daniel W. 1993. "Regulatory Takings: Coherent Concept or Logical Contradiction?" *Vermont Law Review* 17 (3): 647–682.

Clawson, Marion. 1983. *The Federal Lands Revisited.* Baltimore, MD: Resources for the Future.

Coggins, George Cameron. 1990. "The Developing Law of Land Use Planning on the Federal Lands." *University of Colorado Law Review* 61: 307–353.

Coggins, George Cameron. 1994. "Commentary: Overcoming the Unfortunate Legacies of Western Public Land Law." *Land and Water Law Review* 29: 381–398.

Congressional Record. 1964. U.S. Senate. July 23. 16704–16706.

Cronon, William. 1983. *Changes in the Land: Indians, Colonists, and the Ecology of New England.* New York, NY: Hill and Wang.

Epstein, Richard. 1993. *"Lucas v. South Carolina Coastal Council:* A Tangled Web of Expectations." *Stanford Law Review* 45: 1369–1432.

Falk, Donald. 1989. "Bulldozing First Amendment Protection of Indian Sacred Lands." *Ecology Law Quarterly* 16: 515–570.

Foucault, Michel. 1970. *The Order of Things: An Archaeology of the Human Sciences.* New York, NY: Random House.

Friedman, Lawrence M. 1985. *A History of American Law.* Rev. 2d ed. New York, NY: Touchstone.

Gates, Paul W. 1936. "The Homestead Law in an Incongruous Land System." *American Historical Review* 41: 652–681.

Gates, Paul W. 1968. *History of Public Land Law Development.* Washington, D.C.: U.S. Government Printing Office.

Gates, Paul W. 1976. "An Overview of American Land Policy." *Agricultural History* 50: 213–229.

Goble, Dale D. 1986. "The Myth of the Classic Property Clause Doctrine." Natural Resources Symposium. *Denver University Law Review* 63: 495–533.

Gordon, Robert W. 1984. "Critical Legal Histories." *Stanford Law Review* 36: 57–126.

Gordon, Robert W. 1985. "Law and Ideology." *Tikkun* 3: 14–18, 83–86.

Hall, Kermit L. 1989. *The Magic Mirror: Law in American History.* Oxford: Oxford University Press.

Hays, Samuel P. 1979. *Conservation and the Gospel of Efficiency: The Progressive Conservation Movement,* 1890–1920. New York, NY: Atheneum.

Horowitz, Morton J. 1977. *The Transformation of American Law, 1780–1860.* Cambridge, MA: Harvard University Press.

Hurst, J. Willard. 1956. *Law and the Conditions of Freedom in the Nineteenth-Century United States.* Madison, WI: University of Wisconsin Press.

Hurst, J. Willard. 1964. *Law and Economic Growth: The Legal History of the Lumber Industry in Wisconsin, 1836–1915.* Cambridge, MA: Harvard University Press.

Hurst, J. Willard. 1977. *Law and Social Order in the United States.* Ithaca, NY: Cornell University Press.

Jefferson, Thomas. 1955 [1787]. *Notes on the State of Virginia,* edited by William Peden. Chapel Hill, NC: University of North Carolina Press.

Locke, John. 1960. "Second Treatise." In *Two Treatises of Government,* edited by Peter Laslett. Cambridge: Cambridge University Press.

Madison, James. 1981, reprint. *The Federalist no. 10."* In *The Federalist Papers: A Collection of Papers Written in Support of the Constitution of the United States,* edited by Roy P. Fairfield. Baltimore, MD: Johns Hopkins University Press.

Mansfield, Marla E. 1993. "A Primer of Public Land Law." *Washington Law Review* 68: 801–857.

McEvoy, Arthur F. 1986. *The Fisherman's Problem: Ecology and Law in the California Fisheries, 1850–1980.* Cambridge: Cambridge University Press.

Michelman, Frank I. 1981. "Property as a Constitutional Right." *Washington & Lee Law Review* 38: 1097–1981.

Michelman, Frank I. 1993. "Property, Federalism, and Jurisprudence: A Comment on *Lucas* and Judicial Conservatism." *William and Mary Law Review* 35: 301–328.

Miller, Robert J. 1990. "Correcting Supreme Court 'Errors': American Indian Response to *Lyng v. Northwest Indian Cemetery Protective Association."* *Environmental Law* 20: 1037–1062.

Olpin, Owen. 1994. "Toward Jeffersonian Governance of the Public Lands." *Loyola of Los Angeles Law Review* 27: 959–968.

Reich, Charles. 1964. "The New Property." *Yale Law Journal* 73: 733–787.

Renz, Jeffrey T. 1984. "The Coming of Age of State Environmental Policy Acts." *Public Land Law Review* 5: 31.

Ripani, Michael N. 1990. "Native American Free Exercise Rights in Sacred Land: Buried Once Again." *American Indian Law Review* 15: 323–339.

Rohrbough, Malcolm J. 1968. *The Land Office Business: The Settlement and Administration of American Public Lands, 1789–1837.* Oxford: Oxford University Press.

Rose, Carol M. 1984. *"Mahon* Reconstructed: Why the Takings Issue Is Still a Muddle." *Southern California Law Review* 57: 561–599.

Rose, Carol M. 1987. " 'Enough, and as Good' of What?" *Northwestern University Law Review* 81: 417–442.

Sax, Joseph L. 1964. "Takings and the Police Power." *Yale Law Journal* 74: 36–76.

Sax, Joseph L. 1993. "Property Rights and the Economy of Nature: Understanding *Lucas v. South Carolina Coastal Council."* *Stanford Law Review* 45: 1433–1455.

Scheiber, Harry N. 1973. "Property Law, "Expropriation, and Resource Allocation by Government, 1789–1910." *Journal of Economic History* 33: 232–251.

Scheiber, Harry N. 1980. "Public Economic Policy and the American Legal System: Historical Perspectives." *Wisconsin Law Review:* 1159–1190.

Schumpeter, Joseph A. 1950. *Capitalism, Socialism, and Democracy.* New York, NY: Harper and Row.

Spreng, Jennifer E. 1994. "Failing Honorably: Balancing Tests, Justice O'Connor and Free Exercise of Religion." *Saint Louis University Law Journal* 38: 837–879.

Walker, Francis A. 1890. "American Agriculture." In *U.S. Department of the Interior, Bureau of the Census, Tenth Census of the United States.* Vol. III: *Agriculture,* xxviii–xxxiii.

Wilkinson, Charles F. 1987. "The Law of the American West: A Critical Bibliography of the Nonlegal Sources." *Michigan Law Review* 85: 953–1024.

Wilkinson, Charles F. 1989. "The Field of Public Land Law—A Ten-Year Retrospective." *Public Land Law Review* 10: 19–27.

Wood, Gordon S. 1969. *The Creation of the American Republic, 1776–1787.* New York, NY: Norton.

7

Leaving the Land Behind:
Struggles for Land Reform
in U.S. Federal Policy, 1933–1965

Jess Gilbert and Alice O'Connor

In the 1930s, the U.S. government undertook the most significant land reform and planning program in modern U.S. history. Two agencies of the U.S. Department of Agriculture (USDA) carried out these public policies: the Farm Security Administration (FSA) and the Bureau of Agricultural Economics (BAE). The FSA helped landless farmers become landowners, and the BAE set up a national network of grassroots land-use planning committees that combined mass participation with scientific expertise. Almost alone among New Deal agencies, the FSA and the BAE represented the interests of agricultural workers, tenant farmers, and small family farmers.

These programs, however, were not the New Deal's main farm policy, which was embodied in the Agricultural Adjustment Administration (AAA). The AAA introduced production controls and subsidy payments into U.S. agriculture in 1933 and was quickly captured by large-farm interests. In class-divided agricultural regions like California and much of the South, the AAA worked against farm laborers and landless sharecroppers (Saloutos 1982; Badger 1989). This mainstay of New Deal farm policy remains the basis for contemporary agricultural policy. In contrast, because of the potential threat the FSA and BAE posed to the rural power structure both locally and nationally, conservatives abolished the two agencies soon after World War II.

Their histories, however, raise several issues of continuing significance to land policy concerns today. Not only did these innovative programs perish during the early 1940s, but along with them the possibility for a social democratic coalition. Progressive alternatives for rural America became submerged. The underlying issues, however, resurfaced in debates over the War on Poverty during the 1960s. Today, progressive policy options need to be revived and updated. In this chapter, we examine some of the internal difficulties of past land reform efforts that made it hard to overcome conservative opposition. In particular, we focus on three essentials of reform: the social base, visionary leadership, and administrative capacities.

New Deal Land Reform and Planning Programs

The FSA had its origins in the more radical Resettlement Administration, established in 1935 and led by presidential adviser and visionary economist, Rexford G. Tugwell. In 1937, Congress passed the Bankhead-Jones Farm Tenant Act, and Secretary of Agriculture Henry A. Wallace moved the Resettlement Administration (RA) into the new FSA. For the next five years, the FSA was a major and influential New Deal agency that upset the status quo in rural America. It had over 19,000 employees and 800,000 client families. The FSA's largest program, Rural Rehabilitation, offered loans, grants, and technical assistance to tenants, sharecroppers, and other poor farmers. Over 10 percent of all U.S. farmers received such loans from the FSA. Another "rehab" program created over 1,000 successful group medical and dental plans that served approximately 500,000 people, including some of the nation's poorest. The Tenant-Purchase Program provided low-interest, long-term credit for landless farmers to buy land.

More controversial were the FSA's smaller, experimental resettlement programs. The federal government bought nearly 2 million acres of farmland, mostly foreclosed plantations. The FSA resettled local landless farmers into community projects on this land, organized as either individual units or cooperative operations, occasionally with long-term leases. Another resettlement program built migrant labor camps in California (familiar to many from John Steinbeck's *Grapes of Wrath*) and established farm labor standards. Overall, the FSA was the most class-conscious of the New Deal agencies and one of the least racist. Twenty percent of its clients were African-American, including over thirty all-black community projects in the South. The FSA thus affronted the southern plantation/sharecrop system (and much of the dominant class system elsewhere) at all levels: racial, ideological, economic, and political.

Yet the FSA did not come close to dealing with the massive problems it faced. For example, the Tenant-Purchase Program allowed twelve thousand landless families to become landowners, but there were over two million tenants and sharecroppers in the country. The FSA saw its programs as immediate self-help efforts that offered alternatives to public relief and as the basis for long-term reforms; its enemies saw the programs as subversive and un-American. The latter view dominated in Congress, which effectively killed the FSA in 1943 (Baldwin 1968; Mertz 1978; Conkin 1959).

The year before, the same conservative Congress had ended the BAE's federal-county land-use planning program. Less obviously reformist than the FSA, the BAE was the socioeconomic research and planning agency of the USDA in the late 1930s. Secretary Henry A. Wallace and Undersecretary M. L. Wilson set up a national system of local committees. This was a unique undertaking in American history, to combine citizens (farmers), program administrators, and land-grant scientists together to administer and plan public policy. Farmers constituted a majority of each county-level committee. By 1941, the program was in two-thirds of all U.S. counties, with 200,000 farm men and women serving on planning bodies. Forty-five states had state-level committees of farmers, scientists, and administrators, who coordinated the county reports and recommendations for land-use planning. At the federal level, the USDA was reorganized to implement this national-local planning effort. The USDA leaders called it "democratic planning" or "economic democracy in action."[1]

The federal-county planing program, however, did not achieve its democratic vision. For the farmers, it was neither very representative nor fully participatory. Yet, compared to the dominant power structure in rural America, the planning committees were remarkably open and less elitist. The planners' experiments in action research, joining local farmers with social scientists for policy purposes, narrowed the citizen-specialist gap that seems endemic to contemporary society. The effectiveness of the program was barely glimpsed in a few exemplary counties and in national defense planning work—unfulfilled potentials cut short by enemies of mass participation and reformist planning.[2] The BAE tried to democratize agricultural policy and it failed. That failure is testament not only to its own weaknesses but also to the obstacles such an effort still faces today.

Social Base for Reform—Potential and Actual

U.S. agriculture in the 1930s consisted of not one but three class structures that varied by region: family farming in the Midwest, industrial-capitalist farming in the West, and the plantation/sharecrop system in the South. Each major agricultural region had its own set of dominant and subordinate actors and interests. There was "mobilization from below" in each region, but

1. Unlike the FSA, the county planning program has not been well studied by historians. The major exception is Kirkendall (1966, pp. 165–217). For current research on this program see Gilbert (1996).
2. For some successes, see Raper (1943); Tolley (1943, pp. 137–78).

regional peculiarities led to problems of organization and coherence at the national level.[3]

In the Midwest, self-employed landowning farmers suffered from extremely low prices in the early 1930s. Banks threatened nearly half of them with foreclosure. They responded in several states by organizing the Farmers' Holiday Association, largely a radical offshoot of the long-established National Farmers' Union (NFU). The Holiday Association gained support as thousands of farmers picketed, blockaded roads, marched on courthouses, and held "penny auctions" to prevent foreclosures. Five midwestern governors visited President Franklin D. Roosevelt in 1933, warning of violent insurrection and demanding relief, which FDR immediately announced (Gilbert and Howe 1991; Shover 1965).

In the two other main agricultural regions of the country, nonfamily farming predominated. In California and adjoining states, a rural proletariat worked on large-scale industrial farms. Despite their ethnic diversity (e.g., Mexican immigrants and poor whites), radicals and farm workers organized the "factories in the fields." In 1933 alone, there were 37 farm labor strikes in California; these culminated with an 18,000-strong cotton strike, the largest in U.S. agricultural history. The farm workers demanded higher wages and collective bargaining rights. The growers responded violently and were aided by local officials (Daniel 1981; Majka and Majka 1982).

Equally class-conscious were both sides of the plantation/sharecrop economy in the south, especially in the Cotton Belt. Planter-landlords were at the top of a racist, paternalistic social system that dominated landless farmers, both black and white. Class mobilization was most clear in eastern Arkansas, where socialists and sharecroppers organized the Southern Tenant Farmers' Union (STFU) in 1934. Within three years, the union claimed thirty-thousand members in six states. The tenant farmers sought written contracts and their share of New Deal program payments. The plantation owners' reaction was extreme; in 1935, the *New York Post* editorialized that " 'there can be no doubt of the reversion to slave law, mob violence, and Fascist methods in Arkansas' " (quoted in Jamieson 1945; see also Grubbs 1971).

The New Deal's AAA was able to unite dominant farmers in each region because of their common interest in higher commodity prices. Radical New Dealer Rexford Tugwell early on linked "the ruling caste of farmers, the most conservative Farm Bureau leaders, the cotton barons of the South, the emerging Associated Farmers of California, the banker-farmers of the Middle West" (Lord 1947). On the other hand, the subordinate classes in the three regions were structurally differentiated into small farmers, farm work-

3. This section draws from Gilbert and Howe (1991, pp. 204–220).

ers, and sharecroppers. Their divergent interests made it very hard to build a national organization of the "lower third" in U.S. agriculture.

By the late 1930s, the two most reformist agencies of USDA—the FSA and the BAE—constituted a "community of interest" favoring social change. The AAA's "urban liberals" were gone, as was their leader, Rexford Tugwell. His successor, a southern liberal, led the FSA until 1940, when he was replaced by another of Tugwell's aides. Heading the BAE from 1938 until 1946 was economist-planner Howard R. Tolley, who was strongly supported by Secretary Wallace and Undersecretary M. L. Wilson. This powerful group of USDA liberals formed a potential political coalition. First of all, their agency constituents numbered a few million rural citizens. More broadly, they were supported by progressive farm and reform groups around the nation: the NFU, the STFU, and urban liberals. This may be seen as an attempt to create the agrarian wing of a "social democracy" in the United States. In particular, Henry Wallace and the BAE turned increasingly toward the labor movement and issues of full employment, consumption, health, and nutrition (Baldwin 1968; see also Kubo 1991; Tugwell 1937; Tolley 1941, 1943; Wallace 1940).

They were opposed, however, by a more powerful coalition of conservative USDA agencies (including the New Deal AAA), many state Extension Services, the National Cotton Council, California's Associated Farmers, and, most importantly, the American Farm Bureau Federation. This group represented the new status quo in U.S. agriculture. Together with the anti-New Deal coalition in Congress (conservative midwestern Republicans and southern Democrats), they were able to kill the BAE county land-use planning program in 1942 and, in effect, the FSA in 1943. The social base for reform was politically weak and relatively unorganized; it failed to save the progressive New Deal in agriculture.

New Deal Visions of Reform

Just as there were two reformist agencies in USDA, so were they motivated by two different visions for rural America. Each was represented by an articulate spokesperson. Despite his departure from the New Deal in 1936, Rexford Tugwell's spirit (and staff) stayed on; the FSA continued his legacy. His successor as undersecretary, M. L. Wilson, represented the other strand of reformism in USDA, institutionalized in the BAE's county planning program. A summary of their ideological similarities and differences reveals much about the reformist vision of the New Deal Department of Agriculture.

First of all, both Tugwell and Wilson were institutional economists. They believed that the days of laissez-faire economies were over, that the central state necessarily had a positive, developmental role to play in social change. To them, government was the agent for collective security. Both were deep reformers, believing that long-term, substantial changes needed to be made in the economy. They represented the agrarian wing of a budding European-style social democracy in the United States. Tugwell and Wilson linked their vision of change to the "lower third"; they did not isolate a poor underclass from the rest of society. Both were also, in some sense, modernizers with faith in science and reason. Finally, we want to emphasize that Tugwell and Wilson lost in the struggle to achieve their visions, not only programmatically but intellectually. After World War II, their type of thinking virtually died in influential political circles, at least as regards domestic farm policy.

Despite these shared beliefs, Tugwell and Wilson differed significantly on a number of crucial points. Tugwell's thought is more familiar: he was a proponent of centralized planning and governmental coordination of the economy. While allowing a political role for citizens, he believed that planning was a technical task to be done by trained experts. Grassroots efforts to him were usually dominated by local power structures (he called them "grass-tops"). Moreover, he was willing to use the substantial powers of the federal government to reform regional cultures that did not meet his approval—for instance, the southern plantation/sharecrop system. He favored rapid social change and explicitly opposed forces for the status quo. Consequently, he held a dim view of the agricultural power structure, including the traditional land-grant colleges and the state Extension Services. The main group that he worked for in agriculture was the poorest—the clients of the RA/FSA (farm workers, sharecroppers, tenant farmers) (Sternsher 1964; Padilla 1975; Tugwell 1933; 1935).

In contrast, Wilson was more concerned about the mid-sized family farmer; indeed, he thought that most rural residents could achieve middle-class, property-owning status. He believed much more in citizen participation than Tugwell, even to the extent that he thought local farmers could play a major role in planning national agricultural policy. "Grassroots democracy" was not just a slogan to him. Farmers could administer federal policies as well as help make them. Wilson also respected regional differences and local cultures more than Tugwell and thought that social change had to be gradual rather than imposed quickly from Washington. He was a product as well as a shaper of the land-grant and Extension system (representing its left wing), so he was much more willing than Tugwell to work within it (Kirkendall 1966; Wilson 1940a, 1940b, 1941; Kubo 1991). Still,

Wilson's views of participatory planning survived the conservative on-slaught of World War II even less than did Tugwell's seemingly more radical stance, which lived on in some of the resettlement communities.

Institutional Capacities, Administrative and Political

Both the FSA and the BAE had significant administrative capacities. Each was institutionally reinforced in 1937–38 and grew in strength until 1942. Unlike Tugwell's Resettlement Administration, the FSA had legislative sanction; Congress passed the Bankhead-Jones Farm Tenant Act in 1937, and Henry Wallace merged the RA into the new FSA. Over the next five years, it became a major federal agency. Although centralized in decision-making authority, the FSA had a decentralized administrative structure. Its personnel numbered over 19,000, mostly in 2,300 county offices that served more than 800,000 client families. The FSA funded its own program of research, often carried out by social scientists in the BAE. As a leading action agency of the New Deal, it was often seen as a "poor people's USDA." This strong mission orientation (labeled "zealous" by its detractors) soon led to problems that were more political than administrative (Baldwin 1968).

The BAE was not an action agency but rather a research and planning unit. When Wallace reorganized the USDA in 1938, he elevated the BAE to become the central planning agency for the entire department. (Even before the New Deal, however, the BAE was well-known for the quality of its research and expertise. It was probably the largest social science research organization in the world.) With the reorganization, the BAE acquired the AAA's Program Planning Division, which further added to its strength. The BAE was an intellectual powerhouse perhaps unequaled in the New Deal government in terms of policy analysis and formulation. In policy implementation, however, it had a limited field staff and relied on the USDA's traditional outreach arm, the state Extension Services with their county agent system.

That both the FSA and the BAE were within the larger USDA had definite implications. Changes in leadership, political climate, and global affairs could have drastic consequences. Compare, for example, the outlook for the two reformist agencies in mid-1940 with late 1941. In 1940, both had strong support from the secretary and the undersecretary of agriculture (even the president), the conservative power structure of U.S. agriculture was relatively tolerant of the agencies, and the nation was at peace. By the end of 1941, the country had entered World War II, and all priorities changed. FDR announced that "Dr. New Deal" had become "Dr. Win the

War." Conservatives were aroused by the potential threats of the FSA and BAE, and launched a political campaign against them. Both Wallace and Wilson had left the USDA; the former had become vice-president and the latter the federal director of extension work. The new secretary of agriculture did not support the reform agenda as they had (Kirkendall 1966).

Both the FSA and the BAE faced the same political enemies, the "establishment" of U.S. agriculture: the organizations serving large farms and conservatives in Congress as well as those within USDA itself. These groups were powerful both locally and nationally. In the mid-1940s, the BAE was attacked specifically for two pieces of research that threatened local power structures. One was a sociological survey of rural Coahoma County, Mississippi. An internal draft of this short study was leaked to new congressman Jamie Whitten, who represented the county. He and other southerners were outraged that the BAE report detailed racial differences in standards of living. The other study caused even more trouble for the BAE. Anthropologist Walter Goldschmidt investigated the effects of farm size on rural community well-being in the Central Valley of California. He found that a small-farm area had a higher quality of life than did a large-farm area. The Associated Farmers and other supporters of industrial farming attacked the study and its sponsoring agency. Congress forbade the BAE from conducting "sociological surveys," as it had earlier denied funding to the county planning program, drastically weakening both the reform and research capacities of the BAE (ibid.).

The FSA was similarly gutted in 1943. Its enemies charged it with duplication, inefficiency, waste, and radicalism. The STFU, NFU, and USDA economists Tolley and Wilson all mounted a campaign of support. Yet the FSA's stronger adversaries won the day, cutting its budget and personnel in half. In 1946, what was left of the FSA became the moderate Farmers' Home Administration (FmHA) (Baldwin 1968; Conkin 1959).

Land Reform in the War on Poverty

Thus, the history of land tenure reform in the New Deal era reveals the complexities of constituency-building, vision, and institutional capacity—complexities that made it difficult to sustain a reform coalition that could match the powerful enemies of reform and that would continue to hinder the possibility of realizing the New Deal vision in subsequent years. Yet, to understand the post-New Deal fate of rural land tenure reform, it is equally important to consider the broader economic, political, and ideological transformations that changed the rural landscape beginning in the 1940s. Government policies, new technology, and growing consumer demand helped create an economy featuring a highly commercial, more mechanized agricultural sector, and a larger industrial sector, heavily reliant on defense spending as well as more "traditional" industries such as textiles and lumber. These changes, largely brought about through federal government policies, dramatically reshaped the rural labor force by eliminating agricultural jobs, streamlining factories, and spurring vast interregional migrations, particularly among blacks. They also paved the way for the consolidation of more commercial, business-oriented political power bases in the South and West, which were chiefly concerned with economic growth and modernization (Schulman 1991; Nash 1985; Daniel 1986). To accommodate these concerns, postwar liberals embraced growth as the central goal of domestic policy, and de-emphasized economic democracy and redistribution, thus marking a retreat from New Deal reform ideology (Brinkley 1995).

The longer-range implications of these economic, political, and ideological transformations for the New Deal reform vision can be seen in a second land tenure reform episode, this time attached to the War on Poverty in the 1960s. In contrast to the land reform policies of the New Deal era, this episode was brief, narrowly targeted, and left little visible impact on policy: the very limited land reform measures proposed as part of the Economic Opportunity Act of 1964 never made it off the congressional floor, where conservatives purged the act of any provisions that smacked of redistribution. Once again, there is more to the tale than conservative opposition, for the episode also reveals just how deeply submerged the reform tradition of the FSA/BAE "visionaries" had become, at least at the federal level, among liberals.

Land-tenure reform was one feature of Title III, the "rural title" of the Economic Opportunity Act of 1964. Put together by Department of Agriculture staff members James Sundquist and John Baker, Title III was a collection of modest provisions, targeted less to the rural poor as a whole than to the estimated one million farm families who were deemed too old, too uneducated, or otherwise handicapped to be candidates for migration to urban areas. These boxed-in families were being left behind by progress and ignored in existing government policies. "In the absence of special assistance," agency analysts wrote, "they would either remain desperately poor where they are or move to an urban area where their chances of becoming welfare cases are far better than their prospects of earning a decent living" (U.S. Senate 1964a, pp. 90–92). The idea behind legislative proposals was to provide the adults in these families with a basic level of security; meanwhile, their children would be educated for upward and outward mobility. Though the Title III provisions they were couched within the logic of basic subsistence and remediation, they did contain some element of the land-reform strategies of the RA and FSA: modest grants and low-interest loans would extend "middle-class" FmHA-type benefits to the poor, enabling them to improve and eventually purchase their farms; federal funds would also provide assistance for low-income farmers' cooperatives; and, most controversially, a Family Farm Development Corporation would finance nonprofits to purchase large tracts of land for redistribution in small units to low-income farmers.

Title III met with skepticism but not much active opposition in committee hearings, where opponents depicted it as a measure that would simply postpone the inevitable death of the small farm and occasionally, as in the case of Representative William Robert Poage of the House Agricultural Committee, compared its proposals with the sort of "communistic" ideas that had been purged with the demise of the FSA (U.S. House 1964). The more concerted—and theatrical—protestation was reserved for the Senate floor debate, when conservatives led by Strom Thurmond managed to invoke the Bible, communist revolution, racial fear, and the ghost of Rexford Tugwell in one sustained attack. "The poor always ye have with you," he reminded his colleagues, calling the poverty bill "pregnant with racial overtones" and threatening to the basic precepts of a free market economy. The rural title was clearly inspired by the FSA, an "experiment station of un-American ideas and economic and social theories of little or questionable value." Saving his sharpest barbs for the Family Farm Development Corporation, Thurmond also managed to get in a dig against postwar foreign aid policy, warning against the attempt to impose "socialistic devices" of the sort that "we have tried so hard to ram down the throats of our Latin American neighbors" (U.S. Senate 1964b, pp. 16, 704–706).

Given the lukewarm level of support for Title III from the Johnson administration and within Congress, Thurmond's onslaught was enough to pare it down even further. The final bill was passed without the Family Farm Development Corporation and with much-diminished funding for its already minimal loan provisions. Following this brief appearance on the legislative scene, land tenure was simply a nonissue as far as the War on Poverty was concerned. Instead, federal efforts to address rural poverty would be concentrated on education and training and on improving access to services through the Community Action Program.

The preemptive strike against land tenure reform could be seen as a sharp reminder of the power exercised by southern conservative opposition. In reality, it was the liberal camp—as revealed in certain aspects of the War on Poverty planning process—that undermined its viability in the 1960s. Once again, liberal planners encountered problems in organizing a community-based constituency for reform as well as ideological differences within the administration. Even more than in the 1930s, they lacked a politically powerful institutional base for sustaining rural reform efforts.

As suggested above, the demographic profile of rural poverty had become even more diverse since the 1930s, as low-wage industrial workers grew in number compared to the dwindling population of impoverished farm laborers. Though aware of this diversity, the Department of Agriculture analysts proposed an admittedly narrow program in the hope that it would be an opening wedge for further action. To some degree, this narrow focus reflected the larger inability of the federal government bureaucracy to respond to the changing rural scene: despite profound changes since the 1940s, "rural" was still equated with "farming" in the 1960s, and the Department of Agriculture remained the only institutional home for attention to rural issues. Furthermore, in the minds of the poverty planners, the one million poor farm families targeted in Title III fit the image of the hopeless "residual" rural poor depicted in social scientific research and the popular media of the day. The federal government poverty planners were not in a position to build a constituency for a rural antipoverty strategy that could effectively integrate land-tenure issues with the concerns voiced by community-based labor and civil rights advocates, the activists who formed part of a natural constituency to address rural poverty. In the mid-1960s, the NFU sponsored a report by its National Policy Committee on Pockets of Poverty which linked farm problems with other forms of "structural" poverty. The report was released weeks before the Economic Opportunity Act was sent to Congress.[4] The NFU strongly supported Title III and testified on its behalf during congressional hearings, but its broader proposals made little impact on the administration's poverty planners.

The architects of Title III also faced several obstacles within the administration-wide antipoverty planning process, and these obstacles reveal the virtual absence of an elite constituency for land-tenure reform in the 1960s. One obstacle was an overwhelming bias against seeing poverty as having a specifically rural component, let alone as being tied to land tenure. This bias was built into the planning process in two ways. First, the chief responsibility for conceptualizing the War on Poverty rested with the economists at the Council of Economic Advisers (CEA) and the Bureau of the Budget. Unlike the institutionalists who ran the BAE in the 1930s, these economists were confirmed Keynesians who embraced neoclassical principles. Concepts such as land and place were not included in their analytic models, and they tended to see poverty primarily as a problem of low aggregate demand, high unemployment rates, and deficiencies of human capital.[5] Moreover, the administration-backed effort to address "depressed area" poverty in the

---

4. See National Policy Committee on Pockets of Poverty, press release announcing "Poverty in America," 5 March 1964, Wilbur Cohen Papers, Box 125, Folder 1, Wisconsin State Historical Society Archives, Madison, Wisconsin.
5. On the neglect of the land in neoclassical economics, see Geisler 1995; Robert J. Lampman Oral History, Lyndon Baines Johnson Library; and James L. Sundquist Oral History, Lyndon Baines Johnson Library.

1961 Area Redevelopment Act had been disappointing at best, reducing even further the likelihood that the CEA would back a concerted rural focus.

Second, to the extent that administration planners thought about poverty, it was as an urban phenomenon. The awareness of urban poverty was reinforced during the planning process by the influence of a somewhat eclectic network of social scientists, foundation officials, local government officials, and community/labor activists who had been involved in a series of urban demonstration programs since the mid-1950s. Many of these local demonstration programs had come about because of problems associated with the influx of "new migrants," largely from rural backgrounds, into inner-city areas—blacks, Latinos, and white "poor ethnics" who were seen to be unprepared for urban life and who strained urban services. Putatively designed to reform local services to make them more responsive to the needs of the newcomers, the demonstrations contained the seeds of what later became the Community Action Program and emphasized principles of comprehensiveness, coordination, and, more unevenly, local participation. While community action could, and would, be applied in rural as well as urban areas, most of its proponents came from the urban frontlines, where they came to regard the rural poor through the lens of migration, as potential urban newcomers with cultural as well as skill "deficiencies" (O'Connor 1996).

Underlying these built-in biases against the rural perspective was a broader ideological framework that embraced economic growth and modernization as the way to affluence as well as the solution to poverty. In the 1930s, there had been some tension in liberal thought between Tugwell's vision of centralized planning and modernization and Wilson's vision of an economy based on the family farm and rural communities. By the 1960s, modernization was clearly the predominant framework among liberal social scientists and policymakers. As a reform vision, however, this was a narrow, commercialized concept of modernization—one which relied on market-driven growth, minimal central planning, and was complacent about the prospect of uneven development. In this vision, the family farm and traditional gemeinschaft communities were things of the past, the poor were victims of material and cultural deprivation rather than of broader socioeconomic inequality, and it was they, not society, who were in need of rehabilitation. Education, retraining, and outmigration were seen as the keys to fighting rural poverty; the rural poor, in the words of a later commission report, were "the people left behind" (National Advisory Commission 1967; see O'Connor 1992). In this vision, land redistribution was, at best, a means of providing subsistence for those who could not move up and out.

A third factor that presented an obstacle to the land tenure perspective was institutional, and it was rooted in the earlier demise of the FSA and BAE. In the absence of those agencies, the institutional base for the administrative voice for the interests of poor farmers had all but disappeared. As a result, there was no strong constituency within the Department of Agriculture for incorporating the poor into a more modernized agricultural sector; departmental priorities were geared to the larger producers and, overwhelmingly, to commercial farm interests; and the Extension Services had a reputation for being racist. Not surprisingly then, the War on Poverty planners held a deep suspicion of the Department of Agriculture and were not inclined to look to it for ideas (Sundquist oral history; note, though, that Sundquist himself was widely respected and was seen as an exception to the rule). Meanwhile, the visionaries of the earlier era had become engaged in the world of international development, which proved much more promising as a research/action frontier after World War II.[6]

Largely due to the persistence of James Sundquist, the Department of Agriculture analysts did manage to overcome these obstacles and persuade the Poverty Task Force to include a rural title in the antipoverty legislation. Nevertheless, it was treated as an afterthought in packaging the legislation and was not strongly defended in the face of opposition.

A New Deal Legacy

Lest we conclude that the story of federal land reform is simply one of defeat, there remains the question of whether the resettlement programs were successful in achieving their ends. In the 1970s, economist and former Office of Management and Budget official Lester Salamon set out to answer this question, conducting an evaluation of FSA reform with the all-important element of long-term effects factored in. Focusing on programs that distributed land to black agricultural workers, Salamon found evidence of a high level of land retention over time, along with significant improvement in terms of income, assets, health, and overall well-being among program beneficiaries. Significantly, he also found that program beneficiaries were heavily engaged in local politics and community activities, most notably forming the vanguard of local support for the civil rights movement. These findings led him to conclude that the resettlement program "had sig-

6. Rexford Tugwell, who served as governor of Puerto Rico and harbored hopes of using the island as a laboratory for scientifically informed reform, was one of the more prominent "exportations" of social scientific expertise to underdeveloped areas of the world (Lapp 1995, 169–199). Howard Tolley resigned as BAE chief in 1946 to become head economist of the new Food and Agriculture Organization, which he had helped establish. M. L. Wilson remained in the USDA until 1952, when he began working with the Ford Foundation in India.

nificant long-run effects, transforming a group of landless black tenants into a permanent landed middle class that ultimately emerged in the 1960s as the backbone of the civil-rights movement in the rural South." Moreover, this was "social reform on the cheap": for a limited investment, the federal government had been able to change the entire social dynamic in a rural region (Salamon 1979).

Conclusion

The history of federally administered land reform since the New Deal is brief and episodic, but it yields enduring lessons for reform more generally. First, these federal efforts have historically faced difficulties in mobilizing their grassroots constituencies. To some degree these difficulties have been due to the diversity of rural America and the potentially conflicting interests within the social base. They also have been part of the more general institutional weakness in the federal government when it comes to developing rural policy beyond the confines of large-scale agriculture. But they also have been due to the preponderance of top-down planning and the lack of effective mechanisms for linking federal administrators with the localities. Although the BAE offered a model for achieving such linkages, its local constituency did not include low-income and disfranchised community members. In the 1960s, local community action agencies were meant to engage the poor in planning, but they were primarily service-oriented and their impact on the broader direction of federal government policy was negligible. In both reform episodes, problems related to constituency-building at the local and elite levels made it that much more difficult to overcome conservative opposition to reform measures.

Second, the land reform story reveals the limits of liberal reform ideology as it evolved during the post–World War II years. The liberal embrace of modernization, particularly in its narrow, commercialized form, relegated the poor to residual status, neglected the concern for economic democracy that had informed New Dealers, and, in its reliance on neoclassical economic theory, effectively defined land out of the poverty equation. In contrast to this "residualist" vision, the New Deal land reform experiments offered a genuine alternative which, thanks to the Resettlement Administration, is grounded in historical experience. The most far-reaching of the RA programs were redistributive; they challenged a prevailing system that perpetuated inequality; they targeted low-income populations without stigmatizing them; and they acknowledged race, as well as the class dimensions of poverty. However briefly, they shattered the myth that poverty could be addressed without changing the status quo.

Third, the vast changes that separate these two episodes of land reform underscore the overriding impact of federal economic policy on the fate of low-income Americans. Much more than welfare, training, or other types of residual programs, steps taken by the federal government to encourage growth, industrialization, agricultural commercialization, and the military/ defense industry changed the face of poverty in rural America. Important as it is to develop specific reform alternatives that will improve opportunities for low-income Americans, it is also important to keep a critical eye on, and develop alternatives to, the broader macro-level and labor-market policies that form the context of poverty. By the same token, it is important to reconceptualize the links between poverty and land tenure in light of changing political, economic, and environmental realities. For all Americans, land-tenure issues go well beyond ownership and income to include persistent spatial inequality, public health, natural resource protection, and quality of life. The diverse constituency for land-tenure reforms includes the poor and perhaps offers an opportunity to recapture the more-inclusive vision that inspired reform in the 1930s.

References

Badger, Anthony J. 1989. *The New Deal: The Depression Years, 1933–1940.* New York, NY: Farrar, Straus and Giroux.

Baldwin, Sidney. 1968. *Poverty and Politics: The Rise and Decline of the Farm Security Administration.* Chapel Hill, NC: University of North Carolina Press.

Brinkley, Alan. 1995. *The End of Reform: New Deal Liberalism in Recession and War.* New York, NY: Alfred A. Knopf.

Conkin, Paul K. 1959. *Tomorrow a New World: The New Deal Community Program.* Ithaca, NY: Published for the American Historical Association by Cornell University Press.

Daniel, Cletus E. 1981. *Bitter Harvest: A History of California Farm Workers, 1870–1942.* Ithaca, NY: Cornell University Press.

Daniel, Pete. 1986. *Standing at the Crossroads: Southern Life since 1900.* New York, NY: Hill and Wang.

Geisler, Charles C. 1995. "Land and Poverty in the United States: Insights and Oversights." *Land Economics* 71 (1): 16–34.

Gilbert, Jess. 1996. "Democratic Planning in Agricultural Policy: The Federal-County Land Use Planning Program, 1938–1942." *Agricultural History* 70 (Spring): 233–250.

Gilbert, Jess, and Carolyn Howe. 1991. "Beyond 'State vs. Society': Theories of the State and the New Deal Agricultural Policies." *American Sociological Review* 56: 204–220.

Grubbs, Donald H. 1971. *Cry from the Cotton: The Southern Tenant Farmers' Union and the New Deal.* Chapel Hill, NC: University of North Carolina Press.

Jamieson, Stuart. 1945. *Labor Unionism in American Agriculture. U.S. Department of Labor, Bureau of Labor Statistics Bulletin no. 836. Washington, D.C.: U.S. Government Printing Office.*

Kirkendall, Richard S. 1966. *Social Scientists and Farm Politics in the Age of Roosevelt.* Columbia, MO: University of Missouri Press.

Kubo, Fumiaki. 1991. "Henry A. Wallace and Radical Politics in the New Deal: Farm Programs and a Vision of the New American Political Economy." *Japanese Journal of American Studies* 4: 37–76.

Lapp, Michael. 1995. "The Rise and Fall of Puerto Rico as a Social Laboratory, 1945–1965." *Social Science History* 19 (2): 169–199.

Lord, Russell. 1947. *The Wallaces of Iowa.* Boston, MA: Houghton Mifflin.

Majka, Linda C., and Theo J. Majka. 1982. *Farm Workers, Agribusiness, and the State.* Philadelphia, PA: Temple University Press.

Mertz, Paul E. 1978. *New Deal Policy and Southern Rural Poverty.* Baton Rouge, LA: Louisiana State University Press.

Nash, Gerald D. 1985. *The American West Transformed: The Impact of the Second World War.* Bloomington, IN: Indiana University Press.

National Advisory Commission on Rural Poverty. 1967. *The People Left Behind.* Washington, D.C.: U.S. Government Printing Office.

National Policy Committee on Pockets of Poverty. 1964. Press Release Announcing "Poverty in America," March 5. Wilbur Cohen Papers, Box 125, Folder 1, Wisconsin State Historical Society Archives, Madison, WI.

O'Connor, Alice. 1992. "Modernization and the Rural Poor: Some Lessons from History." In *Rural Poverty in America,* edited by Cynthia M. Duncan, pp. 215–233. New York, NY: Auburn House.

O'Connor, Alice. 1996. "Urban Reform, Community Action, and the War Against Poverty: The Ford Foundation's Gray Areas Program." *Journal of Urban History* 22 (5): 586–625.

Padilla, Salvador M., ed. 1975. *Tugwell's Thoughts on Planning.* Rio Piedras: University of Puerto Rico Press.

Raper, Arthur F. 1943. *Tenants of the Almighty.* New York, NY: Macmillan.

Salamon, Lester M. 1979. "The Time Dimension in Policy Evaluation: The Case of the New Deal Land-Reform Experiments." *Public Policy* 27: 129–183.

Saloutos, Theodore. 1982. *The American Farmer and the New Deal.* Ames, IA: Iowa State University Press.

Schulman, Bruce J. 1991. *From Cotton Belt to Sunbelt: Federal Policy, Economic Development, and the Transformation of the South, 1938–1980.* New York, NY: Oxford University Press.

Shover, John L. 1965. *Cornbelt Rebellion: The Farmers' Holiday Association.* Urbana, IL: University of Illinois Press.

Sternsher, Bernard. 1964. *Rexford G. Tugwell and the New Deal.* New Brunswick, NJ: Rutgers University Press.

Tolley, Howard R. 1941. *Report of the Chief of the Bureau of Agricultural Economics, 1941.* Washington, D.C.: U.S. Government Printing Office.

Tolley, Howard R. 1943. *The Farmer-Citizen at War.* New York, NY: Macmillan.

Tugwell, Rexford. 1933. *Industrial Discipline and the Governmental Arts.* New York, NY: Columbia University Press.

Tugwell, Rexford. 1935. *The Battle for Democracy.* New York, NY: Columbia University Press.

Tugwell, Rexford. 1937. "Is a Farm-Labor Alliance Possible?" *Harper's* (May): 651–661.

U.S. House. 1964. Committee on Agriculture. *Hearings on the Economic Opportunity Act of 1964.*

U.S. Senate. 1964a. Committee on Labor and Public Welfare. *Hearings on the Economic Opportunity Act of 1964.*

U.S. Senate. 1964b. Committee on Labor and Public Welfare. *Congressional Record,* July 23, pp. 16704–16706.

Wallace, Henry A. 1940. *Report of the Secretary of Agriculture, 1940.* Washington, D.C.: U.S. Government Printing Office.

Wilson, M. L. 1940a. "Beyond Economics." In *Farmers in a Changing World: The Yearbook of Agriculture, 1940, pp. 922–937.* Washington, D.C.: U.S. Government Printing Office.

Wilson, M. L. 1940b. "Problem of Poverty in Agriculture." *Journal of Farm Economics* 22: 10–33.

Wilson, M. L. 1941. "A Theory of Agricultural Democracy." U.S. Department of Agriculture, Extension Circular no. 355. Washington, D.C.: U.S. Government Printing Office, March.

Ecosystem Management: Who's Entitled?

Charles C. Geisler and Barbara L. Bedford

Introduction

In 1972, Caldwell (p. 413) noted that the "Application of the ecosystem concept implies a whole new way of organizing man's relations with the natural world, an ecosystem approach to public policy implies fundamental changes in the rights and responsibilities of individuals and corporations in the possession and use of land."

This chapter explores the property implications of ecosystem management, now hailed as a new conservation paradigm (Cortner et al. 1994; Jackson and Wyner 1994; Lubchenco 1994) and as a promising next step in federal land management (U.S. General Accounting Office 1994b; Yaffee et al., 1996).[1]

Ecosystem management yields many benefits to society. These include protecting watersheds and soil, maintaining viable populations of plants and animals, improving environmental conditions in surrounding areas and extending vital services to society as a whole (soil replenishment, surface and groundwater protection, oxygen generation and climate amelioration, new scientific/medical/tourist opportunities, to name a few), and the sheltering of replacement cohorts of many life forms on which civilization depends (NPCA 1988). Added to this are a vast array of aesthetic pleasures, economic stocks, and the broad platform of biodiversity without which evolution itself would languish. These imposing attributes suggest a new "estate of mind" with respect to how human society organizes its proprietary relationship to the biosphere.

What is striking about ecosystem management is the unprecedented scale of its reach onto private lands beyond its core protected (usually public) areas. If accomplished in a fashion laid out in assorted conservation manifestos and legislative agendas, ecosystem management promises to re-

---

1. Though only recently coming to the fore legislatively and administratively, ecosystem management is clearly not new to the scientific community (Jackson and Wyner 1994).

draw the metes and bounds of ownership in America in fundamentally new ways. We concern ourselves here with these ownership changes and with their unintended consequences. Foremost among these is a burgeoning number of ecosystem inholdings; that is, ownership units that fall within expanding ecosystem management units.[2] This phenomenon has been likened by Grumbine (1992) to the English enclosure movement of bygone centuries. What is unintended is not the enclosure per se nor the alterations in property rights that follow but the alienation felt by large numbers of threatened property owners toward the theory and practice of ecosystem management.

The property implications of ecosystem management have attracted the prior attention of scholars (Caldwell 1972; Carlton 1986; Cortner and Moote 1994; Geisler and Kittel 1994; Ireland 1994; Albrecht 1994; Trott 1995), not to mention a vast amount of popular writing and editorializing in the mainstream media and in the newsletters of groups opposing and supporting ecosystem management. Combined, these efforts offer a rich archive of debate on the possible effects of ecocentric management on property rights, on property taxes, and on communities depending on both. What is lacking is a full account of the property effects of reorganizing conservation policy on a regional scale in a society generally accustomed to pursuing such ends through public ownership or public control of land, often at a local level.

In what follows, we document both the expansionary potential of future ecosystem management and the magnitude of inholdings likely to accompany it. By inholders we refer to ownership interests that, because they are enclosed by or adjacent to managed ecosystems, have some or all of their property rights encumbered. We suggest that, both in numbers and in background profile, "ecosystem inholders" are distinct from inholders who, for more than a century, have dotted the national parks. To illustrate the complexity of entitlement within managed ecosystems, we offer two contrasting case studies, one old and one new. This provides ample opportunity to comment on both the consequences of ecocentric land use planning on property owners and, conversely, of private property ownership on ecosystem management. It leads, perhaps predictably, to a historical parallel between ecosystem management and the so-called Quiet Revolution of the 1970s. Our conclusion looks to the National Environmental Policy Act (NEPA) as an

2. Inholdings are the private or state parcels remaining within federal boundaries (Lambert 1982). This definition easily can be extended to nonprofit holdings (churches, scout troops) or to any of these property types within state lands as well. Technically speaking, Indian tribes were the earliest inholders. Federal land acquisition for nonconservation ends also creates inholders; for example, energy generation (the Tennessee Valley Authority) and transportation corridors (the Blue Ridge Parkway).

underutilized way to reduce conflict between ecosystem rights and property rights.

Ecosystem Management as Bigger-Is-Better Management

Ever since Arthur Tansley (1935) used the concept of "ecosystem" six decades ago to capture the regional array of biological and physical forces shaping organisms in nature, there has been gradual adoption of the term among resource managers. Similarly, there has been a concerted effort on the part of conservation biologists to move from de facto to de jure recognition of ecosystem units as superior management frameworks. Bills have been proposed to protect ecosystems (Hunt 1989: Liverman 1990; Noss 1991; Grumbine 1992; Jontz 1993; Sierra Nevada Ecosystem Project 1996), federal agencies managing hundreds of millions of federal acres have pledged themselves to ecosystem management, and the Clinton administration's 1995 budget included funding for the initial stages of a government-wide ecosystem management policy (Jackson and Wyner 1994). The White House's Office of Environmental Policy has established an Interagency Ecosystem Management Task Force to advance the concept (U.S. General Accounting Office 1994b; Cortner et al. 1994).

As presently interpreted, ecosystem management implies a radically new and expanded geography of conservation.[3] The quest for increased scale by ecosystem management proponents has antecedents in a seminal report to the Ecological Society of America by Victor Shelford in 1933, in which he called for the expansion of reserve boundaries to match species habitat needs, to achieve representation of ecosystem types, to manage for ecological fluctuations and disturbances, and to accomplish a core-buffer approach to conservation planning (Shelford 1994). In 1972, the National Park Service released its first ever National Park System Plan. An early form of gap analysis, this plan identified discrepancies between what was within national parks and what, from the standpoint of "natural regions," was not. In 1985, a report by the National Parks and Conservation Association (NPCA) stated: "The primary justification for adding new areas to the System should be to preserve nationally significant ecosystems, land forms and cultural resources to the maximum extent possible" (NPCA 1988, pp. 1–10).

Two years later, in 1987, further analysis by the Park Service came to the following startling conclusions (ibid., p. 1–11):

3. Not all ecosystems are inherently large. Grumbine (1990) views ecosystems as scale neutral. Nonetheless, conservation biologists typically seek the protection of more rather than less habitat when circumstances permit.

- 41 percent of the ecosystems identified using the methods in the 1972 plan are probably not represented adequately in the National Park System;
- 42 percent of ecosystems identified using potential natural vegetation maps of the United States are probably not represented adequately in the system;
- 60 percent of the ecosystems assessed at a still-higher, detailed level of ecosystem diversity are probably not represented adequately in the system.

Despite aggressive federal land acquisition in the 1970s, some still considered the National Park System to be more empty than full from an ecosystem standpoint (for example, see Foresta 1984). This skepticism was rooted less in National Park System efforts to expand than in continuing threats to biodiversity. Species extinction today is occurring at rates faster than ever before in the history of the planet (Bird 1989). Two years after Shelford's report, other researchers concluded that the national parks were not fully functional ecosystems by virtue of boundary and size limitations (Wright and Thompson 1935). Since that time, the U.S. National Park System has doubled in size, a national wilderness system has been created, and protected areas worldwide have grown by a factor of six (Grumbine 1994). Yet of the nearly nine hundred species (plants, birds, and mammals) listed under the Endangered Species Act, only a quarter can be found on the 91 million acres of National Wildlife Refuges (U.S. General Accounting Office 1994a). Public forest lands are a relatively small proportion (27 percent) of the total forest land base and cannot be expected to adequately protect biodiversity in ecosystems (Sample 1994). Moreover, federal lands are unevenly distributed, accounting for less than 1 percent in states such as Illinois, Indiana, Iowa, Ohio, and Oklahoma (U.S. General Accounting Office 1995). Grumbine (1994, p. 211) concludes that "ecosystem management restricted to government lands is a prescription for extinction."[4]

Thus, conservation biologists today have broadened their management interest to ecocentric units beyond park boundaries—to whole river basins, watersheds, and landscapes, rather than to homeocentric units such as ownership or governance units. They argue that managing broader geographic areas for multiple rather than single species may be more efficient and effective, reducing the risk that viable species will become endangered and resulting in fewer limitations on human activities (U.S. General Ac-

---

4. Gap analysis, a means of identifying critical vegetative ecosystems still in need of ecosystem-level conservation, has confirmed the inadequacy of current public lands for ecosystem protection and spurred efforts by private sector conservation groups to augment public protection efforts (Grossman, Goodin, and Reussl 1994).

counting Office 1994a). Still others rely on the bigger-is-better approach to sidestep difficult ecosystem delineation issues and contend that eco-centric management must be large enough to capture the complexities and linkages among the components and processes of the ecosystem (Keystone Center 1991; Turner, Gardner, and O'Neill 1995).[5] As Grumbine (1992, p. 187) states:

> [T]hink big and think connected. Bigness and connectivity across our wounded landscapes must be bolstered by a moratorium on habitat degrada-tion and more conservation-biology research. In the present political land-scape, bans on old-growth logging coupled with expensive research, expan-sive wilderness and biological corridors are considered utopian. That may be so. But if they are, then we had better be very clear about the consequences of pragmatism for both species and ecosystems: They will soon disappear, along with Earth's habitability for homo sapiens.

In sum, all else being equal, large reserves are among the few almost universally accepted principles within conservation biology (Noss 1992).

The New Geography of Ecosystem Management

The property implications of ecosystem management would be unremark-able if the spatial requirements just referred to could be satisfied by those lands of the United States in federal ownership. By 1988, more than five hundred boundary adjustments had occurred on nearly two hundred na-tional parks (NPCA 1988). Most were relatively minor in size, however. More importantly, ecosystem managers diversified their conservation ap-proaches and fashioned an extraterritorial strategy extending well beyond national parks. On the one hand, this relied on partnerships among federal landholding agencies administering vast extensions of public land. On the other, it relied on managing and co-managing nonfederal lands through a host of techniques. The Wildlands Project, a vision of how the United States might look after two centuries of ecosystem management, is a notable exam-ple of the latter.

Conceived by David Foreman of Earth First! and elaborated by re-spected conservation biologists, the Wildlands Project (also called the North American Wilderness Recovery Project) is the most ambitious pro-posal for land management since the Louisiana Purchase of 1803 (Mann

---

5. Grumbine (1992, p. 118) hints at the problems of ecosystem delineation in California: "Depending on where we draw ecological boundaries . . . there are anywhere from 15 to 375 natural ecosystems in the Golden State." Bailey (1995) recently updated earlier govern-ment mapping of ecoregions of the entire United States for use in ecosystem management.

and Plummer 1993). If accomplished, it would encompass hundreds of millions of acres, or just under half of the continent. A distant descendent of the Shelford blueprint, 23.4 percent of U.S. land would be wilderness and another 26.2 percent corridors and buffer zones. The result would be an archipelago of human-inhabited islands surrounded by natural areas. Noss (1992, p. 13) translates the Wildlands Plan into a macro land use manifesto consisting of four interwoven strategies:

- rare and endangered species are identified and protected;
- species valuable for pragmatic reasons are maintained (e.g., they play critical roles in the ecosystem; they require large areas to survive, thus serving as "umbrellas" for other species; they are charismatic species that serve as popular symbols for conservation);
- high-quality examples of all natural communities are secured from destruction;
- greater ecosystems or landscapes are identified and managed for biodiversity conservation and sustainable human use.

Noss adds that the heart of the Wildlands Project lies in breaking down the continental geography into subregions such as those proposed in Omernik's (1987) seventy-six ecoregions. Ecoregions and bioregions, for which Noss (1992, p. 13) says many grassroots groups have developed conservation plans, are a convenient scale for planning and "often inspire feelings of belonging and protectiveness in their more enlightened inhabitants." Protected areas and buffer zones would be planned and executed within these regions and then connected via conservation corridors, hence the importance of connectivity as well as size.

Though no single piece of legislation envisages all components of the Wildlands Project, a sampling of recent legislative initiatives suggests that ecosystem management's expanded scale is not hypothetical. In 1989, Congress considered American Heritage Trust Fund legislation that sought to set aside $1 billion annually for environmentally significant land acquisition.[6] The Ancient Forest Protection Act of 1991 sought to establish an ancient forest reserve system based on a year-long scientific study of all unprotected old-growth acres on the federal lands of the Northwest.[7] The American Heritage Areas Act of 1995, following the recommendations of the Mississippi River Parkway Commission and other initiatives dating to

6. H.R. 876 was sponsored by Morris Udall and 179 cosponsors; S.R. 370 by John Chaffee had 38 cosponsors. Funds would come from cigarette taxes and go to federal, state, and local governments, and nonprofit organizations for land acquisition and outdoor recreation development.
7. H.R. 842 was introduced by Jim Jontz of Indiana and had over 100 cosponsors. Bruce Vento of Minnesota sought similar protection (H.R. 1590), extending to 50 percent of remaining old-growth ecosystems.

1984, projected 2,500 miles of the Mississippi River as a semiprotected corridor.[8] The California Desert Protection Act of 1994 became law and was the single largest land withdrawal for conservation in the continental United States.

To this list could be added numerous other broad-gauge ecosystem projects, such as the four-state Northern Forest in the Northeast, the multicounty Sierra Nevada Ecosystem Project of California, the thirteen Adaptive Management Areas in the Northwest, a host of private and private-public ecosystem management schemes in the Texas Canyonlands (Beatley 1994), as well as various "greater ecosystem" projects and biosphere reserves. These illustrations say nothing of the myriad smaller-scale ecological action plans and projects which, cumulatively, add up to millions of additional acres. Noss, LaRoe, and Scott (1995), in the first full review of the health of the American landscape, conclude that major stretches of formerly vibrant habitat, once amounting to over half of the continental United States, have declined to the point of endangerment. Combined, the formal and informal plans to bring about the Wildlands Plan amount to an ecosystem management manifesto for North America.

Ecosystem Inholders

What for conservation biologists is prudent extension of the managed landscape is for many private property owners leapfrog conservation—that is, conservation management of publicly owned lands interspersed among private holdings. It is the principal stimulus for the membership growth of such groups as the National Inholders Association, the National Federal Lands Conference, the American Land Rights Association, and the "wise use" movement in general. The Alliance for America counts over six hundred local property rights groups in its ranks, and the National Inholders Association has well over a million members (NRC 1993). Inholder status will apply to more and more people as ecosystem management gains ground, politically and spatially.

Inholders became an important set of stakeholders over a century ago with the emergence of the national parks system and are a perennial concern on Capitol Hill (Runte 1990). By the 1930s, when the Taylor Grazing Act officially ended the federal land disposition outside of Alaska and the Depression forced many Americans back to the land to survive, inholders became an obstacle to federal land planning. Just after World War II, the direc-

---

8. This bill (H.R. 1301) and others like it are cost-sharing initiatives intended to accomplish protection through heightened public awareness, education, and economic assistance to promote environmentally appropriate development such as tourism.

tor of the National Park Service noted that inholder complications were a major impediment to discharging his mandate (Drury 1946).

By the 1970s, roughly half the land within the fifty-one national forests in the eastern United States remained in private hands, and, nationally, inholder conflicts flared in places as diverse as the Cape Cod National Seashore, the Columbia River Scenic Parkway, the Shenandoah National Park, the Indiana National Lakeshore, Yosemite National Park, the Delaware Water Gap, the New Jersey Pinelands, and New York's Adirondack Park (NRC 1993). Mindful of such conflicts, the federal government made the reacquisition of private lands within federal holdings a priority in the Eisenhower and Kennedy eras through the Land and Water Conservation Fund (Glicksman and Coggins 1984). The overall amount of land owned by the four major federal landholding agencies increased in forty-six states between 1964 (when acquisition started) and 1993 (U.S. General Accounting Office 1995). Had the Bureau of Land Management (BLM) lands not been transferred to the state of Alaska and to Native Alaskans in this period, the net acquisition would have been 34,230,000 acres.[9] But this acquisition favored new conservation coverage rather than buyouts of existing inholders, and the number of inholders actually grew.

Not only has the publicly owned land base grown, but the proportion of this land encumbered for conservation purposes consistent with ecosystem management has also expanded, through legislative or administrative restrictions. In fiscal 1964, such lands stood at 7 percent; by fiscal 1993, they had risen by almost 44 percent (U.S. General Accounting Office 1995). In 1964, with few exceptions, land thus encumbered was exclusively managed by the Fish and Wildlife Service and the National Park Service. By 1993, the two largest federal landholding agencies (BLM and the U.S. Forest Service) similarly had encumbered appreciable portions of their holdings (see Table 8.1). Given the federal government's interest in ecosystem management, the federal lands now in strict conservation status (270 million acres) will continue to grow and, with it, the population of inholders affected by such growth.

Various studies have sought to profile traditional inholders (NRC 1993). Generalizations are hard to come by, as these profiles vary greatly by location and region of the country. The inholders range from marginalized minorities (Hispanic-Americans in various national forests in New Mexico, African-Americans in the Virgin Islands National Park, and Osage Indians in the Tall Grass Prairie Reserve) to urban and suburban second-home owners (in the Adirondacks, Yosemite, the Blue Ridge Parkway). The former have relatively insecure titles (Spanish land grants frequently unrecognized

9. Public Law 85–508, the Alaska Statehood Act of 1958, as amended, stipulated this transfer. The Alaska Native Claims Settlement Act of 1971, as amended, provided for the latter transfer.

Table 8.1 Acres managed by four federal agencies

	Forest Service	Bureau of Land Management	Fish and Wildlife Service	National Park Service	Totals
1964					
Total acreage managed	186,274,576	464,346,607	22,396,317	27,500,745	700,518,245
Conservation acreage	1,435,909	628	22,396,317	27,500,745	51,333,599
Percentage with conservation restrictions	0.77	—[a]	100.0	100.0	7.33
1979					
Total acreage managed	187,422,847	397,505,869	43,045,987	64,961,020	692,935,723
Conservation acreage	22,911,081	74,513	43,045,987	64,961,020	130,992,601
Percentage with conservation restrictions	12.22	0.02	100.00	100.00	18.90
1993					
Total acreage managed	191,525,377	267,640,286	87,375,963	76,571,878	623,113,504
Conservation acreage	49,410,180	57,738,928	87,375,963	76,571,878	271,096,949
Percentage with conservation restrictions	25.80	21.57	100.0	100.0	43.51

Source: GAO analysis of data provided by the Departments of Agriculture and the Interior (U.S. General Accounting Office 1995).
[a]Percentage is miniscule.

by the United States, clouded titles in the case of former slaves in the Sea Islands and the Virgin Islands, and Indian Trust land status, which can be overridden by Congress at will). What traditional inholders have in common, in the end, is their heterogeneity.

Ecosystem inholders are not lacking in diversity but differ from the above in both quantitative and qualitative terms. There are vastly more inholders today than a generation ago, a consequence of the demographic trends colliding with the new geography of ecocentric conservation. The demographic "turnaround" of the 1970s (net population gain of nonmetropolitan over metropolitan areas) appears to be returning in the 1990s, possibly as a long-term trend (Lichter 1993). In addition, the so-called wilderness counties (proximate to wilderness areas) are among the highest-growth counties in the United States (Rudzitis and Johansen 1989). Bullish ecosystem management is encountering swelling population enclaves attracted to the amenities of remote rural areas, greatly increasing the density of inholdings.

The qualitative differences between new and old inholders are many, particularly as regards social class and status. Given the demographic forces currently at work, inholders captured by the ecosystem annexations are apt to be relatively prosperous, well educated, and interested in environmental amenities. They are less likely to produce a living directly from primary-sector pursuits (mining, forestry, agriculture, hunting, trapping, etc.) than to "consume" the environment in more passive ways (recreational, aesthetic, touristic), a condition fostered by their widespread retirement and semi-retirement status. They are apt to commute physically or electronically to urban places for employment, education, or in-service training and to reside in the managed ecosystem seasonally or temporarily. They have, in short, alternatives for sustained livelihood and enjoyment, making their property rights important but not an irreplaceable survival entitlement. Their tolerance for planning and for the regulation of these property rights is generally high, given their retirement or temporary retreat from urban and suburban places where such social controls are taken for granted.

These generalizations are illustrated in the two case studies that follow. One is the oldest and largest initiative in ecosystem management in temperate North America, the Greater Yellowstone Ecosystem (GYE). The other is among the newest ecosystem experiments, the Highlands Project of New York and northern New Jersey. Both are in progress, the latter being far less consolidated in its geographical base and identity. The GYE is in a relatively remote location undergoing intense inmigration, development pressure, and subdivision of ownerships. The latter is immediately adjacent to the nation's largest metropolitan area. In both cases, urban sprawl and conservation sprawl collide.

The Greater Yellowstone Ecosystem

Yellowstone National Park, christened the world's first national park in 1872, is the core of the GYE, which is nearly 20 million acres, or seven times the size of the park and roughly as big as West Virginia.[10] Interagency management coordination for the region began in the 1960s, but delineation as a greater ecosystem came nearly twenty years later when Craighead's (1979) grizzly research first appealed for conservation of a larger natural system to provide a minimal viable habitat for that species. The U.S. Park Service controls 2.5 million acres (Yellowstone and Grand Teton combined), the Forest Service accounts for roughly 11 million acres (seven national forests), the Fish and Wildlife Service manages 89,000 acres in three refuges, and the Bureaus of Land Management and Reclamation control scattered parcels (see Map 8.1). Some twenty-eight federal and state agencies and committees from three states share GYE management duties (Goldstein 1992).[11]

10. This claim rests on whose estimate of GYE is used. Estimates of area included vary widely from 6 to 18 million acres (Grumbine 1990, p. 115).
11. Budd (1991) takes exception to this portrayal of broadly shared management, claiming that, of the twelve members of the Greater Yellowstone Coordinating Committee, nine are Forest Service employees and the remaining three are employees of the National Park Service.

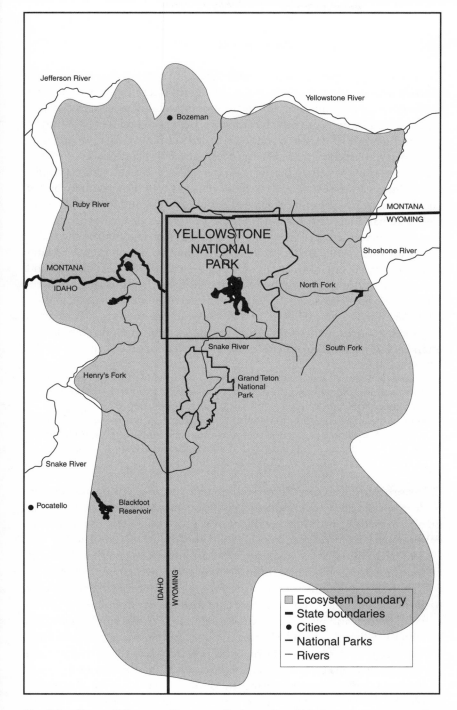

Map 8.1. Greater Yellowstone Ecosystem. Redrawn from U.S. General Accounting Office 1994b.

The GYE is a mosaic of ownership, growing ever more complex as its ecosystem vision expands. State and county lands intermingled with federal holdings comprise public inholdings. Private inholdings are extensive, ranging from 8 to 24 percent of the total system, depending on the definition of GYE used. Some of these are checkerboarded, a holdover of railroad lands granted in the last century. As Forest Service and BLM lands have joined the GYE effort, the owners of permits (timber), leases (oil and gas), and split estates (grazing) have assumed inholder status as well. For example, by the mid-1980s, nearly 5.4 million acres of national forest land (or almost twice the entire national park land within the GYE) was available for oil and gas leasing. This constitutes 55 percent of national forest land within the GYE.

Many owners of partial or full property interests within the GYE claim to be self-styled environmental stewards (Hage 1990; Leal, Black, and Baden 1990). But they pose threats to the GYE by their growing numbers and by their behavior and beliefs about privatization, deregulation, and local ownership (Kwong 1990; Ekey 1994). Although one in four GYE acres may seem an inconsequential ratio of private to public tenures, inholdings often have disproportionate effects on the ecosystem by where they settle:

> People chose to settle in valley bottoms and other level terrain at lower elevations and along water courses where they found milder climates, deeper soils, and a mix of vegetation types. While these lands appeal to people, they also are important habitat for wildlife and birds. For example, in Teton County, Wyoming, half of all bald eagles nest on private land and 90 percent of mule deer migrate onto private lands in search of winter forage. (Harting et al. 1994, p. 12)

Other problems resulting from intermingled and adjacent ownerships include trespassing livestock, industrial pollution, poaching, and the encroachments of roads, power-line corridors, waste-disposal sites, fire, and land development for recreation, housing, and concessions (Jarvis 1982).

Another way of conceptualizing inholder interests is in terms of longevity and intensity. The first group—long-term permanent residents—consists of 300,000 inhabitants of the twenty counties within and adjacent to the GYE. They own, rent, and lease land within the system and depend on grazing, timber, and oil and gas extraction in the GYE for employment and livelihood (Glick, Carr, and Harting 1991), though this may not be their sole source of income. During the early 1980s, when the urban-to-rural population reversal ebbed for much of the country, these same twenty counties grew 33 percent faster per year than Montana, Wyoming, and Idaho as a whole. This led observers to warn of a private land rush in the GYE (Smith 1993). At the other extreme, 34 million tourists a year have an ephemeral yet high-intensity user interest in the GYE for its recreational amenities.

Strains between GYE expansion and the property interests of a prolifer-ating population seem unavoidable. This likelihood increases as population expands or as the GYE extends its territorial reach. Both seem plausible. Demographers project an increase of 70,000 residents by the year 2010 (Harting et al. 1994). If some version of the Wildlands Project is successful, then at a minimum the GYE will eventually be connected to other ecosys-tems through corridors. Consider the management implications of the 1988 Yellowstone fire, which swept through just under half (1.4 million acres) of Yellowstone Park: ecologists believe that land areas at least 50 times the size of catastrophic disturbances should be used to define a minimum scale of the protected ecosystem (Shugart and West 1981; White 1987; Baker 1984). If followed, this formula would yield a managed GYE of an additional 10 to 15 million acres, or more than twice the acreage acquired by the Land and Water Conservation Fund from 1964 to 1989 (NRC 1993).

A final reason to anticipate further expansion of the GYE is the appear-ance in the region of greater numbers of inholders who willingly accept federal land encumbrances. Some private owners view conservation ease-ments, deed restrictions, restrictive covenants, and other limitations on their ultimate use and disposition of land as the "price of admission" to live in an unsullied, high-amenity area of unique beauty and value. Like the High-lands, to which we now turn, conservation easements are spreading via land trusts and other conservation groups which view inholders as potential allies of the GYE (Smith 1993).

The Highlands

Two thousand miles to the east of the GYE, and within an hour of the country's largest metropolitan complex, lie the New York-New Jersey High-lands, a new federal venture in large-scale ecosystem management. The 1990 Farm Bill called for the U.S. Forest Service to conduct a study of the Highlands Region, a million acres stretching from the Delaware River across most of northern New Jersey to the Hudson River in New York, for which Congress appropriated $250,000 in 1991. In the absence of appropri-ate planning, according to the Forest Service, the area's environmental leg-acy was at significant risk. In 1992, the New York-New Jersey Highlands Regional Study was completed for public and congressional review (Mi-chaels et al. 1992), and bills to begin purchasing critical habitats within the region went before the Senate.[12]

12. Two examples are S. 223 and S. 1683, both of which would authorize the secretary of the
    interior to provide funds to the Palisades Interstate Park Commission for acquisition of
    land in the Sterling Forest area of the two-state Highlands, as well as for other purposes.

In contrast to the relatively low population density of the GYE, the thirty-one-county region surrounding the Highlands (extending into Connecticut) is home to some 20 million people, 2.8 million of whom live in the nine counties adjacent to the study area (see Map 8.2). According the 1992 regional study, the tri-state area has seen a 6 percent rise in population and a 60 percent increase in the amount of urban land in the last twenty-five years. Unlike in the West, where federal land forms a significant nucleus of land for ecosystem management and planning, there is virtually no public domain and only 147,800 acres of public land amid 1.1 million acres targeted for protected and buffer-zone ("greenway") status. Federal, state, and local public land constitutes a mere 15 percent of the target area—public inholdings in a sea of private holdings. As in the GYE, private holdings here are under dramatic subdivision pressures. At current rates of land conversion, 15,000 acres of farmland and over 17,000 of forest land will be densely settled by the year 2010, and parcel fragmentation will alter physical, biological, and cultural resources (Michaels et al. 1992).

Assuming the Highlands study area induces special designation and protection beyond what now exists, who will be its inholders and what resemblance to do they bear to those of the GYE? The largest single land use (nearly 50 percent) of the Highlands is forestry. Private ownership dominates, whereas in the GYE public forest lands make up slightly more than half the system. A study of New Jersey forest lands within the study area indicates that in 1988 some 25,000 individuals owned forest land compared to 16,500 in 1972 (Zipperer 1992). This is an increase of 48 percent in two decades and is accompanied by a dramatic increase in holdings of less than 10 acres, particularly by people of retirement age who want to live on or near their parcels and who plan to harvest timber in the next decade. Corporate and partnership owners have increased slightly since 1972, perhaps motivated by land speculation, but own less acreage than previously.

Absentee ownership, declining among individual owners of forest land, is a tenure category of major importance in both ecosystems. In the GYE, it is structurally dictated by the nature of leases and permits for timber and cattle. With certain grazing exceptions, these are transitory rights and, by their nature, invite remote management and control by distant individuals and corporations.[13] Patents to mine, a more permanent property right, open the door to absenteeism, usually after a short burst of prospecting/extractive activity. The Greater Yellowstone Coalition claims that the GYE is afflicted by over 12,000 active and abandoned hardrock mining claims on its federal lands (Glick, Carr, and Harting 1991); these claims threaten to con-

---

13. Some believe that grazing permits are a long-term right that runs with the land, land that is often contiguous to a private holding and cannot be strictly thought of as "absentee owned" (Foresta 1984; Hage 1990).

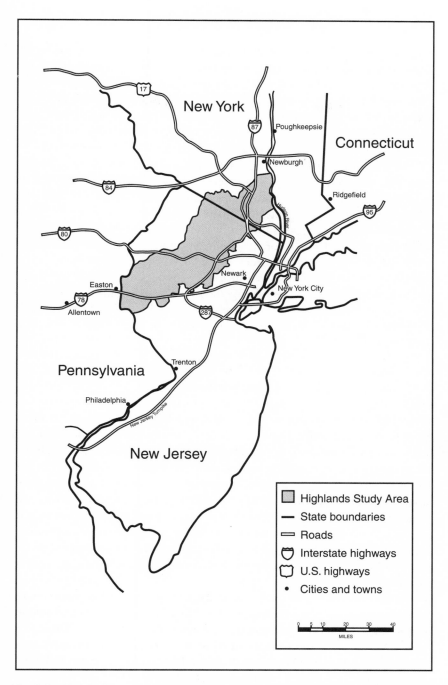

Map 8.2.   New York-New Jersey Highlands Regional Study Area. Redrawn from Michaels et al. 1992.

145

taminate ground and surface waters and indirectly jeopardize the food chain and visual quality in the system. A prominent case is the Noranda Corporation's proposed gold mine less than three miles from Yellowstone National Park in the Gallatin National Forest. Protected by the 1872 Mining Law, Noranda's 200-acre mine hinges on the acquisition of 27 remaining acres, valued at $500 million (*New York Times* 1995). Clearly, inholders are not always small-scale, second-home owners or extractive interests.

In stark contrast to the GYE is the core of the Highlands management plan, the privately owned 17,500-acre Sterling Forest. It is the second largest parcel of relatively undeveloped land under one ownership in the Highlands and the centerpiece of the aforementioned legislation before Congress. Sterling Forest is owned by the Sterling Forest Corporation, a subsidiary of the Home Insurance Company, which, in turn, is a subsidiary of Home Holding, Inc. The latter is owned by a consortium of European investors led by Trygg-Hansa Insurance of Sweden (Michaels et al. 1992). At present, Sterling Forest is being targeted by a consortium of Swiss investors whose primary interest is speculative gain and real estate development. In both the Highlands and the GYE, powerful foreign corporations are important inholders.

"Legacy Inholders"

The Highlands has the potential to serve as a recreational refuge for urban populations, a priority among administrations for at least three decades (NRC 1993), but it comes of age at a time of fiscal austerity and resistance in many quarters to extended federal ownership or control of property rights. Total acquisition of the Sterling Forest's 17,500 acres alone would cost about $70 million. Furthermore, with a 1994 backlog in federal land acquisitions of $1.1 billion, the National Park Service itself opposes diversion of scarce moneys in the Land and Water Conservation Fund toward projects not part of the park service (Finley 1994). Thus, one might expect a proliferation of approaches that control development at a reduced cost, such as conservation easements.

The 1990 Farm Bill introduced the Forest Legacy Program, an approach to conservation that authorizes the U.S. Forest Service to acquire perpetual conservation easements from consenting landowners. Forest Legacy is a federal-state cost-sharing program that targets a variety of pilot areas in the Northeast and in Washington. In the 1993 Appropriations Bill, Congress provided $3 million for the initial acquisition of Sterling Forest lands and other critical parts of the Highlands. The Legacy Program funds cannot be used for eminent domain but can be used for other conservation techniques such as covenants, voluntary deed restrictions, and full-fee acquisition on a willing-seller basis. It thus yields a new type of inholder who, in theory, accepts ecosystem management where there is compensation of foregone property rights.

The Legacy Program is fundamentally tied to ecosystem management principles and, if successful, may spread to other regions of the country where buffer zones, critical corridors, and vulnerable core areas remain unprotected, particularly in forested areas. The words of New Jersey's Forest Legacy Committee (1994, p. 24) are prophetic in this regard:

> Because of the significance of biodiversity, the use of both fee acquisition and conservation easements will be required to protect the biological integrity of selected areas. Timber rights will be acquired on all tracts. Development rights will be acquired on all lands adjacent to streams or wetlands. All subdivision rights will be acquired on all tracts and access will be acquired when property is adjacent to existing parks.

Some will be skeptical that forest landowners will accept encumbrances on their land, even with material incentives. However, over 70 percent of landowners surveyed in the New York-New Jersey Highlands Regional Study mentioned aesthetics and enjoyment as the primary reasons for forest ownership (Michaels et al. 1992). Easements addressing the particular needs of such inholders could be successful in protecting forested ecosystems elsewhere.

Toward a Second Quiet Revolution?

The *Land Rights Advocate,* the newsletter of the American Land Rights Association and the National Inholders Association, recently characterized ecosystem management as old wine in new bottles. It alleged that ecosystem management "won't just stop on the edge of Federal lands. The Forest Service has already been told that this 'planning' will now include any private property 'within the ecosystem.' . . . This is really National Land Planning and Zoning" (Allman 1994). It is accurate to claim that ecosystem management is more than a new conservation paradigm. It remains an open question, however, whether the land-use planning implied herein is old or new. Certainly it evokes parallels with the so-called Quiet Revolution in land-use controls of the 1970s—the broad legislative effort to provide uniform land-use controls at the state and federal levels in the name of environmental necessity (Bosselman and Callies 1971).

The important parallels are these. The Quiet Revolution had antecedents in the 1930s, was national in scale, challenged prevailing notions of public and private interests in property, and, in the end, offered lessons about balancing local and nonlocal interests in pursuing environmental integrity. Indeed, the Quiet Revolution made ample reference to the land ethic of Aldo Leopold (1949), and its mainstay, the National Land Use Policy Act of 1970, cited ecological factors as criteria for sound land-use planning (Caldwell 1972). Though this bill was defeated, its principles permeated subsequent state-level laws and, to some degree, surfaced in the Clean Air Act of 1972, the Clean Water Act of 1972, the Coastal Zone Management Act of 1972, and the Endangered Species Act of 1973.[14]

Yet ecosystem management differs from its predecessor in fundamentally important ways. The Quiet Revolution directed itself to the expanded regulation of private landholding and, arguing that no unconstitutional takings were involved (Bosselman and Callies 1973), foresaw no budget-busting implications in its agenda. This contrasts sharply with the efforts of ecosystem managers to reconstruct the countryside by reformulating both public and private land policy around ecosystem priorities. It concentrates on buffering and protecting privileged ecosystems rather than on uniform protection of the environment across the national geography. What it seeks to safeguard is defined by nature rather than political jurisdictions or the marketplace. In some ways, ecosystem management is quietly revolutionary.[15] Instead of further empowering government as was done in the 1970s, however, it renders it semi-obsolete. As "ecosystem" replaces political jurisdiction, the public interest terms of reference will shift to management units without prior legal standing, legal representation, taxing authority, or budget to carry out their agenda. Of necessity, ecosystem management will require new partnerships, alliances, and social compacts.

Moreover, by using politically rather than ecologically defined boundaries as its point of conceptual departure, the Quiet Revolution sought to centralize authority over land-use planning to state, regional, or federal levels of government (Darin-Drabkin 1977; Popper 1981; Heiman 1988). For the most part, this revolution was an assault on unfettered private ownership of land and on the local control of land use planning (Geisler 1980). Ecosystem management is principally focused on biodiversity and habitat protection and does not presuppose centralization of authority. Its control

---

14. A prominent example is the recent court decision by the Supreme Court granting the Fish and Wildlife Service the power to regulate practices on private lands in relation to the Endangered Species Act in *Sweet Home Chapter of the Communities for a Greater Oregon v. Babbitt,* D.C. Court of Appeals, No. 92-5255, 1993 (Sample 1994, p. 42).

15. Grumbine (1992, p. 11), among others, makes this "revolutionary" inference: "The dilemma posed by the relationship between public and private lands is the beginning of the story of how boundaries drawn in the past are no longer suitable today." Another potentially revolutionary aspect of ecosystem management, not treated here, is the claim that nonhuman organisms in the ecosystem have rights (see Rolston 1990).

mechanisms can be local or nonlocal, private or public, or combined. Ecosystem managers are packaging diverse public ownership mandates with an array of inducements—including compensation, incentive, and benefits-sharing options—intended to attract private owners to participate (see Michaels et al. 1992).

In sum, the former revolution sought sweeping separations of ownership and control in land through macro-zoning of the landscape. Landowners were asked to relinquish certain rights of use in light of a newly defined public interest that emphasized a clean environment. Ecosystem management proposes a new geography of ownership and control that will potentially, but not necessarily, reach the backyard of all landowners. Caldwell clearly hoped that the first Quiet Revolution would go beyond broader land-use regulation: "An ecosystems approach to public land policy assumes a scope that embraces all land regardless of its ownership or custody under law" (1972, p. 412). This hope is more likely to be realized through ecosystem management than the Quiet Revolution, which held little to attract most landowners to its camp.

Conclusion

The rapid expansion of the ecosystem management and its bigger-is-better operating bias makes the property-ecosystem interface a pressing research target at many levels. As the ecosystem management paradigm expands in practice, it subsumes more ownership units and creates new ranks of inholders. It bears repeating Popper's (1979) injunction that ownership factors such as concentration, absenteeism, and owner background and values are an important, though often hidden, dimension in land-use planning. Anyone who doubts this influence need only recall the sovereign hand of railroad companies a century ago in locating, on a national scale, settlements, public infrastructure investments, thoroughfares and major national parks (NPCA 1988). On a regional and local scale, competing ownership claims can cloud title, obstruct land assembly, and stymie property transactions. Prior ownership patterns such as checkerboarding prefigure where settlement and subdivision occur and, of course, the degrees of management freedom retained by ecosystem managers. Monopoly ownership patterns, surprisingly recurrent in the United States (NRC 1993), raise the cost of land for housing, for local livelihoods, and for such basic tools as conservation easements. It also dictates which lands will be exempted from protection and where planning windfalls and wipeouts will occur. The personal values of inholders, turned political, can stampede public opinion for or against ecosystem management.

At the outset of this chapter, we expressed concern over the unintended social consequences of ecosystem management. Chief among these, given its sprawling nature, is the potential public backlash against the principles of such management and against conservation biology more generally. Is compromise possible between the advocates of property rights and ecosystem rights? We believe it is. Where successful to date, ecosystem management rests on environmental education and on what Orr (1992) aptly calls "ecological literacy." It evokes innovative land assembly and compensation strategies, as outlined in Michaels et al. (1992), Endicott (1993), Northern Forest Lands Council (1994), and Wiebe, Tegene, and Kuhn (1996), and invites debate on the public interest in an era of unprecedented environmental stress. Finally, it requires no-nonsense citizen participation and review of alternative approaches to achieving ecosystem management before they are prescribed. We believe that the National Environmental Policy Act (NEPA) of 1970 has much to offer ecosystem management.

NEPA has great potential in reducing unintended backlash in so far as it is valued both by environmentalists and, in its concern for cultural welfare, by followers of the "wise use" movement.[16] As noted by Keiter (1990, p. 46), "The heart of NEPA is the requirement that federal agencies prepare an environmental impact statement (EIS) whenever they contemplate any action significantly affecting the quality of the human environment." NEPA provides for social impact assessments which, like its EIS provisions, are to be executed in the early stages of the environmental review process. It requires that "affected" agencies must be notified of the proposed action and afforded an opportunity to comment on the proposal, and that the EIS include discussion of "possible conflicts between the proposed action and the objectives of Federal, regional, State and local land use plans, policies and controls for the area concerned" (Keiter 1990, pp. 47–48).

Perhaps most relevant to ecosystem management, NEPA recognizes the importance of cumulative impacts, including those extending beyond established boundaries to adjacent and sometimes distant landscapes. In plain terms, this well-established federal law requires that both the social and environmental impacts of significant federal proposals be analyzed in their full geographic scope and be subject to public involvement and participation (Keiter 1990). This investigation must consider alternative ways of achieving a policy objective and include the status quo as a legitimate option. NEPA regulations require full disclosure of serial development proposals

16. For example, the county movement, presumably a foe of ecosystem management, uses NEPA to justify its bold protection of local cultural diversity as recognized by NEPA. As a policy goal, NEPA seeks to ensure "esthetically and culturally pleasing surroundings" and to "preserve important historic, cultural, and natural aspects of our national heritage" (Keiter 1990, p. 58). (For further discussion of this, see chapter 4 of this volume.)

and a comprehensive examination of transboundary impacts (Keiter 1994), certainly the baseline for informed public debate. Where land assembly for ecosystem management does not emanate from federal mandates and initiatives, there are "baby NEPAs" in virtually every state with at least some of the above provisions. Energetically applied, an environmental and social impact assessment is a prudent first step in ecosystem management and a way of incorporating the stakeholders who Slocombe (1993) correctly views as essential to such management. Finally, NEPA requires that mitigation be fully considered, from prevention of harm to compensation (Interorganizational Committee 1993).[17]

We trust this chapter offers convincing evidence of Grumbine's (1992) charge that ecosystem management constitutes a modern enclosure movement, one which is federally significant in a cumulative sense and which, in its own way, amounts to a quiet revolution in land-use planning. Grumbine's concern is that ecosystem management runs the risk of being top-down, of homogenizing people and places, of distancing rather than connecting people from their real interests in the land. The solution he proposes is place-based management, which respects local culture just as it respects biodiversity (ibid.). Among NEPA's policy goals is the preservation of important historic, cultural, and natural aspects of our national heritage (Keiter 1990). Surely this includes the local culture of which Grumbine speaks and is one of the hard-won lessons of the Endangered Species Act (Carlton 1986). Ecological coherency at the landscape level will expand and endure in American cultural landscape to the extent that local property cultures are recognized as management partners.

References

Albrecht, V. 1994. "Ecosystem Management and the Private Landowner." In *Ecosystem Management: Status and Potential,* pp. 107–113. Summary of a workshop convened by the Congressional Research Service (March 1994). 103d Congr., 2d sess. Washington, D.C.: U.S. Government Printing Office.

Allman, P. 1994. "Ecosystem Management Threat to Cabin Owners, Inholders." *Land Rights Advocate* (January/February): 19.

Bailey, R. G. 1995. "Description of the Ecoregions of the United States." 2d ed. U.S.

17. The true sense of mitigation, as elaborated in the Council on Environmental Quality guidelines governing NEPA, requires a sequence of procedures that, first, prevents harm, reduces it to a minimum if it must occur, and, lastly, compensates for damages (Interorganizational Committee 1993, p. 15). Elsewhere, we have discussed the merits of applying NEPA to protected area planning and commented on its potential for public participation among diverse property interests (Rao and Geisler 1988; Geisler 1993; NRC 1993).

Forest Service Miscellaneous Publication 1391. Washington, D.C.: U.S. Department of Agriculture.

Baker, W. L. 1994. "The Landscape Ecology of Large Disturbances in the Design and Management of Nature Reserves." In *Environmental Policy and Biodiversity*, edited by R. E. Grumbine, pp. 75–98. Washington, D.C.: Island Press.

Beatley, T. 1994. *Habitat Conservation Planning*. Austin, TX: University of Texas Press.

Bird, Joan. 1989. "How Big Is Big Enough?" In *Learning to Listen to the Land*, edited by Bill Willers, pp. 68–73. Washington, D.C.: Island Press.

Bosselman, F., and D. Callies. 1971. *The Quiet Revolution in Land Use Controls*. Washington, D.C.: Council on Environmental Quality.

Bosselman, F., D. Callies, and J. Banta. 1973. *The Taking Issue: An Analysis of the Constitutional Limits of Land Use Control*. Washington, D.C.: U.S. Government Printing Office.

Budd, K. 1991. "Ecosystem Management: Will National Forests Be Managed into National Parks?" In *The Greater Yellowstone Ecosystem: Redefining America's Wilderness Heritage*, edited by R. Keiter and M. Boyce, pp. 24–36. New Haven, CT: Yale University Press.

Caldwell, L. 1972. "The Ecosystem as a Criterion for Public Land Policy." In *The Ecology of Man: An Ecosystem Approach*, edited by R. L. Smith, pp. 410–420. New York, NY: Harper and Row.

Carlton, R. L. 1986. "Property Rights and Incentives in the Preservation of Species." In *The Preservation of Species*, edited by B. Norton, pp. 255–267. Princeton, NJ: Princeton University Press.

Cortner, H. J., and M. A. Moote. 1994. "Trends and Issues in Land and Water Resources Management: Setting the Agenda for Change." *Environmental Management* 18: 167–173.

Cortner, H. J., M. A. Shannon, M. G. Wallace, S. Burke, and M. A. Moote. 1994. *Institutional Barriers and Incentives for Ecosystem Management*. Tucson, AZ: University of Arizona Water Resources Research Center.

Craighead, F. C., Jr. 1979. *Track of the Grizzly*. San Francisco, CA: Sierra Club Books.

Darin-Drabkin, H. 1977. *Land Policy and Urban Growth*. New York, NY: Pergamon.

Drury, N. B. 1946. "Private In-holdings in National Park System." *Land Policy Review* 9: 3–8.

Ekey, R. 1994. "Wise Use and the Greater Yellowstone Vision Document." In *Let the People Judge*, edited by J. D. Echeverria and R. B. Eby, pp. 339–347. Washington, D.C.: Island Press.

Endicott, E. 1993. *Land Conservation through Public/Private Partnerships*. Cambridge, MA: Lincoln Institute of Land.

Finley, M. 1994. "Statement of Mike Finley, Associate Director, National Park Service, Department of the Interior, before the House Subcommittee on National Parks, Forests and Public Lands, Committee on Natural Resources Concerning HR 2741 and HR 3107, Bills to Authorize the Secretary of the Interior to Provide Funds to the Palisade Interstate Park Commission for the Acquisition of Lands in the Sterling Forest." May 26. U.S. House. Washington, D.C.

Foresta, R. A. 1984. *America's National Parks and Their Keepers.* Washington, D.C.: Resources for the Future.

Geisler, C. C. 1980. "The Quiet Revolution in Land Use Control Revisited." In *The Rural Sociology of Advanced Societies,* edited by F. H. Buttel and H. Newby, pp. 489–526. Monclair, NJ: Allanheld.

Geisler, C. C. 1993. "Rethinking SIA: Why Ex Ante Research Isn't Enough." *Society and Natural Resources* 6: 327–338.

Geisler, C. C., and S. Kittel. 1994. "Who Owns the Ecosystem? Property Dimensions of Ecosystem Management." Paper presented at the conference "The Institutional Dimensions of Ecosystem Management." Oct. 17. Skamania Lodge, Oregon.

Glick, D., M. Carr, and B. Harting, eds. 1991. *An Environmental Profile of the Greater Yellowstone Ecosystem, Executive Summary.* Bozeman, MT: Greater Yellowstone Coalition.

Glicksman, R. L., and G. C. Coggins. 1984. "Federal Recreational Land Policy: The Rise and Decline of the Land and Water Conservation Fund." *Columbia Journal of Environmental Law* 9: 125–236.

Goldstein, B. E. 1992. "Can Ecosystem Management Turn an Administrative Patchwork into a Greater Yellowstone Ecosystem?" *Northwest Environmental Journal* 8: 285–324.

Grossman, D. H., K. L. Goodin, and C. L. Reussl. 1994. Rare Plant Communities of the Coterminous United States: An Initial Survey. Arlington, VA: Nature Conservancy.

Grumbine, R. E. 1990. "Protecting Biological Diversity through the Greater Ecosystem Concept." *Natural Areas Journal* 10: 114–120.

Grumbine, R. E. 1992. *Ghost Bears.* Washington, D.C.: Island Press.

Grumbine, R. E. 1994. "An Ecological Denouement." In *Environmental Policy and Biodiversity,* edited by R. E. Grumbine, pp. 387–393. Washington, D.C.: Island Press.

Hage, Wayne. 1990. *Storm Over Rangelands: Private Rights in Federal Lands.* Bellevue, WA: Free Enterprise Press.

Harting, A., D. Glick, C. Rawlins, and B. Ekey. 1994. *Sustaining Greater Yellowstone: A Blueprint for the Future.* Bozeman, MT: Greater Yellowstone Coalition.

Heiman, M. K. 1988. *The Quiet Evolution: Power, Planning, and Profits in New York State.* New York, NY: Praeger.

Hunt, C. 1989. "Creating an Endangered Ecosystems Act." *Endangered Species Update* 6 (3–4): 1–5.

Interorganizational Committee. 1993. "Guidelines and Principles for Social Impact Assessment." Interorganizational Committee on Guidelines and Principles for Social Impact Assessment. Washington, D.C.: U.S. Department of Commerce.

Ireland, L. C. 1994. "Getting from Here to There: Implementing Ecosystem Management on the Ground." *Journal of Forestry* (August): 12–17.

Jackson, C. C., and J. S. Wyner. 1994. "The New Hot Doctrine: Ecosystem Management." *The National Law Journal* 17: C6.

Jarvis, T. D. 1982. "Adjacent Lands and Intermingled Ownership Problems." In *National Parks in Crisis,* edited by E. H. Connally, pp. 91–106. Silver Spring, MD: Information Dynamics.

Jontz, J. 1993. "The Sustainable Ecosystem Act." Draft report. Silver Lake, Indiana.

Keiter, R. B. 1990. "NEPA and the Emerging Concept of Ecosystem Management on the Public Lands." *Land and Water Law Review* 25: 43–60.

Keiter, R. B. 1994. "Beyond the Boundary Line: Constructing a Law of Ecosystem Management." *University of Colorado Law Review* 65: 293–333.

Keystone Center. 1991. Final Consensus Report of the Keystone Policy Dialogue on Biological Diversity on Federal Lands. Keystone, CO: (April).

Kwong, J. 1990. "A Private Property Rights Approach to Land Use Conflicts." In *The Yellowstone Primer,* edited by J. A. Baden and D. Leal, pp. 81–93. San Francisco: Pacific Research Institute for Public Policy.

Leal, D., G. Black, and J. A. Baden. 1990. "Oil and Gas Development." In *The Yellowstone Primer,* edited by J. A. Baden and D. Leal, pp. 117–135. San Francisco: Pacific Research Institute for Public Policy.

Leopold, Aldo. 1949. *A Sand County Almanac.* New York, NY: Ballantine.

Lichter, D. 1993. "Migration, Population Redistribution and the New Spatial Inequality." In *The Demography of Rural Life,* edited by D. Brown, D. Field, and J. Zuiches, pp. 19–46. University Park, PA: Northeast Regional Center for Rural Development.

Liverman, M. 1990 "Model Endangered Native Ecosystem Legislation, Third Draft." *Audubon Society of Portland.* Feb. 20.

Lubchenco, J. 1994. "The Scientific Basis of Ecosystem Management: Framing the Context, Language and Goals." In Ecosystem Management: Status and Potential, pp. 33–40. Summary of a Workshop Convened by the Congressional Research Service, March 24 and 25. 103d. Cong., 2d. sess. Washington, D.C.: U.S. Government Printing Office, pp. 33–40.

Mann, C. C., and M. L. Plummer. 1993. "The High Cost of Biodiversity." *Science* 260 (June 25): 1868–1871.

Michaels, J. A., L. Neville, D. Edelman, T. Sullivan, and L. A. DiCola. 1992. *New York-New Jersey Highlands Regional Study.* Washington, D.C.: U.S. Forest Service.

New Jersey Forest Legacy Committee. 1994. *Forest Legacy Statewide Assessment of Need for New Jersey.* March 18. Trenton, NJ.

New York Times. 1995. "Stopping the Yellowstone Mine." *New York Times* (editorial, March 27): A14.

Northern Forest Lands Council. 1994. Technical Appendix. A Compendium of Technical Research and Forum Proceedings from the Northern Forest Lands Council. Concord, NH.

Noss, R. F. 1991. "A Native-Ecosystems Act." *Wild Earth* 1: 24.

Noss, R. F. 1992. "The Wildlands Project." *Wild Earth Special Issue:* 10–25.

Noss, R. F., E. T. LaRoe III, and J. M. Scott. 1995. "Endangered Ecosystems of the United States: A Preliminary Assessment of Loss and Degradation." Biological

Report 28. Washington, D.C.: U.S. Department of the Interior, National Biological Service.

NPCA (National Parks Conservation Association). 1988. "Park Boundaries: Where We Draw the Line." Washington, D.C.: National Parks and Conservation Association. Vol. 5.

NRC (National Research Council). 1993. *Setting Priorities for Land Conservation.* Washington, D.C.: National Academy Press.

Omernik, James N. 1987. "Ecoregions of the Coterminous United States." *Annals of the Association of American Geographers* 77(1):118–125.

Orr, D. W. 1992. *Ecological Literacy.* Albany, NY: State University of New York Press.

Popper, F. J. 1979. "Ownership: The Hidden Factor in Land Use Planning." In *Land in America,* edited by R. N. Andrews, pp. 129–136. Toronto: Lexington Books.

Popper, F. J. 1981. *The Politics of Land-Use Reform.* Madison, WI: University of Wisconsin Press.

Rao, K., and C. Geisler. 1988. "The Social Consequences of Protected Areas Development for Resident Populations." *Society and Natural Resources* 3: 19–32.

Rolston, H. III. 1990. "Property Rights and Endangered Species." *University of Colorado Law Review* 61: 283–306.

Rudzitis, G., and H. E. Johansen. 1989. "Amenities, Migration and Non-Metropolitan Regional Development." Report to the National Science Foundation. Washington, D.C.

Runte, A. 1990. *Yellowstone.* Lincoln, NE: University of Nebraska Press.

Sample, A. V. 1994. "Building Partnerships for Ecosystem Management on Mixed Ownership Landscapes." *Journal of Forestry* (August): 41–44.

Shelford, V. E. 1994. "The Preservation of Natural Biotic Communities." In *Environmental and Policy Biodiversity,* edited by R. E. Grumbine, pp. 25–33. Washington, D.C.: Island Press.

Shugart, H. H., Jr., and D. C. West. 1981. "Long-Term Dynamics of Forest Ecosystems." *American Scientist* 69: 647–652.

Sierra Nevada Ecosystem Project. 1996. Final Report to Congress. Vol. 1, *The Assessment Summaries and Management Strategies.* (Report no. 36.) Davis, CA: Wildlands Resources Center.

Slocombe, D. S. 1993. "Implementing Ecosystem-Based Management." *BioScience* 43: 612–622.

Smith, L. 1993. "The Land Rush Is On." Greater Yellowstone Report 10: 1, 4–5.

Tansley, A. G. 1935. "The Use and Abuse of Vegetational Concepts and Terms." *Ecology* 16: 284–307.

Trott, C. 1995. "Ecosystem Planning for Private Property." *Women in Natural Resources* 16: 4–7.

Turner, M. G., R. H. Gardner, and R. V. O'Neill. 1995. "Ecological Dynamics at Broad Scales." *BioScience Supplement:* 29–35.

U.S. General Accounting Office. 1994a. *National Wildlife Refuge System: Contributions Being Made to Endangered Species Recovery.* Washington, D.C.: U.S. General Accounting Office.

U.S. General Accounting Office. 1994b. *Ecosystem Management.* GAO/RCED-94–111. August. Washington, D.C.: U.S. General Accounting Office.

U.S. General Accounting Office. 1995. *Federal Lands. Fact Sheet for Congressional Requesters.* Washington, D.C.: U.S. General Accounting Office.

White, P. S. 1987. "Natural Disturbance, Patch Dynamics and Landscape Pattern in Natural Areas." *Natural Areas Journal* 7: 14–22.

Wiebe, K., A. Tegene, and B. Kuhn. 1996. *Partial Interests in Land: Policy Tools for Resource Use and Conservation.* Agricultural Economics Report no. 744. Washington, D.C.: U.S. Department of Agriculture, Economic Research Service.

Wright, G. M., and B. Thompson. 1935. *Fauna of the National Parks of the U.S.* Washington, D.C.: U.S. Department of the Interior, National Park Service.

Yaffee, S. L., A. L. Phillips, C. Frentz, P. W. Hardy, S. M. Maleki, and B. E. Thorp. 1996. *Ecosystem in the United States.* Washington, D.C.: Island Press.

Zipperer, W. C. 1992. "Forest Land Ownership." In *New York-New Jersey Highlands Regional Study,* edited by J. A. Michaels et al., pp. 34–44. Washington, D.C.: U.S. Department of Agriculture, Forest Service.

PART III

Land, Culture,
and Place

Cultural Dimensions of Land Tenure in the United States

Sonya Salamon

Introduction

A mosaic of cultural systems exists in America. Each system is unique to a specific place and is a product of who settled a place, when settlement occurred, and what environmental factors—social or physical—were met. Distinctive cultural systems emerged attached to the different places as successive conjunctions left traces in the assumptions people had regarding appropriate behaviors. Thus, distinctive cultural practices such as a kinship system, gender roles, inheritance customs, and attitudes toward land have roots in the original and subsequent peoples who inhabited a particular space. Land-tenure systems, likewise, emerged as part of the local cultural system.

The vast majority of the nation's land is in rural and agricultural use, and this chapter on culture and land tenure focuses on agricultural land tenure. Its main concern is how tenure evolves where family farms dominate (Beale and Kalbacher 1989). In the literature, a family farm is typically defined according to economic criteria, scarcely taking social and cultural dimensions into account; yet culture matters to land tenure and is critical to understanding the implications of who owns America's land.

This chapter considers land tenure as a process produced by various layers of culture. National ideals constitute a broad context in which a specific cultural system operates. At the community level, the meaning of land or land-acquisition goals, originating with a group's ethnic origin, shape a context for the domestic culture of the family. In the family, culture is enacted and social relationships are reproduced in conjunction with the intergenerational transmission of land. Each layer is affected by internal factors but also by external factors (from the other layers), as well as by historical events.

National Culture Shaping Land Tenure

Space is culturally constructed, and thus Americans think about land in distinctive ways. How the nation was settled, how public lands were transferred to private hands, and how newcomers received vast amounts of land all shape how Americans think about land (Johnson 1976). Below is a list of American cultural themes associated with land. While not an exhaustive list, these ideal factors are central to the national culture, in which land is simultaneously the instrument for attaining the ideal and the motivation for action. These factors emerged from the interplay of peoples with the unique landscape features, and the character of the self-chosen immigrants to the New World.

The New World landscape and the subtle communal ownership of American Indians affected how successive waves of newcomers thought about land.[1] Pioneer settlers from western and northern Europe encountered a landscape of a scale previously unknown to them. For peoples hungry for land, encounters with a vast continent with seemingly limitless horizons fostered the emergence of the first cultural theme that shapes American land tenure.

"Bigger is better." "A cult of bigness," in which "size is preferred even in things that might be better small" (Lowenthal 1968), motivates Americans to accumulate, speculate on, and be wasteful of land (Jordan and Rowntree 1982; Zelinsky 1973). Communities spread out as railroads and then automobiles fostered expansion across the nation, logically extending the classic "main street" source of goods and services to the present "galactic city," covering vast areas (Hudson 1985; Lewis 1995).

Abundant lands influenced adoption of the rectangular land survey in much of the nation's regions. The grid system has influenced the way Americans view the land, plan their communities, and perhaps realize dreams to control more and bigger places and things (Johnson 1976). Close to three-quarters of the land in the forty-eight contiguous states and some of Alaska was divided by the rectangular survey. This survey system greatly facilitated

---

1. The influence of the American Indians on land tenure and agriculture is significant but beyond the scope of this chapter. American Indians, the original inhabitants, accounted for the frontier features encountered by subsequent settlers. Whether aboriginal populations lived in permanent settlements, as along the Mississippi and in the Southeast, or were nomads, as in the High Plains, speeded or slowed the inexorable spread of immigrants. European-Americans' adaptation to the local ecology involved adopting some American Indian cultural traits: names for places and species, indigenous foods, native medicinal plants, crops, and farming practices. As a result of the Mexican-American war, Mexicans living in what is now the Southwest were granted citizenship, and their culture interacted with the Pueblos and other tribes to form the distinctive Southwest landscape. Of note is the recent utilization of landholdings by American Indians on reservations for resorts, gambling, or natural resources to enhance the well-being of tribal peoples.

the rapid transfer of vast amounts of land to private ownership because it made possible the unambiguous description of land tracts and guaranteed security of ownership. The system made it simple to transfer land, which aided in the success of claim associations and, incidentally, that of speculators; it also contributed to the attitude that land is a commodity, not a common good under the stewardship of its owners (ibid.).

The United States did not invent the rectangular survey (it was known as early as the Romans) but the survey method is particularly well-suited to level, relatively uninterrupted landscapes. Engraved on the old agriculture college building of the University of Illinois campus is an epigraph that captures the reverence for the land: "The wealth of Illinois is in her soils." Yet farmers exploited the resource, some say, influenced by the notion that good farming, regardless of the slope or contour of the land, was measured by the straightness of the furrow (ibid.).

Abundant land meant that nineteenth-century native-born farmers diverged dramatically from Europeans, who farmed land as a scarce resource. Native-born farmers historically were not considered good stewards of the soil. Though fertility-maintenance methods were known, the abundance of available land encouraged farmers to discard such practices as impractical and unnecessary. By the 1840s, because farmers neglected such practices as manuring fields, some Ohio soils showed the same depletion as those in the East pioneers had left behind. Depleted soils were abandoned as farmers followed the frontier west to new, more fertile land (Danhof 1969).

"Ownership of land is better for society and is a citizen's right." Jeffersonian notions of how democracy is best supported infuse this other cultural belief affecting American land tenure. Jefferson's vision of an ideal democratic society was agrarian; landownership by the citizenry was the bulwark of democracy. Owning land was seen by Jefferson as the means to economic security and freedom. Of course, he thought government should protect the right to property, and the immensity of land available beyond the frontier made such a right feasible (Griswold 1948).

The nation's regard for farming is connected to a cultural belief that democracy is best assured by private ownership, just as Jefferson argued (ibid.). That is, the general welfare of the nation and communities is best served by farmers owning their land (Strange 1988). Public policies, as early as the Homestead Act of 1863, reflect ownership considered as an entitlement. A homestead deeded to a citizen who occupied and cultivated the allotted acreage for five years was "the imprint in law of a concept of land that had emerged gradually with the growth of the Republic: that each head of a family was entitled to a home or farm" (U.S. Department of the Interior 1976, p. 56). Ownership has become firmly embedded in the nation's economy and serves important societal goals (Perrin 1977; Fitchen 1989).

Ownership in the United States incorporates notions of an exclusive relationship to land (Fiske 1991). Owning land has come to mean defending the inviolability of privacy and private property. Outcomes of these culturally shaped relationships to land are apparent in land-use and inheritance patterns. Typically, an American individual or family depends substantially on an inheritance of land from ancestors to achieve status while professing to being self-made (Clignet 1992; Salamon 1992). Property rights are understood to be relatively unlimited in the United States and to carry no obligation for wise use of the land (Strange 1988). Environmental degradation by farming, ranching, or mining that occurs on private property is therefore largely ignored; U.S. land is not considered a public resource or common property (Jorgensen 1984). "Land is a commodity that you can own and if you wish willfully destroy" (Strange 1988, p. 202). Currently, landlords own 70 percent of U.S. farmland and rent out nearly two-thirds of their holdings (Gilbert and Beckley 1993). Majority control of community land thus may be with owners who live elsewhere and have no vested interests in community services (or other indexes of quality) supported by real estate tax dollars.

"Social mobility is a realizable goal symbolized by landownership." Land as a commodity underlies a third cultural ideal, that of social mobility. Our individualistic and capitalistic society is based on the notion that if you work hard you can get ahead and do better than your parents did. Government policies such as the Homestead Act of 1863, inheritance laws that favor equal opportunities to all heirs, and the income tax system's bias toward homeowners exemplify the national value placed on landownership as the means to attain the American dream (Strauss 1971; Perrin 1977). The symbolic ladder of upward mobility is climbed by property ownership; conversely, one moves downward without it. Property is a measure of status, viewed as a source of economic security and a measure of a worthy citizen (Strauss 1971; Tocqueville reprinted 1990).

One passes through progressive stages of landownership if one achieves the American dream (Perrin 1977). One moves from tenant status to that of ownership of successively larger farms, according to this ideal of social mobility. Land simultaneously provides status, as well as shelter or livelihood. Landownership, especially in earlier historic periods, allowed people to use property mobility to attain social mobility without a change in occupation (Thernstrom 1968). In particular, immigrants pursuing the American dream through painstaking accumulation of property holdings have improved their social standing. Property ownership, however, also is an indicator of whether mobility is achieved by being symbolic of income differentials, racial inequalities, or geographical differences (Hacker 1983; Perrin 1977).

Jefferson was opposed to the social immobility and perpetuation of wealth that prevailed among the English with their systems of entail and primogeniture inheritance (Griswold 1948). When he drafted Virginia's laws, he tried to prevent an aristocracy from emerging by mandating an equal division of family property during intergenerational transfers. By such means, he hoped to perpetuate his ideal: a small-farm system that allowed for more of a chance to achieve individual liberty and equal opportunity. That is, there was a moral basis to his small-landowner system; ultimately, though, Jefferson had an agrarian goal that was a political and social ideal rather than an economic one (ibid.).

Inheritance practices reproduce familial relations and the order of groups within a community and the wider society (Clignet 1992; Salamon 1992). Prior to industrialization in the United States, land was the most important source of wealth. Clignet (1992, p. 189) argues that Americans downplay the importance of inheritance, although it is important to social status in the society, because "inheritance offends their belief in mobility and their desire to be liberated from the past." Land, a form of "mechanical" inheritance, remains especially important to enterprise reproduction when families are self-employed (farmers are an example). Land also is a stable resource, carrying little risk to heirs, and its inheritance enhances the ability to accumulate other assets. Yet, when land makes up the bulk of the estate, it is less likely than other assets to be divided equally among heirs (ibid.). Conceivably, inheritance of land acts differently for men and women and thus can perpetuate gender differences in mobility and in the status hierarchy of families and communities. Ethnic origin or cultural difference are critical dimensions of social reproductive processes, for ethnic groups possess distinctive motives for acquisition of land, distinctive beliefs regarding risk, and distinctive inheritance practices (ibid.; Salamon 1992).

Bigness, ownership, and social mobility combine to form a national cultural framework, what Strauss (1971) terms "a context of relevance" that orients people to land. This cultural framework was encountered by the various ethnic groups who came in successive immigrant waves to settle rural America. The ideals motivated many to come and helped shaped new ethnic identities (hyphenated-Americans). In turn, the interplay affected the land tenure where each group settled.

Ethnic Communities and Land Tenure

Culture, Ethnic Identity, and Land

How a group values, transfers, buys, or sells land constitutes its land-tenure system. Those who control land in a community act within a cultural system derived from national, community, and family layers. As a consequence, a community shares a particular repertoire of practices based on beliefs about the goodness of a person, a kin group member, a farmer, and a way of life: these determine how land ought to be handled. Together, the shared set of beliefs constitutes a schema that serves as an interpretive framework and a scenario for decision-making actions (Ortner 1990). Shared cultural practices are typically taken for granted. Beliefs about whether the family or individual is a rightful landowner, who is responsible for intergenerational land transfers, or how much land provides sufficient family support order fundamental decisions across a variety of situations. This view of culture is heavily influenced by "practice model" anthropological theorists (Ortner 1984, 1990). According to this model, culture shapes what people do and believe and also constrains options and regularizes the choices they make, particularly in the repetitive and seemingly trivial aspects of daily life that make up the domestic order (Ortner 1984).

A land-tenure system develops from forces external to the community interacting with families as they are shaped by cultural beliefs and specific environmental constraints. By endorsing some family options and excluding others, land-transaction practices are mechanisms that maintain a cultural system in its special configuration (ibid.). Beliefs about land are fundamental to family and community customary asymmetric relations of gender (men over women), generation (elder over younger), and status or wealth (larger landowners over everyone else). Family practices regarding land ultimately affect whether persistence in farming or continuity of ownership occurs. Cultural systems in which landownership, succession, and inheritance are valued differently cause local land-tenure systems to evolve in distinctive ways (Salamon 1992, 1993).

A community's boundaries are defined by land and its land-tenure system. Land is a component of a local identity and is a particularly powerful force for perpetuating identity. According to Simmel (1898), land provides a concrete, indestructible "material symbol" for family and community attachment. Land has been salient to the expression of ethnic identity. Historically, U.S. immigrants tended to cluster in settlements with those who shared an ethnic origin. Communities evolved as a consequence of chain migration (Conzen 1980) or of church policy that established colonies toward which immigrants had both a duty and a desire to gravitate (Hollingshead 1937). If family farmers maintained continuity tied to land in a particular place, near others sharing an ethnic identity, ethnic communities persisted (Conzen 1990; Salamon 1992). Land was so effective as a symbol of identity that ethnic groups maintained solidarity even in the absence of those experiences identified as reinforcing ethnic differences (Salamon 1992). For instance, given Midwestern checkerboard settlement patterns, ethnic islands were not thrown into competition for land with other ethnic groups, a process thought to enhance ethnic identity (Barth 1969).

Land and Social Structure

There is little corporate farming in the Midwest: the predominant enterprise form is the family farm, where the family makes the operational decisions, provides most of the labor, and generates income to support the household (Johnson 1983; Reinhardt and Barlett 1989). Factors such as the size of farms, tenancy, absentee ownership, or fragmentation of landholdings are variables critical to the region's land tenure (Friedberger 1988; Kramer 1977). The nature of attachment to land, or land tenure—the complex of ownership, rental, farm size, and land transfers—provides the central logic for a rural community's economic and social systems (Bell and Newby 1971; Crocombe 1974).

Early mechanization and the costs of prairie farming made Corn Belt farmland particularly expensive, causing tenancy to become common (Bogue 1963). In the Midwest, tenancy did not automatically mean low social status and a marginal economic existence, as it often did in the South. Typically, most tenants and part owners farmed at least some land rented from relatives, who were commonly local or absentee landlords. Even today in Illinois, 43 percent of landlords rent to tenants who are relatives (Johnson 1972; Kloppenburg and Geisler 1985; Salamon 1992). Renting from a relative means that the relationship between owner and operator is fairly stable and less likely to be exploitative. When a community has many absentee landlords, it is likely that outside investors' control of land was established early (Gilbert and Harris 1984; Salamon 1992). Because an exodus from farming occurred between the 1950s and the 1970s, however, the number of heirs living elsewhere increased for all Midwestern communities. Absentee owners may be good citizens and may be committed to preserving local social infrastructure, but, because they reside elsewhere, they are not subject to the community's cultural system. For them, community identity or integrity may rank lower than profits. For this reason, increased absentee ownership in land tenure can negatively affect community well-being (Mooney 1983).

According to Goldschmidt (1978), land tenure and farm size account for differences in the quality of rural life: schools, infrastructure, and services. In a California community where ownership was in moderately sized family-farm units, the community was superior to the second study community, where farms were larger than family size, ownership was controlled by corporations from outside the community, managers ran the farms, and work was carried out by farm laborers. But regional agriculture in the United States is so varied that, even where absentee ownership or farm consolidations dominate, an inevitable community outcome cannot be predicted (Swanson 1988; Friedberger 1988). Agriculture based on hired farm labor is associated with more stratified social structures, as in the southern plantation/sharecrop system or the corporate farms of California (Pfeffer 1983). The relative absence of hired labor and corporate farms has meant that the midwestern social structure is less stratified; nonetheless, the amount of land owned affects a family's relative position in the status hierarchy (Beale 1989b; Hatch 1975, 1979; Pfeffer 1983).

Manifestations of Land Tenure

Land tenure has two manifestations: geographical/physical and customary practices/social. Both are shaped by culture. In the United States, geographical features such as the layout of a community or the surveying of a territory are heavily influenced by the culture of the original inhabitants. The everyday surroundings of farm and village make up an aesthetic of the landscape—what is taken for granted about how the world should look. That is, culture shapes the physical world, and, correspondingly, culture is acted on by what it created.

Land Tenure and Landscape: Visible Cultural Dimensions

Contemporary rural landscapes are best understood starting with the past, with the cultures that shaped them. Each region of the nation was settled differently and was dominated by particular ethnic groups. Today, the concentration of ethnic populations reflects the intersection of European and U.S. historical events at the time of immigration. For example, the peak of German migration coincided with the opening of agricultural opportunities in the Midwest. Groups remain where they originally settled in significant numbers (Lieberson and Waters 1988). The agricultural landscape, community plans, and land tenure differ among ethnic groups, as a consequence of the intersection of the cultural systems, the historical moment, and the land available at settlement. Families farming in the same region, with similar soils, could be expected to have farms of similar shape or size. Operating according to differing cultural schemas, however, has resulted in differing conceptions of farm and village, as well as differing land-acquisition incentives or intergenerational transfers (Salamon 1992).

From the early seventeenth until the mid-eighteenth century, four different waves of English-speaking settlers brought ways of life that began the formation of distinctive regional cultures: Puritans from eastern England to Massachusetts; Royalist elite and many indentured servants from southern England to Virginia; a largely Quaker movement from the North English and Welsh Midlands to the Delaware Valley; and those from the border areas of north Britain and northern Ireland to the Appalachian highlands. Migrants from these areas fanned out across the East, South, Midwest, and Southern Highland respectively (Fischer 1989). In this period labor was in short supply (especially in the South and far West), racial minorities were used—African-American slaves or Chinese and Japanese recruited as low-paid laborers—to develop the nation's economy. In just fifty years during the mid-nineteenth century, the Midwest was settled through one of the most extraordinary transfers of land and people the world has known. Although the settlers were white and had Christianity, farming, and northern and western European peasant backgrounds in common, their cultural differences led the Midwest in particular to be termed an ethnic mosaic (Conzen 1990).

Ethnic groups, as a consequence of events in their native lands, such as the Irish potato famine, arrived when particular areas of the nation were opening. The immigrants came from places having land-tenure systems that had evolved for centuries. Cultural notions about property rights were imposed on America, where land was in abundance. The Spanish, French, Dutch, and English dealt differently with the tribal peoples and their communal attitude toward land (Hart 1975). The settlement patterns and land survey systems of the newcomers left a distinctive cultural mark on the landscape. The English set the policies in much of the Northeast, with nucleated villages and fragmented farms. The Dutch, in the Hudson River valley, followed a more feudal system, granting large land tracts to individuals. The Spanish in Texas, New Mexico, Colorado, and California granted land in large blocks. Wherever the French settled, they used the "long-lot" system of land division, in which all holdings are set at right angles to road or river frontage, providing access to transportation or fishing, and extended through tillable land to a wood lot (ibid.; Jordan and Rowntree 1982).

Culture affected how people farmed and the quality of life they experienced. Whether farm families lived near neighbors or were dispersed in the countryside affected the mobilization of labor, exchanges, and the support women felt (Salamon and Keim 1979). Farms in the United States, in contrast to Europe's fragmented farms, are more often contiguous unit blocks. The dispersed checkerboard pattern of the Midwest is an example. Geographers connect the unit-block pattern with the conditions that prevailed in much of the U.S.: peace and security in the countryside, settlement by individual families rather than cohesive groups, agricultural private enterprise, well-drained land with available water (Jordan and Rowntree 1982). Unit-block farms in the United States are not uniformly rectangular nor do they resemble the long-lot pattern. Rather, in many instances, irregular shapes result from the metes-and-bounds surveying system, which makes use of natural features such as trees, rocks, and streams. Metes-and-bounds survey-ing dominates the eastern part of the country. Ohio served as a testing ground for several surveying system experiments in preparation for the plot-ting of the Northwest Territory. About one-sixth of Ohio was laid out unsys-tematically in the Virginia Military Survey area. This area has more property litigation over boundaries than the rest of the state combined. The township and range system used in northwestern Ohio was extended to the North-west Territory and is responsible for farmers reckoning their land in frac-tions of 640-acre sections (Hart 1975). The Northwest Territory system dominates most of the country. Culture thus modified the environment, producing a highly varied agrarian landscape across the nation.

European settlers also left distinctive cultural marks in the form of vil-lage land-tenure patterns (ibid.; Jordan and Rowntree 1982). What geogra-phers call the "cultural landscape" reveals traces of "ethnic imprints" that ex-plain the distinctive regional character of the American landscape. Besides favoring different types of land-surveying methods, ethnic groups had pre-ferred styles for houses, farmsteads, barns, communal facilities, churches, and villages. The grid survey and homestead laws favored dispersed settle-ment patterns, but nucleated village plans emerged in some locales, par-ticularly in association with religious-based communities (Conzen 1990). Michael Conzen cites many factors that favored an ethnic imprint on the landscape: volume of immigration sufficient to form a significant spatial cluster, relative isolation for a long period, sufficient economic resources, and strong shared values. In contrast, the combined factors least likely to pro-duce an ethnic imprint on farm and village landscape are "heterogeneous mi-grant streams, dispersed destinations, little tendency to cluster, lack of suc-cess in colonization (leading to geographical mobility), and the pull of the new culture" (ibid., pp. 239–241). Ironically, distinctive ethnic imprints on the rural landscape, once denigrated, are now used to attract tourists.

Land Tenure and Families: Less Visible Cultural Factors

After settlement, a dynamic process took place in which culture, history, and context interacted to shape new ethnic types among the pioneers. Each American ethnic group now differs from the culture in its ancestral home-land and from that brought by immigrant families founding the original community. Yet, because behaviors vested in the family changed more slowly than, for example, language, the emergent cultural structure retains continuity with the past (Salamon 1992; 1993). U.S. farm families, like farmers worldwide, mesh the domestic order with work so that kinship considerations form the context for most actions. As these households go about reproducing family and farm, the cultural system undergoes change: some aspects are altered rapidly and others more slowly. Among farmers, the vested interests of those who control land and thereby dominate families and communities change slowly because actors seek to preserve their social positions and that of their successors (Bloch 1985; Ortner 1990). How land is handled reflects what families consciously want to reproduce for the future and maintain from the past.

Every generation, as owners age and prepare to die, must deal with the transfer of family land. As land control moves through families via intergenerational transfers or through communities via the land market, the transmission is a vehicle for recreating and reenacting the cultural system, even while modifying it. Family relationships linked with land practices in general are taken for granted, carried out in an unthinking manner because "that is how we do things." Maintaining a specific family relationship to land is the way people publicly endorse the compelling and meaningful beliefs that order their lives (Ortner 1984).

A normal intergenerational transfer of farmland occurs about once every twenty-five years, amounting to an annual turnover of approximately 4 percent. Because some land is transferred within families through inheritance, gifts, or preferential sales, only a small amount reaches the open market. Over a generation, however, 4 percent a year can amount to a considerable proportion of land in a rural community (Reiss 1976). The choices of families transferring land and other holdings are shaped by cultural beliefs and specific environmental constraints. These factors also shape how they contend with forces external to the community. The local land-tenure system evolves as a community's families, sharing an ethnic identity, make similar choices over time. Ethnic-group differences pivot on practices derived from beliefs about what land confers, whether the family lineage or the individual owns land, whether siblings cooperate, and whether community allegiance is a commitment associated with the family farm. Cultural distinctions are consequences of the processes of land and farm concentration.

Cultural Dimensions of Family Factors Affecting Agricultural Land Tenure

Family relationships are central to the reproduction of family farms. The kinship system (kin obligations, priorities, and rights) is how the ethnic group perpetuates a distinctive identity. The anthropologist Francis Hsu

(1965, 1971) categorizes kinship systems by linking kin beliefs with family interaction patterns. He argues that a single, primary relationship in the nuclear family—husband-wife or father-son, for example—is dominant, valued, and relied on to perpetuate the group. Accordingly, the other family dyads are subordinated or viewed negatively. When aggregated at the community level, these subtle differences have had implications for how a particular local land-tenure system develops. Intergenerational transfers of land, shaped by culture, can affect persistence in farming, fragmentation of landholdings, and concentration of farms (Salamon 1992, 1993).

Three family-land dimensions, framed below as questions, emerged as pivotal for land-tenure issues in cultural systems. Each of the questions must be viewed as answered according to a cultural schema, by the kinship system, in the nuclear family context, and by land practices.

"Who owns family-owned land?" How this question is answered shapes relations between couples and between parents and children and is evident in practices of farm management, succession, and retirement. Family gender inequalities and, secondarily, inequalities between generations are the products of how land is transferred. Ultimately, such practices have implications for the concentration of landownership.

"Is the group or individual welfare held in highest priority?" How this question is answered shapes family priorities and levels of cooperation among siblings and between generations and is evident in inheritance of farmland. In particular, reproductions of gender inequalities and gender patterns of ownership in families and communities are linked to this dimension.

"Are strong connections between the household and community valued?" How this question is answered shapes access to land and has implications for which families (and who in families) will continue to farm. These practices are particularly linked to the reproduction of community-status and gender inequalities that have implications for land acquisition.

Families of a specific ethnic group answer the above questions with typical land practices that reproduce existing inequalities in the family and community. Subtle practices repeated over generations affect whether a successor is produced, whether a viable farm is kept intact by intergenerational transfers, or whether continuity of ownership is maintained. Such processes affect the availability of land and thus access to farming. Family decisions link a cultural schema and the distinctive outcomes of a local land-tenure system. The key family-land dimensions are likely to be pivotal to land-tenure systems in agrarian societies elsewhere and can be the basis for comparative research (Goldschmidt and Kunkel 1971).

Dimension 1. Who Owns Land: Reproduction of gender and generational inequalities. Cultural beliefs can assign control of family land to the head of household, to both parents, or to parents and children, according to which dyad in the nuclear family is valued for reproduction of the family and farm (Hsu 1965). Typically among white, middle-class Americans, the sexual bond between husband and wife is emphasized and the intergenerational bond between father and son is deemphasized (Schneider 1980; Hsu 1965). This pattern is the reverse of the father-son bond dominant in patrilineal kinship systems, most commonly associated with agrarian societies (Goldschmidt and Kunkel 1971). Dominance of either dyad is implemented through greater control over land and therefore more power over the lives of other family members.

When the husband-and-wife dyad is dominant, exclusiveness expressed by an unwillingness to share resources and a dedication to individualism prevails (Hsu 1965). A married couple who characteristically term themselves business partners expect children to leave the marital household, spurn parental authority, and make their way in the world independently. Household and farm resources in this schema belong primarily to the parents and are rightfully the children's only after parents die. Because the farm is their personal property, parents feel little obligation to involve children in management or plans. The father-and-son relationship may be competitive and acrimonious because the son is not the instrument valued for continuity. The husband-and-wife bond as the dominant dyad creates a family structure less patriarchal with respect to same-generation or intergenerational relations. However, production of a successor is not assured by this system, particularly because the generational inequalities often make the successor role demeaning for sons. Such a kinship emphasis has been found to be associated with farming communities whose ancestry can be traced to the Protestant British Isles (Salamon 1992).

Continuity, according to Hsu (1965), is central to the dominance of the father-son dyad. When continuity is a high priority, the preference for a son to farm means that each father and son relationship forms a link in an unbroken chain. Because of the intergenerational dependence inherent to the dyad, hierarchical lines of authority are clearly drawn. Parents need sons (or a child) to assure continuity of the family farm, and the successor is dependent on the father, who controls the entrance to farming. Authority is male-centered, and the son, who embodies continuity by virtue of carrying the family name, is favored over daughters. A successor is more assured by this cultural system and generational and gender inequalities are reinforced. This type of kinship emphasis has been associated with farming communities whose ancestry can be traced to Germany (Salamon 1992). Because Germans and Protestant British Isles' descendants make up the major ethnic groups farming in the Midwest, their family patterns account for the majority of local land-tenure systems in the region (ibid.).

Dimension 2. Group versus the Individual: Reproduction of gender and gen-

erational inequalities. Cultural schemas enhance generation and gender hierarchies. On midwestern grain farms men are uniformly acknowledged as *the* farmer, though men often say, "You can't farm without a wife." In addition to being the farmer, men market the family grain and control distribution of what is produced (Rosenfeld 1985). Because the producer-manager has the highest family status in farm communities, men control the means for maintaining a superior position in the family's and the community's hierarchy (Friedl 1975). Moreover, inheritance patterns and the legal system have combined historically to maintain the dominance of males in families and communities through their perceived control over land, regardless of actual ownership.

Inheritance is the final intergenerational transfer. Married siblings are torn between the demands of their procreative and natal families, and even so basic a collective goal as the continued viability of the farm may be contested. During parental estate settlements, sibling rivalries may culminate over financial support owed the successor to the farm versus pursuit of the nonsuccessors' self-interests. When heirs keep all land inherited and show a reluctance to sell, land fragmentation occurs, as found among German-Americans. When most children leave farming or the community, the potential for sibling conflict is dampened. Willingness to sell land and less commitment to continuity is linked with fewer fragmented landholdings, more concentration of farms, and more rental land held by absentee owners, as is found among Americans whose ancestors came from the Protestant British Isles (Salamon 1992).

Farm families planning intergenerational farm transfers confront a dilemma: how to treat all members according to the American ideal of equity without destroying the farm in the process. Female heirs present a particular problem for family-farm continuity (Salamon and Davis-Brown 1988). A son is a potential farmer, but a daughter may marry either a farmer or a nonfarmer and leave agriculture. Either way, any land she inherits could be lost to the natal family before the next intergenerational land transfer. Among some American farm families, however, continuity has become secondary to the goal of equality in intergenerational transfer of farm resources. Shifting to absolute equal treatment among children reflects the historic emergence of a U.S. ideal for providing each child with equal resources and an equal opportunity in the world (Farber 1973; Clignet 1992) and an emergent child-rearing philosophy minimizing differences from age, sex, or education (Rosenfeld 1979). The changing customs result in American daughters in urban and rural contexts inheriting equally with sons, regardless of ethnic origin (Clignet 1992).

Despite equal inheritance values and the enhancement of women's right to hold property, the amount of farmland controlled by women in the nation has not increased substantially. As an illustration, only 17 percent of Illinois farmland is owned by women (Geisler, Waters, and Eadie 1985). How did this seemingly illogical state of affairs develop? It may be that what women do with the land they inherit or their discretionary freedom accounts for the continued national dominance of male owners. For example, an early Wisconsin tenure study documented a process whereby owner-operatorship moved out of families as intergenerational transfers were influenced by cumulative "natural" circumstances, such as the timing of retirement and children leaving the farm. The consequences of equal inheritance by both the farming son and the nonfarm siblings were generally negative for the successor (Salter 1943). Thus, the socialization of women, as a variation on Salter's conception of natural circumstance, may shape a woman's commitment toward herself (or family of procreation) versus her natal family—as symbolized by the farm or family land. How women choose or are socialized to choose to use their farmland contributes to distinctive land-tenure patterns among certain religious groups (Salamon and Davis-Brown 1988) and ethnic groups (Salamon 1992).

Another explanation for the dearth of women farmland owners may lie in the discriminatory probate customs that prevailed in the nation until the late 1970s (Geisler, Waters, and Eadie 1985). Although a married couple worked and bought land together, and registered the farm in both names, the courts, prior to reform of the law, considered the male the real owner. Ownership and operation of the farm were equated (Rogers and Vandeman 1993). If the woman died first, the husband paid no inheritance tax. If the man died first, however, the wife was responsible for paying inheritance tax. Even on jointly held land, it was and is common for women to have life use of, rather than full title to, land, securing an income for them and a tax savings for heirs (ibid.). As a consequence, although a woman might have her name on land or life-use, families and communities have viewed males as the true owners of farmland (Salamon 1993; Salamon and Keim 1979). Finally, the practice of men being the farmer and women leaving the farm may mean that urban women are more willing to sell off an inheritance than are their rural brothers.

When land is transferred from one generation to the next, the equal treatment of female heirs favors the individual over the group. When a woman controls land in her name, she is able to wield power by controlling others' lives and influencing the course of events. Control over land is visible to the community and her family. Women who do not inherit land or who do not control land they do inherit have less power in U.S. farming communities (Salamon and Keim 1979; Salamon and Davis-Brown 1988). Commitment to gender equality has been found to be greater among those whose estate consists of stocks and bonds rather than those whose estate is mainly land (Rubinstein 1980; Clignet 1992). Such preferences are central to reproduction of a gender hierarchy in families.

   Dimension 3. Household and Community: Reproduction of status inequalities. The land-tenure system underlies the social divisions in rural society (Goldschmidt 1978; Newby 1980; Salamon 1992). When farm ownership is more concentrated, a few wealthy families control most community land resources. This system is inherently hierarchical, and differences are expressed through striking contrasts in management and living styles. When land resources are distributed more homogeneously and most farms approximate the average in size, a community's social structure more nearly approaches the democratic, egalitarian system envisioned by Jefferson (Griswold 1948). In this latter context, less differentiated strata prevail since families that control relatively equivalent resources and qualities other than wealth can shape the community's social hierarchy (Salamon 1992).

   Success, according to a bigger-is-better standard for land owned and farm size, automatically confers higher status in farm communities. Farm and land consolidation opportunities are linked to stratification of the community's social structure (Schulman, Garrett, and Newman 1989). Social status effectively limits economic options and, along with a family's farm size, its operation type and settlement history. Due to their social connections, households in a community do not have equal access to land. Market information, for instance, flows through social networks, and a family's placement in a network either fosters or hinders its access to land. Those families with the longest legacy and the largest proportion of the community land base are in the best position to accumulate capital for consolidation purposes. Thus, the local land market has tended to facilitate concentration of farm ownership, as large part-owner operators grow bigger, at the expense of tenants and smaller owners. An example of this process is the tendency of farm managers to favor large operators over small; absentee owners or their agents seeking a quick sale follow the same logic. Furthermore, large farm size is wielded to gain a management advantage. Farm managers are impressed with quick planting and harvesting. Because landholdings confer power, landowning families can buttress their position by making use of preferential opportunities available to those with a privileged position in stratified social networks (Salamon 1992, 1993).

Home as Land in a Post-Agricultural Society

Agrarianism is deeply rooted in the American consciousness even though farmers represent less than 2 percent of the population (Beale 1989b). Agrarianism, however, shifted to new contexts as the nation was transformed by urbanization and industrialization. Owning one's own home is agrarianism translated, by industrialization and rising population, from farmland ownership to home ownership of urbanites and especially suburbanites. Among urban and suburban populations, a home (that combines land with a dwelling) represents achievement of the American dream in the same way as does control of farmland in rural areas (Hummon 1989). A newspaper's real-estate headline quotes Abraham Lincoln sounding like Jefferson: "The strength of the nation lies in the homes of its people" (quoted in Fitchen 1989, p. 320).

Agrarian imagery permeates our society, equating goodness, virtue, beauty, and honesty with the countryside (Goldman and Dickens 1983). Our agrarian vision of the wholesomeness of country life for a family is linked to the preference of Americans to live in rural areas or small towns rather than in cities (Hummon 1990). Such a vision fueled the national turnaround in rural migration that has lasted, with few exceptions, since the 1970s (Beale 1989a). This vision also has suburbanized regions adjacent to metropolitan areas throughout the nation.

Housing architecture, like land surveying and town planning, reveals the intersection of geography, history, and ethnicity. Geographers have long known that ordinary house types reveal migration streams, and thus patterns of diffusion and cultural variation (Conzen 1990; Kniffen 1965). American housing, like farmland, follows the national ideals of bigness, ownership, and social mobility. Lavish use of space—for large homes and lots—distinguishes American housing from that of Europe or Asia (Zelinsky 1973). Further, a decided preference exists for the freestanding home on its own land. A disproportionately small fraction of the population lives in apartments or other types of multiple dwellings, typically in or around major cities (Perrin 1977). In fact, when Americans achieve wealth, typically the symbol of upward mobility is a bigger home on a larger lot. Our use of housing is indicative of our high geographic and social mobility. Few expect to live their entire lifetime in the same house. The grand American front lawn, a nonfunctional showpiece, characterizes our extravagant use of space and the importance of the home as a symbol of affluence and achievement (Zelinsky 1973, pp. 88–94).

Status differences based on farmland ownership likewise differentiate property owners in urban and suburban America. Renters have less status than do homeowners, and larger and more ostentatious lots and homes are of higher status yet (Perrin 1977). "Making it," as indicated by the social ranking of dwellings, commonly measures social mobility (Hummon 1989). Success connected with property is good business for the nation. The construction industry's "housing starts" of single-family dwellings typically measures the health of the economy while interests rates are typically evaluated by the affordability of a home mortgage. Perrin (1977), in the Jeffersonian tradition, posits a cultural equation between home ownership and good citizenship. A recent report supports this equation (Rossi and Weber 1995). A study of 13,000 households interviewed once and another 1,500 household interviewed annually between 1988 and 1993 found that owners are more involved in the local community than are renters. Owners are more likely to actively serve in local improvement organizations, attend meetings of the group, and lobby elected officials on issues that concern the community. That is, homeowners are better citizens in the Jeffersonian sense. The study found that, perhaps as a consequence of citizenship, home-owners' children, regardless of income level or race, are less likely to drop out of school, be adolescent parents, or be arrested. Thus, culture and state encourage home ownership and such citizens help to reproduce the culture and state desired by ideology.

Rarely do people treat homes as just a necessity. These critical posses-sions are symbolic of family, a way of life, and a social rank. As such, homes are expressions of identity—who we are, what we value (Fitchen 1989; Hummon 1989). Just as land contributed to perpetuation of an ethnic community and ethnic identity, dwellings that are culturally significant can support a group identity and community (Conzen 1990; Hummon 1989). Gender differences are similarly perpetuated by cultural ties between women and the home (Hummon 1989). Class differences exist for how homes are used, the meaning of neighborhood, and the symbolism a home has for identity (ibid.; Salamon and Tornatore 1994). Such differences can bring families into conflict. Because a home is the major investment of the middle classes, when home values are threatened by another's actions, one's basic identity is also assaulted (Fitchen 1989; Salamon and Tornatore 1994).

Conclusion

Observers of land tenure tend to assume that all Americans, when faced with similar alternatives, are guided by historic national priorities for land: bigger is better; ownership is better for society and is a citizen's right; social mobil-ity is symbolized through and validated by landownership. If cultural dif-ferences once existed and influenced behavior, it is argued, time has homo-genized the once-unique patterns. Thus, culture is often disregarded in analyses of land markets and land tenure. Though distinctive ethnic im-prints on the rural landscape have indeed faded, a superficial sameness masks fundamental contrasts maintained by the original and successive occupants of the land. Rarely do families act purely as individuals unencumbered by demands from and responsibilities toward a community or ethnic group. Culture cannot be ignored as a critical variable for shaping land-tenure systems.

Culture is particularly useful for understanding localized variation in land-tenure patterns. Nonfinancial cultural factors at the household or community level shape choices that, when aggregated, create local land trends that, again when aggregated, produce regional patterns. Thus, grasping that micro-level choices are shaped by culture helps us understand land tenure system developments at the macro level.

A history of culture shaping land tenure in a particular place is revealed in the local landscape. Inheritance patterns, the land market, and social structure help explain unique characteristics such as extent of concentration of farms, land use, or levels of absentee ownership. National priorities for land are tied directly to a preference for agrarian ideals. These preferences, signaled by single homes and vast lawns, set the stage for suburban and exurban expansion once technological advancements made realizing agrarian ideals possible for many. Untangling the meaning of the relatively new land-tenure systems created by the suburbanization of America is best achieved by incorporating culture as well as economic and political explanations. The land tenure system represents the underlying social structure of any society because it is a mechanism for reproducing present gender, generational, and community relations and maintaining continuity with what was valued in the past.

References

Barth, Fredrik. 1969. *Ethnic Groups and Boundaries.* Boston, MA: Little, Brown.

Beale, Calvin L. 1989a. "The Revival of Population Growth in Nonmetropolitan American." In *A Taste of the Country: A Collection of Calvin Beale's Writings,* edited by Peter Morrison, pp. 137–153. University Park, PA: Pennsylvania State University Press.

Beale, Calvin L. 1989b. "Significant Recent Trends in the Demography of Farm People." In *Proceedings of the Philadelphia Society for Promoting Agriculture, 1987–1988* (February): 36–39.

Beale, Calvin L., and Judith Kalbacher. 1989. "Farm Population Trends: Shrinkage, Shifts, and Fewer Heirs." *Farmline* 9 (8): 19.

Bell, Colin, and Howard Newby. 1971. *Community Studies.* New York, NY: Praeger.

Bloch, Maurice. 1985. "From Cognition to Ideology." In *Power and Knowledge,* edited by Richard Fardon, pp. 21–48. Edinburgh: Scottish Academic Press.

Bogue, Allan G. 1963. *From Prairie to Cornbelt.* Chicago, IL: University of Chicago Press.

Clignet, Remi. 1992. *Death, Deeds, and Descendants: Inheritance in Modern America.* New York, NY: Aldine de Gruyter.

Conzen, Kathleen N. 1980. "Historical Approaches to the Study of Rural Ethnic Communities." In *Ethnicity on the Great Plains,* edited by Frederick C. Luebke, pp. 1–18. Lincoln, NE: University of Nebraska Press.

Conzen, Michael P. 1990. "Ethnicity on the Land." In *The Making of the American Landscape,* edited by Michael P. Conzen, pp. 221–248. Boston, MA: Unwin Hyman.

Crocombe, Ron. 1974. "An Approach to the Analysis of Land Tenure Systems." In *Land Tenure in Oceania,* edited by Henry P. Lundsgaarde, pp. 1–17. Honolulu, HI: University Press of Hawaii.

Danhof, Clarence H. 1969. *Change in Agriculture: The Northern United States 1820–1870.* Cambridge, MA: Harvard University Press.

Farber, Bernard. 1973. *Family and Kinship in Modern Society.* Glenview, IL: Scott Foresman.

Fischer, David Hackett. 1989. *Albion's Seed: Four British Folkways in America.* New York, NY: Oxford University Press.

Fiske, Alan Page. 1991. *Structures of Social Life: The Four Elementary Forms of Human Relations.* New York, NY: Free Press.

Fitchen, Janet M. 1989. "When Toxic Chemicals Pollute Residential Environments: The Cultural Meanings of Home and Homeownership." *Human Organization* 48 (4): 313–324.

Friedberger, Mark W. 1988. *Farm Families and Change in Twentieth-Century America.* Lexington, KY: University Press of Kentucky.

Friedl, Ernestine. 1975. *Women and Men.* New York, NY: Holt, Rinehart and Winston.

Geisler, Charles C., William F. Waters, and Katrina L. Eadie. 1985. "The Changing Structure of Female Agricultural Land Ownership, 1946–1978." *Rural Sociology* 50 (1): 74–87.

Gilbert, Jess, and Thomas Beckley. 1993. "Ownership and Control of Farmland: Landlord-Tenant Relations in Wisconsin." *Rural Sociology* 58 (4): 569–579.

Gilbert, Jess, and Craig K. Harris. 1984. "Changes in Type, Tenure, and Concentration of U.S. Farmland Owners." In *Focus on Agriculture: Research in Rural Sociology and Development,* vol. 1, edited by Harry K. Schwarzweller, pp. 135–160. Greenwich, CT: JAI Press.

Goldman, Robert, and David R. Dickens. 1983. "The Selling of Rural America." *Rural Sociology* 48 (4): 585–606.

Goldschmidt, Walter. 1978. *As You Sow: Three Studies in the Social Consequences of Agribusiness.* 2d ed. Montclair, NJ: Allanheld, Osmun.

Goldschmidt, Walter, and Evalyn Jacobson Kunkel. 1971. "The Structure of the Peasant Family." *American Anthropologist* 73 (5): 1058–1076.

Griswold, A. Whitney. 1948. "The Jeffersonian Ideal." In *Farming and Democracy,* pp. 18–46. New York, NY: Harcourt, Brace and Company.

Hacker, Andrew, and Lorrie Millman, eds. 1983. *U/S: A Statistical Portrait of the American People.* New York: Viking.

Hart, John Fraser. 1975. *The Look of the Land.* Englewood Cliffs, NJ: Prentice-Hall.

Hatch, Elvin. 1975. "Stratification in a Rural California Community." *Agricultural History* 49 (1): 21–38.

Hatch, Elvin. 1979. *Biography of a Small Town*. New York, NY: Columbia University Press.

Hollingshead, A. B. 1937. "The Life Cycle of Nebraska Rural Churches." *Rural Sociology* 2 (2): 180–191.

Hsu, Francis L. K. 1965. "The Effect of Dominant Kinship Relationships on Kin and Non-Kin Behavior: A Hypothesis." *American Anthropologist* 67 (3): 638–661.

Hsu, Francis L. K. 1971. "A Hypothesis on Kinship and Culture." In *Kinship and Culture*, edited by Francis L. K. Hsu, pp. 3–29 Chicago, IL: Aldine.

Hudson, John C. 1985. *Plains Country Towns*. Minneapolis, MN: University of Minnesota Press.

Hummon, David M. 1989. "House, Home, and Identity in Contemporary American Culture." In *Housing, Culture, and Design: A Comparative Perspective,* edited by Setha M. Low and Erve Chambers, pp. 207–228. Philadelphia, PA: University of Pennsylvania Press.

Hummon, David M. 1990. *Commonplaces: Community Ideology and Identity in American Culture*. Albany, NY: SUNY Press.

Johnson, Bruce B. 1972. "The Farmland Rental Market: A Case Analysis of Selected Corn Belt Areas." Agricultural Economics Report, no. 235. Michigan State University.

Johnson, Bruce B. 1983. "The Status of Family Farming in Nebraska." *Farm, Ranch, and Home Quarterly* 23/24. Institute of Agriculture and Natural Resources, University of Nebraska-Lincoln.

Johnson, Hildegard Binder. 1976. *Order upon the Land: The U.S. Rectangular Land Survey and the Upper Mississippi Country.* New York, NY: Oxford University Press.

Jordan, Terry G., and Lester Rowntree. 1982. *The Human Mosaic*. 3d ed. New York, NY: Harper and Row.

Jorgensen, Joseph G. 1984. "Land Is Cultural, So Is a Commodity: The Locus of Differences among Indians, Cowboys, Sod-Busters, and Environmentalists." *Journal of Ethnic Studies* 12 (3): 1–21.

Kloppenburg, Jack R., and Charles C. Geisler. 1985. "The Agricultural Ladder: Agrarian Ideology and the Changing Structure of U.S. Agriculture." *Journal of Rural Studies* 1 (1): 59–72.

Kniffen, Fred. 1965. "Folk Housing: Key to Diffusion." *Annals of the Association of American Geographers* 55 (4): 549–577.

Kramer, Mark. 1977. *Three Farms*. Boston, MA: Little, Brown.

Lewis, Pierce. 1995. "The Urban Invasion of Rural America: The Emergence of the Galactic City." In *The American Countryside: Rural People and Places,* edited by Emery N. Castle, pp. 39–62. Lawrence, KS: University Press of Kansas.

Lieberson, Stanley, and Mary C. Waters. 1988. *From Many Strands: Ethnic and Racial Groups in Contemporary America*. New York, NY: Russell Sage Foundation.

Lowenthal, David. 1968. "The American Scene." *Geographical Review* 58 (1): 61–88.

Mooney, Patrick H. 1983. "Toward a Class Analysis of Midwestern Agriculture." *Rural Sociology* 48 (4): 563–584.

Newby, Howard. 1980. "The Rural Sociology of Advanced Capitalist Societies." In

The Rural Sociology of the Advanced Societies, edited by Frederick H. Buttel and Howard Newby, pp. 1–30. Montclair, NJ: Allanheld, Osmun.

Ortner, Sherry B. 1984. "Theory in Anthropology Since the Sixties." *Comparative Studies in Society and History* 26 (1): 126–166.

Ortner, Sherry B. 1990. "Patterns of History: Cultural Schema in the Foundings of Sherpa Religious Institutions." In *Culture Through Time: Anthropological Approaches,* edited by Emiko Ohnuki-Tierney, pp. 57–93. Stanford, CA: Stanford University Press.

Perrin, Constance. 1977. *Everything in Its Place: Social Order and Land Use in America.* Princeton, NJ: Princeton University Press.

Pfeffer, Max. 1983. "Social Origins of Three Systems of Farm Production in the United States." *Rural Sociology* 48 (4): 540–562.

Reinhardt, Nola, and Peggy Barlett. 1989. "Family Farm Competitiveness in United States Agriculture: A Conceptual Framework." In *Food and Farm: Current Debates and Policies,* edited by Christine Gladwin and Kathleen Truman, pp. 389–411. Lantham, MD: University Press of America.

Reiss, Franklin J. 1976. "Decision-Making in the Farmland Market." *Journal of the American Society of Farm Managers and Rural Appraisers* 40 (1): 35–43.

Rogers, Denise M., and Ann M. Vandeman. 1993. "Women as Farm Landlords: Does Gender Affect Environmental Decision-Making on Leased Land?" *Rural Sociology* 58 (4): 560–568.

Rosenfeld, Jeffrey. 1979. *The Legacy of Aging.* Norwood, NJ: Ablex.

Rosenfeld, Rachel Ann. 1985. *Farm Women: Work, Farm, and Family in the United States.* Chapel Hill, NC: University of North Carolina Press.

Rossi, Peter H., and Eleanor Weber. 1995. "A National Statistical Portrait of Homeowners and How They Differ from Renters." *Washington Post* (June 3).

Rubinstein, W. D. 1980. *Wealth and the Wealthy in the Modern World.* New York, NY: St. Martin's Press.

Salamon, Sonya. 1992. *Prairie Patrimony: Family, Farming and Community in the Midwest.* Chapel Hill, NC: University of North Carolina Press.

Salamon, Sonya. 1993. "Culture and Agricultural Land Tenure." *Rural Sociology* 58 (4): 580–598.

Salamon, Sonya, and Karen Davis-Brown. 1988. "Farm Continuity and Female Land Inheritance: A Family Dilemma." In *Women and Farming: Changing Roles, Changing Structures,* edited by Wava G. Haney, and Jane B. Knowles, pp. 195–210. Boulder, CO: Westview Press.

Salamon, Sonya, and Ann Mackey Keim. 1979. "Land Ownership and Women's Power in a Midwestern Farming Community." *Journal of Marriage and the Family* 41:109–119

Salamon, Sonya, and Jane B. Tornatore. 1994. "Territory Contested through Property in a Midwestern Post-Agricultural Community." *Rural Sociology* 59 (4): 636–654.

Salter, Leonard A., Jr. 1943. "Land Tenure in Process." Agriculture Experiment Station Research Bulletin no. 146. Madison, WI: University of Wisconsin.

Schneider, David M. 1980. *American Kinship: A Cultural Account.* 2d ed. Chicago, IL: University of Chicago Press.

Schulman, Michael D., Patricia Garrett, and Barbara Newman. 1989. "Differentiation and Survival among North Carolina Smallholders: An Empirical Perspective on the Lenin/Chayanov Debate." *Journal of Peasant Studies* 16 (4): 523–541.

Simmel, Georg. 1898. "The Persistence of Social Groups." *American Journal of Sociology* 3 (5): 662–698.

Strange, Marty. 1988. *Family Farming: A New Economic Vision.* Lincoln, NE: University of Nebraska Press and San Francisco: Institute for Food and Development Policy.

Strauss, Anselm L. 1971. *The Contexts of Social Mobility: Ideology and Theory.* Chicago, IL: Aldine.

Swanson, Louis E. 1988. *Agriculture and Community Change in the U.S.: The Congressional Research Reports.* Boulder, CO: Westview Press.

Thernstrom, Stephan. 1968. "Urbanization, Migration, and Social Mobility." In *Towards a New Past: Dissenting Essays in American History,* edited by Barton J. Bernstein, pp. 158–175. New York, NY: Pantheon.

Tocqueville, Alexis de. 1990, reprint. *Democracy in America.* New York, NY: Vintage.

U.S. Department of the Interior. 1976. "America 200: The Legacy of Our Lands." *Conservation Yearbook* no 11, 1975–76. Washington, D.C.: U.S. GPO.

Zelinsky, Wilbur. 1973. *The Cultural Geography of the United States.* Englewood Cliffs, NJ: Prentice-Hall.

Forest Tenure and Cultural Landscapes: Environmental Histories in the Kickapoo Valley

Lynne Heasley and Raymond P. Guries

Introduction

During the twentieth century, American forests have come to represent more than the biological sum of their trees. They are the material and symbols society wields in its debates over nature, the environment, natural resources, and property (White 1980; Cronon 1991; Langston 1995). Controversy can erupt in an instant over the smallest public school forest or the largest private timber tract, a farmer's woodlot or a national forest, an urban park or a remote wilderness area. Increasingly, we name these wooded places or affix additional labels to them to gain an emotional advantage while vying for public approval or legislative action. Forests are not simply forests but are now "ancient" or "industrial" forests, satisfying "biodiversity" or "commodity" needs. We also label forests "public" or "private" to identify various forms or degrees of ownership. Together these labels can generate considerable anxiety, especially when the state defines or regulates a public interest in private lands, such as endangered species protection, or a private interest in public lands, such as grazing and mineral leases on national forests.

Forests—often the focus of local, regional, and global environmental disputes—show us the historical roots of conflicts over contemporary environmental policy. Competing groups, which fall along an ideological spectrum from Earth First! to the Center for the Defense of Free Enterprise,

This research is part of a long-term collaboration with Keith Rice and Hawthorne Beyer, both of the University of Wisconsin–Stevens Point, and Steve Ventura of the University of Wisconsin–Madison. We are grateful to Bill Cronon, Don Field, Jess Gilbert, Nancy Langston, and Matt Turner for their thoughtful comments on earlier versions of this chapter. We also thank Matt Dahlen, Ben Gramling, and Mike Stanek for field assistance over two summers. Finally, we owe a special thanks to Jim Dalton, Judy Gates, Phil Hahn, Jeff Hastings, Jim Radke, and Sandra Vold-Brudos, without whose support, expertise, and generosity our research in the Kickapoo Valley would not be possible. Support for this research was provided by the McIntire-Stennis Cooperative Forestry Research Program and the School of Natural Resources, College of Agricultural and Life Sciences, University of Wisconsin–Madison.

maintain a philosophical schism between forest preservation versus development and public or private ownership that goes back to sixteenth-century Europe (Harrison 1992). While competing with each other, these groups also mistrust the modern political process, which most perceive as ignoring their ecological, economic, or cultural fears. Nevertheless, many groups use persuasion or litigation to influence myriad government agencies which have their own institutional agendas for natural resource management, including forests.

Forests, however, are more than mere weapons wielded by interest groups in political battles. First and foremost, they are an enormous material force that has shaped the country's development (Cox et al. 1985; Williams 1989). In Wisconsin, forest historians stress how nineteenth-century efforts to transform a forested landscape into an agricultural landscape continue to shape patterns of forest cover and ownership (Carstensen 1958; Flader 1983). Northern woodlands once cleared by the lumberman's ax grew back to forests when agriculture proved neither practical nor profitable. Many of these cutover lands, whose owners abandoned them to tax delinquency, now form the bulk of federal, state, and county forests. Farther south, in places like the Kickapoo Valley, forests and fields have always shared the landscape, so the issue has not been forests versus farms; rather, it has been the place forests held in farm life on a landscape often too steep or stony to plow. Forests remain an integral part of Wisconsin's rural economy and ecology, a source of clean water, forest products, recreation, and a hedge against inflation. At the same time, forests remain central to how different regions define themselves. Wisconsin's North Woods and the Kickapoo Valley are cultural places in part because they are forested places that shape occupations, customs, and beliefs (Logan 1975; Churchill 1981).

Thus, forests present us with an entry point for studying two vital topics: the dynamic relationship of people to their environment and the role our modern political economy has played in transforming rural areas. We cannot fully understand our material relationships to forests, or cultural conflicts over their use, unless we look closely at the ways in which society allocates access to them through its systems of land tenure; yet it is precisely these systems that environmental histories, and forest histories in particular, tend to oversimplify or ignore (White [1980] and McEvoy [1986] being prominent exceptions). In this chapter, we explore themes of property and nature from a number of perspectives rather than just one; we tie forests to land tenure and, by extension, to the social and ecological upheavals still transforming the rural Midwest.

We focus on the Kickapoo Valley (see Map 10.1), a watershed in southwestern Wisconsin, whose rolling fields and forests unfold as in a pastoral idyll. Beneath that veneer, the shifting control of forests labeled private property or public property has acted as a lightning rod for cultural conflict. Forest ownership has changed dramatically over the past sixty years, with an influx of Amish, urbanites looking for weekend homes or hunting grounds, Ho-Chunk Indians, back-to-the-landers, loggers, developers, speculators, and militia members, all jostling with each other and with long-time dairy farmers for space, profits, and political sway. Moreover, though most land in the Kickapoo is privately owned, the state has asserted its right to influence forest management since the first New Deal conservation programs. One result is that a fluid scientific jargon of degradation, ecology, and bio-diversity has infiltrated the local vernacular, providing a language appropri-ated by competing groups in the fight for their ideal forest, farm, or rural community.

In traversing the Kickapoo Valley, we cross two academic fields—environmental history and landscape ecology—to show how the ecological, cultural, political, and economic facets of forest tenure became entwined in unpredictable ways, creating a twentieth-century midwestern landscape and a contested regional identity. Along the way, we frame our concepts and methods around three sets of questions:

1. Since the end of the Depression, when, where, and why have some people gained access to land in the Kickapoo Valley while others have not? In what ways have the valley's forests changed along with control over them and access to them?

2. What has been the role of overlapping, sometimes competing, his-torical processes in transforming the landscapes of the valley during this century? How have changes in forest tenure affected environ-mental, social, and economic conditions in the Kickapoo Valley?

3. In what ways does forest tenure foster connections of valley residents to their environment, their communities, and the rest of the Mid-west? How have these relationships contributed to the valley's cul-tural identity and development as a distinct rural place?

The Kickapoo Valley

The Kickapoo Valley lies within the unglaciated Driftless Region of south-western Wisconsin, encompassing 766 square miles in parts of Vernon, Monroe, Richland, and Crawford counties. The valley is home to some thirty thousand mostly rural people, who refer to their landscape as "coulee country," a mix of agricultural lands on narrow ridgetops and valley bottoms embedded in a matrix of forests on steep valley slopes. The Kickapoo River and its tributaries, usually tranquil, occasionally rampaging, dissect the land-scape. At the peak of farm ownership in 1935, small farmers held more than

Map 10.1.   Kickapoo Valley in Wisconsin

185

95 percent of Vernon County and 90 percent of Crawford County, the bulk of the Kickapoo Valley. At that time, farmers grazed woodlands too steep to plow, first with sheep, then dairy cattle, and finally beef (Ebling et al. 1948). Today, nearly half of the valley is forested (42 percent), much of it regenerated to young forests, or recovering from earlier cropping and grazing eras, with private owners holding over 90 percent of the forest land (Lamm 1981). In many places in the valley, forest ownership has shifted to absentee owners, who have changed the local ecology and economies of the rural communities in which they hold land.

The valley's forests are slowly turning from oak-hickory communities into more shade-tolerant maple-basswood ones (Hix and Lorimer 1990). Prior to European settlement, the landscape west of the Kickapoo River consisted of oak openings interspersed with prairie fragments. Along the Kickapoo River and to the east, closed canopied forests, dominated by sugar maple, basswood, oak, hickory, and some clusters of white pine, formed a more or less unbroken forest the entire length of the valley (Finley 1976). Fire-prone ecosystems like prairies and oak savannas are now rare features on the landscape here, with closed forests occupying slopes on both sides of the river valley. Researchers attribute this successional trend to anthropogenic changes, especially fire exclusion, timber harvesting, and livestock grazing (Kline 1976).

Many foresters and landowners regard the valley's oaks as crucial for forest products and wildlife and seek to perpetuate them using a variety of silvicultural practices. This mindset tends to obscure the fact that the oak forests were themselves a product of anthropogenic disturbance, a historical convergence of society and nature in the valley during the nineteenth century. Financial pressure on farm economies has tended to increase harvesting of the remaining high-value oaks, a process that generally accelerates ecological succession to other species. In recent years, the Wisconsin Department of Natural Resources, the Nature Conservancy, and Trout Unlimited have taken an interest in the valley's forests, in part because they are an important extractive resource, but also because they support several endemic threatened and endangered plant species and various biotic communities (Nature Conservancy 1989).

As forests have changed, so has the human population, which is shrinking and aging. Southwestern Wisconsin is one of the poorest parts of the state; within the valley, adjusted gross income in 1990 was only 55 percent of the state average (Bureau of the Census 1992). Agriculture still dominates the regional economy, but farming continues on a steady decline. Economists compare the valley to northern Wisconsin, both of which they label "underdeveloped" (Leatherman 1994); some have even referred to the valley as "Little Appalachia," a clear allusion to its poverty and topography.

Nevertheless, the Kickapoo Valley is quite distinct from northern Wisconsin and Appalachia. The latter regions contain vast tracts of public land, highly concentrated corporate ownership of forests, and long-established recreational bases (Gaventa 1980; Appalachian Land Ownership Task Force 1983). In contrast, the valley has little public land, few large landholders, and an emerging but immature recreational base. Therefore, research attributing rural poverty and environmental degradation primarily to concentrated landownership cannot explain conditions in the Kickapoo Valley. We need to look to other tenure relationships and conduct work on local and regional levels in the Midwest to account for social and environmental change.

Toward this end, we have followed cultural landscapes and forest tenure from 1930 to 1995 in three townships within the Kickapoo Valley, with our analyses extending down to the individual parcel. As political subdivisions, townships are small enough to identify, spatially or historically, specific landscape features and tenure dynamics. At the same time, townships provide areas large enough to matter regionally, accounting for changing rural realities such as land fragmentation or concentration, entry into and exit from farming, the establishment of public land conservation programs, crop and timber prices, and land use. Our methodology has involved constructing a geographic information system (GIS), verifying changes in forest composition and quality, and collecting local environmental histories. The GIS incorporates data from historical air photos, parcel maps, property tax rolls, agriculture census data, real-estate transfers, and records of enrollment in public-sponsored conservation programs. This has been crucial for discerning landscape-level patterns in ownership, land use, and landcover. Field visits to every owner-parcel in the three townships provided qualitative and quantitative data on the impacts of different land-use practices on biophysical conditions, in particular timber harvesting and livestock grazing. Oral histories and interviews with landowners, other residents, and resource management specialists related landscape changes to social, economic, and political conditions in the valley during different eras.

Tenure Relations in Three Townships

Twenty-two townships lie within the Kickapoo Valley. Three of these—Clinton, Stark, and Liberty—capture much of the area's cultural, economic, and ecological diversity (see Map 10.2). Today ownership patterns are heterogeneous among the three townships. Clinton presents a relatively uniform distribution of parcel size, with less variation than either Stark or Liberty. Stark contains a large fraction of the only federal land in the valley:

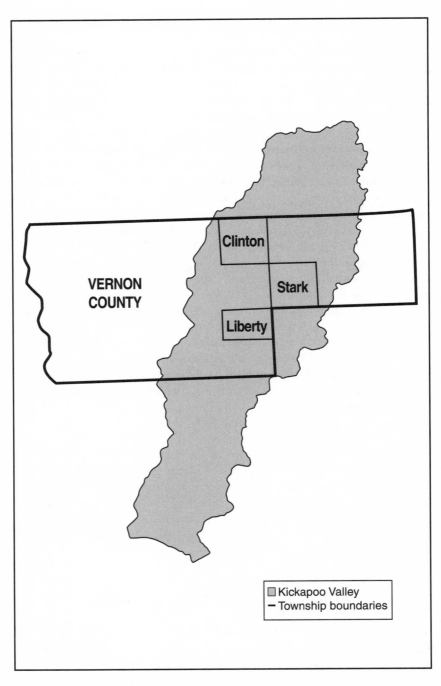

Map 10.2. Townships of Clinton, Stark, and Liberty, Wisconsin

188

8,600 acres that the U.S. Army Corps of Engineers controlled until very recently. In addition, Stark has a more bimodal distribution of larger and smaller parcels than does Clinton. Liberty shows the highest area concentration of large parcels (one holding is 2,600 acres or approximately four square miles) and the greatest fragmentation of small parcels.

Automated parcel maps at six dates (1931, 1939, 1955, 1967, 1978, and 1995) reveal that ownership patterns have changed over time within the three townships. In Stark and Liberty, parcel size and distribution are notably different today relative to sixty years ago. Clinton has experienced a reduction in average parcel size and an increase in the number of parcels, but the change in distribution is not as marked as in Stark and Liberty. Land-use profiles point to a history of cropping in Clinton, while Liberty and Stark, whose landscapes are steeper and stonier, experienced heavier livestock pasturing. In all three townships, forests cover more area today than in the 1930s. Such general trends suggest that landownership in the valley is dynamic, with parcels becoming aggregated or divided as families entered or left farming, changed from cropping to grazing systems, or sold their land. However, a closer inspection of the three townships reveals subtle changes in the valley, changes that link people to their landscapes via land-tenure systems, with social, economic, and ecological consequences for the entire region.

Clinton

The air photos of Clinton reveal distinct changes in land use and land cover since the 1930s. Prior to the 1930s, contour strip-cropping was nonexistent. Farmers increasingly adopted the practice during the 1940s and 1950s, responding to federal and state conservation programs aimed at reducing soil erosion. By the early 1960s nearly every field was in contour strips. Beginning in the late 1960s, contour-plowed acreage began to decline, a trend coincident with the first influx of Amish settlers.

Forest cover increased over the sixty years, while livestock grazing appears to have steadily declined in forests until the 1970s. We can attribute some of the decline in forest grazing to state- and federal-sponsored conservation programs that required enrollees to fence livestock from forests to qualify for reduced property taxes. However, some changes in forest grazing are also related to distinct livestock eras. Sheep grazing was extensive before 1920, followed by a prominent dairy industry, which ultimately gave way in some places to beef cattle operations during the 1960s and 1970s. Stagnant milk prices during the 1960s, together with other economic incentives, prompted many farmers to sell their milking herds and purchase beef herds, freeing them from many daily chores and reducing their need for equipment and labor.

Deed transfers in Clinton reveal that owner turnover has been high during the last sixty years, with turnover occurring at different rates in different sections of the town. Absentee ownership has risen, primarily because of intergenerational transfers to children who inherit their family's land but no longer reside in the area. Even more notable is the migration of Amish farmers into the township since the 1960s. The first Amish families settled in Clinton in 1965, attracted by the valley's remoteness and its inexpensive land (Vernon County Historical Society 1994). The Amish now own more than half of the land in Clinton.

We can attribute many dramatic changes in land use and land cover to increased Amish landownership. Logging has steadily increased in Clinton and now comprises an extensive timber network throughout the township. Perhaps the most revealing statistic here is the presence of approximately one Amish sawmill for every three miles of ridgetop road. The Amish selectively log in their own forests, relying on draft horses for power. They frequently purchase additional timber from other landowners in the area, gaining value-added income when they make secondary products like fine furniture and crafts. Furthermore, they have established a popular niche market for themselves with small inexpensive cabins, which they construct for recreational landowners. Once the Amish built up an impressive capacity for processing logs (using only small gasoline-powered saws), larger sawmills in the region began to subcontract work to them, extending Amish influence on the landscape well beyond their own property boundaries.

Since the arrival of the Amish, regional opinion has vacillated over the impact their land-use practices have on soil fertility, forest condition, and off-site water resources. Urbanites tend toward a romantic view of the Amish, imagining them as the ideal land stewards, a plain people who live a simple life (Worthington 1988; Ladd 1993). Many local residents hold an opposing view, that the Amish "mine" the soil and ruin the forests. To the chagrin of extension agents, when Amish farmers purchase farms, they often remove contour strips from their fields, graze cattle and horses in their forests, and rent forest land from their neighbors for the same purpose. Likewise, they harvest timber without planning for forest regeneration or future management (of course many non-Amish do exactly the same).

The county forester and the district soil conservationist present two alternative views of Amish resource management. The forester takes a "cultural constructionist" position. The Amish, the forester surmises, practice old-fashioned farming and forestry based on their religious beliefs and antitechnology ideology. The district conservationist, on the other hand, adopts an "environmental determinist" stance. According to the conservationist, the Amish in the Kickapoo Valley developed their farming methods in Ohio, where their farmland was flat and the soil rich compared to the valley's. The conservationist sees the Amish slowly adapting to the valley's steep, erosion-prone slopes by changing their techniques. Whether the Amish will thrive at the expense of their local environment is an interesting question that we do not attempt to answer here. We believe we can consider Amish land tenure as another explanation for their success (Kraybill and Nolt 1993). Historical land transfers show that the Amish community successfully provides land to younger generations in established families and to new settlers. The Amish maintain a flourishing civil society in Clinton based on their cultural values, livelihoods, and land-tenure system. At the same time, the land and its forests place them at the edge of a wider economy.

Amish control over land and resources in Clinton acts as a lightning rod for wider cultural conflict. The Amish are succeeding with their agricultural and forest-based enterprises, while many others are experiencing hardship. Some younger non-Amish residents and would-be farmers will never have the opportunity to buy land in the area. Under these circumstances, land-ownership becomes a symbol separating the haves from the have-nots, the Amish from their poorer neighbors. Consequently, local resentment toward the Amish, frequently over issues related to land tenure, can run high. Amish farmers, a few assert, degrade the land and lower property values in the area. Even more vexing, the studded horseshoes Amish put on their horses damage the roads, increasing costs to the township for road repairs (*Epitaph-News* 1983). During a tragic clash in 1995, a non-Amish resident kidnapped and raped an Amish girl. Her assailant claimed an Amish buggy provoked him when it nearly ran his car into a ditch (Renner 1995).

In this case, local and state officials and resource managers assume a dual responsibility to prevent resource degradation and to resolve conflicts. A major problem exists in that the language of degradation inflames cultural conflict. Moreover, local officials have little influence over Amish land use, while courts frequently side with the Amish on matters of lifestyle embedded in religious tenets. Since the Amish do not enroll their land in agricultural commodity or forestry stewardship programs, program administrators cannot prescribe landowner behavior, making public land-use policy irrelevant to the Amish. Public agencies, on the other hand, want very much to be relevant and would prefer that Amish farmers restrict their livestock to pastures, not forests, and fence erodable stream banks. They also would like the Amish to maintain contour strips on their fields. As a result, conservation and extension personnel debate how to change Amish attitudes and behavior and thereby gain influence over Amish land.

Despite the dissension that Amish landownership produced, signs of accommodation have emerged among residents in Clinton. The Amish have begun forging informal tenure relationships with their neighbors, connections that may lead toward reconciliation in the wider community. They seek access to their neighbors' forests for hunting, fishing, berry picking, mushroom gathering, and livestock grazing, even as they offer the same opportunities to others. The reciprocity does not end there; they frequently reach out to non-Amish neighbors in need of assistance. One old farmer in Clinton, now surrounded on all sides by Amish, was reticent toward them for many years. Yet, when his wife died, his Amish neighbors pitched in to help with chores on the farm. He now allows them to keep horses in his forest, acknowledging that his ideas about the Amish have changed considerably. Such tenure relationships—rooted in neighborliness—have profound social implications, as well as ecological consequences, for the land.

Stark

Like Clinton, Stark is not the same social or ecological place today that it was sixty years ago. Though certain historical processes have affected both townships, their histories are not identical. The origins of their differences flow back to the Kickapoo River itself. Its main branch cuts through the middle of Stark from north to southwest, a few miles to the east of Clinton. Locals call the Kickapoo "the crookedest river in America," and, in fact, its name comes from the Algonquin language, meaning "one who goes there, then here" (Kickapoo Valley History Project 1979, p. 1). The name is fitting, for while the valley is only 65 miles long, the river wends 120 miles. The evolution of Stark's landscape and human communities is entwined with the river's twists and turns.

Forestry and farming have been mainstays of Stark's economic and ecological development throughout this century, so much so that photos from the 1930s show denuded hillsides dotted with sheep and cattle. Small farmers owned most of the land, while numerous lumber companies operated sawmills in the area. A combination of deforestation, overgrazing, frequent fires, and steep slopes resulted in some of the worst soil erosion in Wisconsin. This, in turn, led to severe floods, which devastated the valley in 1907 and have continued at frequent intervals to the present. In the 1930s, valley residents started clamoring for congressional action to control flood damage along the Kickapoo River. At the behest of Congress in 1962 the U.S. Army Corps of Engineers drew plans for flood control in the valley; the plans centered on a dam and reservoir near the town of La Farge in Stark, as well as channel improvements and levees farther south. In 1967, the Corps expanded its original proposal to include an 1,800-acre lake (Johnson 1991). Most valley residents wholeheartedly approved the Corps' plans.

Up to this time, landownership patterns in Stark had remained stable. When the Corps began buying 8,600 acres of privately owned forest and farm land for the La Farge dam, 4,968 acres of it came from Stark (Vernon County Historical Society 1994). Hence the federal government became the township's (and the valley's) largest landowner. In anticipation of the new recreational area, speculators began acquiring real estate in the area. Between 1965 and 1975, two-thirds of the land in Stark changed hands, excluding that already acquired by the federal government. On average, only 16 percent of the land in the township sections adjacent to the federal land remained with the same owners. Real estate prices doubled, and the nature of ownership also changed, with sales of forest land to absentee buyers accounting for the majority of transactions (Phillips 1977).

Despite the confidence of valley communities in the project's success, completion of the La Farge dam was not assured even after workers began construction in 1971. The Corps confronted increasing opposition to the project from a coalition of environmental groups, academics, and canoeists determined to stop the project. A study from the University of Wisconsin–Madison's Institute for Environmental Studies demonstrated that sediment would fill the new lake in a short period of time, that water quality would be poor, and that the dam would destroy numerous endangered species and archaeological sites (Institute for Environmental Studies 1974). The project also flunked economic cost-benefit analyses, which considered the feasibility of alternatives to the dam (U.S. Army Corps of Engineers 1977). In response, Wisconsin's governor and two U.S. senators withdrew their approval of the dam. Local residents did not acquiesce quietly; they demanded support from state politicians, wrote countless letters to state newspapers, and heavily attended meetings on the dam's status. The Corps concurred with them, but, in the end, environmental, political, and economic pressures forced it to halt work. The unfinished dam's concrete outlet structure still stands as a sentinel on the Kickapoo River, a monument to an environmental nightmare averted or a tomb marking the death of a community, depending on one's perspective.

Land condemnation, followed by cancellation of the project, provoked a local fury that is still strong today in Stark. Locals aim their anger directly at "the State" and "the University." Since then, numerous academic studies focusing on economic development in the valley and around the federal land have not placated many local residents (for example, Lewis and Lamm 1981; Leatherman 1993; Sancar et al. 1992). Academics, they feel, have profited professionally from their plight, while failing to improve conditions in the valley. Residents perceive clear winners—environmentalists, canoeists, absentee landowners, university researchers, politicians, the federal government, the state of Wisconsin—and unmistakable losers: themselves. Their anger is understandable. During land-condemnation proceedings, Stark lost 60 percent of its population. The Corps moved or tore down all buildings on the site, leaving few signs of that segment of the community, which traced its history to early pioneer settlers in the valley. Adding to a sense of injury, the federal government paid no property taxes, a financial burden to the township. Many longtime residents now proclaim sympathy for the private property rights advocates who reside in the township.

Although Stark's experience may sound like a midwestern replay of old western land wars between locals, outsiders, and the federal government, this saga has an unusual ending. After two decades of political inertia over what to do with the federal land, Congress returned some 7,400 acres to the state of Wisconsin as a provision of the Water Resources Development Act of 1996. This action stands as a unique case of devolution from the federal to the state level. The state, bowing to intense local pressure, agreed not to administer the land under the jurisdiction of the Department of Natural Resources. Instead, the Department of Tourism will manage it primarily as a natural reserve, in partnership with the Kickapoo Valley Governing Board, a governor-appointed group of local and state citizens.

Deauthorization of the flood control project, however, contains a caveat that has renewed the bitterness Stark's residents harbor for intervention by outside forces. As part of the federal-to-state transfer, Wisconsin will cede the remaining 1,200 acres of the reserve containing culturally and religiously significant sites to the Department of the Interior, which will hold it in trust for the Ho-Chunk Nation (formerly known as the Winnebago). The Ho-Chunk relinquished this land to the United States in an 1837 treaty. Significantly, the law provides for an expansion of the 1,200 acres should other sites be discovered, but the precise location of the sites remains secret, in part because of local hostility. Anti-Indian graffiti greets drivers on a concrete bridge bisecting the reserve land. One-time landowners ask whether their land is part of the 1,200-plus acres. They no longer have tenure over their former property, yet they feel some claim to it nonetheless, as do the Ho-Chunk, whose ancestors lived in the valley long before the first white settlers.

At this point, we need to take a closer look at the reserve itself, which local residents refer to as "the Fed." After thirty years of federal tenure, the land is now mostly forested. Until recently, rules and regulations governing land use remained unenforced due to the lack of a federal presence. The federal land has operated under a classic "open access" tenure regime. A variety of users have made a place for themselves there: cross-country skiers, hikers, hunters, snowmobilers, horseback riders, and operators of four-wheel-drive vehicles (mostly pickup trucks). The different user groups have been competitive. One local story tells of a group of horseback riders who protected their trail by laying spikes in the ground to cause blowouts in vehicle tires. As the forest has grown, it has fallen outside of valley society or the law. Occupants in the forest make their own civil arrangements, as in the case of the horseback riders. The pickup drivers are "outlaws" of a sort, generating fear and resentment. Indeed, they find their activity appealing precisely because it is disorganized and wild. Just as the forest provides the space in which people can act with abandon, its trees stand as welcome obstacles, making it a place unlike any other in the valley.

Of the various forecasts for the federal land, none has noted the recent history of uncontrolled access as an issue for future enforcement. Should managers prohibit pickup trucks in the forest? "Yes!" public officials and some residents answer resoundingly. If so, how easy will they find bringing this forest and one group of its "inhabitants" back into the law? The policy rationale for prohibiting trucks speaks to environmental concerns. A common refrain is that pickup trucks are wrecking the federal land. The evidence that vehicles cause severe localized soil erosion on trails is beyond dispute. Still another sentiment lies under the surface of the ecological argument against four-wheel-drive vehicles: only people of a certain class (lower), gender (male), or age (young) drive trucks on the land, and their actions appear antisocial. The policy issue of access now becomes complex and potentially explosive. The social and cultural politics embedded in forest access and control could bedevil the most well-intentioned plans for the new reserve.

In the 1930s, when valley communities urged the federal government to control flooding on the Kickapoo River, they put in motion a number of social and ecological processes, all of which changed the people and landscape of Stark. The government became a major landholder in the area. Absentee landownership increased, as did parcel size, while the number of people declined. Forests returned as new landowners removed more and more land from agricultural production. Sections of the Kickapoo River reverted from a warm-water fishery to a cold-water fishery (i.e., trout) as soil erosion decreased and forest cover shaded the river channel. The return of trout created a modest tourism sector with a small number of guides and bed-and-breakfasts catering to fishers (Marcouiller, Anderson, and Norman 1995). Wildlife populations, especially deer, turkey, and coyote, which were rare in the 1930s, flourished. They, in turn, put pressure on crops and livestock, becoming a nuisance to area farmers.

The advent of a recreational economy is at hand, but any benefits that such economic diversification might provide are offset by a foreboding that the larger world now dictates life's economic and social pace in Stark. The public reserve, a popular and scenic river, and numerous neighbors, whose permanent homes lie hundreds of miles away, have led to revised notions about what makes an ideal community. Commodity futures and the weather still drive the local economy, yet today's "coffee shop economists" also articulate the importance of a moral economy, one based on local landownership and community needs, at the expense of a "free market" if necessary. One local editorialist expounded on this when he wrote, "As the ownership flows out of the valley and away from the farms, so does the power to control our own lives." Real estate transfers on the open market present a problem, he continues: "Instead of seeing dollar signs all over the landscape, sellers should examine more closely who they are selling to and how the buyer proposes to take care of the land. . . . Unless people decide that WHO they sell to is just as important, if not more so, than the price they get, that trend [in absentee ownership] will continue" (*La Farge Epitaph* 1980). Ironically, many absentee owners explain that they bought land in Stark for the same reasons some local residents would like to see them go: a desire to be part of a close-knit rural community and a stunning valley landscape of fields and forests.

Liberty

Liberty's physical features do not differ markedly from Stark's and Clinton's because the three townships share a common landscape. Moreover, the reforestation and contour-plowing methods that photographs chronicled in the other townships also occurred in Liberty. As in the valley as a whole, Liberty has lost population and dairy farms during the past sixty years. But the history of landownership in Liberty diverges from that of Stark and Clinton in ways that shed additional light on forest tenure and cultural landscapes in the Kickapoo Valley.

Parcel maps of Liberty from the 1930s, 1940s, and 1950s present a picture of rural stability, a brief respite between the agricultural distresses of the Depression and the late twentieth century. The maps document an even distribution of parcels ranging from 40 to 350 acres. While land changed hands regularly during these decades, local farm families retained ownership. Between 1960 and 1965, tenure shifts began to appear. One absentee owner acquired 249 acres from two local landowners, while a second absentee couple purchased 950 acres, thereby consolidating five smaller parcels. By 1970, this couple, along with five more local landowners, sold 1,800 acres to an Illinois-based beef ranch. During the same period, a Kickapoo Valley manufacturer bought approximately 1,000 acres from six owners for development of a corporate dairy operation. During the late 1980s, the dairy sold its land to an Illinois man who wanted a vacation retreat and rental income. The beef ranch also sold out; 500 acres went to a real estate speculator and the rest to another out-of-state beef ranch. Today, the beef ranch to the north and the recreational property to the south sandwich several dozen small undeveloped subdivisions (from 2 to 10 acres each), some of whose absentee owners have already resold them.

These trends show a township in flux, with each new configuration of landowners setting in motion additional tenure changes. But real estate transfers alone do not reveal the underlying processes that created these patterns or their less obvious consequences. Many longtime Liberty residents trace the township's transformation back to the advent of the Soil Bank in 1956. With the Soil Bank Act, Congress hoped to eliminate surplus crops and enhance agricultural productivity through conservation (U.S. Department of Agriculture 1958), paying private landowners who converted their cropland into forests, either actively when they planted trees, or passively via "old field" succession.

While its objectives were economic and ecological, the Soil Bank had unintentional demographic effects. According to Danbom (1995, p. 245), the Soil Bank helped empty the countryside because it "allowed farmers to remove their entire farms from production and induced tens of thousands to move away." In this sense, Liberty mirrored larger rural trends, as many farmers did enroll in the program and a number of those ultimately left the area. However, the perspective of people who remain in Liberty does not coincide exactly with that of Danbom. They attribute Liberty's transformation to the death of the Soil Bank. When the Soil Bank ended in 1965, they say, its older participants and their children could not realistically reenter farming, which had grown in scale and capital intensity. At the same time, real estate taxes had increased beyond their ability to pay, so many sold their farms.

If one outgrowth of the Soil Bank Program was a shift in land tenure, another was the realization that the program's goals were of minor consequence to the new owners. Ranchers were drawn to Liberty's cheap land, whose streams, meadows, and forests provided tremendous potential for livestock grazing. Post-Soil Bank ranchers knew when they arrived that intensive livestock operations put them in conflict with a new generation of natural resource managers over conservation issues, especially woodland grazing and stream-bank erosion. They adopt a posture similar to that of the western rancher, invoking a "property-rights" mantra and speaking of public resource agencies as "the enemy." Nevertheless, Liberty's ranching community views itself as a good land steward whose members have avoided or minimized chemical inputs, implemented rotational grazing for livestock, and rehabilitated eroded stream banks. In their eyes, as well as those of local district conservation specialists, soil erosion control has made spectacular gains since the 1930s. Moreover, ranchers like the open look of grazed forests (which also tend to increase populations of deer and other game), despite the concern of foresters and conservation biologists.

Contemporary environmental activists see the Kickapoo Valley differently. They draw on modern scientific insights into ecosystem fragmentation, population biology, and watershed dynamics, finding much to criticize. Livestock still degrade water quality. And despite the reemergence of a forested landscape in the valley, grazing has created forest fragments, taking a slow but steady toll on various nongame wildlife and plant species, some endemic to the Driftless Region. At the moment, environmental aspirations to restore vegetation to presettlement conditions are contradictory to grazing aspirations (Brick 1994). Both ranchers and environmentalists are engaged in a race to create different rural landscapes. Science, ironically, is supplying ammunition to both the ranchers, who look back to the valley's recent degraded past seeing improvement today, and to environmentalists, who gaze farther into the past seeking a more pristine future.

Just as the Soil Bank helped recreate a ranching landscape in Liberty, the two together paved the way for real estate speculators. The most notorious of these has a long history in the Kickapoo Valley, albeit one that is difficult to trace owing to frequent name changes and other efforts to conceal the scope of its activities. Moving throughout the valley, the firm bought cheap forest land, subdivided it, advertised the new parcels in the Chicago area as "abandoned farms," and sold them at an enormous profit. Their deceptive acquisition and marketing techniques have created a furor, generating ill-will with public officials, bankers, extension agents, and clients. One woman recounted how a man knocked on her door asking about her 80-acre forest. He enjoyed hunting with his son, he claimed, and would like to buy her woods for their outings. After some reflection, she agreed to a sale, only to discover later that the new owner was, in fact, a representative of this firm. Almost immediately, they logged the forest for its valuable timber and divided the property into second-home sites. "I felt I had done something awful," she reflected, embarrassed that her trust in human nature had such negative consequences for her neighbors and her former forest. In Liberty, where landownership had changed and the population dwindled, this firm found little difficulty in quietly buying land, mostly forested, and dividing it soon thereafter. Such sales drove up land prices, making it difficult for young farmers to acquire farmland. Many buyers of the small tracts belatedly found that their sites could not support septic systems, making second-home construction impossible. Some would like to sell their lots but refuse to "lose money" on a resale. In fact, few buyers exist for such properties, which have become overpriced rural pariah lands.

In addition to second-home sales, land speculators in the Kickapoo Valley have started capitalizing on the demand of urban and suburban sportsmen for hunting land. Hunting has increased in the valley because wildlife populations, especially deer, have skyrocketed since the 1930s. Competition for hunting land is now intense, and many farmers and ranchers have discovered that hunting rights are a valuable commodity. In Liberty, moreover, some landowners have come to rely on hunting leases for protection from the game-seeking masses. According to them, poaching, especially deer and turkey, is so common that landowners have been forced to sell hunting rights to groups, who, in their own self-interest, enforce property boundaries and minimize trespass. Liberty's landholders blame their conflicts with outside hunters on the state's "industrial hunting mentality," which aspires to open up as much private land as possible to hunters in return for millions of dollars in licensing fees. "The materialistic greed of our lawmakers has spilled over upon the participants of this fiasco and he who spends bucks expects 'Buck' and will pursue his course with rugged determination involving trespass and illegalities with no love or thought of safety for his fellow men," bemoaned the editor of the *La Farge Epitaph* (1978).

There is a paradox in the state's claim of ownership to wildlife that live and feed mostly on private land. The state must respect private landowners while assuring the public access to its game. For example, Wisconsin's Managed Forest Law, which the legislature enacted to enhance reforestation and timber production on private lands, is evolving into an "open lands" law linking property tax deferrals to guaranteed public access to private forests, especially for hunting. Together, state game policy and private hunting leases have added seasonal layers to tenure relationships in the valley, connecting rural and urban people during hunting season for better or worse. Hunting in Liberty's forests, as much as any other activity, underscores the fluidity of the ideas people hold about private and public land and resources, property lines on paper notwithstanding.

Conclusion

We provide a broad perspective on forest tenure in this study, in part to benefit from a recent spate of international tenure research that crosses spatial and temporal scales, incorporates multiple viewpoints, and investigates causes and solutions for tenure conflicts (e.g., Bruce and Fortmann 1988; Peluso 1992; Heasley and Delehanty 1996). An expansive approach also gives voice to another key figure, Nature, whose features help shape society's tenure relationships even as they are altered by them. Researchers who study land tenure in the United States must come to terms with the American ideology of private property along with one of its central features: boundaries on the landscape. These boundaries, which separate people, places, and activities, hold out to an individual owner the possibility of wealth, work, success, and self-sufficiency. Despite the ideology, this century has shown that landownership is not synonymous with self-sufficiency, and rural landowners are as likely to be near the bottom of the economic ladder as at the top. A more inclusive concept of land tenure moves beyond property lines and the individual, allowing for connections and interdependence, the dissolution of boundaries as well as their creation, even the condition of becoming landed poor. The ways in which boundaries emerge or dissolve mediate our connections to each other and the natural world, and it is the outcome of these patterns and processes in the Kickapoo Valley that we attempt to explain.

Forests in the Kickapoo Valley, as in much of eastern North America, have been in transition since European settlement. In the late twentieth century they are still central to regional or national conservation and development scenarios, many of which fail to account for their multiplicity of owners or their small size. Commodity extraction offers a case in point. Since the 1930s, the USDA Forest Service has advanced the notion that private nonindustrial forests could provide for the nation's hardwood fiber needs should public supplies dwindle (Carpenter 1985; Birch and Pywell 1986). Toward this end, the Forest Service has supported hundreds of ownership studies on nonindustrial private forests with the intent of making them more industrial and less private (Young and Reichenbach 1987; Alig, Lee, and Moulton 1990). Two important assumptions undergirded the Forest Service's outlook: that private landowners held a utilitarian "wood basket" vision of their forests, and that private ownership patterns were stable insofar as farmers held the majority of these woodlands (Stoddard 1961).

The valley's history illustrates that foresters were only partially correct on the first point and mostly wrong about the second. The reasons people own forest land are as numerous as the owners themselves, with timber production just one motive among many (Healy and Short 1979; Force et al. 1993). While nonindustrial forests may provide wood fiber, neither rural populations nor their forests are stable but continue to change in age, size, and composition, far from demographic or ecological equilibrium. Timber production on these lands is unpredictable, occurring outside the bounds of conventional economic wisdom, with many owners foregoing economic benefits in favor of esthetics (Roberts, Tlusty, and Jordahl 1986). In addition, loggers and forest owners tend to make impromptu arrangements to harvest timber without regard to market conditions or professional advice. Generalizing from an ownership study is daunting at best given the array of owners no longer bound by common livelihoods, customs, identity, or purpose, and the uncertain future they face with regard to taxes, markets, and legal constraints.

An environmental history like this one offers a counterpoint to more simplistic ownership surveys, providing insight into the ways that rules and rights surrounding land tenure shape rural societies. In the Kickapoo Valley, tenure patterns reveal socioeconomic relations within communities, and between communities and a wider regional, national, and global political economy. At the same time, property lines have immediate local effects, giving a select group—"owners"—the power to carve up the landscape in new ways, to create particular ecosystems, and to keep people out. Landowners also let people in. When, where, why, and under what conditions owners restrict or permit access has always been critical to rural life in areas like the Kickapoo Valley. The livelihoods of those without property, as well as neighboring landowners, have depended on their access to land through rental or tenant agreements for farming, grazing, or housing. Likewise, loggers and sawmill owners have relied on timber they harvested from private forests. Informal customs whereby forest owners allowed neighbors to hunt, harvest mushrooms, pick berries, or collect firewood strengthened community relations while contributing to the region's informal economy. Rural people use these tenure arrangements to measure the strength of relationships with neighbors, making them as valuable as more formal contacts. Hence, it is important to assess their meaning for people and natural resources at any moment, together with implications of changes in them over time.

Land tenure in the valley also reflects the cultural and ideological forces that shape how people interact with their environment. Cultural ideas that categorize land as urban, suburban, rural, or wilderness come into play, as do parallel notions separating land management into leisure, recreation, or work (Cronon 1995; White 1995). Few would deny that a suburban resident in Madison manages her land differently than does a dairy farmer in the Kickapoo Valley. One "rests" in her backyard while the other "works" her land. Yet both individuals may raise domesticated animals, apply fertilizers and pesticides, cultivate fruits and vegetables, cut and plant trees, and otherwise alter their immediate environments in profound ways. In this instance, we must be careful that we do not casually label people who subsist directly from their land "worse" or "better" managers. To do so steers us away from the important question of what different categories of property tell us about our material relationship to the nonhuman world, the cultural meaning we give different natures, class hierarchies, and social structures (Field and Burch 1988).

Contemporary debate about nonmarket values in forests, water, and biological diversity focuses upon how to fairly value goods and services not traditionally traded in the marketplace (for example, see Swanson and

Loomis 1996). This study suggests a different facet of nonmarket valuation, one involving how individuals decide to buy or sell land. An economist analyzing land tenure in the valley might study "arm's-length" property transactions between a willing buyer and a willing seller, both with perfect knowledge of the land, the deal concluding at fair market value. Such an "objective" analysis fails to account for assumptions the seller makes about the use to which a buyer will put the property. Many property transactions in the valley have occurred between relatives at below-market value, between like-minded neighbors intent on continuing their customs, or even between individuals who feel they must hide information to conclude a transaction. Conversely, transactions have taken place at above-market value with absentee buyers who are unfamiliar with the area, local land prices, or environmental constraints to development. The idea of "implied use" reflects a landowner's desire to control the future of her land, even as she relinquishes ownership to someone else.

Another dimension of land tenure involves overlapping, sometimes conflicting interests in "private property" or "public property," where both the state and the public(s) struggle to control both classes of property (Bromley 1993). Events in the Kickapoo Valley reflect wider debates in American society over how clear the line between public and private was in the past and how blurred it might become in the future. The ill-fated La Farge dam project acquired private land through condemnation, then set up a public forest reserve when the project was canceled. Although no formal management plan yet exists for the reserve, its oversight by the State Department of Tourism and the U.S. Department of the Interior suggests that preservation and recreation interests will dominate the reserve's future. These actions have generated both criticism and praise of state and federal agencies who retained the land for uses that many former owners did not support. During the same period, increasing numbers of forest owners enrolled their property in Wisconsin's Managed Forest Law program, which lowered property taxes in exchange for management planning and expanded public access. Hunters felt they held a legitimate, though temporary, right to access private land because they had purchased public hunting licenses. As rural and urban populations ebb and flow, mechanisms that protect the public's interest in natural and biotic resources on private land, or widen public access to private land, surely will increase, ensuring that the meaning of public and private property remains open to reinterpretation and change.

Public resource policy is sometimes at the mercy of this ambiguity. Bureaucracies that treat land and resource tenure relationships as static rather than dynamic have tended to frustrate their own objectives, while fostering adversarial relationships and unintended changes on the land-scape. One problem is that policymakers assume that the government influences the individual, rather than the other way around, thus failing to recognize the interplay between society and the state (Gilbert and Howe 1991). As a result, resource managers may not be able to address cultural factors that stymie their plans, like scenic values or culturally based management practices. They have a hard time responding to unforeseen trends, such as ownership shifts, which change or narrow their sphere of influence. Wisconsin's history shows how the interests of many groups diverge from those of public agencies in questions of resource management. A striking example appears in the forestry realm when public foresters and private industries emphasize industrial timber production to the exclusion of other practices. Foresters and loggers prefer to work with owners of large tracts and those who are willing to harvest their timber intensively. In the Midwest, though, small tracts predominate, not large forests, and landowners must choose between heavy harvesting or no action at all. The Amish have shown us a third possibility because they operate on a small scale using "low-tech" methods, a practice public forest policy does not as yet address. In order to keep abreast of a rapidly changing social and ecological landscape, policy-makers must readjust to new configurations of public and private interests in land.

Research that aspires to discuss people and their environment must find ways to keep both in sight. To do otherwise risks ignoring our mutual engagement with nonhuman phenomena, a relationship that is not entirely culturally constructed or environmentally determined. Just as land tenure opens the door to a subject as vast as society, forests offer a gateway into nature. In the end, the Kickapoo Valley's history underscores what is at stake in the concept of forest tenure: community and environmental well-being. It reveals the changing political, cultural, and environmental contexts with which communities must cope. It shows how shifting public and private interests in forests have acted as catalysts for wider cultural conflict, conflict that is bound to regional ecological transformation. Forests, still essential sources of lumber, fuel, pasture, and other "products," also have become protectors of the soil, watersheds for trout streams, habitat for turkey and deer, refuge for songbirds and endangered plants, weekend lodging for city-dwellers, workplaces for state conservation agents, and sacred ground for Indians. That is a heavy load. As society seeks a middle ground where these different worldviews can coexist, our tenure relations become increasingly complex—buffeted by law and custom, nature and culture, past and future—but our changing cultural landscapes force hard choices upon us.

References

Alig, Ralph J., Karen J. Lee, and Robert J. Moulton. 1990. "Likelihood of Timber Management on Nonindustrial Private Forests: Evidence from Research Studies." Asheville, NC: USDA, U.S. Forest Service, Southeastern Forest Experiment Station, GTR-SE-60.

Appalachian Land Ownership Task Force. 1983. *Who Owns Appalachia? Land Ownership and Its Impact.* Lexington, KY: University Press of Kentucky.

Birch, Thomas W., and Nancy A. Pywell. 1986. "Communicating with Nonindustrial Private Forest-Land Owners: Getting Programs on Target." Upper Darby, PA: USDA, U.S. Forest Service, Northeastern Forest Experiment Station, NE-RP-593.

Brick, Ed. 1994. "Ten Thousand Years of Land Management in Vernon County." In *Vernon County Heritage,* edited by the Vernon County Historical Society, pp. 14–16. Dallas, TX: Taylor Publishing Company.

Bromley, Daniel W. 1993. "Regulatory Takings: Coherent Concept or Logical Contradiction?" *Vermont Law Review* 17 (3): 647–682.

Bruce, John W., and Louise Fortmann. 1988. "Why Land Tenure and Tree Tenure Matter: Some Fuel for Thought." In *Whose Trees? Proprietary Dimensions of Forestry,* edited by Louise Fortmann and John W. Bruce, pp. 1–10. Boulder, CO: Westview Press.

Carpenter, E. M. 1985. "Ownership Change and Timber Supply on Non-Industrial Private Forest Land." St. Paul, MN: USDA, Forest Service, North Central Forest Experiment Station, NC-265.

Carstensen, Vernon. 1958. *Farms or Forests: Evolution of a State Land Policy for Northern Wisconsin, 1850–1932.* Madison, WI: University of Wisconsin, College of Agriculture.

Churchill, Josie. 1981. *Dirt Roads: A Collection of Stories.* Westby, WI: Josie Churchill.

Cox, Thomas R., Robert S. Maxwell, Phillip Drennon Thomas, and Joseph Malone. 1985. *This Well-Wooded Land: Americans and Their Forests from Colonial Times to the Present.* Lincoln, NE: University of Nebraska Press.

Cronon, William. 1991. *Nature's Metropolis: Chicago and the Great West.* New York, NY: Norton.

Cronon, William. 1995. "The Trouble with Wilderness; or, Getting Back to the Wrong Nature." In *Uncommon Ground: Toward Reinventing Nature,* edited by William Cronon, pp. 69–90. New York, NY: Norton.

Danbom, David B. 1995. *Born in the Country: A History of Rural America.* Baltimore, MD: Johns Hopkins University Press.

Ebling, W., C. D. Caparoon, E. C. Wilcox, and C. W. Estes. 1948. *A Century of Wisconsin Agriculture.* Madison, WI: Wisconsin Crop and Livestock Reporting Service, Bulletin no. 290, p. 119.

Epitaph-News. (La Farge, WI). 1983. "Road Damage and Horseshoes: Town of Clinton Tries to Talk it Out." July 21, vol. 2, no. 4.

Field, Donald R., and William R. Burch, Jr. 1988. *Rural Sociology and the Environment.* New York, NY: Greenwood Press.

Finley, Robert W. 1976. *Original Vegetation Cover of Wisconsin.* (Compiled from notes on the original vegetation cover of Wisconsin. Transcribed by Finley [1951] from information recorded in the original government land survey.) St. Paul, MN: North Central Forest Experiment Station, USDA, U.S. Forest Service.

Flader, Susan L., ed. 1983. *The Great Lakes Forest: An Environmental and Social History.* Minneapolis, MN: University of Minnesota Press.

Force, Jo Ellen, Gary E. Machlis, Lianjun Zhang, and Anne Kearney. 1993. "The Relationship between Timber Production, Local Historical Events, and Community Social Change: A Quantitative Case Study." *Forest Science* 39: 722–742.

Gaventa, John. 1980. *Power and Powerlessness: Quiescence and Rebellion in an Appalachian Valley.* Chicago, IL: University of Illinois Press.

Gilbert, Jess, and Carolyn Howe. 1991. "Beyond 'State vs. Society': Theories of the State and New Deal Agricultural Policies." *American Sociological Review* 56: 204–220.

Harrison, Robert Pogue. 1992. *Forests: The Shadow of Civilization.* Chicago, IL: University of Chicago.

Healy, Robert G., and James Short. 1979. "Rural Lands: Market Trends and Planning Implications." *Journal of the American Planning Association* 45 (3): 305–317.

Heasley, Lynne, and James Delehanty. 1996. "The Politics of Manure: Resource Tenure and the Agropastoral Economy in Southwestern Niger." *Society and Natural Resources* 9: 31–46.

Hix, David M., and Craig G. Lorimer. 1990. "Growth-Competition Relationships in Young Hardwood Stands on Two Contrasting Sites in Southwestern Wisconsin." *Forest Science* 36: 1032–1049.

Institute for Environmental Studies. 1974. *Environmental Analysis of the Kickapoo River Impoundment.* University of Wisconsin–Madison, IES report no. 28, Nov. 1.

Johnson, Leonard C. 1991. *Soil Conservation in Wisconsin: Birth to Rebirth.* Madison, WI: University of Wisconsin–Madison, Department of Soil Science.

Kickapoo Valley History Project. 1979. *Kickapoo Pearls.* 1:4. 16 pp.

Kline, Virginia M. 1976. "Dynamics of the Vegetation of a Small Watershed." Ph.D. diss. Madison, WI: University of Wisconsin.

Kraybill, Donald B., and Steven M. Nolt. 1993. *Amish Enterprise: From Plow to Profits.* Baltimore, MD: Johns Hopkins University Press.

Ladd, Ann. 1993. "In Harmony with God." *La Crosse Tribune.* Wednesday, September 1.

La Farge Epitaph. (La Farge, WI). 1978. "Surge." May 17.

La Farge Epitaph. (La Farge, WI). 1980. "Absentee Land Ownership in the Kickapoo Valley." September 24.

Lamm, Thomas. 1981. *Forest Resources in the Kickapoo Valley: Issues and Opportunities.* Madison, WI: Environmental Awareness Center, University of Wisconsin–Madison.

Langston, Nancy. 1995. *Forest Dreams, Forest Nightmares: The Paradox of Old Growth in the Inland West.* Seattle, WA: University of Washington Press.

Leatherman, J. 1993. "An Economic Analysis: Helping Valley Residents Understand the Challenge and the Opportunities." In *At Work in the Kickapoo Valley,*

Annual Report 1992, edited by S. Johnson, pp. 7–10. Madison, WI: School of Natural Resources, College of Agricultural and Life Sciences, University of Wisconsin–Madison.

Leatherman, John C. 1994. "Input-Output Analysis of the Kickapoo River Valley." Center for Community Economic Development Staff Paper 94.2. Madison, WI: University of Wisconsin–Madison/Extension.

Lewis, P. H., and Thomas Lamm. 1981. *Recreation and Tourism Resources in the Kickapoo Valley.* Madison, WI: Environmental Awareness Center, University of Wisconsin–Madison.

Logan, Ben. 1975. *The Land Remembers: The Story of a Farm and Its People.* Minocqua, WI: Heartland Press.

Marcouiller, D., A. Anderson, and W. C. Norman. 1995. *Trout Angling in Southwestern Wisconsin and Implications for Regional Development.* Madison, WI: University of Wisconsin Extension/Center for Community Economic Development.

McEvoy, Arthur F. 1986. *The Fisherman's Problem: Ecology and Law in the California Fisheries, 1850–1980.* Cambridge: Cambridge University Press.

Nature Conservancy. 1989. "A Future for the Kickapoo River Watershed." Madison, WI: Wisconsin Chapter, unpublished report.

Peluso, Nancy Lee. 1992. *Rich Forests, Poor People: Resource Control and Resistance in Java.* Berkeley, CA: University of California Press.

Phillips, Guy D. 1977. "Environmental Assessment of the Kickapoo River Impoundment II: An Assessment of Economic Impact." IES Report no. 91. Madison, WI: Institute for Environmental Studies, University of Wisconsin–Madison.

Renner, Maxene. 1995. "Police Seeking Man in Kidnapping, Rape." *Wisconsin State Journal.* November 4.

Roberts, John C., Wayne G. Tlusty, and Harold C. Jordahl. 1986. "The Wisconsin Private Nonindustrial Woodland Owner: A Profile." Madison, WI: University of Wisconsin Cooperative Extension Service Occasional Paper Series no. 19.

Sancar, Fahriye, H. Macari, T. Barman, K. Onaran, and G. Sargin. 1992. "Development of an Action Plan for the Kickapoo River Valley of Southwestern Wisconsin. New Visions for the Kickapoo: Regional Design Proposals for Future Development." Madison, WI: Department of Landscape Architecture, University of Wisconsin–Madison.

Stoddard, Charles H. 1961. *The Small Private Forest in the United States.* Washington, D.C.: Resources for the Future.

Swanson, C. S., and J. B. Loomis. 1996. "Role of Nonmarket Economic Values in Benefit-Cost Analysis of Public Forest Management." Portland, OR: USDA, U.S. Forest Service PNW-GTR-361.

U.S. Army Corps of Engineers. 1977. "Alternatives for Flood Reduction and Recreation in the Kickapoo River Valley, Wisconsin: Special Report." St. Paul, MN: St. Paul District, U.S. Army Corps of Engineers.

U.S. Bureau of the Census. 1992. 1990 *Census of Population and Housing for Wisconsin.* Washington, D.C.

U.S. Department of Agriculture. 1958. *Land: The 1958 Yearbook of Agriculture.* Washington, D.C.: U.S. Government Printing Office.

Vernon County Historical Society. 1994. *Vernon County Heritage.* Dallas, TX: Taylor Publishing Company.

White, Richard. 1980. *Land Use, Environment, and Social Change: The Shaping of Island County, Washington*. Seattle, WA: University of Washington Press.

White, Richard. 1995. " 'Are You an Environmentalist or Do You Work for a Living?' Work and Nature." In *Uncommon Ground: Toward Reinventing Nature*, edited by William Cronon, pp. 171–185. New York, NY: Norton.

Williams, Michael. 1989. *Americans and Their Forests: A Historical Geography*. New York, NY: Cambridge University Press.

Worthingon, Rogers. 1988. "Amish Are Survivors in the Drought of '88." *Chicago Tribune*. August 9.

Young, Robert A., and Michael R. Reichenbach. 1987. "Factors Influencing the Timber Harvest Intentions of Nonindustrial Private Forest Owners." *Forest Science* 33: 381–393.

11

Land Tenure and Ecosystem
Management in Indian Country

Ronald L. Trosper

Introduction

Many studies of land tenure in Indian country address the relationship between land tenure and economic development; this chapter addresses the
relationship between land tenure and ecosystem management. Management
of ecosystems requires goals that include the needs of humans and ecosystems. An ecosystem usually needs a form of sustainability, which has also
been described as health or integrity. Human needs can be defined with
reference to economic valuation as expressed by market prices, or by bringing in aspects of ecological systems that provide additional values. This chapter addresses institutional aspects of implementing ecosystem management
as they relate to the present structure of land tenure in Indian country.

One reason for examining the relationship between land tenure and
ecosystem management is that Indian tribes are regaining control of their
land as a result of at least forty years of their efforts to remove federal controls. Self-determination has given Indian tribes a chance to practice what
their values preach: ecosystem management. The failure of many tribes to
implement management practices consistent with their environmental values is a puzzle. Indian leaders, both traditional and contemporary, emphasize the importance of treating the land with respect, and polls such as those
conducted by the Indian Forest Management Assessment Team (1993) reveal that the Indian public wants its forests protected; yet, in some cases, the
land is not treated with respect. One reason for this is that traditional institutions no longer have the management role they once had.

Although tribes in the United States are achieving formal self-determination, they have limited control over their internal institutions (Anders
1989; Goodman-Draper 1994; Grinde and Johanson 1995; Harris, Blomstrom, and Nakamura 1995). The dominant society, through its formal and
informal powers, appears to set limits upon the types of organizational options available to a tribe. Cornell and Kalt (1992, 1995), among others, are

right to emphasize that Indian Reorganization Act constitutions are in many cases not consistent with traditional political structures. Federal institutions favor two types of land management: private property and open access.[1] Both make ecosystem management difficult. The difficulty has roots in the view that land is either under human control or wild and open to all. This dichotomy has been translated into institutions, with the consequence that a list of alternatives taken from the dominant society may not include an approach that is consistent with the worldview of an Indian society. Preservation of Indian culture, in the context of land management, necessitates the ability to practice ecosystem management.

Contrasting Values

American Indian cultures share an attitude of respect toward the world (Callicott 1989; Nelson 1983, 1993). In a 1995 paper, I presented evidence from a variety of Indian traditions describing four basic components as a way to characterize the American Indian definition of respect: community, connectedness, the seventh generation, and humility. Each of the components can be contrasted with those of an ethic that emphasizes the utility of nature for human purposes. Table 11.1 summarizes these ethics.[2]

Accompanying these different attitudes is a contrast in assumptions about the human motivation that should be used to organize institutions. Native peoples place generosity on top; European settlers and the U.S. government place self-interest on top. This can be illustrated by quoting the policymakers who set out to take apart native institutions that were organized to utilize generosity rather than self-interest. For example, one may cite Senator Dawes's description of one of the Five Civilized Tribes (quoted in Otis 1973, pp. 10–11):

> The head chief told us that there was not a family in that whole nation that had a home of its own. There was not a pauper in that Nation, and the Nation did not owe a dollar. It built its own capitol . . . and it built its schools and its

1. Instruments exist that allow portions of the tribal estate to be allocated to individuals with considerable private property rights to the land. Instruments also exist to assure that lands that are not allocated to individuals be used to benefit all tribal members equally. Getches, Wilkinson, and Williams (1993, pp. 453–458) emphasize that the protection of tribal governments from state law has been based upon the legal principle of *preemption* in its application to Indian country; however, "cases rejecting assertions of state law over Indians have repeatedly emphasized the primacy of federal law in the field of Indian policy" (ibid., p. 454). This means that the institutions of land management that govern federal land management are duplicated on reservations.
2. Illustrations of the mainstream attitude and assumptions can be found in economics texts such as Gregory (1987) and Tietenberg (1992).

Table 11.1. Contrasting assumptions

Assumptions in a native ethic	Assumptions in the mainstream
Community	*Dominion*
Humans are members of a community that includes all beings; we have our proper roles.	Humans have dominion; the natural world is for our use.
Connectedness	*Commodity relations*
Everything is connected; treating parts in isolation is unwise. Humans are part of the world, of Nature.	Interconnections are unimportant; commodity relations through markets work best. The world outside of humans is a supply of "natural resources."
The seventh generation	*The next generation*
Among humans, past generations left us a legacy, and we have a duty to our great-grandchildren and beyond to do the same.	We have no expectation from the past, and owe nothing to our grandchildren; they are our children's responsibility.
Humility	*Hubris*
Nature is powerful, well able to cause trouble if not treated with due respect.	Humans can control nature; we understand the consequences of our acts; caution is not required.

hospitals. Yet the defect of the system was apparent. They have got as far as they can go, because they own their land in common. It is Henry George's system, and under that there is no enterprise to make your home any better than that of your neighbors. There is no selfishness, which is at the bottom of civilization. Till this people will consent to give up their lands, and divide them among their citizens so that each one can own the land he cultivates, they will not make much more progress.

Dawes was such a supporter of this analysis that the primary act to impose private property on Indians, the General Allotment Act, is best known as the Dawes Act. Implementation of the allotment policy led to both the taking of land from Indians and the imposition of a private property system on a portion of tribal lands throughout the country (Carlson 1981; McDonnell 1991; Geisler 1995).

The potlatch of the Northwest Coast Indians can illustrate the use of generosity to support sustainable-resource use. The potlatch was outlawed in Canada in 1885 for reasons very similar to those given by Senator Dawes for the allotment policy. Historians Cole and Chaikin (1990, p. 20) summarize the motivation behind the suppression of the potlatch:

Condemnation of the potlatch's demoralization of the Indians was much less on ethical grounds than on economic. [By] far the most frequent and serious arguments against the potlatch were those that touched on the system's incompatibility with settled habits of labour and industry: the loss of time from agriculture, ranching and even fishing, and the potlatch's destructiveness of the accumulation of savings. Work and savings were directed, not towards material progress, but to hoarding and then the extravagant dispersal of money and goods. Even the West Coast agent, Harry Guillod, who found the Nootkan potlatch largely inoffensive, agreed that it was "much against the habits of saving" and [Indian agent] Lomas, who estimated that his Cowichans had earned over $15,000 in the 1881 Fraser River fishing season, regretted that the greatest portion of this sum would be spent on blankets to be given away. . . . Few would have disputed [Indian reserve commission member Gilbert] Sproat's judgment that material progress was impossible while the potlatch existed. "It produces indigence, thriftlessness, and a habit of roaming about," he wrote, "which prevents home associations and is inconsistent with progress."

The Canadian government outlawed the potlatch and associated ceremonies in 1885; the law remained on the books until 1951 (ibid.).

Respect for Land Is Consistent with Ecosystem Management

Economic development maximizes wealth generation or the generation of income for individuals. Ecosystem management could be said to maximize ecosystem health, which is a concept that is consistent with respect for the land. Ecologist Robert Costanza (1992, p. 248) provides the following recently developed ecological definition:

> To be healthy and sustainable, a system must maintain its metabolic activity level as well as its internal structure and organization (a diversity of processes effectively linked to one another) and must be resilient to outside stresses over a time and space frame relevant to that system.

He proposes that a health index be defined as the product of three separate indices: vigor, organization, and resilience. Vigor is measured by productivity, the output of food or other measure of biomass.[3] Organization is measured by the complexity of the structures (the connections between species and the abiotic environment) and by the diversity of the species present. Resilience is hard to measure, because it describes the response of a system to disturbance. When long time frames are involved, as is the case with ecosystems, a simulation model is needed to predict results, yet such models are hard to construct.

This three-part definition of ecosystem health embodies the basic components of respect. Vigor describes a characteristic of community: if all members of a community have their right to a livelihood respected, then

---

3. Economists measure productivity as output per unit of input; in an ecological system, the input is energy from the sun, a constant, unless humans supply additional inputs.

each will perform his or her role in the production of useful products for others, thereby contributing to the community. Respect for community means respect for diversity, which relates to the ecosystem health concept of organization. Connectedness is also related to organization: although "connectedness" is vague about the type of connections, "organization" suggests a structure. A healthy ecosystem will have resilience, which will help it survive until the seventh generation. The difficulties in constructing adequate simulation models for measuring resilience is consistent with humanity's need for humility. If the residents of a reservation want to use their ecosystems in a manner consistent with respect, they will preserve or promote ecosystem health. In greatly disturbed ecosystems, however, identifying the proper policies may be difficult.

Principles of Ecosystem Management

Academic and public interest in ecosystem management has increased, as the danger of significant loss of ecosystem structure and function has become more evident in many different situations. Jensen and Everett (1994) provide one summary of the principles of ecosystem management, and Holling et al. (1995) provide another. The principles can be placed into three categories: hierarchy theory, coarse-filter conservation of diversity, and natural variability.

Hierarchy Theory

Hierarchy theory asserts that ecological systems must be understood as different systems operating in different spatial and temporal scales. In forests, for example, the spatial scale moves from the parts of a tree, to a tree, to a stand, to a watershed, to a forest, to a biome. Corresponding to the spatial hierarchy is a temporal one: the life cycle of a stand is shorter than that of a forest, which is shorter than that of a biome. The smaller the scale, the shorter the time period; the larger the scale, the longer the time period. Much of landscape ecology is about describing the relationships between large-scale and small-scale patterns and processes.

Costanza (1995) has pointed out that a common goal of ecosystem management—the preservation of sustainability—should be defined in terms of scale. What is sustainable at a small scale is different from what is sustainable at a larger spatial or temporal scale. An individual member of a population, for instance, has a finite life, much shorter than the lifetime of the entire population of a species, and the death of one population (defined spatially) may not mean the extinction of a species.

Holling et al. (1995) use the example of the boreal forest biome to illustrate the concepts of connectedness among different scales. Within a stand, balsam fir can outcompete spruce. If there were no larger-scale processes occurring, fir would dominate the landscape. But although balsam fir is vulnerable to outbreaks of spruce budworm, spruce is less vulnerable, and birch not at all. Because of the dynamics of insect outbreaks, a single landowner wishing to grow only balsam fir within a region subject to outbreaks cannot control all the variables relevant to growing fir.

Coarse-Filter Conservation of Diversity

The distinction between coarse-filter and fine-filter approaches to conservation can be illustrated by considering the protection of endangered species. A fine-filter approach looks at the specific habitat requirements of a short list of threatened or endangered species. Policy is directed at those habitats. A coarse-grained approach would examine the entire landscape in which the habitats exist and would examine the landscape-level processes that may govern the sustainability of particular habitats. Jensen and Everett (1994, p. 11) state, "This approach assumes that if landscape patterns and process (similar to those that species evolved with) are maintained, then the full complement of species will persist and biodiversity will be maintained."

Natural Variability

Ecosystems have multiple equilibria, depending upon the interaction of the large-scale and small-scale processes. A change in the species composition of an ecosystem can lead to a "flip" to a different equilibrium. A commonly cited example is the flip of a grassland to a shrubland in response to cattle grazing. Intensive cattle grazing, by reducing the fuel load in the grassland, can eliminate fire as a process. Without fire to remove competition from woody species, the grass is replaced by shrubs. An equilibrium with a high proportion of grassland is replaced by one with a high proportion of brush, and there is a consequential change in the types of animals that can live in the ecosystem (Perrings and Walker 1995). The term "succession" is a common description of cycles in many plant communities. Models of succession provide descriptions of temporal variability in particular sites, such as a stand or a watershed. Ecosystem management requires institutions and policies that recognize the reality of hierarchy, coarse-filter conservation, and natural variation.

Private Property Is Not Consistent with Ecosystem Management

In the United States, private property in land is not consistent with the principles of ecosystem management. The primary reason is that the owner of a parcel of land regards that parcel, alone, as the system within which he or she can operate. A landowner has full rights to manage his or her parcel, sell commodities from it, and dispose of the property, including as a bequest to his or her children. He or she can exclude other persons from the land and sue in cases of trespass or damage. The role of government is to enforce these rights and any contracts mutually agreed to by a landowner and other persons (Schlagger and Ostrom 1992; Christman 1994).

Drawing clear boundaries ignores hierarchy theory (Rosser 1995). If the parts of an ecosystem are subdivided into private property parcels, the owners must relate to each other through market exchanges such as leases, contracts, sales, and purchases of goods. In this way, self-interest overrides connectedness. While ecosystem function is not disturbed, individual parcel productivity will be maintained. As owners use their land for their own purposes, however, connections will be broken and productivity will fall. To maintain parcel productivity, each owner will have to import resources, such as fertilizer.

When resources such as water or migratory animals affect the productivity of land, some argue that the institution of private property can be extended to include these resources, to assure that everything of importance has an owner (Anderson and Leal 1991). But high costs of enforcing such rights often prevent implementation. Further, large-scale dynamics involve noncorporal problems such as disease or fire. In ecosystems where fire is common, control of fire on a parcel basis, through a general increase in fuels, can generate periodic catastrophes. In a watershed in which periodic floods contribute to repairing the ecosystem function by setting succession back and renewing soil nutrients, controlling water through diversions, dams, and levees can have system-wide consequences. In ecosystems where large migrating animals are significant, fences and other characteristics of private property can remove species whose contribution to system productivity may be important (Allen and Hoekstra 1992).

If private property rights are fully defined, and if all participants understand the connections within an ecosystem, then each owner will have an interest in purchasing the needed ecosystem inputs from other owners. But private property systems rarely assign ownership rights to everything; as a result, a private property system is capable of fine-filter management while coarse-filter management is difficult. Rights are defined as particular goods become scarce; enforcing rights to nonvaluable components is not cost-effective. In addition, parcel owners learn about their own land exclusively; information becomes private. Under a private property system, there is little incentive to share knowledge. If one owner hurts the resources of another, recourse is to the courts.

The above comments, although brief, establish a clear case that private property—what Christman (1994) calls "liberal private property"— through its assignment of control and income rights to parcel owners, cannot deal with the landscape and other issues of connectivity raised by ecosystem management.

Federal Institutions That Support Private Property

Under current federal policy, there are five ways land in Indian country can be owned and used. These are: fee simple, subject to state jurisdiction and taxes; individual trust, subject to the regulations of the General Allotment Act and succeeding amendments to that act; tribal trust, managed by tribal government as supervised by the Bureau of Indian Affairs (BIA) pursuant to federal law; federal land; and state school lands.

The first two are private-property systems. Land held in fee simple is land like any other in the United States that is privately held. Individual trust lands—allotments—are also under the control of the landowner, subject only to some supervision by the BIA. A great deal of the individually held land is leased. Much of the individual trust land is held by multiple heirs, which complicates management of the land by the owners.

Tribal trust land management is guided by the rules of Volume 25 of the Code of Federal Regulations, which in turn depends on federal law. Use of this land is controlled through leases, permits, assignments, timber sale contracts, and tribal ordinances. These *contractual* tools for using land are part of the private-property, market-based approach to land management in the United States. Even though the land is held in trust, its use is governed by the institutions of private property. Some Pueblo tribes in the Southwest, however, have retained their clan-based system of assigning use rights within their reservation boundaries; their systems aren't described in the Code of Federal Regulations but do govern surface land use.

Other Federal Institutions That Impede Ecosystem Approaches

The federal administrative division of activities into separate areas impedes tribal ecosystem management. For instance, the structure of the "trust" division of the BIA divides different resource responsibilities into different parts of the organizational chart: timber, minerals, real property. Also, governance of hunting and fishing is part of police work, not land management.

Some federal institutions encourage management of common resources with principles of open access, based on the idea that individuals in the tribe have the right to their equal share of the tribal estate. Examples include per capita distribution of the proceeds of land sold for homesteading; per capita distribution of land-claims settlements; grazing access on some reservations; hunting regulations on many reservations; the form of specific grazing leases; and tribal off-reservation hunting and fishing rights. In some cases, tribes have asserted their rights to control these on their own terms, but, when they have not done so, the problem of open-access management occurs.

Recent Pollution Control Laws

Given the many national laws enacted in the 1970s and later to protect the environment, one can no longer maintain that federal law is completely determined by the principles of selfishness that motivated the allotment policy and subsequent leasing laws. Citing *Davis v. Morton*,[4] Getches, Wilkinson, and Williams (1993, p. 735) write: "Although Indian land is held in trust, and some think it is a different category than other federal land, the provisions of the National Environmental Protection Act apply to the approval of tribal land leases." Thus, the requirements of the National Environmental Policy Act (NEPA) can be used by tribes to examine interactions among ecosystem components when a federal action occurs.[5]

NEPA's approach is more general than pollution-control laws. Other environmental laws enforced by the Environmental Protection Agency (EPA) focus on specific components of the environment or on specific sources of pollution: the Clean Air Act, the Clean Water Act; the Safe Water Act; the Comprehensive Environmental Response, Compensation, and Liability Act (Superfund); and the Federal Insecticide, Fungicide, and Rodenticide Act all have provisions that allow the EPA to treat tribes as states in carrying out the acts. Only the Resource Conservation and Recovery Act does not have specific authority to delegate control to tribes (Getches, Wil-

4. 469 F. 2d 593 (10th Cir. 1972).
5. See chapter 4 of this volume for more background on NEPA.

kinson, and Williams 1993; Suagee 1990). These laws recognize that activities on a person's land can have impacts outside of that land and, therefore, that regulation is needed. Some tribes have used federal environmental laws to protect themselves, as, for example, the Isleta Pueblo in enforcing the Clean Water Act and the Northern Cheyenne in obtaining Class I air-quality designation.

Do these laws, however, promote the type of ecosystem management that Indian values support? One argument on the negative side is that the laws supporting the EPA encourage direct regulation of pollution, with an emphasis on point rather than nonpoint sources. Each law is enforced by its own set of rules and with funding determined by national compromises in the enforcement of environmental laws. The implementation model is direct control by a bureaucracy. Although this approach can be beneficial, it is based upon exclusivity in regard to each of the sources of pollution.

An Indigenous Institution That Recognizes Connectedness

Private property, accompanied by institutions that protect the landowner's right to the full net return from his or her property, fail to provide incentives for good ecosystem management. The potlatch is an alternative approach, based upon institutions that force a land- or resource-owner to share the net return from his or her property with other owners participating in the same ecosystem. The institution is the potlatch, the resource is the fishing sites that shared common runs of salmon, and the case is that of the Kwakiutl people of the Northwest coast, chosen because the ethnographic evidence is extensive.[6]

Among the Kwakiutl, the potlatch system was part of the winter ceremonials that occurred each year. The Kwakiutl divided the year into a summer secular season during which people fished and collected other foods, and a winter sacred season in which they conducted their ceremonies. The villages of the Kwakiutl were organized into clan-like entities called *numaym*; property rights in fishing and gathering sites belonged to the *numaym*, and the activity of the *numaym* was under the direction of its leaders (Galois 1991). In addition to directing and coordinating food-gathering activities, the heads of the *numaym* were responsible in the winter for the ceremonies that ensured the salmon were given proper respect and would return in the next secular season (Walens 1981). Part of the sacred duties of the leaders was the distribution of wealth to the other *numaym* that were in the village or neighboring villages. These were the potlatches, or giveaways,

---

6. See Trosper (1996) for a more detailed treatment.

originally described by Franz Boas (1966), who asserted that the purpose of the potlatch was to establish the status of the man giving away wealth (see also Cole and Chaikin 1990; Rosman and Rubel 1971). Subsequent commentators have disputed that interpretation. Drucker and Heizer (1967) argued that rank was inherited, and high rank came with a duty to conduct potlatches: "The potlatch did not give, or create, social status. Present data make abundantly clear that this was as true of the Southern Kwakiutl as it was of other northwest coast groups. No matter how many potlatches a chief gave, he did not alter his formal rank one whit beyond that to which he was legally entitled through heredity or acquisition of rights in marriage."

The duty to conduct potlatches was based on the Kwakiutl view of the cause of the return of salmon each year:

> [W]e must examine carefully those qualities the Kwakiutl themselves consider to be the return given to [a] person who gives to others at a potlatch. . . . This return is not considered to be given by humans, but is given by the spirits to humans: that is, the man who gives the potlatch receives his reciprocal gift in spirit-power, which will directly enable him during the coming years to secure, by the grace of the spirits, a plentiful supply of food. Prestige has nothing to do with it. The results are considered to be tangible, meaningful, and essential, and they can be achieved only by the giving away of wealth. (Walens 1981, pp. 33–34)

Although the Kwakiutl gave a spiritual explanation for the way in which the potlatch caused food to be plentiful, one can also provide an explanation based on economic analysis: if fishers are placed in a situation in which they must share the surplus of their fishing activities, then the common-pool dilemma they all face has been removed.

One must emphasize the fact that giving away wealth was required; this was not a system in which people voluntarily gave away their wealth in order to obtain prestige or to have their rank recognized:

> Moreover, it could be argued that the potlatch system itself was coercively intolerant of dissent. Agents noted again and again that some, especially younger natives, did not wish to participate but could find no escape. Kwakiutl children were involved long before they had reached any age of conscious decision and marriage was arranged without choice. . . . Younger Gitksan were intimated into participation by ridicule, insults and other means. "If we do not participate," said one young man, "you know there are still *nadowigets* (witchcrafters) and there are yet many ways of making you embarrassed among our people. So we have to subscribe to their views." Another said that "we have to do this or our lives will be miserable amongst our people." The potlatch as a "total social phenomenon," precluded alternatives necessary to real choice. (Cole and Chiakin 1990, p. 178)

In addition, although chiefs held potlatches, everyone was involved in giving and receiving wealth:

> The usual conceptualization of a redistributive system is that goods move up from followers to a chief of a group, these goods being redistributed by the chief at large feasts and potlatches. Our analysis has shown the model to be more complex. The chief of a group decides to give a potlatch. He requests assistance in the form of goods from the members of his group. He amasses these goods and distributes them to chiefs of other groups at the potlatch. These chiefs return to their homes and hold feasts at which they distribute what they have received at the potlatch to their followers. Conversely, when the first chief goes as a guest to the potlatch of another chief, he will make a feast and distribute what he has received to his followers on his return. The redistributive process in this case involves relations between, as well as within, groups. (Rosman and Rubel 1971, p. 203)

The Kwakiutl were organized into what Drucker and Heizer (1967) called festival groups. There were five or six of the groups. "Feasts were normally given among groups that were in frequent, friendly contact: the several groups sharing a winter village or neighbors within a well-marked physiographic region, such as an inlet" (ibid., p. 142). Galois (1991) provides detailed maps of the festival groups, showing that they shared fishing areas in the secular season.

The Prisoner's Dilemma Model of a Fishery

Neighboring Kwakiutl sharing an inlet would face a common-pool problem. The prisoner's dilemma is often presented to illustrate the fundamental puzzle that faces two or more persons harvesting from a common-pool resource (Binmore 1994; Ostrom, Gardner, and Walker 1994). The dilemma occurs because if some fishers restrain their harvest, other fishers are free to expand their harvest. If all fishers would use restraint, the total net returns would be maximized. But with open access, no sensible fisher will use restraint, total effort will be too great, and the fishery will be stressed. If those who aggressively harvest fish *must* give a share of their harvest to the other fishers, then a sensible fisher can restrain his or her effort, knowing he or she will receive a share of the rivals' catches. The requirement to share—as among Kwakiutl festival groups—resolves the dilemma (Trosper 1996).

If this solution is so simple, why have so few commentators stressed it? Most assume that an agreement to share the outcomes is not enforceable (Sugden 1984; Binmore 1994; Varian 1994). In a society that requires giveaways, however, the enforcement mechanism is credible. Given its ability to solve the common-pool prisoner's dilemma, the Kwakiutl were right to believe that the winter ceremonials, with their potlatches, were responsible for "a plentiful supply of food" in the coming years.

Usufruct Tenure: Another Native Institution

Likewise, other native institutions may plausibly support ecosystem management. Consider, for instance, the use of usufruct tenure. Under this system, the right to "own" land is contingent on the use of it: individuals or families can have exclusive control of land they use; upon cessation of use, the land is once again controlled by the community. This system was used throughout native North America and was usually combined with giveaway institutions. Consider the nature of wealth-sharing in New England and the associated system of access to ecosystem outputs. Historian William Cronon (1983, pp. 62–64) provides the following description for New England:

> Property rights . . . shifted with ecological use. . . . Hunting grounds are the most interesting case of this shifting, nonagricultural land tenure. The ecological habits of different animals were so various that their hunting required a wide range of techniques, and rights to land use had to differ accordingly.
>
> What the Indians owned—or, more precisely, what their villages gave them claim to—was not the land but the things that were on the land during the various seasons of the year.

The rights to use things on the land were allocated to individuals; but the right was one of use, not ownership in the sense of exclusive control, including buying and selling and owning all of the net return from using the land. Other uses may overlap in the same geographical area. Ultimate ownership remained with the village as a whole. With ownership dependent on use, exclusivity is determined by the territorial extent of each community of Indians.

Cronon (ibid., pp. 61–62) provides the following evidence of sharing among one group of New England Indians: "The Micmac of Nova Scotia . . . were 'so generous and liberal towards one another that they seem not to have any attachment to the little they possess, for they deprive themselves thereof very willingly and in very good spirit the very moment when they know that their friends have need of it.' " Property ownership also existed in these traditional societies, but it was not private property ownership, as understood in the European tradition; income from land was shared.

This assignment of hunting or use rights to particular resources rather than particular areas suggests that attention to the hierarchical structure of ecosystems could be recognized. In addition, because any user of community resources has a right that is contingent, the community can place limits on overexploitation. Among the Kutenai of the inland Northwest, for instance, chiefs could award the right to fish to particular individuals, but this was conditional:

> An Upper Kutenai could build a fish trap only after obtaining permission from the chief. No one could build more than one. The fisher was given a definite franchise for a specific stream, in return for which he entered into a contractual relation with the band in the person of its chief. The chief guaranteed him exclusive right to the site, but the owner had to share the product of the weir with some eight or nine families. Since he got the lion's share of the trout per diem in the right season, this sharing worked no hardship on the fisher. . . . But they [the fishers] did not own the stream. This was the property of the people at large under the direction of their principal socio-economic functionary, the Guide Chief. The stream could not be abused or the fishermen were punished. (Turney-High 1941, pp. 47, 52)

Thus, the seventh-generation principle, which would not allow abuse of the stream, could be enforced by the community leader as a condition on the right to use the community's resources. The requirement that individuals be generous with their neighbors could also be a contingency: if an individual did not share his or her surplus, his or her community membership might be at issue, and usufruct rights depended upon community membership.

How Might a Tribe Organize Its Economy to Support Ecosystem Management?

Although the positive value of sharing one's wealth has survived the process of forced cultural change undertaken by the federal government on Indian reservations, the institutions that carried out the sharing of wealth have been fairly well disempowered or dismantled. While they may conduct give-aways, fishing tribes of the Northwest do not conduct them in the context of the "total social phenomenon" that once characterized the potlatch. Gloria Cranmer Webster (1991, pp. 231–232), a Kwakiutl and trained anthropologist, participates in the modern Kwakiutl potlatch and describes its preparation as follows:

> A typical modern potlatch is much shorter than in the past, when one potlatch might last over several days or a week. [Today], a potlatch must be compressed into less than twenty-four hours, beginning in the afternoon, so that mourning songs can be sung before sunset, and ending in the late evening or early hours of the next morning. . . . Several days before the potlatch, relatives and friends begin arriving, staying with local families and visiting other homes,

while there is time. . . . Everyone works together with incredible energy and enthusiasm to ensure that everything will be ready on time. While the food and big house crews are finishing their jobs, others are loading trucks with potlatch goods and ceremonial gear to deliver to the big house. Such cooperative effort seems to surface only during potlatch time and is probably indicative of another change in our lives; that is, we are no longer able to help each other in any kind of ongoing way. However, it is of some consolation that such cooperation has not completely disappeared and that it does emerge for the right reasons.

As Northwest Coast tribes lost control of their fisheries, the potlatch declined. The decline was greater in the United States than in Canada, where the legal prohibition of the potlatch may have aided its preservation in form, but its role as an institution that helped in the cooperative management of fisheries declined in both countries. When the *Boldt* decision gave half of the salmon catch back to Indians in the United States, the Northwest Tribes did not recreate potlatch-like institutions, even among themselves (Cohen 1986). The analysis in this chapter suggests that one way to address the open-access problems of the salmon fishery would be to establish a potlatch-like method of sharing the net returns to salmon fishing.

A more interesting approach to some of the problems of ecosystem management involves the interaction of different types of commodity harvests. Consider the interaction between forests and salmon. The simple model of this interaction is that the clearcutting of too great a percentage of a watershed increases silt deposition in the watershed's streams to a level that reduces salmon survival in the streams' spawning areas. A potlatch-type institution would give a share of the net returns from timber management to fishers and a share of net returns from salmon harvest to the owners of timberland. Similarly, because of the role of hydroelectric dams in reducing salmon harvests, it could be argued that the net returns from electricity sales should be shared with the fishers.[7]

Usufruct tenure also has implications, in that property owners would not have extensive rights to the use of their land. As with timber-sale contracts, the right to use land would be limited in time, space, and according to the type of product that could be harvested. The interesting institutional possibilities, however, are in the interactions between usufruct tenure and forced generosity.

7. One problem with defining the net return from hydroelectric dams is that public regulation of electricity rates distributes a portion of the economic value of hydroelectric dams to the consumers of electricity. In the presence of cost-of-service rate regulation and large electricity markets, the true economic value of electricity is determined by fossil-fuel plants, which have higher marginal costs (when measured without accounting for external effects) than hydroelectric dams.

Conclusion

A well-known Native American institution, the potlatch of the Northwest Coast, provides an incentive to consider connections in the spatial and temporal hierarchy of a fishery. Fishers who need to share their surplus harvest do not have a prisoner's dilemma, can generate a social surplus each year, and also can restrain themselves from destroying future harvests. If the potlatch, as a prototypical case of "forced generosity," addresses an ecosystem issue, perhaps other native institutions can do so as well. Usufruct tenure systems may assist ecosystem management. With ownership rights based on use, the community can place conditions on landownership consistent with ecosystem needs.

The policy context of this argument is the increasing self-determination of tribal governments. More control of resources, however, is not sufficient if a tribe both retains private-property institutions and wishes to be true to traditional values that support the goal of ecosystem health. To resolve the resulting conflicting incentives, tribes must consider ways to restore their institutions in the modern age.

As ecosystem management becomes more important for mainstream society, interest may grow in the institutions used by native peoples to channel the self-interest of their community members in directions that promoted the sustainable use of their ecosystems. That the Indians of the Northwest Coast achieved high levels of wealth while utilizing fisheries, a notoriously difficult type of resource to manage, provides evidence that their institutions were successful. That the potlatch was so foreign to the invading Europeans, however, suggests that today these institutions might appear to be extremely strange to people who are considering the types of institutional reform needed to manage sustainable ecosystems.

Among those who are considering alternative arrangements, the recent work of David Korten (1995) is noteworthy. He examines the consequences of extending private property rights and self-government rights to corporations and concludes that the short-term profit-making focus of corporations, among their other characteristics, is a major cause of worldwide difficulties in ecosystem sustainability. He recommends reinvigoration of local communities throughout the world. This chapter suggests that, as part of such reorganization of local economies, the role of gift-giving among users of a common ecosystem be given serious consideration.

Another author proposing alternative arrangements is Christman (1994). He argues for a distinction between the right to control property and the right to have income from property. In order for a society to have distributional justice, he argues, private property rights should not include the right to income from property, only the right to control property. This proposal resembles usufruct tenure combined with requirements to share the surplus from land use. Christman's motive is to set background conditions for the pursuit of income equality as an issue of social justice. In the process of his argument, he considers, but does not stress, externalities as a reason to separate the ownership of income from the right to control an asset. That proper treatment of externalities may require relinquishing the right to income from property would further support Christman's proposals to separate the right to income from the right of control in the social definition of ownership of land and its associated resources. But the requirements of hierarchy, coarse-filter management, and attention to natural variability may require limits on the control of property as well as limits on an individual's rights to full ownership of the income from property.

References

Allen, Timothy F. H., and Thomas W. Hoekstra. 1992. *Toward a Unified Ecology.* New York, NY: Columbia University Press.

Anders, Gary C. 1989. "Social and Economic Consequences of Federal Indian Policy: A Case Study of the Alaska Natives." *Economic Development and Cultural Change* 37 (2): 285–303.

Anderson, Terry L., and Donald R. Leal. 1991. *Free Market Environmentalism.* Boulder, CO: Westview Press.

Binmore, Ken. 1994. *Playing Fair.* Cambridge, MA: MIT Press.

Boas, Franz. 1966. *Kwakiutl Ethnography,* edited by Helen Codere. Chicago, IL: University of Chicago Press.

Callicott, J. Baird. 1989. "Traditional American Indian and Western European Attitudes toward Nature: An Overview." In *In Defense of the Land Ethic: Essays in Environmental Philosophy,* edited by J. Baird Callicott, pp. 177–201. Albany, NY: SUNY Press.

Carlson, Leonard A. 1981. *Indians, Bureaucrats, and Land: The Dawes Act and the Decline of Indian Farming.* Westport, CT: Greenwood Press.

Christman, John. 1994. *The Myth of Property: Toward an Egalitarian Theory of Ownership.* New York, NY: Oxford University Press.

Cohen, Fay G. 1986. *Treaties on Trial: The Continuing Controversy over Northwest Indian Fishing Rights.* Seattle, WA: University of Washington Press.

Cole, Douglas, and Ira Chaikin. 1990. *An Iron Hand upon the People: The Law against the Potlatch on the Northwest Coast.* Seattle, WA: University of Washington Press.

Cornell, Stephen, and Joseph P. Kalt. 1992. "Reloading the Dice: Improving the Chances for Economic Development on American Indian Reservations. What Can Tribes Do?" In *Strategies and Institutions in American Indian Economic Development,* edited by Stephen Cornell and Joseph P. Kalt, pp. 1–59. Los Angeles, CA: American Indian Studies Center, UCLA.

Cornell, Stephen, and Joseph P. Kalt. 1995. "Where Does Economic Development

Really Come From? Constitutional Rule among the Modern Sioux and Apache." *Economic Inquiry* 33 (3): 402–26.

Costanza, Robert. 1992. "Toward an Operational Definition of Ecosystem Health." In *Ecosystem Health: New Goals for Environmental Management,* edited by Robert Costanza, Bryan G. Norton, and Benjamin D. Haskell, pp. 239–256. Washington, D.C.: Island Press.

Costanza, Robert. 1995. "Defining and Predicting Sustainability." *Ecological Economies* 15 (3): 193–196.

Cronon, William. 1983. *Changes in the Land: Indians, Colonists, and the Ecology of New England.* New York, NY: Hill and Wang.

Drucker, Philip, and Robert F. Heizer. 1967. *To Make My Name Good: A Reexamination of the Southern Kwakiutl Potlatch.* Berkeley, CA: University of California Press.

Galois, Robert. 1991. *Kwakwaka'wakw Settlements, 1775–1920: A Geographical Analysis and Gazetteer.* Vancouver, BC: University of British Columbia Press.

Geisler, Charles C. 1995. "Land and Poverty in the United States: Insights and Oversights." *Land Economics* 71 (1): 16–34.

Getches, David H., Charles F. Wilkinson, and Robert A. Williams. 1993. *Federal Indian Law.* 3d ed. St. Paul, MN: West.

Goodman-Draper, Jacqueline. 1994. "The Development of Underdevelopment at Akwesansne: Cultural and Economic Subversion." *American Journal of Economics and Sociology* 53 (1): 41–56.

Gregory, G. Robinson. 1987. *Resource Economics for Foresters.* New York, NY: John Wiley and Sons.

Grinde, Donald A., and Bruce E. Johansen. 1995. *Ecocide of Native America: Environmental Destruction of Indian Lands and Peoples.* Santa Fe, NM: Clear Light.

Harris, Richard R., Greg Blomstrom, and Gary Nakamura. 1995. "Tribal Self-Governance and Forest Management at the Hoopa Valley Indian Reservation, Humboldt County, California." *American Indian Culture and Research Journal* 19 (1): 1–38.

Holling, C. S., D. W. Walker, Brian W. Schindler, and Jonathan Roughgarden. 1995. "Biodiversity in the Functioning of Ecosystems: An Ecological Synthesis." In *Biodiversity Loss: Economic and Ecological Issues,* edited by Charles Perrings, Karl-Goran Maler, Carl Folke, C. S. Holling, and Bengt-Owe Jansson, pp. 44–83. Cambridge: Cambridge University Press.

Indian Forest Management Assessment Team. 1993. *An Assessment of Indian Forests and Forest Management in the United States.* Portland, OR: Intertribal Timber Council.

Jensen, M. E., and R. Everett. 1994. "An Overview of Ecosystem Management Principles." In *Volume II. Ecosystem Management: Principles and Applications,* technical editors M. E. Fensen, and P. S. Bourgeron; Assessment Team Leader, Eastside Forest Ecosystem Health Assessment Richard L. Everett, pp. 6–15. Gen. Tech Rep. PNW-GTR-318 ed. General Technical Report, PNW-GTR-318. Portland, OR: U.S. Department of Agriculture, Forest Service, Pacific Northwest Research Station.

Korten, David C. 1995. *When Corporations Rule the World.* West Hartford, CT: Kumarian Press.

McDonnell, Janet A. 1991. *The Dispossession of the American Indians, 1887–1934.* Bloomington, IN: Indiana University Press.

Nelson, Richard. 1983. *Make Prayers to the Raven.* Chicago, IL: Chicago University Press.

Nelson, Richard. 1993. "Searching for the Lost Arrow: Physical and Spiritual Ecology in the Hunter's World." In *The Biophilia Hypothesis,* edited by Stephen R. Kellert and Edward O. Wilson, pp. 201–228. Washington, D.C.: Island Press.

Ostrom, Elinor, Roy Gardner, and James Walker. 1994. *Rules, Games, and Common-Pool Resources.* Ann Arbor, MI: University of Michigan Press.

Otis, D. S. 1973. *The Dawes Act and the Allotment of Indian Land.* Norman, OK: University of Oklahoma Press.

Perrings, Charles, and Brian W. Walker 1995. "Biodiversity Loss and the Economics of Discontinuous Change in Semiarid Rangelands." In *Biodiversity Loss: Economic and Ecological Issues,* edited by C. A. Perrings, Karl-Goran Maler, Carl Folke, C. S. Holling, and Bengt-Owe Jansson, pp. 190–210. Cambridge: Cambridge University Press.

Rosman, Abraham, and Paula Rubel. 1971. *Feasting with Mine Enemy: Rank and Exchange among Northwest Coast Societies.* New York, NY: Columbia University Press.

Rosser, J. Barkley, Jr. 1995. "Systemic Crises in Hierarchical Ecological Economies." *Land Economics* 71 (2): 145–172.

Schlagger, Edella, and Elinor Ostrom. 1992. "Property-Rights Regimes and Natural Resources." *Land Economics* 68 (3): 249–262.

Suagee, Dean B. 1990. "The Application of the National Environmental Policy Act to 'Development' in Indian Country." *American Indian Law Review* 16 (2): 377–495.

Sugden, Robert. 1984. "Reciprocity: The Supply of Public Goods through Voluntary Contributions." *Economic Journal* 94: 772–787.

Tietenberg, Tom. 1992. *Environmental and Natural Resource Economics.* 3d ed. New York, NY: HarperCollins.

Trosper, Ronald L. 1995. "Traditional American Indian Economic Policy." *American Indian Culture and Research Journal* 19 (1): 65–95.

Trosper, Ronald L. 1996. "How the Potlatch Contributed to Fisheries Management." Paper presented at the Sixth Annual Conference of the International Association for the Study of Common Property, Berkeley, California.

Turney-High, Harry Hobert. 1941. "Ethnography of the Kutenai." *Memoirs of the American Anthropological Association* no. 56.

Varian, Hal R. 1994. "A Solution to the Problem of Externalities When Agents Are Well-Informed." *American Economic Review* 84 (5): 1278–1293.

Walens, Stanley. 1981. *Feasting with Cannibals: An Essay on Kwakiutl Cosmology.* Princeton, NJ: Princeton University Press.

Webster, Gloria Cranmer. 1991. "The Contemporary Potlatch." In *Chiefly Feasts: The Enduring Kwakiutl Potlatch,* edited by Aldona Jonaitis, pp. 227–248. Seattle, WA: University of Washington Press.

12

The Political Economy of Land Tenure: Appalachia and the Southeast

John Gaventa

Introduction: The Centrality of Land Tenure

The political economy of the South is deeply rooted in the land. In much of the rural deep South, local economies were shaped by the cotton plantations; in the Appalachian region, by coal and mineral exploitation. Timber extraction for wood and paper, tourist development along the coasts and in the highlands, agricultural land use—all have shaped the history, culture, and, most essentially, the power and politics of the region. While love of the land and sense of place have been important in the culture of the region, "The greater cultural tradition of the South," wrote southern sociologist Howard W. Odum, "has been one of exploitation of the land and its resources" (quoted in Goldfield 1987, p. 197).

My own introduction to the importance of landownership to the region came some twenty-five years ago when, as a student at Vanderbilt University, I joined two other students to conduct what now would be called a "service learning project" sponsored by the Student Health Coalition. We were asked to pursue these questions in our study of five of eastern Tennessee's coal-rich counties: Why was there a lack of local revenues for health projects amidst such coal wealth? Who owned the coal lands and what taxes did they pay? By sifting through hundreds of courthouse records, we discovered what many of the residents of the coal region already knew: although nine large coal corporations controlled 34 percent of the land and approximately 80 percent of the coal wealth, they paid less than 4 percent of the local property taxes (Gaventa, Ormond, and Thompson 1971). The most important result of this exercise was what the citizens did with the information. Meeting in the basement of a local church to discuss the findings, the citizens decided to form a group to challenge the inequities. Their effort led to the formation of Save Our Cumberland Mountains (SOCM), which for

Thanks to Chris Pelton, who recently received his master's in sociology at the University of Tennessee, for his research assistance.

the last twenty-five years has been challenging land-based inequities in the region.

During that first study, I also learned that one of the largest landowners in the region was a British company by the name of the American Association. Since I was going to Britain to graduate school, the citizens in the community asked if I would help research who really owned this company, and if I would take the word to them about the conditions of poverty and environmental and human abuse associated with their holdings in the valley. That led me to spend the next several years trying to understand the historical impact of the corporate control of land in that one Appalachian community, which was documented in the book *Power and Powerlessness: Quiescence and Rebellion in an Appalachian Valley* (Gaventa 1980).

My early experiences with community-based research helped shape my perception of the centrality of land, which I could not have gleaned simply from reading the literature of the region. In the midst of my research some years ago, I wrote to the Land Tenure Center at the University of Wisconsin–Madison to request a list of their publications, because we needed models, literature, and assistance as we began to investigate these issues. I remember the excitement when I got the return packet and the disappointment we felt when we discovered the absence of systematic work on land tenure in North America.

This chapter will not attempt to be a complete overview of land tenure in the South or the Appalachian region. That task is too broad, and the research does not yet exist for it to be done. Rather, I will summarize some of the findings of some key studies in the region, especially drawing from the large study of the Appalachian Land Ownership Task Force (ALOTF). Then I suggest that land tenure patterns are deeply connected to the economic, human, environmental, and social development of communities in Appalachia and the South, and the study of one must involve the study of the other. While I will refer to issues across the region, most of my examples will be drawn from Appalachia and the upper South, which has been the site of most of my own research and experience.

Who Owns the Land?

The historical literature of Appalachia and the South evokes themes of rugged individuals and self-sufficient farming families who eke an existence from small landholdings in the hills of Appalachia and in the Black Belt South. That image is not supported by the data on patterns of landownership and land concentration in the region.

In the spring of 1977, heavy rainfall on the strip-mined mountains of eastern Kentucky and West Virginia led to devastating floods. Thousands of families were made homeless, driven from their house trailers and previously owned company houses that lay along the creeks and valleys. In Mingo County, West Virginia, relief trailers sat empty on the roadsides for days. Why? There was no land available for the trailers to occupy, even in this rural county. Some 90 percent of the land was owned by several absentee coal corporations, which would not make land available for housing, even in an emergency. The crisis spawned citizen protest throughout the region. A new coalition, the Appalachian Alliance was formed. The number one issue identified by the coalition was landownership in the region.

The citizens joined forces with researchers from local colleges and universities, and with the help of the Highlander Center, formed the ALOTF. The group, which enlisted local civic organizations, set out to document landownership and its impact in eighty counties in six states across Appalachia and the upper South, including parts of Alabama, Tennessee, North Carolina, Virginia, Kentucky, and West Virginia (see Map 12.1). The resulting study, *Who Owns Appalachia?* (Appalachian Land Ownership Task Force 1983), remains one of the largest studies of land tenure in our region and one of the few such studies across the country. (For summaries of the study and follow-up, see also Gaventa [1984] and Horton [1993].)

ALOTF members sifted through property tax and other records in the eighty counties, gathering data on the ownership of over 20 million acres: 13 million acres of surface rights and 7 million acres of mineral rights. This included information on 55,000 property parcels, owned by 33,000 owners. The sample represented 53 percent of the total land surface in these counties. Since this study is now out of print, it is worth summarizing some of its findings (Appalachian Land Ownership Task Force 1983, pp. 14–18):

- Only 1 percent of the local population, along with absentee holders, corporations, and government agencies, controls at least 53 percent of the total land surface in the eighty counties. This means that 99 percent of the population owns, at most, 47 percent of the land. Of the 20 million acres of land and mineral rights owned by more than 30,000 owners in the survey, 41 percent (over 8 million acres) are held by only fifty private owners and ten government agencies.
- Seventy-two percent of the 13 million acres of surface sampled were owned by absentee owners, 47 percent of whom were out-of-state residents, and 25 percent of whom were state, but not county, residents.
- Corporations hold almost 40 percent of the land in the sample and 70 percent of the mineral rights. Forty-six of the top fifty private landowners are corporations, including some of the largest corpora-

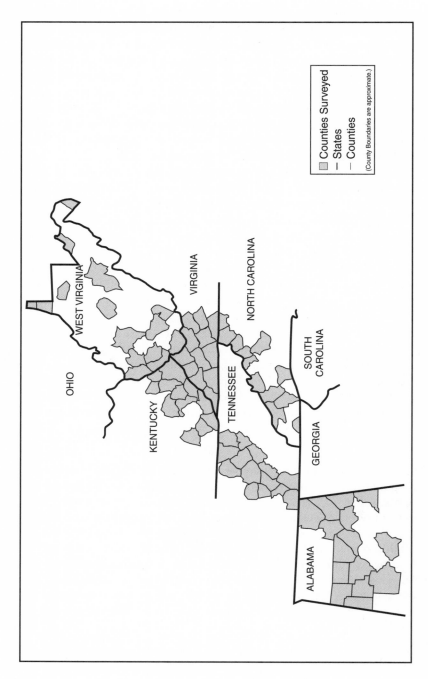

Map 12.1. Appalachian Landownership Counties Surveyed. Redrawn from Appalachian Land Ownership Task Force 1983 with permission of the University Press of Kentucky.

tions in the country. Individuals own some 45 percent of the land in the sample, but well over half of this land is owned by absentee individuals. The remaining portion of the land in the sample (16 percent) is owned by the government and nonprofit bodies. Ten government agencies account for 97 percent of this public ownership.

- In many areas of Appalachia, who owns the mineral rights is just as important as who owns the surface. Although millions of acres of mineral rights in Appalachia are simply not recorded for tax purposes, the study discovered almost 7 million mineral acres, equal to 28 percent of the total surface area of the eighty counties. Four-fifths of the mineral rights in the survey are absentee-owned.
- The ownership of land in Appalachia is highly concentrated in relatively few hands. The top 1 percent of the owners in the sample own 44 percent of the land in the sample—over 1,400 times what is owned by the bottom 1 percent of the owners in the sample. The top 5 percent own 62 percent of the land; the bottom 5 percent own .25 percent, or about 250 times less than what the top 5 percent own. The top half of the owners in the sample control 94 percent of the land, the bottom half control under 6 percent.
- The ownership data for minerals is less complete than the data for land. Nevertheless, the pattern of concentration is similar. The top 1 percent of the recorded mineral-rights owners control 30 percent of the mineral rights in the sample—some 15,000 times more than what is owned by the bottom 1 percent. The top 5 percent of the recorded mineral-rights owners own 62 percent of the recorded mineral rights; the top 50 percent own 97 percent of these rights.

Even though the Appalachian Land Ownership Study (ALOS) is over a decade old, the data are still significant for many reasons. First, it is important to recognize that these patterns were found not only in the coal fields of central Appalachia, which are known to be controlled by the coal industry, but also in portions of the six states, including rural agricultural, timber, and recreational areas. The concentration of ownership is similar to patterns found in some developing countries and led the Appalachian Alliance and Appalachian scholars to dub the region an "internal colony."

Second, the ALOS is significant because of its method. The participatory research of local citizens and citizen-university teams demonstrates that such research can be done and that it can contribute to local action. This was a labor-intensive process made possible by the desire of citizens to document land patterns and impacts in their regions. (Today, the computerization of property tax records and the availability of scanners and portable computers would make the process somewhat simpler.) Using investigative techniques, field work, and analysis, the task force traced real owners and their holdings throughout the region. Though the results were controversial and were never completely published by the Appalachian Regional Commission (which funded the study), the project helps demonstrate the power of participatory land research led by those most affected by land issues.

Finally, though the ALOS is over a decade old, there is little evidence that the overall patterns have changed or that the concentration and absentee nature of the ownership patterns have declined. In a number of areas, larger owners have been bought out by yet larger multinationals. Timber land and timber use have risen in significance as timber production moves from the Northwest to the Southeast. With the decline of livelihoods of rural landholders due to such trends as loss of rural jobs and decline in agricultural prices (e.g., tobacco), we might expect that small landholdings will continue to be lost.

While the ALOS and much of the other scholarship on the region assumes that the land tenure patterns were established with the industrialization of the South around the turn of the century, more recent work suggests that these patterns have deeper historical roots. Wilma Dunaway (1994) reviewed thousands of census and other records about land in Appalachia. She found that, far from being the land of the self-sufficient family farm, the region's pattern of inequitable land tenure was structured very early. By 1800 or so, the bottom half of the Appalachian frontier population owned less than 1 percent of the land, and nearly 60 percent of all households in the region were landless. These people worked as tenants, sharecroppers, and slaves (ibid.). By 1860, the inequities and the concentration of landownership in Appalachia were already in place. There has been little change in this structure or in the level of poverty in the region since. As Dunaway concludes, "Land provided the economic basis for the structuring of a polarized Appalachian society in which the wealthy landed gentry amassed a majority of the acreage while more than half the settler households remained landless" (ibid., p. 222).

While the ALOS focused on the issues of concentration of land by corporate and absentee owners, issues of land loss by the small owners received more attention in other parts of the South, especially in the deeper South, where a great deal of other work has documented the loss of African-American-owned land. Black landownership reached its peak around 1910, with blacks owning an estimated 15 million acres of land. Since 1910, however, this acreage has steadily declined—to less than 6 million by 1969 (McGee and Boone 1977). Since the 1970s, blacks have been losing land nationwide at a rate of nearly 500,000 acres per year (Pennick 1990). While this loss has often been explained by the migration of large numbers of blacks northward during the 1940s, 1950s, and 1960s, a closer look reveals that African-Americans were often stripped of their land by a variety of means, contributing to this migration. The use of eminent domain and other acts by white land officials to take advantage of black landowners through (often illegal) foreclosures and tax delinquency seizures are now considered to be the dominant causes of black land loss in the South (Marable 1979; Nelson 1978). The steep decline of African-American land-ownership has serious political and social implications for the South and elsewhere. As the Black Economic Research Center reported in 1973 (quoted in Beauford, Miller, and Walker 1984, p. 417), "[L]and owner-ship . . . confers on blacks a measure of independence, of security and dig-nity, and perhaps even of power, which is of crucial importance to the eleva-tion of the status of the black community generally."

Land Tenure and Community Development

What is the relationship of land tenure to the broader development patterns of the region? Political economists often analyze the ownership and flow of capital (and its links to power) to explain development. But increasingly, sociologists, community developers, economists, and others have begun to understand development not only in economic terms but in human, environ-mental, and social terms as well. Recently, for instance, Cornelia and Jan Flora (1994) have argued:

> Community sustainability is based in part on the resiliency of that community to respond to changes in the larger environment. . . . Resilience depends in part on the resources available to the community. Those resources can be viewed as forms of capital, which are to be reinvested locally to produce new wealth. Capital can be thought of as any resource capable of producing new resources. Two forms of capital have conventionally been viewed as important for community development: financial and manufactured capital and human capital. When looking at community sustainability, it is also important to ana-lyze environmental capital and social capital.

In this definition, land itself may be understood as a form of capital, a resource capable of producing new resources. Access to and ownership of land will affect the resilience of a community. Equally importantly, land-tenure patterns contribute to and are linked with each of these other forms of capital, especially in rural areas. We can see these interrelationships in examples from Appalachia and the Southeast.

Land Tenure and Economic Capital

What is the relationship of land tenure to the economic development patterns of the region, especially to the patterns of financial and manufactured capital? In much of the literature, the argument goes something like this: The development of Appalachia and the South is related to the "colonial" nature of the region. Absentee and concentrated ownership of the land and natural resources means that wealth has been drained from the region and its people. As the Appalachian Land Ownership Task Force (1983, p. 65) put it, "Through control of the region's land and natural resources, these forces prevent the formation of the indigenous financial control and other requisites for economic development. For development to occur, in this view, strategies must be developed that deal with the problems of ownership and control of land and mineral resources." Similarly, Pennick (1990) points out that the decline in black-owned land results in an estimated net annual loss of some $2.5 billion to the African-American community. "The first and most important step in achieving economic independence is the ownership and control of the land" (ibid., p. 44).

These assertions have been confirmed by a series of other studies. In a study of one hundred North Carolina counties, Donald Tomaskovic-Devey and Mark Prather (1990) found that both poverty and inequality increase when the concentration of landholding increases; likewise, rates of poverty and inequality rise in communities with high minority populations. But "in general, landowning concentration is a better predictor of economic development patterns and the degree of poverty and inequality than the racial composition of the community." Similarly, in a study of the predominantly rural region around the south-central stretch of the Mississippi River, Ciaramitaro et al. (1988) examined the relationship between economic development, land tenure, and rural poverty. They found a predominance of large-scale white farmers, who exerted considerable economic and political power. Perhaps most interestingly, they also found these farmers actively impeded economic development in the region, primarily because manufacturing-based economic development would tend to lower unemployment and raise wages—two developments that might threaten the profitability of their large farms. Thus, the authors argue that, although the underdevelopment of the rural South is enormously complicated, an important factor in the persistence of rural poverty and economic underdevelopment in the Mid-South is the role of large landowners.

Eban Goodstein (1989) also has pursued this relationship between landownership patterns and Appalachian economic and social development. His results only partially confirm ALOTF findings. "Empirical evidence provides support for the claim that absentee ownership is inversely associated with measures of economic and social well-being. However, concentration of ownership is found to be positively related to these same measures" (ibid., p. 510). He speculates that concentration also has to do with other forms of investment, such as coal extraction, which may also be producing income for local residents. Goodstein's analysis, like those of the other studies, also suggests that the link between land tenure and rural poverty is not necessarily a direct one. Rather, land tenure affects the development or lack of development of other forms of investment as well.

Understanding the link between land and investment is also important in times of disinvestment and de-industrialization. The rural southern and Appalachian workforce has long been associated with natural-resource-based industries such as textiles, coal, and chemicals, which came to the region in part because of its raw materials (cotton, minerals, water). During the 1980s, however, many of these industries (and the capital associated with it) left the region or automated their production, leaving behind rural communities with massive unemployment. The departure of these companies is often followed by the decline in other forms of infrastructure, such as roads and housing, which the industries created. When one McDowell County, West Virginia, company closed shop, it took the streetlights down as well, because it had put them up when it built the community many years before (Gaventa, Smith, and Willingham 1990; Gaventa, Lewis, and Williams 1992). The decline of land-based industries leaves rural people in the South in a double bind, with access neither to the land nor the jobs historically associated with it.

The loss of many of the formal jobs associated with the land makes an understanding of the relationship between the informal economy and the land all the more important. People of the region have long survived in hard times, from one bust to the next boom. The ability to grow vegetables, dig coal, gather ginseng, raise livestock, or cut wood has been an important part of survival (Williams 1993). For women in the region, the production of capital associated with the informal economy on the land has been particularly important, but often unrecognized. In a series of work histories of women in the South, Helen Lewis (Lewis, Selfridge, and Merrifield 1986, p. 30) cites the life story of one family in which

the mother left the mountain farm to work in a hotel in the nearest town. After marriage she returned to farming and when her husband deserted the family, she raised the family by farming, plowing for hire and picking up coal, hauling it and selling it. The daughters grew up with farm land destroyed by strip mining but still operating in and out of the economic system. They preached, did domestic work, ran a used clothing story, cut and sold timber, worked in sewing factories, moved to the city to work and returned to rebuild their land and community.

"The work histories," Lewis (ibid., p. 30) notes, "make clear that many women in the rural South have been working very hard and living in poverty for a long time."

Given the current rate of traditional job loss in rural areas, access to the land for survival in the informal economy is all the more important. At the same time, holding on to the land, even for survival through informal means, is becoming increasingly difficult for poor families in the South, especially for African-Americans. Pennick points out that, "At a time when money is extremely tight, the black farmer finds it almost impossible to borrow enough to develop a successful operation. Where once it was too little too late, today two out of ten black farmers receive nothing at all. Primarily because of this lack of access to capital, nearly two-thirds of all black farmers went out of business during the period 1982–1987" (1990, p. 43). Again, rural poverty is perpetuated by the link to the land: control of the land *by* capital limits the ownership of and use of the land by the rural poor; lack of access *to* capital by the poor adds to the loss of the land.

Land and Human Capital

As the Floras (1994) and many others observe, human capital, in addition to economic capital, is also important for community sustainability. Although it encompasses factors such as "individual capacity, human health, values and leadership" (ibid., p. 2), human capital is most conventionally thought of in terms of education and training. What is the relationship between land-tenure patterns and human capital?

A primary linkage has to do with taxes. In rural and urban communities, property taxes are a key source of local revenue, which in turn is vital to the support of local schools and other human services. In Appalachia and other parts of the South, where coal, timber, and other natural resources contribute substantially to the property wealth of the region, one might expect to find substantial tax revenues from the land. In fact, the opposite was found to be true: the region's abundance of coal and timber failed to produce sufficient local revenues for schools, health care, and the other services necessary for developing human capital.

The data from ALOS were startling: Over 75 percent of the mineral owners in the survey paid less than $.25 per acre in property taxes; 86 percent paid less than a penny an acre. In the twelve counties of eastern Kentucky, which include some of the region's major coal-producing properties, the average tax per ton of coal was about 1/50th of a cent, amounting to a total of approximately $1,500 (Appalachian Land Ownership Task Force 1983, p. 48). Similar patterns could be seen not only for other coal-rich lands across the region but also for timber lands, where large companies like Weyerhauser or Champion owned vast tracts of forest yet paid the local counties only a few cents per acre.

The impact of these patterns is obvious in places like rural Martin County, where Lyndon Johnson went to announce the War on Poverty. Martin County was one of the largest coal-producing counties in 1980, yet 86 percent of its budget had to come from state and federal aid because of its inadequate property-tax base. One company owned 55 percent of the county's surface. It leased that land to mining companies, which were projected to make money off that land at a handsome rate for the next fifty years. Yet, as Appalachian Alliance activists often pointed out, "The amount of property taxes paid by the company on the surface land to the county wasn't enough to buy the county a school bus, and the $76 a year received for the mineral rights wouldn't even replace its blown out tire!" Meanwhile, per-pupil expenditures in that county were 24 percent below the state average and 43 percent below the national average.

The link between landownership and taxation, and taxation to human services, has provoked citizen action in the region. Groups like SOCM and Kentuckians for the Commonwealth (originally Kentuckians for Fair Taxation) have worked hard to challenge the inequities. A West Virginia supreme court case (known as the *Recht* decision) found that children in communities with large corporate ownership of land did not receive an equal education, leading to a revamping of the state's school-finance policies. Other cases pitting rural schools against the urban areas have been heard in Kentucky and Tennessee. Yet the problems continue: only recently in Campbell County, Tennessee, where large coal and timber companies own over 50 percent of the land, the county stopped running the school buses one spring because it had run out of revenues. Children in rural areas could not get to school, let alone get an equal education once they arrived.

Land and Environmental Capital

In terms of community sustainability, the role of environmental capital is just beginning to be understood. "Environmental capital encompasses air, water, soil, biodiversity and landscape" (Flora and Flora 1994, p. 2). To explore the relationship of land tenure to environmental capital is also to explore the relationship of land tenure to land use. These issues are deeply intertwined in our system of private ownership, particularly in rural areas where landowners have had the political power to do whatever they want with the land they own.

There are numerous examples in Appalachia and the South where land tenure has affected the use of the land, which, in turn, affected the environmental capital available to a given area. In some cases, such as the ownership of the Great Smoky Mountain National Park or protected areas along the coast, public ownership of the land, many argue, has contributed to the environmental capital. But in much of the South, where more land is in private and corporate lands than in many other regions, environmental capital derived from the land has often been sacrificed for the sake of quick economic exploitation of the land, through strip-mining, clear-cutting, strip development, soil erosion, toxic pollution, or scores of other examples.

Two particularly important conflicts that are emerging in the South today have to do with the use of timber lands, and with the location of solid and hazardous wastes. These issues often occur in areas where land uses are changing.

Timber land and issues

Probably the most well-known conflicts involving environmentalists and the timber industry have occurred in the Northwest; environmental regulations and movements regarding timber have not been so strong in Appalachia and the South. Yet, about 70 percent of southern Appalachian lands are still forested, and more timber is in private or nongovernmental hands than in other parts of the nation. Bullard and Straka, in their study, conclude that this area represents "the greatest potential for increased timber supply in the nation" (1985, p. 5). They continue, "The availability of adequate timber supplies, when combined with a favorable business climate towards the forest products industry, makes future expansion of the Mid-South's timber-processing industry a certainty" (ibid.). Such re-investment in timber resources also has increased concern for the environmental capital of the area.

One controversy concerns a rural Tennessee county where 50 percent of the county has been owned by absentee coal companies. In 1994, Champion International acquired 85,000 acres of Tennessee mountain land located in rural Anderson, Scott, and Campbell counties for harvesting timber. The company also has applied for permits to build a chipmill in Campbell County for chipping hardwood for export. The two mining firms that had previously owned the land are working with Champion and planning to mine for coal on this same acreage using a process called "highwall mining," which relies almost exclusively on robots and computers and disturbs both the surface and underground. Concerned with Champion's disregard for the environment in a nearby North Carolina paper mill, the residents of these counties, through SOCM, are fighting Champion's proposed clear-cutting and chip-milling and the mining companies' proposals, as well as the proposed state legislation providing for extremely weak regulation of the timber industry (*SOCM Sentinel* 1994).

Dumping in the South

The South, particularly the rural South, has been a favorite location for solid and hazardous waste disposal sites, as Bullard (1990) and others make clear. By the end of the 1970s, four of the five states with the largest number of incoming pollution industries were in the South (ibid.). Siting of hazardous and solid waste disposal sites in rural areas has been associated with environmental racism and high poverty rates.

However, siting of wastes also is associated with the types of land use and the level of environmental capital (as well as economic or social capital) in the region. Studies done by waste-management associations on where to locate waste sites with the least resistance have concluded, "[I]t seems to be advantageous to site a new landfill at a location where there has already been some invasion of the environment [and] where there has been mining activities, quarrying, [etc.]" (Johnson 1985). In other words, waste industries may seek an area that has already suffered a loss of environmental capital, perceiving it to be less resistant to further environmental costs.

Moreover, the availability of large plots of land that have been controlled by mining or timber firms make parts of Appalachia and the South ideal locations for solid- and hazardous-waste disposal. Studies of the region have shown that landfills are often sited in poor, rural areas that have been mined for coal or cut for timber. These sites are chosen, at least in part, because they consist of huge tracts of land held by absentee corporations (see Highlander Research and Education Center 1993).

The garbage trade, for instance, has targeted the deep South and coal fields for mega-landfills. In eastern Kentucky, a new landfill company, named GICO (Garbage In, Coal Out), was started. They proposed to lease hundreds of strip mines for out-of-state garbage dumps. Similarly, in West Virginia, Berwind, a large corporation that had mined coal in McDowell County since the 1800s, formed Capels Resources, Inc. in 1991 for the sole purpose of developing the mining site into a mega-landfill designed to accept out-of-state waste. The company used the promise of new jobs to pressure the impoverished community and limit local opposition to its plans. While effective citizen resistance did develop, the key in this case was that the Berwind Corporation's decision to site the mega-landfill in McDowell County was "directly related to the county's persistent poverty and Berwind's ownership of vast tracts of land in the county" (quoted in Highlander Research and Education Center 1993, chapter 3, p. 70).

All of these examples suggest, then, that land-tenure patterns and previous land uses will affect the environmental capital of the region.

Land Tenure and Social Capital

Recently a number of theorists of development also have written about the importance of social capital—in addition to economic, human, and environmental capital—and its relationship to development. The Floras refer to social capital as "the mutual reciprocity and mutual trust that exists among its citizens" (1994, p. 2). Robert Putnam defines social capital as the "features of social organization, such as networks, norms, and trust that facilitate coordination and cooperation for mutual benefit" (1993, pp. 35–36). Communities with large amounts of horizontal social capital, which refers to norms of reciprocity and mutual exchange, "value solidarity, civic participation, and integrity" (ibid., p. 36). Communities characterized by vertical social capital tend to be ones where dependency, patron-client relationships, and corruption prevail. Horizontal social capital can strengthen participatory democracy. Vertical social capital works against it.

What is the relationship of land tenure to social capital? Here there have been some pioneering studies, but there is much more work to be done. In Latin America, Paulo Freire (1970) has written about the culture of silence and fear that exists in latifundia communities. Walter Goldschmidt (1947) documented the relationship between large absentee ownership and weak social institutions. I documented how control of land also translated to political power and a lack of civic engagement based on a sense of powerlessness as well as the fear and distrust that grow out of coercion of the land companies over people (Gaventa 1980). Billings (1979) and others have written of the culture of paternalism and domination that was developed by the planter-industrialists of the South.

Historically, then, the corporate and political power derived from the land-tenure patterns has prevented the development of horizontal social capital in many parts of the region. Company towns promoted patterns of paternalism, patronage, and dependency in which skills and traditions of civic engagement did not flourish. In many communities characterized by such power, patterns of intimidation persist. Only last year when a citizen from SOCM testified regarding the siting of a waste dump on the land near his home, he was attacked and beaten in the hearing room by company thugs.

But, it is important to point out the social capital that has sometimes been created through the development of alternative ownership patterns or when the power of the dominant owner has changed. For instance, groups like the Federation of Southern Cooperatives have strengthened the social capital and civic engagement of empowerment of more than thirty thousand black farmers across the South, organized into dozens of cooperatives. In the midst of the valley where I studied the power gained from corporate and absentee control of land, the Woodland Land Trust has provided a "free space" where different kinds of social relationships are constructed. In Mc-Dowell County, West Virginia, in the wake of mining company closures, democratic participatory planning has emerged in an unprecedented way. Frankie Patton (quoted in Gaventa, Lewis, and Williams 1992, p. 22), one of the leaders of the effort, describes the change in norms:

> Even though the leaving of the coal industry resulted in the loss of jobs, incomes and services, for the first time in my life I feel free from the control of the company. Even though the situation is bad and we have few resources, we can now make decisions ourselves and we can organize to help ourselves without company supervision. It is a feeling of liberation, and for the first time, great hope.

Social capital has also been developed in the growth of democratic, citizen-based organizations that have sprung up in the region around land-based issues, often in response to the dominant forms of power. Groups such as SOCM, the Kentuckians for the Commonwealth, the Federation of Southern Cooperatives, the Rural Consortium of Land-Based Training Centers, and others have provided forums for the development of community leadership, for citizen engagement, and for effective citizen action on land issues. In many cases, they have been successful both at changing the sense of powerlessness and dependency historically instilled by the dominant landowners, as well as in changing land-tenure patterns. For instance, in Kentucky, a state historically dominated by the coal industry, the group Kentuckians for the Commonwealth was able to change the broad-form deed law that for almost a century had allowed the mineral owners to mine coal without respect to the rights of the surface owners. (Several case studies on the rise of citizen-based organizations on land issues may be found in Fisher 1993.)

To explore the relationship of land tenure to social capital, then, is not only to explore how ownership patterns have affected civic participation and reciprocity; it also requires looking at the effects of citizen actions and the effects of land-reform experiments and alternative forms of land tenure on attitudes, participation, and empowerment. The expression of these norms may sometimes be part of what Scott (1990) would call the "hidden transcript" of the community. They may also be expressed through music, song, story-telling, just as strongly as in the dominant political economy. Research on land tenure and social capital therefore must involve understanding the culture of communities affected by the relationship to the land and the indigenous knowledge that has been drawn from it. In ALOS, we made the mistake of focusing too closely on the data and knowledge about the land drawn from the "official" records. In a later workshop at Highlander, we began to document and uncover the richness of knowledge about the land carried through the culture of the region.

Conclusion

The examples given above help us understand that land tenure is intertwined with the development and revitalization of sustainable communities. Land-tenure patterns contribute to, and are shaped by, the financial, human, environmental, and social capital of any community or region. While there is much more research to be done to understand the interrelationship of these issues, one point should be clear: community- or economic-development strategies that fail to understand the centrality of land tenure will not be successful. Likewise, land-tenure reforms that fail to understand the interrelationships of the land to all facets of community life will be limited.

At the same time, the links between land and capital at the community level must be understood in the context of global capital in each of its forms. The movement of financial capital, in the form of investment or disinvestment, affects what happens to the land. U.S. participation in NAFTA and GATT will have implications for land-based economies. Land affects human capital, not the least through the movement of human resources in new streams of migrant workers who may have been displaced from their land in Mexico or El Salvador and who now seek agricultural work in Florida, Georgia, and Tennessee. The uses of the land affect environmental capital not only locally but also globally, as can be seen from the impact clear-cutting has on ozone depletion. Even social capital, which is perhaps most rooted in the community, is linked to global networks. Experiments in social forestry or micro-lending for credit, for instance, which developed in the context of Third World, are now being used as approaches for strengthening communities in this country. Although it is beyond the scope of this chapter, the relationship of land and capital at the community or regional level must include analyses and understanding of the global context.

Further research is needed to deepen our understanding of and action on these issues. Such research also must be useful and accessible to the communities affected by land-based issues. Research that replicates land-tenure patterns (e.g., findings concentrated in a few hands and not accessible to the people directly affected by the land) will do little to alter the patterns of power and powerlessness that landownership patterns have helped to create. ALOTF helped to show that scholars and citizens can work together successfully to develop research that is both valid and empowering. The challenge is not only to strengthen knowledge about land tenure, but to do so in a way that strengthens the economic, human, environmental, and social capital of communities whose futures are bound to the land.

References

Appalachian Land Ownership Task Force. 1983. *Who Owns Appalachia?* Lexington, KY: University Press of Kentucky.

Beauford, E. Yvonne, H. Max Miller, and Melvin E. Walker, Jr. 1984. "Effects of the Changing Structure of Agriculture on Nonwhite Farming in the United States, the South, and Georgia: 1954–1978." *Sociological Spectrum* 4: 405–420.

Billings, Dwight B. 1979. *Planters and the Making of a "New South."* Chapel Hill, NC: University of North Carolina Press.

Bullard, Robert D. 1990. *Dumping in Dixie.* Boulder, CO: Westview Press.

Bullard, Steven H., and Thomas J. Straka. 1985. "Business Aspects of the Mid-South Forest Economy." *Mid-South Business Journal* 5: 3–6.

Ciaramitaro, Bridget, Stanley Hyland, James Kovarik, and Michael Timberlake. 1988. "The Development of Underdevelopment in the Mid-South: Big Farmers and the Persistence of Rural Poverty." *Humanity and Society* 12 (4): 347–365.

Dunaway, Wilma. 1994. "The Incorporation of Southern Appalachia into the Capitalist World-Economy, 1700–1860." Ph.D. diss., University of Tennessee, Knoxville.

Fisher, Stephen L., ed. 1993. *Fighting Back in Appalachia.* Philadelphia: Temple University Press.

Flora, Cornelia B., and Jan L. Flora. 1994. "Community Sustainability and Forms of Capital." A paper excerpted from Cornelia B. Flora, "Sustainable Agriculture and Sustainable Communities: Social Capital in the Great Plains and the Corn Belt." Unpublished manuscript. Department of Sociology. Iowa State University, Ames.

Freire, Paulo. 1970. *The Pedagogy of the Oppressed.* New York, NY: Continuum.

Gaventa, John. 1980. *Power and Powerlessness: Quiescence and Rebellion in an Appalachian Valley.* Urbana, IL: University of Illinois Press.

Gaventa, John. 1984. "Land Reform in Appalachia." In *Land Reform, American Style,* edited by Charles Geisler and Frank Popper, pp. 233–244. Totowa, NJ: Rowman and Allanheld.

Gaventa, John, Helen Lewis, and Susan Williams. 1992. "Disposable Communities: Picking Up the Pieces after the Company Leaves Town." *Dollars and Sense* (March, no. 174): 12–14, 22.

Gaventa, John, Ellen Ormond, and Bob Thompson. 1971. "Coal Taxation and Tennessee Royalists." Study for Vanderbilt Student Health Coalition, Nashville, Tennessee.

Gaventa, John, Barbara Smith, and Alex Willingham, eds. 1990. *Communities in Economic Crisis: Appalachia and the South.* Philadelphia: Temple University Press.

Goldfield, David R. 1987. *Promised Land: The South Since 1945.* Arlington Heights, IL: Harlan Davidson, Inc.

Goldschmidt, Walter. 1947. *As You Sow: Three Studies in the Social Consequences of Agribusiness.* 1st ed. Glencoe, IL: Free Press.

Goodstein, Eban. 1989. "Landownership, Development, and Poverty in Southern Appalachia." *The Journal of Developing Areas* 23: 519–534.

Highlander Research and Education Center. 1993. *Dismantling the Barriers: Rural Communities, Public Participation, and the Solid Waste Policy Dilemma*. New Market, TN: Highlander Research and Education Center.

Horton, Billy D. 1993. "The Appalachian Land Ownership Study: Research and Citizen Action in Appalachia." In *Voices of Change*, edited by Peter Park, pp. 85–102. Westport, CT: Bergin and Garvey.

Johnson, Charles A. 1985. "Successes in Siting Solid Waste Facilities." Paper presented at the Eighth Annual Madison Waste Conference, September 18–19, 1985, University of Wisconsin–Madison.

Lewis, Helen M., Linda Selfridge, Juliet Merrifield, eds. 1986. *Picking Up the Pieces: Women In and Out of Work in the Rural South*. New Market, TN: Highlander Research and Education Center.

Marable, Manning. 1979. "The Land Question in Historical Perspective: The Economics of Poverty in the Black Belt South, 1865–1920." In *The Black Rural Landowner—Endangered Species: Social, Political, and Economic Implications*, edited by Leo McGee and Robert Boone, pp. 3–24. Westport, CT: Greenwood Press.

McGee, Leo, and Robert Boone. 1977. "Black Rural Land Decline in the South." *Black Scholar* 8 (7): 8–11.

Nelson, William E., Jr. 1978. "Black Political Power and the Decline of Black Land Ownership." *Review of Black Political Economy* 8: 253–265.

Pennick, Edward J. 1990. "Land Ownership and Black Economic Development." *Black Scholar* 21(1): 43–46.

Putnam, Robert D. 1993. "The Prosperous Community: Social Capital and Public Life." *American Prospect* 13: 35–42.

Scott, James C. 1990. *Domination and the Arts of Resistance: Hidden Transcripts*. New Haven, CT: Yale University Press.

SOCM Sentinel. 1994. Lake City, TN: Save Our Cumberland Mountains, November/December newsletter.

Tomaskovic-Devey, Donald, and Mark Prather. 1990. "Elite Concentration and the Political Economy of Poverty in North Carolina." Paper prepared for presentation at the annual meeting of the American Sociological Association, Washington, D.C., August.

Williams, Lee Lyle. 1993. "The Semiproletarianization of the Household: Making Ends Meet in Rosey Hollow." Master's thesis. University of Tennessee, Department of Sociology.

CONCLUSION

Who Owns America?

Harvey M. Jacobs

The title of this book poses a provocative question, one the authors have addressed in a variety of ways. Yet no one has provided a straightforward and simple answer. Why?

The question of who owns America, it turns out, is very difficult to answer for a number of reasons. One reason has to do with the administrative structure of the United States. Unlike many developed countries, the United States does not have a national land law or database on landownership. Land is considered to be largely a local matter (the basis of the local property tax); thus, records on landownership are among the most decentralized public ledgers kept in the country. It is to the thousands of county courthouses and city halls that one must go to begin piecing together a picture of landownership.

What is found if one does this? Confusing and difficult to use land data, much of which is inaccurate or incomplete for the purpose of identifying who owns America. In the New England states, for example, it is not uncommon for local land records still to be drawn from the original metes-and-bounds survey approach, which describes a particular tree, stone, or wall as the basis for distinguishing boundaries. In the states established after the country's founding, more accurate survey methods prevailed, but even here local records are less useful than one would like. The impetus through much of the eighteenth and nineteenth centuries was the transfer of large amounts of public lands into private hands so as to secure Euro-American settlement of the continent. Lack of land never seemed to be an issue. The precise boundary of one parcel versus another was generally of little concern.

The very nature of land itself adds another layer of difficulty. As noted in the preface, land is treated by the legal and economic systems as a bundle of rights. Rights can be separated from the bundle and can be bought, sold, leased, traded, inherited, and so on. A courthouse record shows that I am the owner of record of a parcel of land. What if, while owning my land, I sold the mineral right to a multinational mining corporation, sold the right to harvest old-growth timber to a paper company, donated the development right to a local land conservation organization, and leased the access right for the fall hunting season to a local hunting club? I am the owner of record; I get the local property tax bill; yet, who owns the land? I own the soil, maintain the fences, and pay the bills, while others own key rights, some of which may be more valuable than the rights I have left in my portion of the property bundle.

In the last two decades, some states and federal agencies have wanted to know more about who owns America. Their efforts reveal the difficulties in seeking a simple answer. In the early 1980s, the U.S. Department of Agriculture wanted to know who was buying and selling rural land in the United States. They commissioned a feasibility study on a national rural land-transfer database, for which I served as one of the key researchers. Our conclusion: a database of this sort would likely end up being a garbage-in, garbage-out situation. Why? To put together a national database you would need to draw on the information already gathered by states for tax purposes. On average, in most states, the data available publicly and considered useful for tracking market trends represent, at best, one-third of the total transactions that actually occur (Jacobs and Moyer 1986). This is before you even get to the issue of tracing ownership of severed property rights from the owner-of-record's main bundle.

The difficulty of discovering who owns America is further evidenced by the results of one of the major ownership studies conducted in recent times. In the 1970s, John Gaventa, author of the previous chapter, codirected a major study of landownership in the Appalachian region (Appalachian Land Ownership Task Force 1983). A small army of trained citizens were deployed into over eighty local record offices in six states to ferret out and piece together information on large-scale ownership. They found the information difficult to get, use, and interpret. One of the goals of the study was to understand the network of corporate control of valuable mineral and other natural resources, but the very nature of corporate ownership— interlocking directorates controlling land through companies with different names but singular goals—made it very difficult to find a clear and simple answer to who owns Appalachia.

We do have some information about landownership patterns in the United States. The U.S. Department of Agriculture regularly collects information on farmland ownership as part of the Census of Agriculture. For privacy reasons, the names of owners are not revealed, and counties with a small numbers of owners may not report data at all since owners could be identified; yet, the data allow for trend analysis on one component of U.S. land. Also, in the late 1970s, the U.S. Department of Agriculture undertook one of the few national studies of landownership ever by a federal agency

(Lewis 1980). The results are disturbing. It suggests that concentration of landownership, a rationale used frequently by the U.S. government to promote land reform in developing countries, is surprisingly high in the United States. The top 5 percent of landowners own nearly 75 percent of the U.S. land base; the remaining 78 percent own only 3 percent (Geisler 1993). Despite the perception of widespread landownership among America's peoples, the 1980 study found private land in the United States in the hands of only 34 million owners. Nothing in the last two decades suggests that this pattern of private landownership is changing for the better.

Despite the difficulty in answering it, the question of who owns America keeps popping up in the American public policy dialogue. In the late 1970s and early 1980s, the U.S. Congress focused on the foreign ownership of American farmland and wanted to know who owned America's food production base (U.S. Department of Agriculture 1980). The heady economic activity of the 1980s led to foreign purchase of key American properties, such as Rockefeller Center in New York City, with another round of consternation in newspapers and legislative forums about who owns the country. As the background research for the Appalachian Land Ownership Task Force study (1983, pp. 178–217) shows, there actually have been a lot of studies about ownership in America. Despite these, we know very little. Most ownership studies are of little real value. They can be criticized for being flawed in methodology, scope, and interpretation. Also, of course, they are merely snapshots. Landownership is dynamic, changing, often dramatically, as the studies are being conducted.

A more fundamental question nags the primary question of who owns America. Why does land matter? The answer of why it matters who *owns* the land is taken up in the two chapters that frame this volume, those by Louise Fortmann and John Gaventa. Fortmann and Gaventa point out that ownership patterns have a direct relationship to issues such as social and political power, and community diversity and vitality. To late-nineteenth- and early-twentieth-century social theorists and activists, these observations were self-evident, but at the close of the twentieth century the place of landownership and land itself is not as prominent. Why?

In classical economic theory there are three factors of production: land, labor, and capital. Land has always been important because it denotes access—access to transportation, labor, expertise, and information (thus, for example, urban land always has been more expensive than rural land). One of the first things students in real estate programs throughout the United States are taught is that the three principles of real estate are location, location, and location. Where a piece of land is located tells you everything about its value.

Yet, as capitalism has matured over the course of the last one hundred-plus years, and especially in the last twenty-five years, land seems to be ever more irrelevant. With the advent of a global economy, supported by global jet-based transportation and Internet-based information systems, location seems to be less and less important. From the production side, it is no longer necessary to have immediate, spatial access to either materials or experts. From the consumption side, depending on one's occupation, one can live quite removed from one's "place of work," and one can have access to the world's goods, often delivered right to your door, no matter where you are.

But land still matters in a fundamental way. For the vast majority of Americans, the principal economic asset is ownership of a house and land. Land defines the very nature of communities; that people will turn out in droves for a zoning hearing on a controversial land-use proposal because it is a threat to their property values and sense of community integrity reflects individual sensitivity to this fact and the inherent understanding of the precariousness of the location factor. Marketers know this. The whole phenomenon of ZIP-code marketing, where marketers peddle selected goods and services based on your address, is premised on the fact that location tells a great deal about social class, tastes, values, and disposable income.

Land means something more to people, however, than just a raw economic asset. If people didn't care about land, they wouldn't lovingly invest countless hours on their grounds, gardens, and homes. Whether Americans have a low or high income, or live in rural or urban places, land matters to them because its ownership, use, and development (including, importantly, its nonuse and nondevelopment) can be pivotal to the economic and social health of a rural area, city, and region, and to the ability of individuals to acquire and maintain residences in stable yet vibrant rural and urban neighborhoods. Land matters to Americans because it symbolizes so many things about what it means to be American. It is land, especially the wide open lands of the West, that beckon so many. The idea of wild land, whether it is in Alaska, the Adirondack Mountains of northern New York State, or the Everglades of Florida, says something pre-verbal to Americans about their frontier-ness and connection to nature. And land matters because it is intimately connected to ideas of political freedom and personal autonomy that help to define the American character. The ability of people to say and believe, "It's my land and I can do what I want with it" (even though this isn't true!), shows that land is a vehicle through which Americans experience and express other social and cultural values.

If we cannot say anything precise about landownership in America and yet know that land matters, what can we say about the future of landownership? I believe we can say a lot.

America is changing. As it changes, ownership changes. We are becoming a country with a shrinking middle-class, a growing lower class, and a growing income disparity between the top and the bottom. Access to land-ownership and the pursuit of public policies to protect that ownership (for example, federal tax and local zoning policies) mirrored the growth of the middle class after World War II. We are becoming a more (sub)urban and less rural nation. The 1920 Census was the official count of the flipover from our agrarian past to our urban present. With each passing decade, the per-centage of the U.S. population that lives in city-regions increases. As we become more urban and less middle-class, desirable land becomes more expensive.

This is a paradoxical time. Increasingly, we are aware of the limited resources on the planet, and yet the trend in American housing and city planning is to build ever larger houses—mega-homes. Everyone, it seems, from the president to local clergy, talks about the breakdown of community in American life, but the communities we build, the communities of mega-homes, are gated communities, completely shut off from their neighbors, self-contained enclaves with their own security forces, where children go to private schools. The market and capitalism are said to have triumphed over socialism and communism, and yet (as many of the authors in this book discuss) we seem to be seeing a continual growth of social property and a shrinking of private property.

Land will matter for a long time in America. A new book by a member of the property rights movement is titled simply *Property Matters* (DeLong 1997). The authors in this volume help to explain why—though Jess Gil-bert and Alice O'Connor argue that our political system, legislatively and administratively, has not been particularly adept at taking up new challenges in the land arena, and Arthur McEvoy shows how our legal system, the arbiter for social conflict, has difficulty with new ideas about land. Nonethe-less, as the population grows and becomes more concentrated in urban ar-eas, more ethnically diverse, and more economically stratified, people who believe in the American dream and the myth that is America will continually push upon the political, administrative, and legal systems to give them jus-tice through land.

Many of the authors in this volume refer to Thomas Jefferson and the legacy of his ideas about land in America. It is almost impossible to discuss land without bringing Jefferson into the conversation. Jefferson left us a powerful challenge. His image of America was one of decentralized owner-ship of land, where this ownership would serve as both the basis for in-formed democratic decision-making and a linkage for residents to take seri-ously their role as citizens and members of a community. To the extent that fewer and fewer people own America, it is possible that the proponents of the property rights movement are partially correct. If, in the Jeffersonian tradition, landownership is inextricably linked to the essence of Americanism, then perhaps democracy and America as we know it are threatened by the shrinking options for ownership.

The truth is we do not know who owns America, but we need to. We also need to know *how* America is owned (the forms that ownership takes) and *why* America is owned (the motivations that drive ownership). When we have this information, then we might be able to answer the question of who owns America and understand what it means—for the present and the future.

References

Appalachian Land Ownership Task Force. 1983. *Who Owns Appalachia?* Lexington, KY: University Press of Kentucky.

DeLong, James V. 1997. *Property Matters: How Property Rights Are under Assault—and Why You Should Care.* New York, NY: Free Press.

Geisler, Charles C. 1993. "Land Ownership: An Overview." *Rural Sociology* 58 (4): 532–546.

Jacobs, Harvey M., and D. David Moyer. 1986. "Constructing a National, Rural Land Transfer Data Base." *Journal of Soil and Water Conservation* 41 (4): 231–234.

Lewis, James A. 1980. *Landownership in the United States.* Economics, Statistics, and Cooperatives Service Staff Report 80–10. Washington, D.C.: U.S. Department of Agriculture.

U.S. Department of Agriculture. 1980. *Foreign Ownership of U.S. Agricultural Land.* Washington, D.C.: U.S. Department of Agriculture.

Contributors

Index

CONTRIBUTORS

BARBARA L. BEDFORD is a wetland plant ecologist and ecosystem scientist. She is an associate editor of *Wetlands,* chair of the Scientific Oversight Committee for the restoration of wetlands within Everglades National Park, and a Senior Research Associate in the Department of Natural Resources at Cornell University.

DANIEL W. BROMLEY is Anderson-Bascom Professor of Applied Economics at the University of Wisconsin–Madison and has served as editor of the journal *Land Economics* since 1974. He is now writing *Rousseau's Revenge: An Economic History of Private Property.*

RICHARD CASTELNUOVO is an attorney who is pursuing a Ph.D. in land resources at the University of Wisconsin–Madison. He practiced law in the field of regulatory enforcement in state government.

LOUISE FORTMANN is Professor of Natural Resource Sociology in the Department of Environmental Science, Policy and Management, and chair of the Center for African Studies at the University of California, Berkeley. She has done fieldwork on property in southern Africa and northern California.

JOHN GAVENTA was a Fellow at the Institute for Development Studies, University of Sussex, for the academic year 1997–98. He was on leave from the University of Tennessee, where he is Professor of Sociology. Formerly a staff member at the Highlander Center, he served as a co-coordinator of the Appalachian Land Ownership Study.

CHARLES C. GEISLER is Professor of Rural Sociology at Cornell University; he works on land and environmental issues in the United States and Latin America. His research focuses on owners and users within protected areas. He has written on land reform traditions in the United States and is currently researching the environmental side effects of land reform, from resource abuse and natural habitat destruction to new conservation behaviors among land reform recipients.

JESS GILBERT is Professor of Rural Sociology at the University of Wisconsin–Madison and a member of the North American Program of the

Land Tenure Center. He is writing a book on democratic planning in agricultural policy during the late New Deal.

RAYMOND P. GURIES is a professor in the Department of Forestry and Institute for Environmental Studies, University of Wisconsin–Madison. His research responsibilities include the selection and breeding of elms for disease-resistance amenity values; germplasm evaluation; selection and breeding of economically important forest tree species for reforestation programs in Wisconsin; conservation biology of temperate and tropical forest ecosystems; and silviculture and forest management.

LYNNE HEASLEY is pursuing a Ph.D. in the Department of Forestry at the University of Wisconsin–Madison. She has been affiliated with the Land Tenure Center since 1991 and is currently researching the environmental history of the Kickapoo Valley in southwestern Wisconsin, focusing on forest tenure, cultural landscapes, and social change.

HARVEY M. JACOBS is Professor and Chair of the Department of Urban and Regional Planning, and Professor in the Institute for Environmental Studies at the University of Wisconsin–Madison. His research and teaching program focuses on public policy, theory and philosophy of land use, and environmental management. A prominent aspect of his current research focuses on the rise and significance of the property rights movement in the United States.

BETSEY KUHN is Director of the Food and Consumer Economics Division of the USDA's Economic Research Service (ERS). She received an M.A. and a Ph.D. from the Food Research Institute of Stanford University, where she specialized in the economics of futures markets, consumption theory, and international trade and finance. She is responsible for ERS's research on the economics of diet and health, food safety, food markets and retail food price behavior, and food assistance and consumption.

DONALD LAST has been providing information on natural resource management to government officials, landowners, and agency staff since 1970. He has a joint appointment as Professor in the College of Natural Resources, University of Wisconsin–Stevens Point and as University of Wisconsin–Extension Natural Resource Policy Specialist. He publishes *Law of the Land Review*, a monthly newsletter on contemporary topics focused on natural resource policy and law.

ARTHUR MCEVOY is Professor of Law, History, and Environmental Studies at the University of Wisconsin–Madison. He has a J.D. from the Stanford Law School and a Ph.D. in history from the University of California at San Diego. He is currently at work on a history of industrial safety law in the United States.

ALICE O'CONNOR is Assistant Professor of History at the University of California, Santa Barbara, and was a Visiting Scholar at the Russell Sage Foundation for the academic year 1995–96. Her principal research interests are in the recent history of U.S. social policy. She is at work on a book on the history of U.S. poverty research since the 1920s.

SONYA SALAMON is Professor of Family Studies in the Department of Human and Community Development at the University of Illinois at Urbana-Champaign. She holds M.A. and Ph.D. degrees in anthropology and has conducted ethnographic research in Illinois farming and small town communities for over twenty years. She is at work on a book detailing how a diversity of newcomers are changing small Illinois communities in the 1990s.

ABEBAYEHU TEGENE is an economist in the Natural Resources and Environment Division of the USDA's Economic Research Service, where he focuses on land use and land conservation policy. His research interests also include time-series analysis, forecasting, and asset pricing. He holds B.Sc. and M.Sc. degrees in statistics, and a Ph.D. in economics from Iowa State University.

RONALD L. TROSPER is Director of the Native American Forestry Program and a professor at the School of Forestry, College of Ecosystem Science and Management, Northern Arizona University. A Harvard-trained economist, he has taught at the University of Washington and Boston College. He also worked six years as tribal economist for his tribe, the Confederated Salish and Kootenai Tribes of the Flathead Indian Reservation, Montana.

KEITH D. WIEBE is an economist in the Natural Resources and Environment Division of USDA's Economic Research Service. His current work focuses on the use and conservation of a variety of natural resources, including farmland, wetlands, floodplains, grazing land, and wildlife habitat. His research interests also include land tenure, resource use, and food policy in developing countries. He holds an M.A. and a Ph.D. in agricultural economics from the University of Wisconsin–Madison.

INDEX